Proceedings of the

Twenty-Eighth Hawaii International Conference on System Sciences

Overview

Volume I — *Architecture Track*:

High Performance Computing and I/O Systems
Reflective Memory and Distributed Shared Memory
   Architectures for OLTP
Instruction Level Parallelism
Scalable Shared-Memory Architectures
Low Energy ILP Processors

Volume II — *Software Technology Track*:

Parallel Algorithms
Partitioning and Scheduling in Parallel and Distributed
   Systems
Program Development Tools and Environments for
   Parallel and Distributed Systems
Directions in Software Engineering for Parallel Systems
Performance Evaluation and Prediction of Parallel
   and Distributed Systems
Fault Tolerance in Distributed/Parallel Systems
Communication in Parallel and Distributed Systems
Distribution and Concurrency in Persistent Systems
Object Oriented Multidatabase Systems

Volume III — *Information Systems Track*:
Decision Support and Knowledge-Based Systems

Emerging Paradigms for Intelligent Systems
Executive Information Systems
Forecasting Support Systems
Graph-Based Methods in Software Technology and
   Information Systems
Hypermedia in Information Systems and Organizations
Information Sharing and Knowledge Discovery in
   Large Scientific Databases
Logic Modeling
Methods and Tools for Information Systems Development
Modeling Technologies and Information Systems
Multi-Media Information Systems
Technology Management: Systems and Processes

Volume IV — *Information Systems Track*:
Collaboration Systems and Technology

Distributed Group Support Systems (DGSS)
Electronic Support for Learning
Geographic Information Systems
Group Support Systems
Group Support Systems Applications
Negotiation Support Systems
Organization Memory
Business Process Re-Engineering
Telework: The Borderless Organization
Groupware: User Experiences

Organizational Systems and Technology

Creativity/Innovation in I.S. Organizations
INTERNET and the Information Superhighway
Issues in Technology Transfer
Measuring the Effectivenss of Emerging Technologies
Modelling the Dynamics of Organizations and
   Information Systems
Organizational DSS
Strategic and Competitive Information Systems
Special Topics

Volume V — *Biotechnology Computing Track*:

Project-Oriented Databases and Knowledge Bases in
   Genome Research
Computational Biology and Parallel Computing
Stochastic Models and Grammars for Bioinformatics
Computer Tools for Molecular Modeling
Protein Structure Prediction

Proceedings of the

Twenty-Eighth Hawaii International Conference on System Sciences

Volume I:

Architecture

Edited by Trevor Mudge and Bruce D. Shriver

Sponsored by
The University of Hawaii
The University of Hawaii College of Business Administration

In cooperation with
The IEEE Computer Society
The Association for Computing Machinery
PRISM

IEEE Computer Society Press
Los Alamitos, California

Washington   •   Brussels   •   Tokyo

IEEE Computer Society Press
10662 Los Vaqueros Circle
P.O. Box 3014
Los Alamitos, CA 90720-1264

IEEE Computer Society Press Order Numbers:
5-Volume set: 6920-99
Volume I only: 6930-02
ISBN 0-8186-6930-6 (paper)
ISBN 0-8186-6931-4 (microfiche)
ISSN 1060-3425

Additional copies may be ordered from:

IEEE Computer Society Press	IEEE Service Center	IEEE Computer Society	IEEE Computer Society
Customer Service Center	445 Hoes Lane	13, Avenue de l'Aquilon	Ooshima Building
10662 Los Vaqueros Circle	P.O. Box 1331	B-1200 Brussels	2-19-1 Minami-Aoyama
P.O. Box 3014	Piscataway, NJ 08855-1331	BELGIUM	Minato-ku, Tokyo 107
Los Alamitos, CA 90720-1264	Tel: +1-908-981-1393	Tel: +32-2-770-2198	JAPAN
Tel: +1-714-821-8380	Fax: +1-908-981-9667	Fax: +32-2-770-8505	Tel: +81-3-3408-3118
Fax: +1-714-821-4641			Fax: +81-3-3408-3553
Email: cs.books@computer.org			

Editorial production by Mary E. Kavanaugh and Robert Werner
Cover production by Joseph Daigle
Printed in the United States of America by Braun-Brumfield, Inc.

 The Institute of Electrical and Electronics Engineers, Inc.

Volume I
Table of Contents

ARCHITECTURE

Preface

The Proceedings of the Twenty-Eighth Hawaii International Conference on System Sciences (HICSS-28), held in Wailea, Hawaii on January 3-6, 1995, consists of five volumes:

Volume I **Architecture**
Editors: *Trevor N. Mudge and Bruce D. Shriver*

Volume II **Software Technology**
Editors: *Hesham El-Rewini and Bruce D. Shriver*

Volume III **Decision Support and Knowledge-Based Systems**
Editors: *Jay F. Nunamaker, Jr., and Ralph H. Sprague, Jr.*

Volume IV **Collaboration Technology**
Organizational Systems and Technology
Editors: *Jay F. Nunamaker, Jr., and Ralph H. Sprague, Jr.*

Volume V **Biotechnology Computing**
Editor: *Lawrence Hunter*

HICSS provides a forum for the interchange of ideas, advances, and applications among academicians and practitioners in the information, computing, and system sciences. HICSS is sponsored by the College of Business Administration and the University of Hawaii. These proceedings consist of papers that have not been previously published and have undergone a detailed peer review process. The 28th conference emphasizes developments in the areas of software, architecture, decision support systems, knowledge-based systems, collaboration systems and technology, organizational systems and technology, and biotechnology computing. Our most sincere thanks to all the authors, attendees, coordinators, chairpersons, task force members, advisory committees, and administrative support staff who make the conference a success.

Bruce D. Shriver and **Ralph H. Sprague, Jr.**
HICSS-28 Conference Co-Chairmen
E-mail addresses:
Shriver@genesis2.com *and* Sprague@uhunix.uhcc.hawaii.edu

Introduction To The Architecture Track Of The Twenty-Eighth Annual Hawaii International Conference On System Sciences

Trevor Mudge
Electrical Engineering & Computer Science Department
University of Michigan,
Ann Arbor, MI 48109-2122

Bruce Shriver
17 Bethea Drive
Ossining, NY 10562-1620

A total of five Minitracks make up this year's Architecture Track of HICSS-28. The emphasis is on parallel processing. Two of the tracks address issues in instruction level parallelism. This is an idea that is finally finding widespread use in many recent commercial microprocessors. It is should come as no surprise, then, that both minitracks are organized by individuals from industry.

At the processor level of parallelism there are two minitracks. One is on scalable shared memory architectures, a subject that has been very popular in recent years. The other is on systems that employ reflective memory to share memory. This is a technique that has been around for some time but that is just beginning to become popular. The fifth minitrack addresses applications that require a great deal of computer power and I/O bandwidth. These applications are also likely to be the users of parallelism if they are to obtain their performance targets.

We would like to take this opportunity to thank this year's advisory committee for their help and guidance in assembling the Architecture Track's program. They were: Dennis Allison, Stanford University, Tom Conte, University of South Carolina, Ed Davidson, University of Michigan, Joel Emer, Digital Equipment Corporation, Bill Mangione-Smith, Motorola, Alex Nicolau, University of California - Irvine, Yale Patt, University of Michigan, Bob Rau, Hewlett-Packard Laboratories, Jim Smith, University of Wisconsin, Mike Smith, Harvard University, Guri Sohi, University of Wisconsin and Wayne Wolf, Princeton University. Finally, we would also like to thank the minitrack coordinators for all their work to make the Architecture Track a vital part of the conference.

Architecture Track Referees

S. Abraham – *Purdue University*

S. Anik – *Hewlett-Packard Laboratories*

P. Banerjee – *Kansas State University*

L. Barroso – *University of Southern California*

J. Baxter – *California State University Los Angeles*

G. Bewick – *Sun Microsystems, Inc.*

R. Bringmann – *University of Illinois*

R.E. Bryant – *Carnegie Mellon University*

K. Burch – *Motorola*

J. Carter – *University of Utah*

E. Cerny – *Université de Montréal*

T-F. Chen – *National Chung Cheng University*

W. Chen – *California State University, Los Angeles*

H. Cheong – *IBM - Austin*

L. Choi – *University of Illinois, Urbana-Champaign*

A.N. Choudhary – *Syracuse University*

J. Cloutier – *Université de Montréal*

W. Coates – *Sun Microsystems, Inc.*

G. Cybenko – *Dartmouth College*

J. Eifert – *Motorola*

M.I. Elmasry – *University of Waterloo*

J. Fu – *Intel Corporation*

D. Gallagher – *University of Illinois*

C.H. Gebotys – *University of Waterloo*

Il. Gertner – *Encore Computer Corporation*

K. Gharachorloo – *Stanford University*

E. Gornish – *University of Illinois, Urbana-Champaign*

A. Gottlieb – *New York University*

J. Gyllenhall – *University of Illinois*

R. Hank – *University of Illinois*

S. Hong – *Georgia State University*

C-L. Hwang – *Kansas State University*

W-M. Hwu – *University of Illinois, Urbana-Champaign*

P. Konas – *University of Illinois, Urbana-Champaign*

C. Lee – *Motorola*

J. Lexau – *Sun Microsystems, Inc.*

B. Lucas – *Motorola*

S. Mahlke – *University of Illinois, Urbana-Champaign*

B. Mangione-Smith – *Motorola*

K. Moat – *Motorola*

T. Mudge – *University of Michigan*

A. Nowatzyk – *Sun Microsystems Computer Group*

S. Pakin – *University of Illinois, Urbana-Champaign*

J.H. Patel – *University of Illinois*

P. Perdolos – *University of Florida*

T.M. Pinkston – *University of Southern California*

P. Raghavan – *University of Illinois*

M. Rahman – *Motorola*

D. Rivera – *Motorola*

R.H. Saavedra – *University of Southern California*

H. Scales – *Motorola*

S. Scott – *Cray Research*

W. Shi – *Encore Computer Corporation*

G. Silberman – *IBM - T.J. Watson Research Center*

N. Warter – *California State University, Los Angeles*

W-D. Weber – *Hal Computer Systems*

N. Wilhelm – *Sun Microsystems, Inc.*

Y. Wu – *Sequent Computer Systems*

R. Yung – *Sun Microsystems, Inc.*

Z. Zhang – *University of Illinois, Urbana-Champaign*

ARCHITECTURE

Track Coordinators:

Trevor Mudge and Bruce D. Shriver

HIGH-PERFORMANCE COMPUTING AND I/O SYSTEMS

Minitrack Coordinators:

L. Ridgway Scott and Trevor Mudge

High Performance Computing and I/O Systems

L. Ridgway Scott and Trevor Mudge

University of Houston and The University of Michigan

The HICSS-27 meeting featured a very successful Minitrack [2] which highlighted grand challenge computational problems arising in the design of computer systems. This has helped to explore their role in the national High-Performance Computing and Communications (HPCC) Initiative [1].

Computational tools are extensively used in designing computers, yet "grand challenge" level computations remain rare. The primary object of the Minitrack is to bring together people who specialize in the use of modern parallel supercomputers and computer architects who are using extensive amounts of computing in computer design.

This second year will continue this research interaction but is extended to cover the equally important issue of high performance I/O systems. This has been a year of consolidation in the MPP computer market, with the entrance by established manufacturers IBM and Cray, and the demise of industry pioneers Thinking Machines and Kendall Square Research. On the other hand, virtually all "workstation" manufacturers now feature symmetric multiprocessors in their product line. Correspondingly, this year's minitrack is experiencing a similar consolidation, with a smaller number of presentations than last year.

References

1. Grand Challenges 1993: High Performance Computing and Communications, available from the NSF Computing and Information Science and Engineering Directorate, 1800 G Street, N.W. Washington, D.C. 20550.

2. Scott, L.R., Computer design: a new grand challenge, In Proceedings of the 27th Annual Hawaii International Conference on System Sciences, vol.1, T.N. Mudge and B.D. Shriver, ed's, IEEE Computer Soc. Press, 1994, pp. 3-6.

Performance Tuning of a Multiprocessor Sparse Matrix Equation Solver

K Y Wu, P K H Ng, X D Jia, R M M Chen and A M Layfield

Department of Electronic Engineering
City Polytechnic of Hong Kong
83 Tat Chee Avenue, Kowloon
Email: kywu@cpeelgx03.cphk.hk

Abstract

Solving a system of linear simultaneous equations representing an electrical circuit is one of the most time consuming tasks for large scale circuit simulations. In order to facilitate a multiprocessor implementation of the circuit simulation program SPICE, a decomposition algorithm is employed to partition the sparse matrix equation of an overall circuit into a number of sub-circuit equations for parallel processing. In this paper, various implementation and performance tuning issues of a parallel direct method matrix equation solving routine is reported. This routine is written in such a manner that the data structure is compatible with SPICE Version 3C1. The speed-up obtained for the simulation of several test circuits on a message passing multiprocessor system built on Transputers will be reported.

Introduction

Computer-aided circuit simulation is one of the most important and time consuming computational tasks in VLSI circuit design. For VLSI circuit design, circuit simulation using standard circuit simulators like SPICE[1], ASTAP[2], and SLATE[3] may require many days on a computer system with one processor. Although some simulators based on relaxation methods[4,5] can perform circuit simulations up to two orders of magnitude faster than SPICE, convergence can not be guaranteed for all class of circuits.

Solving the large sparse matrix equation representing the circuit equations is one of the most time consuming tasks for large scale circuit simulations. By employing parallel processing technique, the runtime of circuit simulation can be reduced[6,7,8]. To facilitate a multi-processor implementation of circuit simulation based on direct-method[1], the matrix equation decomposition algorithm proposed by Chen [9] was employed to decompose the

sparse matrix into several sub-matrices, of which can computation be arranged for parallel processing on a multiprocessor system. The speedup achieved by the decomposition algorithm, the effect of communication overhead and the relative merits of different multiprocessor topologies were previously estimated by a multiprocessor simulator and reported in [10]. The target platform under consideration is a cost-effective system built on Transputers.

In this paper, various implementation issues and performance tuning aspects of the parallel linear simultaneous equation solving routine will be reported. The routine is implemented in such a manner that the data structure is fully compatible with SPICE Version 3C1. The speedup obtained for the simulation of several test circuits will be reported.

Decomposition Algorithm

The decomposition algorithm used for this work was derived in [9]; a brief outline is included here.

Let the overall circuit equation be written as

$$A\underline{x} = \underline{y} \qquad (1)$$

A is a sparse matrix of dimension M. After the circuit is partitioned into ℓ sub-circuits, the equations of the sub-circuits can be re-written in the following form:

$$\underline{y}^i = B^i \underline{x}^i + D^i \underline{z}^i \qquad (2)$$

where B^i is the circuit matrix of the sub-circuit i with the dimension of $N_i \times N_i$. D^i is an $N_i \times n_i$ circuit matrix, and $\underline{z}^i$ is an n_i-vector obtained from $\underline{x}$ by retaining the elements corresponding to the columns of D^i.

The ith sub-circuit solution can be obtained from Eq(2) as

$$\underline{x}^i = (B^i)^{-1}(\underline{y}^i - D^i \underline{z}^i) \qquad (3)$$

or

$$x^i = v^i + E^i z^i \qquad (4)$$

where

$$v^i = (B^i)^{-1} y^i \qquad (5)$$

and

$$E^i = -(B^i)^{-1} D^i \qquad (6)$$

All items on the right-hand side of Eq.(4) are known except z^i. Z is an m-vector whose elements consist of all the elements of z^i, for i=1,2,.....,ℓ, without any duplication in terms of the elements of x. It was shown in [2] and [4] that:

$$Z = HZ + w \qquad (7)$$

or

$$Z = (I - H)^{-1} w \qquad (8)$$

Eq.(8) is called the interconnection level equation. Once Z is calculated from Eq.(8), all sub-circuit solutions can be computed in parallel from Eq.(4).

After the circuit (or the circuit matrix) is partitioned, instead of one circuit matrix, B matrix and D matrix are formed for each sub-circuit. A new data structure is required in order to store all the information related to each sub-circuit in the problem. This new data structure stores the B matrix and D matrix in the SPICE sparse matrix form. Apart from storing these two matrices, the structure also stores the E^i, v^i, and z^i and the y^i vectors associated with each sub-circuit.

Implementation on Multi-transputer System

Initially, the algorithm was implemented on the processor farm architecture connected in the pipeline form as shown in Figure 1. Figure 2 shows the tasks allocation table of the program for the case when three processors are used to solve three sub-matrix equations. The program flow is as follows:

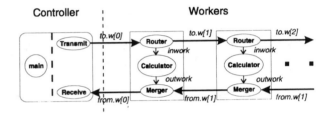

Figure 1. *Farm Architecture Connected in Pipeline Form*

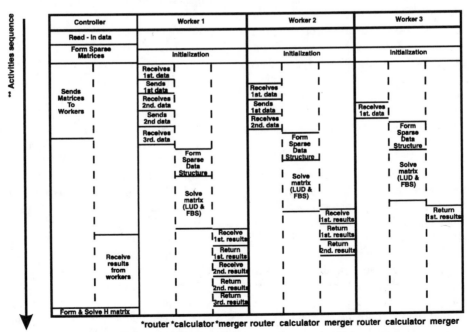

Figure 2. *Tasks Allocation of the Matrix Equation Solving Program*

The controller of the system first reads in the input files consisting of circuit matrices of the partitioned sub-circuits. They are stored as the SPICE sparse matrix data structure in the program. Depending on the number of workers available in the system, the sub-matrices along with the other data required to compute the results, are sent to the unoccupied workers. The workers then perform all sub-circuits LUD (LU decomposition) and FBS (forward-backward substitutions) operations concurrently. The sub-circuit results are sent via another set of channels back to the controller. This procedure is repeated until all sub-matrices are solved by LUD and FBS. By combining the results obtained, the H matrix and $\underline{w}$ vector are then formed. Finally by solving the H matrix equation Eq. (8) in the controller and the solution of the inter-connections is then substituted into Eq.(4), the final sets of results are obtained.

Due to the limitation of the communication mechanism in the transputer "C" language, during the data passing procedure, the controller needs to pass the content of the sparse matrix to the workers. For every data transfer in the system via the external link, there is an associated communication protocol overhead. In order to minimize this communication overhead, the elements in each sparse matrix are grouped into sets of arrays for data transfer. The controller converts the circuit matrix from the sparse data form into a set of arrays, passes these through the communication link, and re-forms them back into the sparse data structure form at the destination workers. It is to be expected that there will be a substantial overhead with this conversion to and from the SPICE sparse data structure format. The existing sparse data structure format is preserved in this implementation because one of the original objectives is to implement a parallel version of SPICE with minimal modifications to the original code.

Since the multi-transputer system is a message passing distributed memory system, each transputer cannot directly access the memory located remotely, so data must be passed to the appropriate memory space through the transputer link. This affects the system when the computation to communication ratio is low. Furthermore, the language used for implementation is the high level "C" language, and the implemented program has a complicated data structure. Due to the limitation of the communication mechanism used in the transputer "C" language, this data structure must be converted into sets of arrays, and then re-formed back to the original data structure at the workers. For some cases, the overhead generated by this conversion and re-formation process can be as high as 40% of the overall simulation time.

Therefore, this portion of program must be optimized in order to reduce the overhead.

SYSTEM PERFORMANCE TUNING

Four test circuits were chosen for the evaluation purpose. The first circuit is taken from [10] and is used for verification purpose. The circuit consists of four 741 op-amps, and the model of the op-amp is an artificial linear network consisting of 40 resistors. This will avoid any convergence problem. Circuit II is similar to Circuit I, but a different model of the op-amp is used. Instead of a resistive network of forty resistors, the number of resistors for the resistive network is increased to 180. This results in an overall circuit matrix size of about 1600. Circuit III is a 4th order Chebyshev active RC band-pass filter. The 741 op-amp model used in this circuit is an active model commonly used. Finally, Circuit IV is a seventh-order Butterworth low-pass filter consisting of 12 op-amps and the schematic diagram of the circuit is shown in the Appendix. The op-amp model used is the same as Circuit III. The circuit is partitioned into different numbers of sub-circuits with different size for evaluation, the methods of partitioning are also shown in the Appendix.

To improve the system performance, the following changes were implemented:

- Changing the communication mechanism - One of the largest overheads is the process associated with the re-generation of the sparse matrix structure. This can block the upstream communication links. To overcome this problem, the new communication mechanism of the processor-farm operates as follows: instead of computing the data in "first-come-first served" manner, a worker processor will transmit the n sets of data received to n neighbor workers downstream and perform computation on the (n+1)th set of data itself, as shown in Figure 2. This mechanism can prevent blocking of communication during the re-generation of data structure. It also allows the re-generation of different sets of data structure to be performed concurrently.

- Buffering the data. The concurrent processes, routers and mergers in the workers are assigned to handle the data communication. To obtain an optimum performance, an extra memory buffer is allocated at each router and merger.

- To re-form the sparse data structure at each worker involves two phases of work:

- to clear up the memory space used to store the sub-matrix previously assigned to the worker, and
- to allocate new memory space for storing the matrix.

The first phase involves a lot of looping which are extremely time consuming. The clearing and allocating memory processes are combined to limit this overhead. The contents of the sparse data structure are used to re-fill the memory space allocated for the previous computation. This can speedup the process dramatically.

- Since the size of each sub-matrix is not identical, the computation time for solving each sub-matrix is different. Although automatic load-balancing among worker processors is achievable for the processor-farm architecture, solving the sub-matrix equations with different sequence may also produce different overall computation time. The scheduling scheme employed in the program is based on the largest-processing-time (LPT) technique [12]. In brief, this scheduling strategy is to assign the task whose execution time is largest with highest priority. Estimation of the execution time can be accomplished by the size of each sub-matrix.

- Tuning of compiling parameters can affect the memory management scheme in a transputer. There are 4K bytes of on-chip internal memory in each T800 transputer which can be used to store the run-time stack. Programs with size of stack exceeding 4K bytes must use external memory instead, and this will result in a decrease in the speed of calculation. The size of the stack is optimized to ensure that it is placed in the on-chip memory, which gives a speedup of performance.

- An alternative tree structure as shown in Figure 3 is also built. This topology was chosen in view of its higher degree of connectivity for the controller processor. A version of the matrix equation solving program is implemented to use this topology, and the performance of this topology is compared with the pipeline version.

Figure 3. *Tree Connection Topology*

- When the workers are solving the matrix equations concurrently, the controller is assigned to monitor and handle the inter-processor communications, and in some period of time, the controller may remain idle. In order to fully utilize all the physical resources in the system, the controller can be assigned to perform calculation work as well especially when there is only a small number of processors. Since the controller can directly access its own memory space where the original matrix elements are stored, this can eliminate the communication overheads and the sparse matrix data structure conversion and re-formation overheads associated with that calculation. The system is also implemented in this manner (defined as Configuration B).

RESULTS

By incorporating the changes in the previous section, the performance results are as tabulated in Table 1 and Table 2. The speedup figures are defined as followings:

1. **Speedup due to the decomposition, S_d.** This is the speedup obtained from the decomposition algorithm only, and can be calculated by:

$$S_d = \frac{t_1}{t_{1d}} \qquad (9)$$

where

t_1 = computation time for 1 Transputer without decomposition

t_{1d} = simulation time using 1 Transputer with decomposition

To access the speedup offered by the decomposition algorithm only, the communication overheads have to be ignored in the Eq.(9). This can be achieved by assigning all the computation to the controller processor (for both decomposition case and without decomposition case). This is the condition under which the 'simulation time' is recorded.

Circuits	S_d	$S_t'(1)$	$S_t'(2)$	$S_t'(3)$	$S_t'(4)$	$S_t'(5)$	$S_o'(1)$	$S_o'(2)$	$S_o'(3)$	$S_o'(4)$	$S_o'(5)$
Circuit I	1.33	1.00	0.83	1.07	1.25	1.15	1.33	1.11	1.43	**1.67**	1.54
Circuit II	1.13	1.00	1.73	2.10	3.48	3.69	1.13	1.96	2.38	3.95	**4.18**
Circuit III	1.19	1.00	1.19	1.66	1.57	1.53	1.19	1.42	**1.99**	1.88	1.82
Circuit IV Scheme A	1.20	1.00	1.15	1.59	1.54	1.41	1.20	1.38	**1.90**	1.85	1.69
Circuit IV Scheme B	1.20	1.00	1.27	1.52	1.48	1.46	1.20	1.53	**1.83**	1.78	1.75
Circuit IV Scheme C	1.20	1.00	1.39	1.67	1.62	1.60	1.20	1.53	**1.83**	1.78	1.75
Circuit IV Complex	1.51	1.00	0.90	1.19	0.99	0.97	1.51	1.36	**1.79**	1.50	1.47

Table 1. *Speedups obtained Pipeline Connection Topology and Configuration B*

Circuits	S_d	$S_t'(1)$	$S_t'(2)$	$S_t'(3)$	$S_t'(4)$	$S_t'(5)$	$S_o'(1)$	$S_o'(2)$	$S_o'(3)$	$S_o'(4)$	$S_o'(5)$
Circuit I	1.33	1.00	0.83	1.07	1.25	1.25	1.33	1.11	1.43	**1.67**	**1.67**
Circuit II	1.13	1.00	1.73	2.10	3.49	3.82	1.13	1.96	2.38	3.96	**4.32**
Circuit III	1.19	1.00	1.19	1.71	1.61	1.61	1.19	1.42	**2.05**	1.93	1.93
Circuit IV Scheme A	1.20	1.00	1.15	1.79	1.47	1.59	1.20	1.38	**2.14**	1.76	1.90
Circuit IV Scheme B	1.20	1.00	1.27	1.55	1.55	1.52	1.20	1.53	**1.86**	**1.86**	1.83
Circuit IV Scheme C	1.20	1.00	1.39	1.70	1.70	1.67	1.20	1.53	**1.86**	**1.86**	1.83
Circuit IV Complex	1.51	1.00	0.90	1.24	1.04	1.03	1.51	1.36	**1.87**	1.57	1.56

Table 2. *Speedups obtained for Tree Connection Topology and Configuration B*

2. **Speedup due to multi-processor system, $S_t'(N_t)$.** This is the speedup obtained by adding more processors into the system. This value is equal to:

$$S_t'(N_t) = \frac{t_{1d}}{t_{Nd}} \qquad (10)$$

where

t_{1d} = computation time for 1 Transputer with decomposition

t_{Nd} = computation time for N_t Transputers with decomposition

Again, the numerator used in Eq.(10) is the simulation time using the controller for all the computation. $S_t(n)$ is defined as the speedup of a system consisting of n worker processors plus a controller, and the controller does not participate in the parallel computation work as the farm worker do (as the case of Figure 4a). $S_t'(N_t)$ is defined as the speedup of a system consisting of (N_t-1) worker processors plus a controller, and the controller also participates in the parallel computation work as the farm workers do (as the case of Figure 4b).

3. **Overall speedup, $S_o'(N_t)$.** This is the speedup contributed by the decomposition algorithm as well as the multi-processor system. The value of the overall speedup can be obtained by:

$$S_o'(N_t) = S_d \times S_t'$$
$$= \frac{t_1}{t_{Nd}} \qquad (11)$$

For a small multiprocessor system, there is always a question of whether the controller should be assigned for calculating the sub-matrix equations. A program was implemented in the manner that the controller is assigned for calculation when it is in idle state waiting to send or receive. Conversely, another program was implemented so that the controller is not assigned for calculating the sub-matrix equations. Figure 4 shows the processes allocated to the controller in these two programs, the

8

speedups obtained from these two programs were then compared.

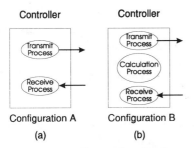

Figure 4. *Processes Allocated to the Controller in Two Different Configurations*

The sub-matrices generated from the Circuit II were used as input; the circuit was partitioned into four sub-circuits, and the size of the sub-matrices generated from the sub-circuits are 404, 400, 400 and 400. Figure 5 shows the speedup curves obtained from the two configurations (as shown in Figure 4) with either pipeline or tree connection topology. The dotted lines represent the speedups obtained from Configuration A, and the solid lines represent the speedups obtained from Configuration B.

First, let us study the speedups obtained from Configuration A. From the graph in Figure 5, it can be seen that S_O obtained from the pipeline topology increases almost linearly with the number of processors, which is not the situation as expected; Figure 6 shows the task allocation for N_t=3 (Figure 6a) and N_t=4 (Figure 6b), the diagram illustrates why the simulation time and the speedups obtained for the two cases should be the same.

The continuous increment in speedup between N_t=3 and N_t=4 shows that there are some overheads associated with the system which affect the performance of the system when N_t=3.

The curves show that the tree topology does not perform as the same as the pipeline topology. In fact, the tree topology shows the expected effect in this problem: the speedup obtained when N_t=3 is nearly equal to the speedup gained when N_t=4. Since the only difference between the pipeline and the tree is the connection topology, but there is a difference in actual performance, this shows that the overheads associated with pipeline topology are mainly communication overheads.

Now let us study the speedup factors obtained from Configuration B. By observing the results, the difference between the two connection topologies is not as significant as in Configuration A. The reason is because some of the calculations were assigned to the controller (see Figure 6) which does not require the inter-processor communications, and hence the communication overhead is reduced. As mentioned before, the difference in performance between the two topologies is due to the communication overheads, therefore in Configuration B, the difference is not as significant as Configuration A.

When the number of worker processors is equal to the number of sub-circuits, the controller in Configuration B only handles the inter-processor communication, and this is equivalent to Configuration A, then there is a difference in the speedups obtained between the two topologies.

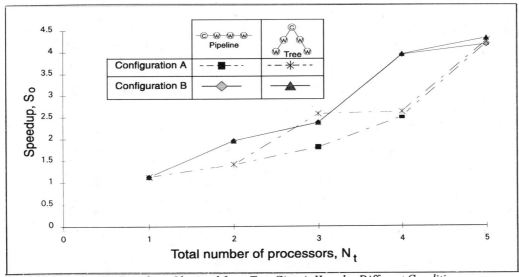

Figure 5. *Speedups Obtained from Test Circuit II under Different Conditions*

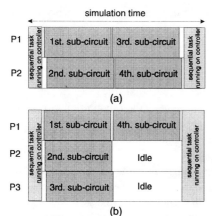

Figure 6. *Tasks Allocation on*
(a) Two Worker Processors P1 and P2,
(b) Three Worker Processors P1, P2, and P3

And in this situation, the tree topologies obtained a slightly better performance as predicted.

Note that for the case when N_t =3, the speedups from the tree topology in Configuration A is better than the speedups in Configuration B, this is due to the following reason:

The tasks allocation diagram for Configuration B shows that one of the worker processors was assigned to compute two sub-matrix equations, which implies that this worker processor finished its first calculation before the controller. Hence for some period of time, the controller was required to handle both communication and computation. As such, the controller was required to perform context switching between the calculation and communication. By assigning the calculation locally to the controller, the communication, conversion and re-formation overheads can be eliminated. However, the overhead required for context switching is higher than the eliminated overheads in this case. Therefore, the overall speedup obtained when N_t=3 is smaller than the overall speedup in Configuration A.

Also, it is worth to mention here that after a lot of testing, another factor which affect the speed of the

system has been found. When the allocated heap size in a transputer is increased, the speed of calculation on that transputer will be decreased. This fact is not mentioned in the transputer ANSI C manual. This is probably due to the hardware architecture of transputers and/or the transputer C compiler. Investigation of this problem is out of the scope of this research work. The speed reduction in the controller as mentioned in the last paragraph may also due to this fact.

After studying the speedups obtained from these two configurations, it was found that when the number of worker processors is less than the number of sub-circuits partitioned, the system performance is better for Configuration B. However, if the number of processors in the system is substantially increased, it is better to dedicate the controller to handle only the inter-processor communications.

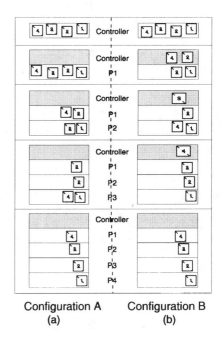

Configuration A   Configuration B
(a)   (b)

Figure 7. *Tasks Allocation for The Two Configurations*

Partition Schemes	Number of sub-circuits	Size of sub-matrices generated from sub-circuits	No of interconnections
A	3	198, 196, 196	6
B	5	198,148,148,52,52	10
C	4	150,148,148,148	16

Table 3. Information of the sub-matrices generated from Circuit IV
by using different Partition Schemes

In the following, the performance of the complex version of the parallel matrix equation solving program is being studied.

The speedup obtained from the complex number version of the program is compared with the speedup obtained from the real number version for the same test circuit; Circuit IV (Scheme A) and Circuit IV (Complex) are two identical circuits and partitioned in the same way (see Figure A1 in Appendix), but Circuit IV (Scheme A) was solved by the real number version of the program, whereas the Circuit VI (Complex) was solved by the complex number version to find the solutions in complex numbers. Since there are real and imaginary parts for each element in the matrix and the vectors, the communicated data size of the complex number version is therefore doubled from the real number version. However, the solving time for sub-matrix equations did not increase doubly, therefore the computation to communication ratio obtained from the complex number version is less than the real number case. This is the reason why the speedup obtained from the complex number version in this test is less than the real number version.

Discussion and Conclusion

By observing all the other speedups obtained, the following factors were found:

- It can be seen that to obtain a better performance, the controller can be assigned to solve the sub-matrix equation(s) as well. Usually, assigning the smallest sub-matrix (or sub-matrices) to the controller may improve the speedup as well as efficiency to the system.

- As shown in the results, when all the sub-circuits are of about similar sizes, usually the maximum speedup can be obtained when the total number of processors in the system (include controller) is equal to the number of sub-circuits; this is due to the fact that all the processors are fully utilized and part of the communication and data reform overheads have been eliminated. However, if there is a large number of worker processors in the system, or the computation to communication ratio is high, i.e., long calculation time is required, a better speedup can be obtained if all the calculations are evenly assigned to the worker processors.

- For most of the cases, the speedups obtained from the pipeline do not different significantly with the tree topology for the configuration where the controller is assigned for calculation.

- As shown in Table 1, Circuit IV was partitioned in different ways. It was shown that a maximum speedup can be achieved from Circuit IV (Scheme A) given in Figure B2(a) in Appendix B. It is because the sub-matrices formed in Scheme A have the largest grain size. Also the number of interconnections in Scheme A was the smallest, hence the time required to solve the interconnection equation as well as the overall solution for Scheme A is the shortest.

- In some of the test circuits, the sizes of the sub-circuits are not large, therefore the speedups achieved are not as good as predicted. If the size of each sub-circuit is large (sub-matrix size is larger than 400), speedup close to the total number of processors can be achieved (such as Circuit II).

By summarizing the results, the overheads or the factors which directly affect the system performance in our implementation are:

- Communication overheads - These depend on the communication data size, the speed of the communication channel, and the traffic in the system.

- Computational overheads - These include the sparse data structure conversion and reformation overheads and memory management overheads.

- Computation to communication ratio - If the data communication size is large, and the time for computation is relatively small, no matter how many processors are available, the maximum speedup is limited. This ratio is directly affected by the sub-matrix size and the complexity of the problem.

- System resources - These include the number of processors (transputers) in the system and the size of memory available for each processor.

- Method of circuit partition - Different methods of circuit partition may give different size of the sub-matrices generated, different numbers of sub-matrices, and different numbers of interconnections. Best speedup can be obtained when the size of the sub-matrices is large, the number of sub-matrices is equal to the total number of processors in the system, and the number of inter-connections among the sub-circuits is small.

- Complexity of problem - This includes:
  - the size of the circuit; in order to obtain a high speedup, the size of the problem i.e. the size of the simulated circuits must be large (e.g. the dimension of each sub-matrix generated is over 400).
  - the kind of analysis to be performed; whether only the real part of the results is required (e.g. DC operation point, DC transient analysis), or both the real part and the imaginary part of the results are concerned (e.g. AC analysis).

- System configuration and connection topologies. - These concern with the hardware as well as the structure of parallel programming. Both factors will affect the performance of a multi-processor system, and can limit the maximum speedup of the system.

Acknowledgments

The authors are grateful to the University and Polytechnic Grants Committee of Hong Kong for their support of this research project.

References

1. L.W.Nagel, "SPICE2: A computer program to simulate semiconductor circuits", Electronics Research Laboratory Report No. ERL-M520, University of California, Berkeley, May 1975.

2. T.Weeks, A.J.Jimenez, G.W.Mahoney, D.Mehata, H.Qassemzadeh, and T.R.Scott, "Algorithms for ASTAP - A network analysis program", IEEE Trans. on Circuit Theory, Vol.. CT-20, no.6, pp.628-634, Nov.1973.

3. P.Yang, I.N. Hajj and T. N. Trick, "SLAVE:A circuit simulation program with latence exploitation and node tearing", Proc. IEEE Int. Conf. on Cir. and Comp., pp.353-355, Oct.1980.

4. E.Lelarasmee, A.E.Ruehli, and A.L.Sangiovanni-Vincentelli, "The waveform relaxation method for time domain analysis of large scale integrated circuits", IEEE Trans. on CAD of IC and Systems, Vol. 1, No.3, pp.131-145, July 1982.

5. J.K.White and A.L.Sangiovanni-Vincentelli, *Relaxzation Techniques for the Simulation of VLSI Circuits*, Norwell, MA, Kluwer Academic Publishers, 1986.

6. R A Saleh et al, "Parallel Circuit Simulation on Supercomputers", Proc IEEE, Vol. 77, No. 12, pp.1915-1931, December 1989.

7. T Nakata et al, "CENJU: A Multiprocessor System for Modular Circuit Simulation", Computing Systems in Engineering Vol.1, No.1, pp.101-109, 1990.

8. P.F.Cox et al, "Direct Circuit Simulation Algorithms for Parallel Processing", IEEE Trans on Computer-Aided Design, Vol.10, No.6, pp.714-725, June 1991.

9. R.M.M.Chen, "Solving a Class of Large Sparse Linear Systems of Equations by Partitioning", pp.223-226, Proc. IEEE International Symposium on Circuit Theory, Toronto, Canada, April 1973.

10. A.M.Layfield, R.M.M.Chen and P.K.H.Ng, "Multiprocessor Simulator Evaluation of A Circuit Partitioning Algorithm for Parallel Execution of SPICE", Pg.440-444, Proc. 1992 European Simulation Multiconference, The Society for Computer Simulation International, York, UK, pp.440-444, June 1992.

11. A.M.Layfield, R.M.M. Chen, L.S. Lim, and W.C. Siu, "Implementation of Multi-processor SPICE", Proc. 6th International Forum on CAD, EUROTEAM, University of Leicester, U.K., pp.316-325, Sept. 1991.

12. E.G.Coffman Jr., P.J.Denning, *Operating System Theory*, Prentice Hall, 1976.

Appendix

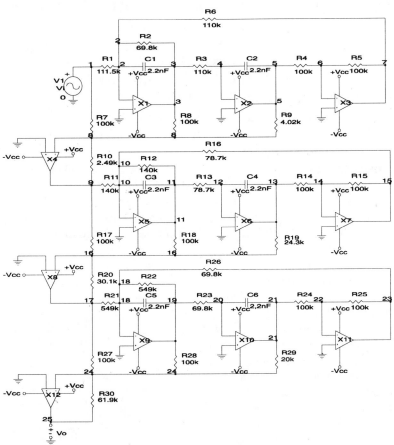

Figure A1. *Schematic Diagram of Circuit IV*

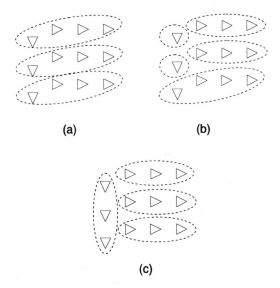

(a)   (b)

(c)

Figure A2. *Ways of Partition of Circuit IV*
(a) Scheme A, (b) Scheme B, (c) Scheme C

Architectural Synthesis with Possibilistic Programming

Ireneusz Karkowski

Delft University of Technology

Faculty of Electrical Engineering

Mekelweg 4, 2628 CD Delft, The Netherlands

e-mail: irek@muresh.et.tudelft.nl

Abstract

The knowledge about available resources during high-level synthesis is usually imprecise. Previous methods seem to have ignored this fact, possibly to avoid an increase in the, already high, computational complexity. In this paper an approach based on so called "possibilistic" programming, a kind of fuzzy mathematical programming, is presented. Using this method we can improve existing mathematical programming methods for the architectural synthesis while keeping their good properties. Not only architectures which optimize the most possible value of the cost function can be generated, but more importantly, also the tradeoff between this goal and reducing the probability of obtaining worse solution and enhancing probability of obtaining a better solution is controlled. At the same time, an increase in the computational complexity of the algorithms is avoided. To show the validity of the approach an application to simultaneous scheduling, selection and allocation of functional units is described. The approach has been implemented in a system called FOAS. Experimental results confirm the advantages of the proposed methodology.

1 Introduction

The design flow of digital systems can be divided into three phases: high-level (architectural) synthesis, logic synthesis and layout synthesis. The earlier stages have many degrees of freedom, but only little information about the final circuit parameters to guide the design. Nevertheless, the quality of the final results can be affected considerably by the decisions made at this stage. Wrong decisions made here are the most "expensive". If a mistake is discovered after placing and routing, the whole design process might have to be restarted.

Most existing methods use some estimated values for the coefficients of cost functions guiding the design. Due to advances in computer technology and numerical methods

nowadays, it is possible to obtain architectures which are globally optimal with respect to these cost functions. But what is the use of this potential if our predictions are far from real values? Attempts to improve the prediction are hampered by many difficult to model design processes. Prediction of the interconnection length is an example of a problem that is quite difficult to handle [Don79][Sec87].

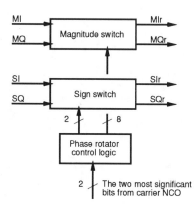

Figure 1: The phase rotator.

Example 1 *We design a GPS correlation engine for the* **GOLLUM** *navigation system [EA92] and we are not sure what kind of phase rotator (figure 1) we should use: A-type or slower but smaller B-type. We estimate that 350 and 310 transistors, respectively are needed to realize them. Since it has to fit into given small area, we decide to use smaller phase rotators. We design our circuit, place it and discover that our layout is too dense and therefore cannot be routed, partly because the final size of B-type rotator is 362 transistors. The redesign of the whole circuit is necessary. We recall the previously ignored suspicion that some logic minimization algorithms could decrease the size of A-type phase rotator to a larger degree than in case B-type was chosen. We use A-type and we obtain a fast and smaller phase rotator using 306 transistors. Place&route complete successfully. Had we known that the logic representation* *for phase rotator of* A-type *can be better optimized, we would have chosen this one from the beginning.*

In a different approach all parameters are assumed random variables with given probability distributions and expected values. Further, we could try to take the randomness into account and modify existing algorithms. There are good reasons to expect that algorithms based on probabilistic information would be more useful. However we then need good methods for generating these probability distributions, and must avoid increasing the, already high, computational complexity. Both problems are not trivial. Generating good probability distributions of circuit parameters is, if feasible, difficult and expensive. Also, methods of stochastic programming do not seem to satisfy our requirements. Combined with integer linear programming formulations only problems with very limited size can be solved.

The approach we propose here is based on possibilistic programming [Zad78], a kind of fuzzy mathematical programming. Methods belonging to this category have their roots in the theory of fuzzy sets and solve optimization problems on fuzzy numbers. It turns out that it is quite easy to generate fuzzy numbers for the design parameters of circuits and that the methods are efficient and flexible. The proposed methodology is very general and can be applied to many optimization problems which arise during design of digital systems. Whenever mathematical programming formulations of problems are used and we deal with imprecise data this method can be applied. Retiming [LS91] and transistor sizing [BJ90] are well known examples of such problems.

The paper is organized as follows. Possibility distributions and possibilistic mathematical programming are introduced in section 2. The problem of simultaneous scheduling, selection and allocation of functional units is introduced in section 3. In section 4 we show how to solve this problem for fuzzy cost function. Experimental results are presented in section 5.

2 Possibilistic programming

2.1 Possibility distributions

To define fuzzy/imprecise numbers, we use possibility distributions[1], as introduced by Zadeh [Zad78], see e.g. figure 2. In this study, the possibility measure of an event might be interpreted as the possibility degree of its occurrence under the possibility distribution, $\pi(.)$, (analogous to a probability distribution).

---

[1]in fuzzy mathematical programming we use membership functions instead.

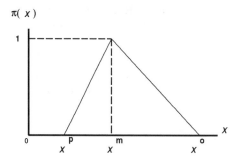

Figure 2: The triangular possibility distribution of fuzzy number x.

Among the various types of distributions, triangular and trapezoid are the most common in solving possibilistic mathematical programming problems. We will concentrate only on triangular fuzzy numbers.

The triangular fuzzy number is denoted by $X = (x^m, x^p, x^o)$, where x^m is the *most possible* value (possibility function $\pi(x) = 1$), x^p and x^o are lower and upper bound values of the acceptable events, respectively. These bound values can be interpreted as the most pessimistic and the most optimistic values. Which one is pessimistic and which optimistic depends on the context.

Example 2 *Consider such a fuzzy number to be the size of the phase rotator unit from example 1. Recall that it was difficult to estimate. Therefore, instead of a poor approximation, we represent the size as a triangular fuzzy number. For example:* $size(A) = X = (350, 300, 370)$ *means that the most possible size of* A-type *unit is 350, we do no expect it to be smaller than 300, nor larger than 370 transistors. In this context* $x^p = 300$ *is our most optimistic value,* $x^o = 370$ *most pessimistic.*

Exact values of x^m, x^o and x^p can be derived from technology parameters, placement and routing methods used, and other information about the structure of the circuit.

Example 3 *In the* **Ocean** *sea-of-gates system [GS94] we have to decide what might be the size of our placement region before performing placement. This is not easy because of two reasons:*

1. *We want to generate layouts as small as possible.*

2. *We do not want to generate too dense layouts since later we may not be able to route them[2].*

Consequently, the existing software tries to guess this size based on factors such as the shapes of cells or the amount of wiring. Retries however are still necessary.

---

[2]In *sea-of-gates* the routing is performed over the cells, there are no special channels for routing.

How can we construct the fuzzy number representing the area of such functional unit? The lower bound can be easily calculated as the sum of areas of all cells to be placed. In practice such a dense placements can hardly ever be routed successfully. Every circuit can be placed and routed if we define our placement region size to be large enough (the software can easily calculate it). This can be used as x^o. Also the most possible size (x^m) can be estimated on the basis of experience.

2.2 Stochastic versus possibilistic programming

Stochastic programming [Sen72] [SM84] can be applied to decision problems where input data have some given probability distributions. Unfortunately these methods are still limited in solving practical problems. The main difficulties are:

1. low computational efficiency,

2. inflexible probabilistic doctrines which hamper modeling the real imprecise meaning of decision makers,

3. the meaning of randomness for some imprecise situations may not be correct either.

Since its introduction by Zadeh, there has been much research on the possibilistic theory. Possibilistic decision making models have provided an important tool in handling practical decision making problems. Unlike stochastic linear programming, possibilistic linear programming methods provide:

1. computational efficiency,

2. flexible doctrines.

Example 4 *The timing specification for our phase rotator (figure 1) contains the following timing constraint:*

> *The delay between arrival of the signal on the "control" input and the time when the data becomes available at the "MIr" output should be about 10ns. In any case the signal should not appear at the output sooner than 5ns or later than 15ns.*

The most straightforward way of modelling this constraint is to express it as the following fuzzy constraint:

$$delay_{control,MIr} \leq X = (10, 5, 15)$$

On the other hand if we were using stochastic programming, X would have to be a random variable with a given probability distribution. It is clear that such a model would not represent the real meaning of our constraint.

Of course, it does not mean that possibility theory can be a substitute in all instances for probability theory.

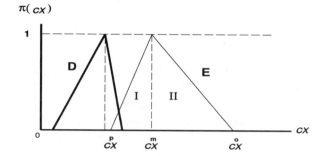

Figure 3: The strategy to solve " $\min \tilde{c}x$ ". We prefer the possibility distribution of D to that of E.

2.3 Linear programming with imprecise objective coefficients

We define the following Possibilistic Linear Program (**PLP**):

$$\min \quad \tilde{c}x \tag{1}$$
$$s.t. \quad \tilde{A}x \leq \tilde{b}, and \quad x \geq 0 \tag{2}$$

where $\tilde{c}$, $\tilde{A}$, and $\tilde{b}$ may consist of imprecise numbers with possibilistic distributions.

Without loss of generality [LH92] we may concentrate on the case when only c is imprecise. For given x, the value of the fuzzy objective function (eq. 1) is a fuzzy number defined by three corner points $(c^m x,1),(c^p x,0)$ and $(c^o x,0)$. Thus, minimizing the fuzzy objective can be obtained by pushing these three critical points to the left. To keep the triangular shape (normal and convex) of the possibility distribution function, instead of minimizing these three objectives simultaneously, we are going to minimize $c^m x$, maximize $[c^m x - c^p x]$ and minimize $[c^o x - c^m x]$, see figure 3.

In this way we obtain the following auxiliary program:

$$\max \quad z_1 = (c^m - c^p)x$$
$$\min \quad z_2 = c^m x$$
$$\min \quad z_3 = (c^o - c^m)x$$

$$s.t. \, x \in X = \{x : Ax \leq b \,, \, x \geq 0\} \tag{3}$$

This Multiple Objective Linear Program (**MOLP**) is equivalent to minimizing the *most possible* value of the imprecise cost (at the point of possibility degree = 1). At the same time, we minimize the "risk of paying higher cost" (see region II in figure 3), and maximize "the possibility of the lower cost" (region I).

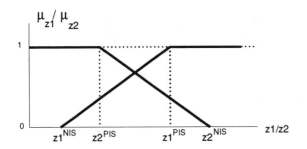

Figure 4: The membership functions of the objectives, z_1 and z_2.

To solve problem 3 we may use any **MOLP** technique such as utility theory, goal programming, fuzzy programming or interactive programming. We have however chosen Zimmermann's fuzzy programming method [Zad65] with the normalization process proposed by Lai and Hwang [LH92].

First we calculate the following Positive Ideal Solutions (PIS) and Negative Ideal Solution (NIS) of the objective functions:

$$
\begin{aligned}
z_1^{PIS} &= \max_{x \in X} (c^m - c^p)x \\
z_2^{PIS} &= \min_{x \in X} c^m x \\
z_3^{PIS} &= \min_{x \in X} (c^o - c^m)x \\
\\
z_1^{NIS} &= \min_{x \in X} (c^m - c^p)x \\
z_2^{NIS} &= \max_{x \in X} c^m x \\
z_3^{NIS} &= \max_{x \in X} (c^o - c^m)x
\end{aligned}
\tag{4}
$$

where the feasible solution space $x \in X$ is the same as in eq. 3. The linear membership functions of these objective functions can now be computed as (see also figure 4):

$$
\mu_{z1} = \begin{cases}
1 & if \quad z_1 > z_1^{PIS} \\
\frac{(z_1 - z_1^{NIS})}{(z_1^{PIS} - z_1^{NIS})} & if \quad z_1^{NIS} \le z_1 \le z_1^{PIS} \\
0 & if \quad z_1 < z_1^{NIS}
\end{cases}
\tag{5}
$$

$$
\mu_{z2} = \begin{cases}
1 & if \quad z_2 < z_2^{PIS} \\
\frac{(z_2^{NIS} - z_2)}{(z_2^{NIS} - z_2^{PIS})} & if \quad z_2^{PIS} \le z_2 \le z_2^{NIS} \\
0 & if \quad z_2 > z_2^{NIS}
\end{cases}
\tag{6}
$$

and μ_{z3} is similar to μ_{z2}. Finally we solve the following Zimmermann's equivalent single-objective linear programming program:

$$\max \alpha$$

$$s.t. \quad \mu_{zi}(x) \ge \alpha, \; i = 1, 2, 3 \; and \; x \in X. \tag{7}$$

The optimal solution of equation 7 will provide a satisfying solution under the previous strategy of maximizing the

chance of higher profit, and minimizing the most possible value and the possibility of lower profit.

If A or b is also imprecise the same methodology with only small extensions can be used.

3 Simultaneous scheduling, and selection and allocation of functional units

3.1 Problem formulation

> **PROBLEM**
>
> Given:
>
> 1. DAG (Directed Acyclic Graph) representing an algorithm to be synthesized.
>
> 2. Interface constraints (synchronous or asynchronous).
>
> 3. Other constraints given by user.
>
> 4. Specifications of available functional units.
>
> Produce a schedule, by mapping each code operation to a time (maintaining the partial order among operations), and map each operation to a functional unit. Simultaneously select and allocate functional units, and schedule operations to minimize the area cost function.

3.2 Solution

The deterministic (non-possibilistic) version of the problem from section 3.1 can be solved optimally using the methods of integer linear programming (**IP**) [GE90]. Thanks to recent advances in integer programming even quite large examples can be solved within reasonable CPU time.

Here follows the integer programming formulation of the problem:

$$\min f(x_{i,j,k}) \tag{8}$$

Minimize this linear or piecewise linear function of variables, subject to:

- Operation Assignment Constraints:

$$\forall_k \left[\sum_i \sum_{j \in R(k)} x_{i,j,k} = 1 \right] \tag{9}$$

They ensure that each code operation will be assigned to one control step and functional unit.

- Functional Unit Constraints:

$$\forall_{i,j} \left[\sum_{\substack{k \in Op(C,L)}} \sum_{\substack{j_1=j \\ j_1 \in R(k)}}^{j+L-1} x_{j,j_1,k} \leq 1 \right] \quad (10)$$

Prevent more than one code operation from being assigned to the same functional unit at the same control step.

- Precedence Constraints:

$$\forall_{\substack{k_2 <\bullet\ k_1 \\ j \in R(k_z) \\ z=1,2}} \left[\sum_i \left(\sum_{\substack{j_1 \leq j+C_2-1 \\ j_1 \in R(k_1)}} y_{i,j_1,k_1} + \sum_{\substack{j \leq j_2 \\ j_2 \in R(k_2)}} y_{i,j_2,k_2} \right) \leq 1 \right]$$
$$(11)$$

Prevent an operation, $k2$ from being scheduled after operation $k1$ whenever there is a partial order between these operations such that $k2 < \bullet\ k1$ (that means $k2$ must be scheduled before $k1$). The constraints form integral facets for the system of linear inequalities and thus better bounds on variables and decrease in computation time result.

- Interface or user specified constraints.

where : $x_{i,j,k}$ - binary variables which assume value 1 if code operation k has been scheduled at the j-th cstep (clock cycle), using functional unit i, 0 otherwise.

C - execution time of functional unit

L - latency time (minimum time between successive data input accepted by the unit)

$k \in Op(C, L)$ - means all codes which could be implemented by a unit with values C,L.

$j \in R(k)$ - means all csteps to which k-th code can be assigned, calculated using *critical path method* [Fou81].

4 The FOAS system

Our system called **FOAS** (Fuzzy Optimization Architectural Synthesis) combines methods of possibilistic programming and integer programming to efficiently solve problem defined in section 3.1. It has been programmed in $C++$ on HP9000/735 computer. Its block diagram is presented in figure 5.

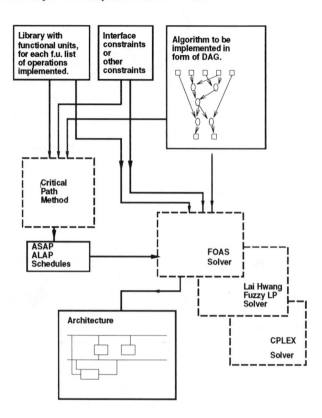

Figure 5: The FOAS System.

The major change that we make is in assuming that our cost function is imprecise. The reason is the fact that the area of available functional units is defined in terms of triangular fuzzy numbers. Also other timing parameters of our units or interface constraints may be defined in terms of fuzzy numbers. As a result we obtain a possibilistic integer program (**PIP**). To increase the power of the system, we decided to include support for multiple types of functional units. This extension was straightforward and caused only a small increase in the number of constraints. For example, every constraint of eq. 11 had to be repeated for each type of functional unit implementing operation $k2$.

The objective function or cost function can be formulated as any linear or piecewise linear function of the variables. The FOAS system supports two different formulations which can be selected by the user:

$$\min \sum_i \sum_k \sum_{j \in R(k)} \tilde{s}(i) x_{i,j,k} \quad (12)$$

$$\min \sum_t \tilde{s} I^t \quad (13)$$

$$\sum_{k \in t} \sum_{i \in t} x_{i,j,k} \leq I^t, \forall_{t,j}$$

where : $x_{i,j,k}$ - the same as in section 3.2,

I^t - number of units of type t used,

$\tilde{s}$ - vector with imprecise costs of functional units,

$k \in t$ - means all codes which can be implemented by units of type t,

$i \in t$ - means all units of type t.

The first cost function (eq.12) is very simple and adds no extra constraints. To handle the possibility of using many units of the same type we add a small constant to the cost of every next unit used. This function has the advantage that it simultaneously optimizes for time and area.

The second function (eq.13) has the advantage that it optimizes the area of the obtained architecture.

The system reads input data, specified in a user friendly format, from a file. That file contains description of the available functional units (including fuzzy cost, C and L parameters, and functions implemented), algorithm to be implemented in form of a DAG, inputs/outputs, mapping from code operations into functional units (we allow units implementing many code operations), requested execution time and interface constraints. Based on this data, we first calculate *asap* and *alap* schedules[Fou81] using the *critical path method* algorithm of complexity $\mathcal{O}(n^2)$. These schedules are later very useful because they allow us to restrict the size of the solution space (only *csteps* between $asap(k)$ and $alap(k)$ need to be considered). Next, we generate the cost function and constraints of the **PIP**. It is then piped into the Lai-Hwang solver which we implemented separately as a general **PIP/PLP** solver. The result of this call is the 0-1 solution to our problem. We only need to scan the variables to which has been assigned the value 1 (that means that a code operation k, has been assigned to cstep j and to functional unit i). After sorting these variables, the system displays the resulting schedule.

We implemented the Lai-Hwang method as a general **PIP/PLP** solver. It accepts input in a comprehensive text format in which the cost function, constraints and definitions of integer/binary variables can be written line by line. All coefficients in these expressions can be fuzzy. We have built it on the top of efficient optimizer called **CPLEX** ([CPL93]). The Lai-Hwang solver generates 7 specially formulated crisp **IP**'s and calls **CPLEX** to solve them. We observed that usually most of the computation time is required to solve Z_2^{PIS} and the final "alpha" program (see for details section 2.3). Since Z_2^{PIS} is equivalent to solving normal non-fuzzy **IP**, solving **PIP** may take in worst case 7 times longer. In practice it is however less. After some experiments, we decided to make a small extension to the original Lai-Hwang method. We added the possibility to define weights for the tree subgoals of the

MOLP (eq. 3). In this way the user can decide what is for him more important - *most possible* area, left or right spreads. In the FOAS program we use as default the highest weight for z_2, then for z_3 and z_1. This very simple extension gives the user extra control over the generated results.

5 Experimental results

In this section we would like to present two examples. First one is a very simple algorithm called "neuzel" which we analyze in detail, the second one is the Elliptical Wave Filter example.

5.1 "Neuzel" example

The algorithm that has to be implemented is shown in figure 6. The available functional units are listed in table 1.

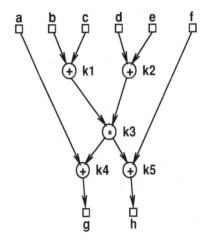

Figure 6: Algorithm to be synthesized (neuzel ex.).

We compute the optimal schedule and functional unit assignment using FOAS system. We specify timing constraints on the required output time to be 4 csteps. Our program produced schedule **A** (table2). Notation $unitname^i(codename)$ means that i-th unit of type $unitname$ is used to implement code operation $codename$ at given cstep. The cost function value for this solution is equal $(37, 29, 44)$ and can be seen in figure 7. We conclude that the *most possible* size of this architecture is 37, it should never be lower than 29 or higher that 44 (left spread of fuzzy cost is equal 8, right 7).

Now we make a small modification. We change the characteristics of available alu's in such a way that x^o for them is much higher. It means that they could be much bigger than the *most possible* size (see value with index

Unit	C	L	Size (fuzzy)	Func tions
add1	1	1	(12,8,15)	+
add2	2	1	(8,7,12)	+
mul1	1	1	(15,11,19)	*
mul2	2	1	(11,10,15)	*
alu1	1	1	$(25,21,29^A/39^B)$	+,*
alu2	2	1	$(19,18,23^A/33^B)$	+,*

Table 1: Functional units specifications (neuzel ex.). C - execution time, L - latency time (minimum time between successive data input values being accepted by the unit), both in clock cycles.

cstep	assignment
1	$alu1^1(k1)$ $add1^1(k2)$
2	$alu1^1(k3)$
3	$alu1^1(k4)$
4	$alu1^1(k5)$

Table 2: Schedule A.

cstep	assignment
1	$add1^1(k1)$ $add1^2(k2)$
2	$mul2^1(k2)$
3	
4	$add1^1(k4)$ $add1^2(k5)$

Table 3: Schedule B.

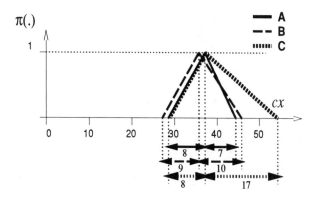

Figure 7: Optimal solutions (neuzel ex.).

B in the table 1). Now we run our system again without changing the other parameters. The resulting schedule is presented in table 3. The program detected the potential "danger" of using alu's and decided for a solution with two adders and one multiplier (cost function value $(35, 26, 45)$, see fuzzy number **B** in figure 7). Comparing this solution to solution **A** we can see that the *most possible* size of the architecture **B** is 35, which is better by 2 units compared with architecture **A**. The right spread, representing the risk of obtaining worse solution, is higher than in architecture **A**. This higher risk was the reason why this solution has not been chosen before. In figure 7 also another, 3rd fuzzy number can be seen (with name **C**). It represents that value of the cost function which we would get if we kept the architecture **A** despite the fact that characteristics of our alu's have changed. Such solution would have the same value of the *most possible* size but in the worst case it could be even 17 units bigger. Solution **B** is much better than **C**.

Concluding this very simple example, it is interesting to point out very important characteristic of our methodology. There may exist many solutions with a similar *most possible* value of the cost function (very close to the global optimum). The system was in both cases able to choose such an architecture which had very small *most possible* size but simultaneously, had a minimal risk of running out of space during layout design and a maximal *possibility* of obtaining even smaller sizes.

5.2 EWF example

We also run our program on the obligatory Elliptical Wave Filter example [Dep88]. The available functional units are listed in table 4.

Unit	C	L	Size (fuzzy)	Func tions
add	1	1	(12,8,15)	+
mul1	1	1	(15,11,19)	*
mul2	2	1	(11,7,20)	*

Table 4: Functional units specifications (EWF).

Figure 8 shows the schedule which we obtain when we use only x^m values (traditional way). In figure 9 the schedule generated by our system using fuzzy costs is shown. We optimize for area and for latency $T_e = 19$. As can be seen, both solutions use 2 adders and 1 multiplier. First schedule uses pipelined multiplier $mul2$ while the second a single cycle $mul1$. The fuzzy cost function values are $(35, 23, 50)$ and $(39, 27, 49)$. The most possible cost in the second solution is a little bit higher. In the same time this solution is less "risky" since the right spread is by 5 units smaller.

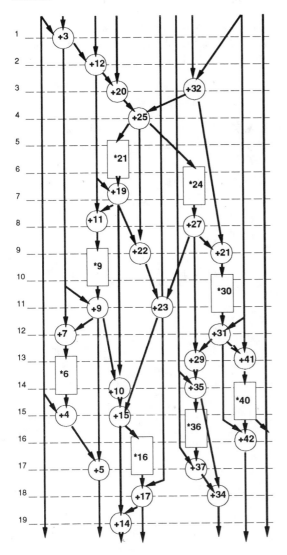

Figure 8: EWF schedule optimized using *most possible costs* only.

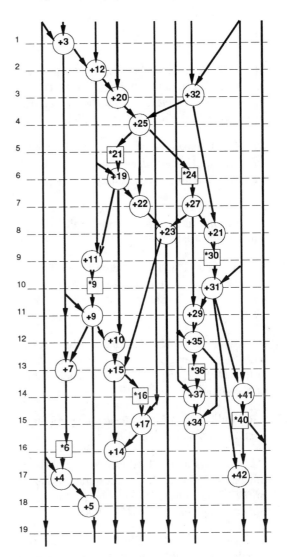

Figure 9: EWF schedule optimized using fuzzy costs.

6   Conclusions

In this paper we presented an extension to the **IP** formulations of the architectural synthesis problems. We described one of its applications - *simultaneous scheduling, selection and allocation of functional units* [3]. It can be very easily applied to other models as *3-D scheduling and allocation* or *simultaneous scheduling, and allocation of functional units, busses, and registers*[GE91]. We have

shown that this extension is very simple, efficient and powerful. We believe that it can also be successfully applied during other stages of computer system design, whenever mathematical formulations of problems are used and we have to deal with imprecise data. As examples we mention here retiming or transistor sizing.

Acknowledgements

The author wishes to thank Prof. Ralph Otten for helpful discussions and Dr. Mirosław Kwiesielewicz for the introduction to the fuzzy sets theory. He is also very grateful to Prof. Giovanni De Micheli of Stanford University, Dr. Patrick Groeneveld, Jacek Serafin, Jack Glas and Cezar Bruma for their valuable remarks. Dr. Tamas Terlaky was very helpful in choosing the right linear optimizer package.

---

[3]another name is 2-D scheduling and allocation

References

[BJ90] M.R.C.M. Berkelaar and J.A.G. Jess. Gate sizing in mos digital circuits with linear programming. In *Proceedings of the European Design Automation Conference*, pages 217–221, 1990.

[CPL93] CPLEX Optimization Inc. *The CPLEX Linear Optimizer and Mixed Integer Optimizer with Barrier. User manual*, second edition, 1993.

[Dep88] Ed F. Deprettere. *SVD and signal processing; applications and architectures*. North-Holland, Amsterdam, 1988.

[Don79] W.E. Donath. Placement and average interconnection lengths of computer logic. *IEEE Trans. on Circuits and Systems*, CAS-26(4):272–277, 1979.

[EA92] E.Aardoom and A.K.Nieuwland. Gollum: A vlsi multi-system navigation receiver. In *Proceedings of ION GPS-92*, pages 1111–1116. The Institute of Navigation, September 1992.

[Fou81] L.R. Foulds. *Optimization Techniques: An Introduction*. Springer-Verlag, 1981.

[GE90] C.H. Gebotys and M.I. Elmasry. A global optimization approach to architectural synthesis. In *IEEE International Conference on Computer Aided Design*, pages 258–261, 1990.

[GE91] C.H. Gebotys and M.I. Elmasry. Simultaneous scheduling and allocation for cost constrained optimal architectural synthesis. In *ACM/IEEE Design Automation Conference*, pages 2–7, 1991.

[GS94] Patrick Groeneveld and Paul Stravers. A robust design environment for vlsi training with a very short learning curve. In *Proceedings of the fifth Eurochip workshop on VLSI training*, October 1994.

[LH92] Y.J. Lai and C.L. Hwang. A new aproach to some possibilistic linear programming problem. *Fuzzy Sets and Systems*, 49:121–133, 1992.

[LS91] C. Leiserson and J. Saxe. Retiming synchronous circuitry. *Algorithmica*, 6(1):5–25, 1991.

[Sec87] Carl Sechen. Average interconnection length estimation for random and optimized placement. In *Proceedings of the International Conference on Computer-Aided Design*, pages 190–193, 1987.

[Sen72] J.K. Sengupta. *Stochastic Programming*. North Holland Publishing Company, 1972.

[SM84] I.M. Stancu-Minasian. *Stochastic Programming with Multiple Objective Functions*. D. Reidel, Dordrecht, 1984.

[Zad65] L.A. Zadeh. Fuzzy sets. *Information and Control*, 8:94–102, 1965.

[Zad78] L.A. Zadeh. Fuzzy sets as a basis for a theory of possibility. *Fuzzy Sets and Systems*, 1:3–28, 1978.

Symbolic Incompletely Specified Functions for Correct Evaluation in the Presence of Indeterminate Input Values

Glenn Jennings

Division of Computer Engineering

Luleå Institute of Technology

S-971 87 Luleå, Sweden

glenn@sm.luth.se

Abstract

We describe the Ordered Ternary Decision Diagram (OTDD) which can be directly evaluated even when given any number of undefined input logic values. Based on Kleenean strong ternary logic, the OTDD unifies the concepts of "unknown input" with "don't-care output" for incompletely-specified Boolean functions. The OTDD permits functions having nontrivial don't-care sets to be represented as single diagrams and to be directly processed against each other. We define the full OTDD and the abbreviated OTDD. We examine advantages of the OTDD over the commonly-used dual-OBDD method of representing incomplete functions, for LGSynth93 standard benchmarks. We outline a single package for computations with both shared, reduced OTDDs and OBDDs.

1 Introduction

The computer engineer is often confronted by complex Boolean functions having nontrivial don't-care sets, in contexts where it is desirable to manipulate those functions symbolically. Examples include multilevel logic synthesis [JT93] and compiled logic simulation [CG85]. When working on such problems, we were repeatedly finding that strictly Boolean symbolic calculi, such as the OBDD [Bry86] became awkward to work with as we sought to answer questions such as the following:

- given functions F and G having nonempty don't-care sets, what symbolic representation should be used for F and for G?

- what is the function *(not F xor G)* and how do we compute it symbolically?

- can we defend the semantics of our result for *(not F xor G)*, is it really meaningful?

- can we evaluate the function *(not F xor G)* even when one or more values for the support set variables are indeterminate ('U')?

The disadvantage of using the OBDD for working with 'U' as an *input* value is that an OBDD needs to be given a firm '0' or '1' for each variable in the support set; and for dealing with 'U' as an *output* value, every path in an OBDD leads of course to a firm '0' or '1' terminal. Therefore to deal with the "unknown" value, using the OBDD meant that we needed multiple diagrams, multiple diagram variables per true problem variable [Bry90], or multiple diagram traversals to deal with the problems above. Using two completely-specified Boolean diagrams, that is, a pair of OBDDs to represent a single incompletely-specified Boolean function had been used by Bryant in the COSMOS simulator, and the encoding is described in [Bry87].

Furthermore the problem of accurate evaluation in the presence of unknowns (an NP-complete problem [CA87]) has never previously been addressed for incomplete Boolean functions, neither for functions represented by decision diagram. Only complete functions in SOP/POS form have been investigated [CP89]. This is a critical problem in simulation, since a symbolic "don't-care" value 'U' produced by an upstream simulation module becomes the "unknown" value 'U' to downstream modules which receive it [JIL94] [Jen94]. This is the intuition for needing a rigorous semantical unification of input 'U' with output 'U', that is, the ternary logic system to be used must be carefully chosen and specified. Such an "unknown" value is used for example in [L+88] as the initial value for all binary signals in the simulation.

This paper reports our development of the Ordered Ternary Decision Diagram, together with its algorithms, toward dealing with the problems mentioned above. The insight was to use a three-branched three-terminaled decision diagram, a well-founded and well-understood extended logic system [Kle52] as the diagram's formal basis, and a very particular semantics for the new 'U' branch of the diagram nonterminals. The OTDD solves the accurate 'U'-evaluation problem posed in [CA87] and our results hold for incompletely-specified functions as well, as we will

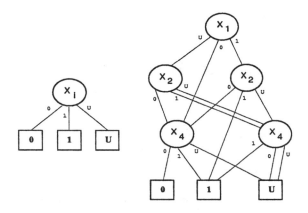

Figure 1: Simple (full) Ordered Ternary Decision Diagrams. To left: the identity function for variable x_i. To right: the function $((x_1$ and $x_2)$ or $x_4)$.

formally prove here. The OTDD permits incompletely-specified functions to be represented by a single diagram, and permits us to compute with them in exactly the same way that the OBDD permits computations on completely-specified functions, yet with lower memory requirements than using the prevalent dual-OBDD encoding [Bry92]. Because the OTDD has an "abbreviated" form, it is possible to compute with the OTDD in its most memory-compact form, expanding to the "full" OTDD only when necessary, which we will also explain.

2   Relationship to Earlier Work

Of course we attribute the Ordered Binary Decision Diagram (OBDD) to Bryant [Bry86] [Bry92], but we point out that the OBDD was developed for manipulation of *Boolean functions,* that is, it is *not* merely a syntactical data structure devoid of any such semantics. At about the same time as the development of the shared, reduced OBDD having a strong canonical form [BRB90] one begins to find the notion of a *binary* decision diagram (two-branched nonterminals) having multiple *terminal* vertices, as in the recent Algebraic Decision Diagrams (ADD) of [BF⁺93]. Some of these two-branched diagrams have *three* terminal vertices, for '0', '1' and "undefined." The "undefined" terminal of the Ordered Partial Decision Diagram (OPDD) [RB⁺91] [PM93] arises due to incomplete OBDD evaluation. In the "ternary-valued BDD" of [MIY90], and more recently the Modified Ordered Binary Decision Diagram (MBD) of [JT93], this 'U' terminal is used to represent "don't-care" function values. As we will review below, no OBDD-type algorithms were provided with those proposals, because the proposals were entirely syntactical: no *semantics* were specified for the proposed ternary systems. More abstract efforts, seeming to lay claim to general "*n*-ary decision diagrams" for all cardinals *n*, can be cited such as the MDD of [SKMB90] (a work of value to us here, see Section 3) and the NDD of [KP⁺92]. Here we find nonterminal vertices

having *more* than two branches; however, the definitions also tend mainly to be syntactical, not semantical, leaving us often to wonder whether any *meaning* [YM88] can be attached in general to such "*n*-ary decision diagrams."

However by our use of the word "ternary" we are designating a diagram having a *very* specific semantics, founded upon Kleenean strong ternary logic [Kle52],[1] and not merely to designate a three-branched syntax. In none of the above cited works on three-branched or three-terminal decision diagrams do we find Kleenean strong ternary logic semantics being assigned to the diagrams, nor do we find any proposal to further process such diagrams against each other using Kleenean strong ternary logic. Even in the "fuzzy logic" community, where there is considerable interest in Kleenean logic [HNY93], we are aware of no previous work for representing nor manipulating Kleenean strong ternary logic functions by decision diagram.

Neither is Kleenean strong ternary logic used by most other authors. For example, Bryant (when describing his two-diagram encoding) defines a MOS-dependent 'U' which means a "potentially nondigital voltage" [Bry92] [Bry87]. However choosing Kleenean *strong* ternary logic as the semantical foundation, as opposed to other ternary logics (including the "weak" ternary logic discussed by Kleene in [Kle52]) places the restriction that 'U' may *not* mean "neither zero nor one" (as in, for example, Post ternary logic [WF80]), nor mean an illegal logic voltage [DL93], nor be part of a pseudo-continuum of distinct values '0'→'U'→'1'. Rather, the Kleenean strong 'U' means a

---

[1] Although we cite [Kle52], Kleene himself cited his earlier work from 1938; see also [Urq86].

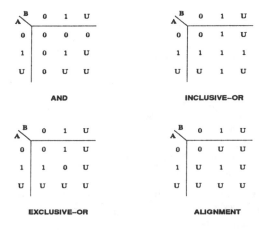

Figure 2: Examples of Kleenean strong ternary logic functions for common functions, including the "alignment" operation underlying the 'U'-branch semantics of the OTDD. The entry in the 'U' column for any given row of a Kleenean strong truth table is zero (one) if and only if the other two entries in that same row are both zero (one); similarly for entries in the 'U' row for any given column.

valid logic one or logic zero, but we don't know *or don't care* which.[2] As early as [Bre72] we see a non-Kleenean-strong ternary logic used in an investigation (as in others which followed in its steps [BS87] [Bry90] [BS91]) which combines a non-Kleenean-strong ternary logic together with a *temporal* model to reason about circuit timing. Also, the technology-dependence of Bryant's 'U' [Bry87] means that the COSMOS dual-OBDD is *not* semantically equivalent to the OTDD; and the effect of this is to leave us without the algorithms necessary for processing dual-OBDDs under Kleenean strong ternary logic. In this paper we are not confusing logic with timing, nor incomplete functions with their many possible implementations. The Kleenean strong definition of 'U' is in fact the one which most often occurs in the logic synthesis and testability literature [Bra83], although Kleenean strong ternary logic *itself* is generally not explicitly appealed to. This Kleenean strong restriction on 'U', which at first glance appears to be a disadvantage, is for our (technology independent) purposes the strength of the OTDD since it permits us to unify an "unknown input" with a "don't care output." Furthermore it is critical toward defining the composition of two incompletely-specified functions, which we will discuss later in Section 5.

Although our contribution is a diagram plus algorithms for Kleenean strong ternary logic (as opposed to the Boolean foundation of the OBDD) yet we make another (and in our view a more important) semantical contribution for applications in computer engineering, namely the particular semantics we assign to the 'U' branch of our nonterminal vertices (Section 3, below). Those semantics permit us to predict the value of the function represented by the OTDD even though *any* number of input variables to the function may be unknown. The result is that we are able to unify the notions of "unknown" and "don't care" within the formal framework of Kleenean strong ternary logic.

3 OTDD Definition and Properties

Using the notation of [SKMB90] we syntactically define the OTDD as a rooted, ordered directed acyclic multigraph containing zero or more nonterminal vertices v having index $i = index(v)$ representing variable x_i, where x_i may take on the values $\{U, 0, 1\}$ $\forall i$, and having children $\{child_u(v), child_0(v), child_1(v)\}$. Furthermore the OTDD contains one or more terminal vertices v having $value(v)$ $\in \{U, 0, 1\}$. A reduced OTDD contains no nonterminal v such that $child_0(v)$ is isomorphic to $child_1(v)$ (in which case, as we will show below, we would also always have an isomorphic $child_u(v)$ as well so that the reduction criteria

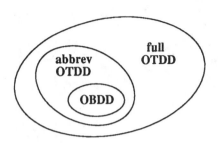

Figure 3: Venn diagram showing the relationship among full Ordered Ternary Decision Diagrams (OTDD), abbreviated OTDDs, and Ordered Binary Decision Diagrams (OBDD).

of [SKMB90] apply to the OTDD). Since we consider the shared reduced OTDD here, which contains no distinct vertex pair v and v' which are isomorphic, we therefore have that $child_0(v) \neq child_1(v)$ for all nonterminal vertices. Examples of OTDDs, corresponding to Figure 1 in Bryant's [Bry86], are shown in Figure 1 above. If we remove the 'U' branch from all nonterminals, we obtain the abbreviated OTDD;[3] and if we further forbid the 'U' *terminal* vertex, we will have an OBDD. These relationships are shown in Figure 3.

We give the intuition behind our chosen 'U'-branch semantics by showing how the Ordered Ternary Decision Diagram for $(x_1 \text{ and } x_2) \text{ or } x_4$ of Figure 1 is derived from its corresponding OBDD. In Figure 4 A we first expand the binary function $(x_1 \text{ and } x_2) \text{ or } x_4$ into its full binary decision *tree* [RB+91] [Bry92], see Figure 4 B. Consider now the top variable; it has two child subtrees, one for each of its '0' and '1' branches. We will create a new third subtree (for the new 'U' branch) as a function of these first two subtrees, a function which we call *alignment*, see Figure 2. The result is a third subtree which differs from the original two in that a 'U' *terminal* appears in the new tree wherever the two corresponding original terminals do not match each other, see Figure 4 C. Here one can see why alignment on isomorphic $child_0$ and $child_1$ will in fact give a $child_u$ which is also isomorphic to both. The same alignment procedure is now carried out on all three sons of the top variable, and so on recursively down the entire tree. The result is a ternary decision tree as in Figure 4 D which can then be reduced to a directed acyclic graph giving the final result of Figure 4 E. Clearly the 'U' branch at any nonterminal has a very specific relationship to the '0' and '1' branches for the same nonterminal, namely that the 'U' branch represents the *alignment* of its '0' and '1' brothers.

---

[2] We cite the late Professor Kleene: "Here 'unknown' is a category into which we can regard any proposition as falling, whose value we either do not know or choose for the moment to disregard; and it does *not* then exclude the other two possibilities 'true' and 'false'." [Kle52]

[3] Syntactically the abbreviated OTDD looks like a "ternary-valued BDD" [MIY90] or MBD [JT93] however the latter are not defined upon Kleenean strong ternary logic, therefore any claim to *semantical* equivalence to the OTDD must be challenged.

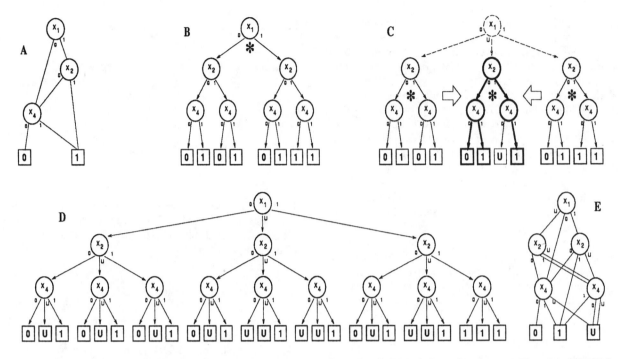

Figure 4: Developing the full OTDD for $((x_1 \ and \ x_2) \ or \ x_4)$ from its OBDD (A) by first expanding the OBDD into its corresponding decision tree (B) and preparing for the topmost alignment (asterisk, B) of '0' and '1' subtrees. The resulting alignment subtree (center, C) receives a terminal 'U' wherever the corresponding terminal in the '0' subtree differs from that of the '1' subtree. The alignment subtree becomes the new 'U' child to the top node. The process is then repeated recursively down the tree (asterisks, C). The resulting full ternary decision tree (D) can then be reduced to a directed acyclic graph (E) which is the final full OTDD.

A full OTDD (by definition) must always have this specific 'U'-branch semantics.

Theorem: *the reduced, shared (full) OTDD has a strong canonical form.*

Proof: by direct appeal to [SKMB90] plus the observation that the various $child_j(v)$ need not all have been *generated* by the same operators for the results on canonical function graphs in [SKMB90] to hold.

Theorem: *the (full) OTDD will evaluate to the correct value for the function, that is '0', '1', or 'U', in the presence of any number of 'U' values for the input variables x_i.*

The proof of this theorem implicitly uses the critical Kleenean strong ternary logic restriction that 'U' cannot mean *"neither zero nor one,"* plus the fact that a full OTDD reduces to a valid abbreviated OTDD or OBDD when the 'U'-branches are eliminated, as we had pointed out earlier (Figure 3).

Proof: by induction on those members x_i of the support set having the value 'U'. We order the members of this (nonempty) subset by ascending variable number; let the member of lowest index be x_A, and for two adjacent members x_B and x_C we assume $B < C$.

Basis: The path from the top variable to variable x_A does

not involve any 'U'-branch. At x_A we will find $child_0 \neq child_1$, and within both $child_0$ and $child_1$ we will not traverse any 'U'-branch had it been possible to determine which of these children to select. We consider the outcome of selecting $child_0$, that is, assuming $x_A = 0$, and then of selecting $child_1$, that is, assuming $x_A = 1$. There are only two cases: (1) both choices lead to the same terminal value, notice that 'U' is possible as a common result, or else (2) the two choices lead to different terminals. In case (1) the correct function value is the common terminal value, but this is the value obtained by the *alignment* operation on those two terminals; and in case (2) the correct function value must be 'U', since the path from the top variable through x_A leads to differing results depending on x_A, so we must produce 'U'; but 'U' is the value obtained by alignment on differing terminals. Therefore we may now consider the choice $child_u$, note that we will not traverse any 'U'-branch within it, and by straightforward *Apply* construction according to the *alignment* function it is clear that selecting $child_u$ will yield the correct function value for the unknown x_A.

Induction step: Assume that all full OTDDs for $x_A, ..., x_B = $ 'U' evaluate to the correct result. Consider any path from any vertex x_B which passes through vertex x_C, where $B < C$, so that at x_C by the induction hypothesis the evaluations of *child*$_0$ (if we had $x_C = 0$) and *child*$_1$ (if we had $x_C = 1$) will yield correct results, neither do we traverse any 'U'-branch within either child. But by the construction of *child*$_u$ at x_C, which is by direct alignment of *child*$_0$ against *child*$_1$ which are correct, then evaluation of *child*$_u$ at x_C will give us the common value of *child*$_0$ and *child*$_1$ if they are the same, else 'U' if they differ; and since this is the correct behavior of the function for both cases, then the correctness of the full OTDD for $x_C = $ 'U' is established, which establishes the correctness of the full OTDD for $x_A, ..., x_C = $ 'U'.

4 Computing with the OTDD

We express our clear debt to Bryant's landmark article [Bry86] by describing OTDD pseudocode in terms of the functions taught there. The basic data structure for a diagram node in our package is given here in pseudocode:

```
node {
   index:       int
   val:         {0,1,U,X}
   low,high,und: *node  }
```

where 'U' is the "don't care" terminal, and 'X' means a nonterminal vertex. We give an *Apply* interface here [Bry86] (rather than an *ITE* approach [BRB90]) because 'U' could appear as both input value and terminal result. The *Apply_step* routine of [Bry86] uses a routine *Op* which receives the "val" of the top variables for the subfunctions being processed and seeks controlling and terminal cases. We can use the fast isomorphism capability to pass not only those values plus opcode, but also a Boolean ("iso") set to "true" if the two subgraphs are isomorphic:

```
char Op( a, b, opcode, iso ) {
  (opcode == IDENT)        => return a;
  (opcode == NOT):
    (a == 'X')             => return 'X' else
    (a == '0')             => return '1' else
    (a == '1')             => return '0' else
    return 'U';
  (opcode == OR):
    ((a == '1')||(b == '1')) => return '1' else
    ((a == 'X')||(b == 'X')):
      (iso)                => return 'F' else
      (a == '0')           => return 'G' else
      (b == '0')           => return 'F' else
      return 'X';
    ((a == '0')&&(b == '0')) => return '0' else
    return 'U';
  (opcode == AND):
    ((a == '0')||(b == '0')) => return '0' else
    ((a == 'X')||(b == 'X')):
      (iso)                => return 'F' else
      (a == '1')           => return 'G' else
      (b == '1')           => return 'F' else
      return 'X';
    ((a == '1')&&(b == '1')) => return '1' else
    return 'U';
```

```
  (opcode == XOR):
    ((a == 'X')||(b == 'X')):
      /* (iso) => return '0' NON-KLEENEAN */
      return 'X';
    ((a == '1')&&(b == '1')) => return '0' else
    ((a == '1')&&(b == '0')) => return '1' else
    ((a == '0')&&(b == '1')) => return '1' else
    ((a == '0')&&(b == '0')) => return '0' else
    return 'U';
  (opcode == A_AND_NOT_B):
    ((a == '0')||(b == '1')) => return '0' else
    ((a == 'X')||(b == 'X')):
      /* (iso) => return '0' NON-KLEENEAN */
      (b == '0')             => return 'F' else
      return 'X';
    ((a == '1')&&(b == '0')) => return '1' else
    return 'U';
  (opcode == OR_B_TO_U):
    ((b == '1')||(b == 'U')) => return 'U' else
    ((a == 'X')||(b == 'X')) => return 'X' else
    return a;
  (opcode == ALIGNMENT):
    ((a == 'U')||(b == 'U')) => return 'U' else
    ((a == 'X')||(b == 'X')):
      (iso)                  => return 'F' else
      return 'X';
    (a == b)                 => return a else
    return 'U'; }
```

'F' and 'G' signify the entire incoming functions f and g having top node "val" fields "a" and "b" respectively. Taking "OR" as an example, the code above includes not only that (f *or* 1) = 1 but also (f *or* f) = f and (f *or* 0) = f for any incomplete function f. This information is used in *Apply_step* below. The performance gain from having this information is examined briefly in Section 6. Notice that function "IDENT" contains no such shortcuts, but forces an exhaustive descent into the corresponding subgraph; its purpose will be explained below. The reader will recognize the Kleenean strong truth tables of Figure 2 in the code above. Furthermore, we note that all Kleenean strong logic functions in the code above (with two exceptions to be indicated below) reduce to simple Boolean operations upon removing the 'U' row and column of those tables, that is, our *Apply* reduces to the Boolean semantics of the OBDD [Bry86] in the absence of 'U'.

We point out a pitfall indicated in the code above, with the comment "non-Kleenean" (more properly, "not-Kleenean-strong"). Considering "XOR" as an example, we cannot simply declare (f *xor* f) = 0 since, if f has a nontrivial don't-care set, then we could have ('U' *xor* 'U') = 0 contrary to Kleenean strong ternary logic, see Figure 2. To give some insight into why the identical-'0' would be incorrect in general, consider two logic modules X and Y, both implementing function f, both sharing the same inputs, yet having differing resolutions for the don't-care set of f. Then there will be some input vector such that (f *xor* f) = ('1' *xor* '0') $\neq$ 0. Kleenean strong ternary logic therefore deals correctly with 'U' in the absence of any additional knowledge about the inputs. Cases where the inputs may have been similarly implemented, where reconvergent fanouts in Boolean networks of incomplete functions are involved and so forth [CA87] [DD93] [SS93] are not discussed further here, the reader is referred to [Jen94].

As described in [BRB90] and also as employed in [SKMB90] we accomplish reduced canonicity by using a *unique-table* with its insertion/lookup function "ut_insert", and by having a *memory function* which caches operations into a *computed-table* with lookup function "mf_find" and insertion function "mf_insert". [BRB90] discusses how these can be implemented by hashing, together with garbage-collection concerns. As in [Bry86] the *Apply* operation invokes recursive routine *Apply_step*, adapted for this package as follows:

```
*node Apply_step( f, g, opcode, sw )
  f,g:  *node;
  sw:   {ABBREV,FULL}  {

  res  = Op( f.val, g.val, opcode, (f == g) );
  (res == 'F') => return f;
  (res == 'G') => return g;
  (res != 'X') => return ut_insert(res,-,-,-,-);

  lookup = mf_find( opcode, sw, f, g );
  (lookup defined) => return lookup.result;

  dx = MIN( f.index, g.index );
  (f.index == dx) => lo_f = f.low, hi_f = f.high else
                     lo_f = f, hi_f = f;
  (g.index == dx) => lo_g = g.low, hi_g = g.high else
                     lo_g = g, hi_g = g;
  lo = Apply_step( lo_f, lo_g, opcode, sw );
  hi = Apply_step( hi_f, hi_g, opcode, sw );

  (lo == hi):
     mf_insert( opcode, sw, f, g, lo ), return lo;

  (sw == FULL)=> un = Apply_step(lo,hi,ALIGNMENT,FULL);
  (sw == ABBREV) => un = ut_insert('U',-,-,-,-);
  result = ut_insert( 'X', dx, lo, hi, un );
  mf_insert( opcode, sw, f, g, result );
  return result; }
```

Some obvious details are not shown, for example, handling unary operations (no function *g*), or of optimizing *mf_find* by transformations on the incoming function, as in [MIY90] (which we did not pursue). We take clear advantage of the benevolent OTDD feature of being able to avoid computing the *'und'* branch should we find that the *'zero'* and *'one'* branches are equal. The input flag "sw" determines whether an abbreviated or full OTDD is computed. If an abbreviated OTDD is computed, the meaningless "und" child pointer is (arbitrarily) made to point to the 'U' terminal. It should be clear that if abbreviated OTDDs are input which contain no 'U' terminal (accessible from paths consisting exclusively of "low" and "high" child pointers), and if an abbreviated OTDD is to be computed, and finally if opcodes "OR_B_TO_U" and "ALIGNMENT" are not invoked by the user, then *Apply_step* is operating on, and will produce, OBDDs. This is because *Op* will

never receive nor return the terminal 'U' under those circumstances.

However it should also be clear from the code above that a full OTDD can in fact be derived *post facto* from its abbreviated form. Therefore if we wish to carry out an OTDD *Apply*, we could save considerable computation time by carrying out the computation with abbreviated OTDDs, and then at the last possible moment convert the final abbreviated result to a full OTDD. We will confirm this savings in Section 6 below. To implement this, we choose the following structure for our outer routine *Apply*:

```
*node Apply( f, g, opcode, sw )
  f,g: *node;
  sw:  {ABBREV,FULL}  {

  (opcode != IDENT)
        => mid = Apply_step(f,g,opcode,ABBREV) else
           mid = f;
  (sw == FULL)
        => res = Apply_step(mid,-,IDENT,FULL) else
           res = mid;
  return res; }
```

Notice that the caller of *Apply* himself chooses whether an abbreviated or full OTDD is to be produced. This permits him to carry out a lengthy sequence of computations in abbreviated mode, and if and when he finally requires a full OTDD, he may produce it with the following call:

```
full_otdd = Apply( abbrev_in, -, IDENT, FULL );
```

This is why a full-descent "IDENT" is implemented in *Op*; it forces *Apply_step* to traverse the entire abbreviated OTDD, converting all subgraphs to full OTDDs, in order to produce a full OTDD as the final result.

5 Composition of OTDDs

In [Bry86] we find the following definition for composition of two *complete* functions F and G:

$$G|_{v_i=F} = F \cdot G|_{v_i=1} + (\neg F) \cdot G|_{v_i=0}$$

however this formula *does not hold* for incomplete functions. The problem is that if the upstream function F is 'U' then (even when using the Kleenean strong definitions for *"and"* and *"inclusive or"* as shown in Figure 2) this formula will *always* compute $G|_{v_i=F} = $ 'U' for all cases where $F = $ 'U'. That result may possibly be valid for some other ternary logics where 'U' may mean *"neither zero nor one,"* but it is *incorrect* for Kleenean strong ternary logic.

The correct definition for the composition of two *incompletely-specified* functions under Kleenean strong ternary logic is:

$$G|_{v_i=F} = \begin{cases} G|_{v_i=1} & \text{if } F=1, \\ G|_{v_i=0} & \text{if } F=0, \\ G|_{v_i=U} & \text{if } F=U \end{cases}$$

```
function compose_step( vlow1, vhigh1, vund1, v2 )
{        /* v1 | m = v2 */
  if ((vlow1.index) = m) vlow1 ← vlow1.low;
  if ((vhigh1.index) = m) vhigh1 ← vhigh1.high;
  if ((vund1.index) = m) vund1 ← vund1.und;
        /* terminal ? */
  if (v2.val = '1'): if (vhigh1.val terminal) return(<vhigh1.val>);
  if (v2.val = '0'): if (vlow1.val terminal) return(<vlow1.val>);
  if (v2.val = 'U'): if (vund1.val terminal) return(<vund1.val>);
  u.index ← Min(vlow1.index,vhigh1.index,vund1.index,v2.index);
  if (v2.index = u.index)
     then begin v2low ← v2.low; v2high ← v2.high; end
     else begin v2low ← v2; v2high ← v2; end;
  if (vlow1.index = u.index)
     then begin vll1 ← vlow1.low; vlh1 ← vlow1.high; end
     else begin vll1 ← vlow1; vlh1 ← vlow1; end;
  if (vhigh1.index = u.index)
     then begin vhl1 ← vhigh1.low; vhh1 ← vhigh1.high; end
     else begin vhl1 ← vhigh1; vhh1 ← vhigh1; end;
  if (vund1.index = u.index)
     then begin vul1 ← vund1.low; vuh1 ← vund1.high; end
     else begin vul1 ← vund1; vuh1 ← vund1; end;
  u.low ← compose_step( vll1, vhl1, vul1, v2low );
  u.high ← compose_step( vlh1, vhh1, vuh1, v2high );
  u.und ← apply( u.low, u.high, ALIGNMENT, FULL );
  return(u);
}
        compose_step( v1, v1, v1, v2 );
```

Figure 5: Pseudocode to implement the OTDD symbolic composition $v1|_{m=v2}$ for the incomplete functions $v1$ (the downstream function G) and $v2$ (the upstream function F). $v1$ (G) must be a full OTDD, but $v2$ (F) may be an abbreviated OTDD.

where we must now digress to consider the restriction $G|_{v_i=U}$ which shall be seen need not be identically 'U'. It should be apparent that

$$G|_{v_i=U} = \begin{cases} G|_{v_i=0} & \text{if } G|_{v_i=0} = G|_{v_i=1}, \\ U & \text{otherwise.} \end{cases}$$

That is, if the value we obtain for G by restricting v_i to '1' is the same as the value we obtain by restricting v_i to '0', then not knowing the value for v_i does not matter, so we simply use the value of the common result. However if the values differ, then the result is genuinely unknown ('U') in the face of unknown v_i. (This is why we do not use, for example, the smoothing or consensus operations from logic synthesis as our definition for $G|_{v_i=U}$.)

Now we will show that symbolic composition of two incomplete functions, according to the correct definition given above, is easily implemented by using Ordered Ternary Decision Diagrams. The critical observation is that the definition of $G|_{v_i=U}$ given above is *precisely* the *alignment* (Figure 2) of the cofactors $G|_{v_i=0}$, $G|_{v_i=1}$. That is, $G|_{v_i=U}$ is precisely the information contained in the *child$_u$* branch at each node of the (full) OTDD for G. This permits a straightforward algorithm for symbolic composition of two incomplete functions. Pseudocode is presented in Figure 5, and is an extended variant of Bryant's composition algorithm as found in [Bry86]. In fact we are aware of no previously published algorithm for symbolic

composition of incompletely specified functions according to Kleenean strong ternary semantics as defined above.

6   Results on Benchmarks

We chose construction of an OTDD from typical benchmark descriptions as a performance experiment, since this exercises *Apply* across many opcodes. For example, building an abbreviated OTDD from an input cube involves a sequence of "AND" operations on identity (Figure 1) or inverted identity OTDDs. Assembling the entire function's abbreviated OTDD from those cubes depends on whether the ON-set and DC-set (DC = "don't care") have been specified, or whether ON- and OFF-sets were given. Cubes belonging to distinct sets are "OR"ed together, since this permits us to check afterwards that the sets are disjoint. For an ON and DC specification we create an initial constant-'0' OTDD as "accumulator": the ON-set is "OR"ed into the accumulator, while the DC-set (as second operand to *Apply*) is "OR_B_TO_U"ed into the accumulator. "OR_B_TO_U" removes cubes from the initial accumulator OFF-set (the initial '0' OTDD) giving them a terminal value 'U'. If ON and OFF sets are given, we begin with a constant-'U' OTDD (that is, all minterms are initially assumed to be in the DC-set) and use "OR" (moving cubes to the ON set, that is, a '1' terminal) and "A_AND_NOT_B" (moving cubes to the OFF set, that is, a '0' terminal). Finally we can exercise "ALIGNMENT" by

	abbr OTDD	full, post	post, no F,G	full, running
b12	2.83	3.39	8.41	38.3
bw	.587	1.08	2.03	2.99
clip	2.56	6.73	13.3	70.2
con1	.018	.051	.074	.073
ex5p	27.6	34.2	71.2	
inc	.362	.798	1.33	4.50
misex1	.110	.231	.340	.442
misex2	.255	18.9	34.0	33.3
rd53	.143	.210	.413	.758
rd73	1.25	1.97	5.70	22.0
rd84	3.94	5.64	26.1	
sao2	1.15	8.62	13.5	
sqrt8	.190	.420	.938	2.92
squar5	.223	.285	.529	1.28
t481	23.5	37.8	655.	
xor5	.077	.125	.206	.359

Figure 6: CPU time in seconds on a Sun SPARC (ELC) for: (a) forming the abbreviated OTDD, (b) forming the abbreviated OTDD and then the full OTDD from it, (c) the computation of "b" without using 'F' and 'G' information from "Op" and (d) using 'F', 'G' but computing the full OTDD at every *Apply_step*.

	in	out	prod	DC $\neq \emptyset$	COSMOS [Bry92]			OTDD	
					A-set	B-set	**A+B**	**abbrev**	full
b12	15	9	431		93	93	**174**	**94**	277
bw	5	28	87	*	121	116	**221**	**182**	275
clip	9	5	167		256	256	**452**	**257**	1038
con1	7	2	9		20	20	**36**	**21**	52
ex5p	8	63	256		313	313	**536**	**314**	713
inc	7	9	34	*	88	91	**151**	**119**	261
misex1	8	7	32		49	49	**82**	**50**	137
misex2	25	18	29		142	142	**272**	**143**	318
rd53	5	3	32		25	25	**34**	**26**	42
rd73	7	3	141		45	45	**62**	**46**	87
rd84	8	4	256		61	61	**84**	**62**	124
sao2	10	4	58		156	156	**310**	**157**	594
sqrt8	8	4	40		44	44	**76**	**45**	113
squar5	5	8	32		40	40	**70**	**41**	87
t481	16	1	481		34	34	**42**	**35**	69
xor5	5	1	16		11	11	**12**	**12**	12

Figure 7: Dimensions of, and number of nodes in unique-table for LGSynth93 benchmarks, for both abbreviated OTDD form, and for full OTDD form. The package used does not have an "inverting edge" as described in [BRB90]. The fourth column indicates those benchmarks having a nontrivial DC-set. The boldface columns compare space needed for dual-OBDD vs. abbreviated OTDD representation.

constructing the full OTDD from the abbreviated OTDD.

In Figure 7 we see that the abbreviated OTDD is more memory-efficient than the dual-OBDD representation defined by Bryant [Bry87] [Bry92] for representing the same syntactical information. Coarse CPU-time results for constructing LGSynth93 benchmarks on a rudimentary package are shown in Figure 6. Not using isomorphism information in *Op*, that is, discarding 'F' and 'G' returned by *Op*, increases computation time by a factor of 2.6 on the average. Attempting to work entirely with full OTDD computations is clearly wasteful, so that the structure of *Apply* given above, plus the advice of not computing a full OTDD until it is needed, is the preferred use of the package.

It would be premature of the present author to give exhaustive memory and CPU time results for the primitive package described in this paper, which is given mainly to illustrate principles rather than to expound any optimal implementation. For example, the present package (used for obtaining all memory usage values in Figure 7) does not use an "inverting edge" as taught in [BRB90], making any package-against-package comparisons of little value at this point. As pointed out in Section 4, we do not yet perform any *mf_find* transformations on the incoming function [MIY90]. For OTDD composition, there is in fact no need to have the downstream OTDD in "full" form as indicated in the caption of Figure 5. Rather, near the top of that pseudocode, the value "vund1.und" (if not defined) can be computed from "vund1.low" and "vund1.high" by

using an abbreviated "alignment" computation. Also, the full "alignment" computation of "u.und" prior to the "return" statement can be replaced so as to yield an abbreviated rather than a full OTDD for the composed result. Lindgren has observed important and exploitable OTDD canonicity properties [Lin94].

7 Conclusion

We have presented the Ordered Ternary Decision Diagram (OTDD), which combines the notions of "unknown" and "don't-care" into a single data structure, and which correctly evaluates its function in the presence of any number of indeterminate input values. Although this was formally proven in this paper, we have also validated this by exhaustive evaluation of the benchmarks of Figure 7. The OTDD uses Kleenean strong ternary logic as the semantical basis for performing *Apply* operations on symbolic functions containing nontrivial don't-care sets. We have presented a correct definition for the composition of two incomplete functions under the semantics of Kleenean strong ternary logic, and have given pseudocode for its OTDD implementation.

The implicit 'U'-decision problem has been examined by [CP89] for single Boolean functions expressed in both sum-of-products and product-of-sum forms. Here we have contributed a solution to that problem for functions represented by decision diagrams, and furthermore [CP89] does not consider incompletely-specified functions as we do here. Of course we do not claim to have overcome the NP complexity of the problem. The OBDD for the function may still be exponential in the number of variables, and the full OTDD cannot be smaller than the OBDD (Figure 4). However it should be clear that once the full OTDD has actually been constructed, that the correct result for any given input vector can be computed in $\mathbf{O}(n)$ time, where n is the number of input variables.

We have also outlined a single package combining OBDD, abbreviated and full OTDD computations, and have examined its performance. The package exploits the strong canonical forms of all these diagrams, with the property that OTDD computations may be coerced into more efficient abbreviated OTDD computations, with the full OTDD constructed *post facto*.

References

[BF+93] R. Iris Bahar, Erica A. Frohm, et al. Algebraic Decision Diagrams and their Applications. In *Proceedings, Int'l Conference on Computer-Aided Design (ICCAD '93)*, pages 188–191, November 1993.

[Bra83] Daniel Brand. Redundancy and Don't Cares in Logic Synthesis. *IEEE Transactions on Computers*, C-32(10):947–952, October 1983.

[BRB90] Karl S. Brace, Richard L. Rudell, and Randal E. Bryant. Efficient Implementation of a BDD Package. In *Proceedings 27th DAC*, pages 40–45, June 1990.

[Bre72]   M. A. Breuer. A Note on Three-Valued Logic Simulation. *IEEE Trans. on Computers*, pages 399–402, April 1972.

[Bry86]   R. E. Bryant. Graph-Based Algorithms for Boolean Function Manipulation. *IEEE Transactions on Computers*, C-35(8):677–691, August 1986.

[Bry87]   Randal E. Bryant. Boolean Analysis of MOS Circuits. *IEEE Trans. on Computer-Aided Design of Integrated Circuits*, CAD-6(4):634–649, July 1987.

[Bry90]   Randal E. Bryant. Symbolic Simulation – Techniques and Applications. In *Proceedings 27th DAC*, pages 517–521, June 1990.

[Bry92]   Randal E. Bryant. Symbolic Boolean Manipulation with Ordered Binary-Decision Diagrams. *ACM Computing Surveys*, 24(3):293–318, September 1992.

[BS87]   Janusz A. Brzozowski and Carl-Johan Seger. A Characterization of Ternary Simulation of Gate Networks. *IEEE Transactions on Computers*, C-36(11):1318–1327, November 1987.

[BS91]   Randal E. Bryant and Carl-Johan H. Seger. Formal Verification of Digital Circuits Using Symbolic Ternary System Models. In E. M. Clarke and R. P. Kurshan, editors, *Proceedings, 2nd Int'l Conference on Computer-Aided Verification (CAV '90)*, pages 33–43. Springer-Verlag, 1991. LNCS 531. Conference June 1990, New Brunswick NJ.

[CA87]   Hongtao P. Chang and Jacob A. Abraham. The Complexity of Accurate Logic Simulation. In *Proceedings, IEEE Int'l Conf. on CAD (ICCAD '87)*, pages 404–407, November 1987.

[CG85]   E. Cerny and J. Gecsei. Simulation of MOS Circuits by Decision Diagrams. *IEEE Transactions on CAD*, CAD-4(4):685–693, October 1985.

[CP89]   Susheel J. Chandra and Janak H. Patel. Accurate Logic Simulation in the Presence of Unknowns. In *Proc. Intl. Conf. on Computer-Aided Design (ICCAD '89)*, pages 34–37, November 1989.

[DD93]   Maurizio Damiani and Giovanni De Micheli. Don't Care Set Specifications in Combinational and Synchronous Logic Circuits. *IEEE Transactions on Computer-Aided Design*, 12(3):365–388, March 1993.

[DL93]   Peter Dahlgren and Peter Liden. Efficient Modeling of Switch-Level Networks Containing Undetermined Logic Node States. In *Proceedings, Int'l Conference on Computer-Aided Design (ICCAD '93)*, pages 746–752, November 1993.

[HNY93]   Yutaka Hata, Kyoichi Nakashima, and Kazuharu Yamato. Some Fundamental Properties of Multiple-Valued Kleenean Functions and Determination of Their Logic Functions. *IEEE Transactions on Computers*, 42(8):950–961, August 1993.

[Jen94]   G. Jennings. Experience Using Ordered Ternary Decision Diagrams for Compiled Logic Simulation. In *Proceedings, SIMS '94, Stockholm*. Scandinavian Simulation Society, August 1994.

[JIL94]   G. Jennings, J. Isaksson, and P. Lindgren. Ordered Ternary Decision Diagrams and the Multivalued Compiled Simulation of Unmapped Logic. In *Proceedings, 27th Annual Simulation Symposium*, pages 99–105, April 1994.

[JT93]   Ricardo P. Jacobi and Anne-Marie Trullemans. A New Logic Minimization Method for Multiplexor-Based FPGA Synthesis. In *Proceedings, European Design Automation Conference (EURO-DAC '93)*, pages 312–317, September 1993.

[Kle52]   Stephen Cole Kleene. *Introduction to Metamathematics*. Wolters-Noordhoff, North-Holland Publishing, 1952. Chapter 12, Section 64: The 3-valued Logic.

[KP+92]   Ken Kubiak, Steven Parkes, et al. Exact Evaluation of Diagnostic Test Resolution. In *Proceedings 29th DAC*, pages 347–352, 1992.

[L+88]   M. Loughzail et al. Experience with the VHDL Environment. In *Proceedings of the 25th Design Automation Conference*, pages 28–33, June 1988.

[Lin94]   Per Lindgren. Private communication on research in progress, September 1994. Luleå Institute of Technology, Luleå, Sweden.

[MIY90]   Shin-ichi Minato, Nagisa Ishiura, and Shuzo Yajima. Shared Binary Decision Diagram with Attributed Edges for Efficient Boolean Function Manipulation. In *Proceedings 27th DAC*, pages 52–57, 1990.

[PM93]   Jaehong Park and M. Ray Mercer. An Efficient Symbolic Design Verification System. In *Proceedings, ICCD '93*, pages 294–298, 1993.

[RB+91]   Don E. Ross, Kenneth M. Butler, et al. Fast Functional Evaluation of Candidate OBDD Variable Orderings. In *Proceedings of the 1991 European Conference on Design Automation (EDAC 1991)*, pages 4–10, February 1991.

[SKMB90]   Arvind Srinivasan, Timothy Kam, Sharad Malik, and Robert K. Brayton. Algorithms for Discrete Function Manipulation. In *Proceedings, Int'l Conference on Computer-Aided Design (ICCAD '90)*, pages 92–95, November 1990.

[SS93]   Ted Stanion and Carl Sechen. Maximum Projections of Don't Care Conditions in a Boolean Network. In *Proceedings, Int'l Conference on Computer-Aided Design (ICCAD '93)*, pages 674–679, November 1993.

[Urq86]   Alasdair Urquhart. Many-Valued Logic. In D. Gabbay and F. Guenthner, editors, *Handbook of Philosophical Logic*, chapter III.2, pages 71–116. D. Reidel, 1986.

[WF80]   Anthony S. Wojcik and Kwang-Ya Fang. On the Design of Three-Valued Asynchronous Modules. *IEEE Transactions on Computers*, C-29(10):889–898, October 1980.

[YM88]   Yoshinori Yamamoto and Masao Mukaidono. Meaningful Special Classes of Ternary Logic Functions – Regular Ternary Logic Functions and Ternary Majority Functions. *IEEE Transactions on Computers*, 37(7):799–806, July 1988.

AN IMPLEMENTATION OF HASH BASED ATM ROUTER CHIP

Dejan Rašković, *Emil Jovanov, Aleksandar Janićijević, and Veljko Milutinović*

Department of Computer Engineering
School of Electrical Engineering,
University of Belgrade
POB 816
11000 Belgrade
Yugoslavia

fax: +381-11-762-215
email: emilutiv@ubbg.etf.bg.ac.yu

*Department of Computer Engineering
Institute "M. Pupin"
University of Belgrade
POB 15
11000 Belgrade
Yugoslavia

fax: +381-11-775-835
email: ejovanoe@ubbg.etf.bg.ac.yu

ABSTRACT *Routing in the ATM environment requires fast handling of large size routing tables, forcing high speed network nodes to implement appropriate hardware support for routing. Traditional solution for this problem is to use associative memories; however, for the ATM router, this solution may require an excessively large chip area and power consumption. This paper presents an original architecture of the hash-based hardware accelerator which makes use of standard RAM. Results of analytical, simulation, and implementation analysis given in the paper indicate the price/performance ratio which is up to an order of magnitude better compared to some of the existing solutions.*

1. INTRODUCTION

The ATM (Asynchronous Transfer Mode) networking standard holds high expectations of computer and communication society, to enable large scale cooperation and support for multimedia services in wide area networks. Based on 53-byte cells (48 bytes for data and 5 bytes for header), the ATM also tends to intersperse the voice and data cells, in order to balance the network workload. Basic characteristics of the environment are a large number of simultaneously active connections and high transmission rates. Therefore, the efficient support for switching and routing is the main technological issue here. This paper presents an original, hash based, approach to routing in the ATM environment.

This research was partially sponsored by the FNRS. For further information refer to emilutiv@ubbg.etf.bg.ac.yu

Proceedings of the twenty-eight IEEE/ACM Hawaii International Conference on System Sciences, Maui, Hawaii, U.S.A., January 3-6, 1995.

Routing is one of major functions of the network layer. In the ATM environment, destination address is given as a two-level address pair VPI/VCI (Virtual Path Identifier/Virtual Channel Identifier). A network node performs flexible routing by replacing the address of the incoming cell with a new (pre-defined) address stored in the routing table. This has to be performed within one cell time, to avoid latency and queuing of incoming cells.

Having in mind the fast transfer rate and the large directory size (in some cases extremely large), most ATM routers will require hardwarized routing tables [Killat89], to satisfy the requirement for on-chip search of large directories within one ATM cell time. The traditional solution to the problem implies the use of associative memories. Such approach is not applicable here, because of the size of the directories involved. Consequently, we decided to realize a pseudo-associative memory taking the following approach: the router has to be based on a standard off-the-shelf RAM, and accelerated with fast search hardware. A block diagram for the approach of our research is given in Figure 1. Advantages of the proposed approach are: a) fast development cycle based on the standard cell VLSI design, and b) large and flexible routing table size. These advantages imply the lowest cost and the shortest time to market, for the currently available technology.

In the second section, we present the essence of our approach to the problem of hardware support for the ATM routing. Brief overview of the possible hardware implementations of routing tables is given in the third section. The fourth section presents hash based hardwarization of the routing table, which leads to a new price/performance measure in the ATM environment. Conditions and assumptions of the analysis are introduced in the fifth section. The results of the simulation analysis are given in the sixth section. The seventh section presents the implementation of one possible architecture of the hash based routing table. Finally, in the last section, the conclusion of our analysis is given. It is shown that the efficient pseudo associative memory approach could make possible efficient handling of very large routing tables, and offers a new price/performance measure.

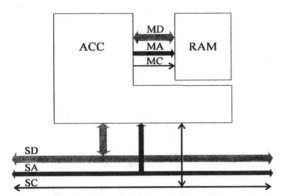

Figure 1: Block diagram of the hardwarized routing table based on standard RAM;
ACC - Accelerator of table operations, **SD** - System Data bus, **SA** - System Address bus, **SC** - System Control bus, **MD** - Memory Data bus, **MA** - Memory Address bus, **MC** - Memory Control bus

2. PROBLEM STATEMENT

Routing workload is characterized with frequent searches and moderate update/write frequencies that depend on the current traffic. The main goal of this research was to find the optimal organization of the routing table and the architecture of the accelerator that makes use of standard RAM.

The essence of existing approaches is to maintain both the peak and the average search time bellow one cell time, to avoid the queuing of cells. On the contrary, *the essence of our approach is to obtain low average search time, allowing that the maximum search time may exceed one cell time (but in very rare situations — less frequently than once in 10^7 cells, which is in-line with the overall ATM philosophy).* In the first case, associative memory seems to be the preferred solution, because of the short and predictable search time. In the second case, the best search hardware algorithm is the one which is characterized with a relatively large ratio of the worst case search time and the average search time. *The hardware implemented hashing algorithms [Knuth73] belong to this type.* Hence, this type of algorithm is expected to be the source of the most suitable search algorithm for ATM routers.

Deficiency of the hash-based approach is that it is possible to loose some cells because of the router chip's causes. *Having in mind the tolerable cell loss rate in the ATM environment (from 1 in 10^6 to 1 in 10^{10}), we have shown that it is possible to maintain the cell loss rate one order of magnitude bellow the inherent ATM standard level (from 1 in 10^7 to 1 in 10^{10}), by adjusting the system buffer size.* As a consequence, it is possible to have a wider choice of possible price/performance alternatives for different speeds and different system architectures. *This approach is especially appreciated by our research sponsor and his application.*

3. HARDWARE IMPLEMENTATION OF ROUTING TABLES

Implementation of a routing table is essentially a practical realization of address translation in a given address space. When the address space is small it is possible to realize the routing table in conventional standard RAM memory. It can be realized either as direct address mapping, or as a search through an unordered list of addresses. In the case of ATM, where the address is 24 or 28 bits wide, the routing tables could not be realized using direct address mapping. Possible realizations of hardwarized routing tables for the ATM environment are:

- Associative memory, Content Addressable Memory (CAM)
- Standard RAM memory with on-chip ALU for searching (RAM+ALU)
- Trie-based architectures (TRIE)
- Insertion Sort Binary Search pseudo-associative memory (ISBS)

Associative memory approach is ideal for small routing tables, or for a cache in larger directories. However, excessive area and power consumptions makes it inappropriate for larger routing tables in the ATM environment [Jovanov94].

The advantage of the second approach is the small complexity and use of off-the-shelf components. The smallest complexity is achieved if the list is unorganized, and faster search is realized using parallel search on multiple units. Nevertheless, sequential search of unordered lists requires a large degree of partitioning, to satisfy tough ATM requirements, which is too complicated for high speed networks [Jovanov94].

Trie-based architectures make use of a hierarchically organized retrieval structure for search of the stored table values. The address is partitioned into sections, and every section addresses a different level of the search tree. An efficient implementation of the trie-based ATM router is given in [Pei92]. Trie-based routers would have a reasonable and predictable search time. The main disadvantages are the additional memory space for maintaining the list of pointers in the search structure, and the large overhead for the table write/update. The table maintenance could be left to the main processor, but this can be very time consuming. On the other hand, full hardware implementation of table maintenance operations drastically increases the complexity of control logic.

Pseudo associative memory could be realized by maintaining an ordered list of table entries, using insertion sort. It makes possible a binary search, and therefore a high speed predictable search time. Compared with the TRIE approach, the ISBS does not require additional memory space for the search structure, and features a comparable search time. Unfortunately, table write/update may, in some cases, take an excessively long time. Although relatively unfrequent, table write/update operations may have a critical impact on system performance. This is because they consume few orders of magnitude larger processing time (compared to the table lookup operation), and therefore the queuing delay of messages could become uncontrollable. The AMD already implemented such approach, referred to as the Content Addressable Data Manager [Segal86], using custom designed memory array for fast insertion of new table entries. However, increased complexity of the custom designed memory array decreases the technological flexibility and the table capacity, and makes the CAM solution more appropriate.

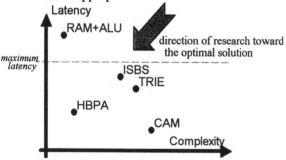

Figure 2: The space of possible solutions for hardwarized routing tables;
CAM - Content Addressable Memory, **ISBS** - Insertion Sort Binary Search pseudo associative memory, **TRIE** - Standard memory with the reTRIEval structure, **RAM+ALU** - Standard RAM and ALU, **HBPA** - Hash Based Pseudo Associative memory, *maximum latency* - Maximum table access latency for a given application

During this research, we analyzed a number of solutions making use of standard RAM, and have found that the hash-based hardware accelerator with standard

RAM may be efficiently implemented in the ATM environment. Figure 2 presents an approximate distribution of candidate architecture in the price/performance space. This is a symbolic representation of possible solutions, from our point of view. Detailed explanation on how it was obtained can be found in [Raško94] and [Janići94]. Optimal solution should have a minimal complexity with the performance equal to (or better than) required for a given application. Minimal requirement of the application is presented as the maximum latency line, while the *optimal direction of research should correspond to the direction of the arrow* in Figure 2.

4. SUGGESTED SOLUTION AND ITS ESSENCE

This paper introduces a hash-based acceleration of the routing table operations, which are relatively easy to parallelize and implement. *The accelerator performs the search, on average, within a few RAM read cycles, which is much shorter than the ATM cell time, and the search time starts to increase only when the routing table becomes almost full, which can be **easily** avoided by using a larger memory.*

Hashing is used to find the starting address from which the table is sequentially searched in order to find the requested key value for retrieval, or an empty location for writing. The hash function could be realized trivially, taking only m bits of the key (where m is the RAM address length), or XOR-ing segments of the key. We analyzed several hashing functions to be incorporated into our accelerator, and we concluded the following:

- All hash types have a low implementation complexity
- Optimal hash type depends on application characteristics (distribution of hash values)
- All hash types have an extremely good performance, for low values of the load factor (percentage of occupied locations in the hash table)

The HBPA is realized as a high performance hardwarized routing table based on standard random access memory. The capacity of the accelerator is 4K 64-bit words. Every table entry contains a 32-bit key and a 32-bit data field. Although the HBPA is designed to serve as a routing table in the ATM node, it can also be used in Database and File Servers [Jovanov93], Image Processing, Neural Networks, and many other applications. The parallelization of multiple HBPA chips could be accomplished using simple external logic, to decrease access latency. Detailed block diagram of the HBPA architecture is given in Figure 3, and state diagram of the control logic is presented in Figure 4. Those figures contain only the details which are available in the open literature. All lower level details are of the proprietary nature.

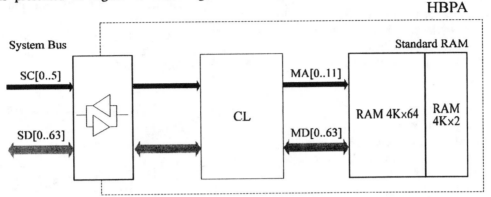

Figure 3: Detailed block diagram of the HBPA architecture;
SD - System Data bus (64 bits), **SC** - System Control bus (6 bits), **MA** - Memory Address bus (64 bits),
MD - Memory Data bus (12 bits), **CL** - Control Logic

Description: Both the internal data path and the external interface are 64 bits wide. The chip is designed to minimize the external logic for expansion and control in the case of parallel implementation. It is controlled with 6 control signals, and by commands loaded into the Control Register. The least significant 32 bits (key) of System Data bus are used to calculate the hash address. This is the starting address from which the table is searched, in order to find an empty location or a specific key. Two bits of RAM are appended to each 64-bit word, to indicate the validity of the location (Empty, Skip, Deleted, Valid). The Status Register contains flags indicating Match and Full.

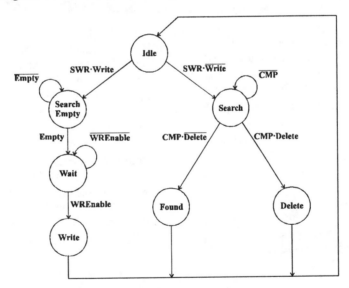

Figure 4: State Diagram of the Control Unit;
SWR - System Write, **CMP** - Comparison result, **WREnable** - Write Enable

Description: Idle, Search Empty, Search, Wait, Write, Found, and Delete are states of the state machine. Write and Delete are command bits indicating the operation mode. In the case of the write operation, the table is searched in order to find an empty location, and if found, chip waits for signal WREnable from the external logic (only if it works in a multi-chip system). When the signal WREnable is received (in single-chip systems, this signal is always active), the datum is written into the table. In the case of the search or delete operations, the table is searched in order to find the given key. When found, if the Delete bit in the Status Register is set, the table entry is deleted. Otherwise, the Match flag is set, and the appropriate signal is sent to the system.

5. CONDITIONS AND ASSUMPTIONS OF THE ANALYSIS

In our research methodology, the term condition refers to the specification of the real environment. The term assumption refers to the simplifications which make the analysis either possible or easier, without any negative impact on the generality and representativeness of the results.

Basic conditions of our research are:
- Standard RAM table realization.
- Memory organization is based on a 64-bit word: 32-bit key and 32-bit data. The whole table entry could be accessed in one memory cycle.
- The RAM capacity is 4K words.
- Search, write, and delete operations have to be completed within the specified time.
- Design is oriented to the standard cell VLSI implementation.
- The utilized architecture is scalable and technology independent.
- Distribution of key values is equal to the ATM address distribution.

We adopted the following assumptions:
- Average search time must be within the specified time.
- Maximum search time can exceed the specified time.
- Each ATM node contains a buffer for queuing of incoming messages, to decrease the cell loss probability. Probability of cell loss (because of the buffer overflow) should not exceed 10^{-7} (an order of magnitude less than the allowed cell loss rate of the ATM network, for applications tolerating the cell loss of 10^{-6})

The performance of hash-based algorithms depends on the "quality" of the hash function. Number of collisions generated by the ideal hash function could be approximated with the Poisson distribution. Probability that, after writing the N entries into a table of the size M, the hash function generated k collisions, is equal to:

$$p_k = e^{-\lambda} \cdot \frac{\lambda^k}{k!}$$

where $\lambda = N/M$ is the table loading factor.

Therefore, probability of collisions can be reduced (and thus the table access performance increased) by selecting the appropriate table size. With the assumption that the maximum access time could exceed the specified time, we have to provide buffering of incoming cells. The buffer length determines directly the cell loss probability.

The results of the queuing analysis are shown in Figure 5. It can be seen that the cell loss probability could be below the predefined maximum, by adjusting the buffer length and the table size, according to the requirements of the application under consideration. For the given example, a buffer for seven cells maintains the cell loss probability below 10^{-7}, and a buffer for 11 cells maintains the cell loss probability below 10^{-11}.

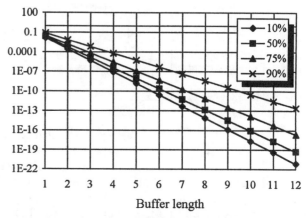

Figure 5: Cell loss probability as a function of buffer length with the table loading factor as a parameter

6. SIMULATION ANALYSIS

The simulation analysis was conducted to indicate the HBPA performance in the ATM and the database environments. Basic characteristics of the simulated environments are:
- Distribution of key values in the database environment is uniform (key values are between 0 and $2^{32} - 1$)
- Distribution of key values (addresses) in the ATM environment is as follows:

    VPI is a uniformly distributed random number between 0 and 127 (maximum 128 paths)

    VCI is a uniformly distributed random number between 0 and $2^{16}-1$

    The adopted distribution of addresses increases the number of collisions for all hash functions, but depicts the distribution of addresses in the ATM-like traffic.
- Transmission rate is 155 Mbps (equivalent to SONET).
- Channel usage is 80%.
- Network data distribution is equal to 10% for data, and 90% for voice and video.

The purpose of the simulation analysis was to attain performance measures of the hash-based routing table in the ATM environment. Two groups of simulations were done: for an ATM and for a database environment. In each group, the following operations were simulated: initialization, write, search (successful and unsuccessful), and delete. Simulation involved over 1,000,000 simulation passes per operation, to decrease the influence of the random number generator. Simulation results are expressed as a number of memory cycles to complete the operation, in order to create technologically independent performance measures. We simulated the performance of the HBPA with five hash functions in the ATM environment:

- **OH** Ordered hash
- **H1** The 12-bit segments overlapping
- **H2** The 12-bit segments overlapping and rotate [Inoue91]
- **H3** The 8-bit segments overlapping version 1
- **H4** The 8-bit segments overlapping version 2

The ordered hash is trivial, taking only m (length of hash value) significant address bits as a hash function, and therefore does not increase hardware complexity. All hash types are made to generate a 12-bit hash value for the routing table of 4K entries. The only difference between hash types **H3** and **H4** is in the way of generating the first four bits of the hash value.

Numbers of memory cycles for the successful search are given in Figures 6 and 7. In Figure 6, the average number of memory cycles per search for a given key is presented, while Figure 7 shows the maximal values. It can be seen that the hash based approach has an acceptable worst case performance. Hence, it can be used in environments where the search operation time is limited.

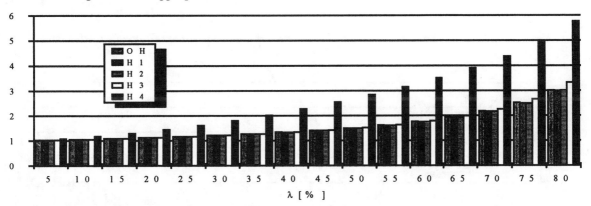

Figure 6: The average number of memory cycles per successful search

λ – Loading factor (percentage of occupied locations), **OH** - Ordered hash, **H1** - The 12-bit segments overlapping, **H2** - The 12-bit segments overlapping and rotate, **H3** - The 8-bit segments overlapping version 1, **H4** - The 8-bit segments overlapping version 2 (Definitions are the same for all figures that follow)

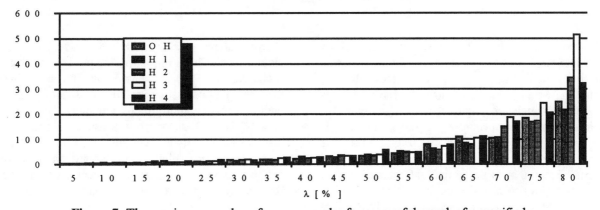

Figure 7: The maximum number of memory cycles for successful search of a specific key

In Figure 8, the average number of memory cycles for writing one key into an already loaded table is given (inserting a new table entry). For example, the hash type **H2** with the loading factor 75%, requires 8.52 memory cycles on average. On the other hand, from Figure 9 (which shows the maximum number of memory cycles for writing a key into an already loaded table), it can be seen that the hash type **H2** has the best performance — 189 memory cycles for the same loading factor (75%).

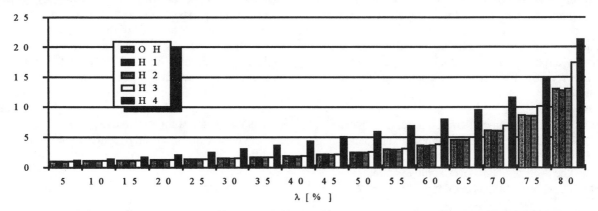

Figure 8: The average number of memory cycles for writing one key into the already loaded table

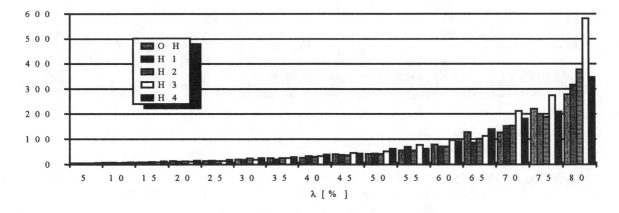

Figure 9: The maximum number of memory cycles for writing one key into the already loaded table

The minimal number of memory cycles for writing one key into an already loaded table is 1. It happens when the hash function, using a key, generates the address of an empty RAM location. Percentage of write operations completed in a single memory cycle is given in Figure 10.

Information that a specific key is not in the table is also crucial for routing. The HBPA makes this information available soon after the request. From Figure 11, it can be seen that, with hashing, the average number of memory cycles per unsuccessful search for a given key is about 8.5, when the loading factor is 75%. That makes this approach appropriate for vertical cascading.

Simulations in a database environment have shown similar results; however, all hash types have almost equal performance. This is caused by the fact that the distribution of key values used in simulation of a database environment was uniform. As a matter of fact, the hash type **H2** is the best, which was expected, because of its complexity (it includes rotation after each overlapping). As an illustration, Figure 12 is given, which shows the average number of memory cycles per successful search, for a given key in a database environment.

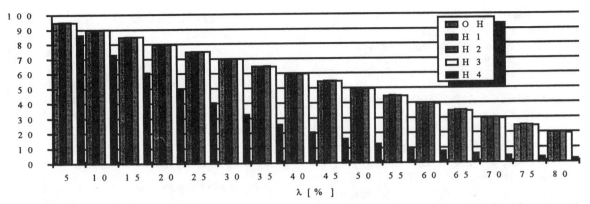

Figure 10: The average number of write operations completed in a single memory cycle (given in percents)

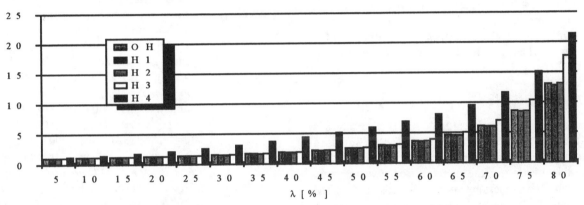

Figure 11: An average number of memory cycles per unsuccessful key search

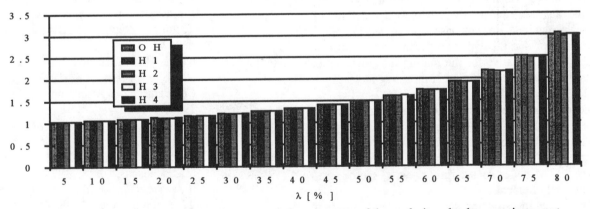

Figure 12: The average number of memory cycles per successful search, in a database environment

7. IMPLEMENTATION ANALYSIS

The HBPA router chip is implemented in the standard-cell VLSI methodology, using the $2\mu m$ CMOS technology. The complexity of the implemented HBPA routing table accelerator is estimated according to the complexity of static RAM and static CAM:

Complexity of static RAM: $T_{RAM} \approx$ 4K words$\times$66 bits$\times$6 transistors = 1622016 transistors

Complexity of the accelerator : T_{ACC} = 5179 transistors

Complexity of the routing chip: $T_{HBPA}=T_{RAM} + T_{ACC} = 1622016+5179 = 1627195$ transistors

The transistor count increase for the implemented accelerator: $\Delta T = \dfrac{T_{ACC}}{T_{HBPA}} = 0.32\%$

Complexity of static CAM: $T_{CAM} \approx 4K\ words\times66\ bits\times9$ transistors = 2433024 transistors

It can be seen from the presented analysis that the HBPA generates only a slight increase in chip area, in comparison with the standard RAM cell. The hash module complexity is 20 XOR cells, i.e. 180 transistors, for hash types H1-H4, or 0 for the ordered hash function! The ordered hash function takes only the most significant 12 bits of interest, without any processing, and therefore has the zero complexity.

Simulation in the conservative 2μm CMOS technology revealed that the minimal cycle time is 82ns plus the RAM access time.

8. CONCLUSIONS

Efficient implementation of large size routing tables is one of the crucial issues in wide area ATM networks. In this research, we have investigated the use of standard RAM for realization of the pseudo associative memory, which can be important not only for the ATM environment, but for other fields of data communications/processing, as well.

Many authors excluded the hash-based algorithms from the analysis, due to the relatively large ratio of average to maximal time of basic operations. However, we have shown that this type of algorithm may represent an important alternative for the routing table design, as long as the appropriate buffering of incoming messages is provided.

The proposed approach could be important for the commercialization of ATM. High performance multi-gigabit networks should take advantage of associative memories, but the HBPA approach could be advantageous for many ATM nodes considering capacity, speed, area, and power requirements.

The further investigation should include a collection of "real" ATM address traces, to reveal the performance for different ATM hardware configurations. Also, we are currently preparing our architecture for implementation in the 0.8μm CMOS technology.

9. ACKNOWLEDGEMENTS

We would like to express our sincere appreciation to Dr. Mirjana Zafirović-Vukotić, from IMP, and Dr. Tom Brumett, from the QSI, for helpful and inspiring discussions about the ATM requirements, and suggestions concerning possible hardware realizations of the routing table.

10. REFERENCES

[DePrycker93] Prycker, M., de, "Asynchronous Transfer Mode: Solutions For Broadband ISDN," Elis Horwood Limited, Hertfordshire, Great Britain, 1993.

[Inoue91] Inoue, U., Satoh, T., Hayami, H., Takeda, H., Nakamura, T., Fukuoka, H., "RINDA: A Relational Database Processor with Hardware Specialized for Searching and Sorting", *IEEE Micro*, December 1991, pp. 61-70.

[Janići94] Janićijević, A., *"Architecture of the ISBS ATM Router Chip,"* IFACT Technical Report TR-IFACT-94-AJ001, 1994.

[Jovanov93] Jovanov, E., *"The Architecture of Accelerator for Database Operations,"* Ph.D. Thesis, School of Electrical Engineering, University of Belgrade, 1993.

[Jovanov94] Jovanov, E., *"Comparison of the ATM Router Chip Architectures,"* IFACT Technical Report TR-IFACT-94-EJ001, 1994.

[Killat89] Killat, U., "ATM and Its Challenges to VLSI," *Proceedings of the 3rd European Computer Conference*, pp. 4.56.- 4.61., 1989.

[Knuth73] Knuth, D., E., *"The Art of Computer Programming, Vol. 3: Sorting and Searching,"* Addison-Wesley, Reading, Massachusetts, U.S.A., 1973.

[Raško94] Rašković, D., *"Architecture of the HBPA ATM Router Chip"*, IFACT Technical Report TR-IFACT-94-DR001, 1994.

[Pei92] Pei, Tong-Bi, Zukowski, C., "Putting Routing Tables in Silicon", *IEEE Network*, January 1992, pp. 42-50.

[Segal86] Segal, M., "Hardware sorting chip steps up software pace", *Electronic Design*, June 26, 1986, pp. 85-91.

Optimized Mapping of Video Applications to Hardware-Software for VLSI Architectures

Catherine H. Gebotys   Robert J. Gebotys

Department of Electrical and Computer Engineering

University of Waterloo,   Wilfrid Laurier University,

Waterloo, Ontario. Canada   Waterloo, Ontario. Canada

This research presents for the first time an integer optimization approach for scheduling video computations on bus-constrained VLSI architectures or on an existing VLIW processor. For many video systems a combination of processor and VLSI chip provides a low cost solution that meets given performance requirements. Thus tools for analyzing whether a video function is best implemented in hardware (VLSI) or in software (on a VLIW processor) are valuable. An optimization approach is presented in this paper which can efficiently map video computations to hardware or software. The technique maps fast (I)DCT-II applications to an existing VLIW video signal processor chip. Our research shows that the optimized mapping to VLSI architectures provides up to 66% fewer busses than previous research. This research is important for Industry since the partitioning of applications into software or hardware has a significant impact on the overall cost and performance of video processing systems.

1.Introduction

Video signal processing is an exciting area that has recently received a tremendous amount of interest due to advancements in standards, networks, and VLSI [1]. Many new applications are being developed based on compressed video. A great number of video tasks belong to the class of DSP algorithms, however they have much higher throughput requirements than audio applications (for which a large number of DSP processors were designed). Video computations include coding, filtering, quantization, and compression. The discrete cosine transform is a very popular compression technique[4]. Approaches to designing these video signal processing systems involve decisions as to whether a video function should be implemented in hardware as a VLSI custom chip (ASIC) or as software code on an existing or newly developed video signal processor. Many video systems are a combination of a core processor with VLSI custom chips [10,1].

Performance is a major advantage of a full custom VLSI implementation, whereas flexibility is an advantage of a software implementation. Some researchers [11] believe the best solution may lie in between the software and hardware implementations. Specifically they are designing programmable hardware or application specific instruction processors (ASIPs) [11]. The ASIPs are expected to provide performance equivalent to ASICs along with the flexibility of software implementation, that may also support late design specification changes. Although there is controversy over whether certain video computations are best implemented in hardware or software, there is a lack of CAD tools to perform the required analysis.

Tools to allow exploration of different hardware or software implementations are necessary in order to make the best decisions which will yield low cost high performance solutions. These high level implementation decisions have a significant impact on the cost and performance of the final video signal processing system. The CAD tools must provide the mapping of video computations into hardware (architectural synthesis), programmable hardware (application specific instruction processors, ASIPs), or into software (highly constrained scheduling).

Although research in mapping computations to hardware (architectural synthesis) has been active and developing over the last 10 years, it has had very little impact in Industry. Two reasons contributing to this lack of impact are 1) few synthesizers have been able to produce high quality architectures and 2) synthesizers have not addressed minimizing interconnect complexity. Both are important for VLSI technologies in the 90's. Some approaches to application-specific architectural synthesis[1] have used a random topology architecture (which uses individual registers connected to/from functional units, such as an adder or multiplier, through multiplexors) however for video signal processing computations the registerfile architectures[2,3,12] are more appropriate. The registerfile architectures have lower interconnect complexities[2], efficiently support larger data structures, and are better suited for programmability. Some researchers[2,3] have used two port registerfiles connected to busses, to hold intermediate data values, and use the busses for writing/reading data values from/to functional units. Functional units may have latched inputs and possibly latched outputs as well, depending

41

upon the timing scheme used.

There is a great deal of interest in mapping video computations into software. This is due to the fact that new video signal processors are extremely powerful and support a large amount of parallelism. A number of these processors resemble VLIWs in that they have a large number of functional units. Previous attempts at designing VLIWs for general purpose computing were not successful largely due to the fact that the VLSI technology and CAD tools was not available to support it. Now VLSI technology is extremely powerful and VLIW-like processors are being investigated [11,19] for audio and video applications. The VLIW processors are particularly suitable for areas such as video signal processing which have higher throughput requirements than audio applications (targeted by DSP processors) and therefore require large degrees of parallelism that VLIW processors can provide.

Some of the earliest tasks to be performed in the mapping of video computations into (programmable) hardware or software are that of scheduling and binding. Scheduling involves assigning each operation (such as an addition or multiplication etc) to a time when it can start its execution. Binding involves assigning each operation to a specific functional unit (ie. alu, multiplier etc) that will execute the operation. It is well known that these early scheduling and binding decisions have a large impact on the final implementation. These early tasks are highly interdependent, thus in order to obtain high quality architectures one must attempt to solve them simultaneously. Unfortunately the mapping problem is believed to be NP-hard [13], since many of its subtasks have been defined as NP-complete. NP-hard means that there will exist some problems which require exponential time to solve[13]. However the research presented in this paper and others show that many problems can be solved in reasonable cpu times to optimal solutions.

The objective of mapping video computations to hardware/software is to transform the function (represented as a data flow graph, DFG) into a hardware architecture or into software that satisfies performance constraints (throughput, latency), architecture constraints, and minimizes cost, such as area for the case of hardware mapping and the number of instructions for software mapping.

2. Problem Descriptions and Previous Research

The following two problems, describe important parts of code the mapping problems that will be examined in this paper. We will represent the video computations by a data flow graph (DFG, or also known as a DAG) where the vertices are the operations (such as addition, multiplication) and the arcs are data transfers between operations. Problem 1 and 2 represent an important part of the (pro-

grammable) hardware mapping and the software mapping problems respectively.

Problem 1 (hardware mapping): *By mapping each vertex (operation) of the DFG to a time (a clock cycle or control step) when it starts executing, produce a schedule such that the estimated area (as a function of number/type of functional units and number of busses) is minimized, while performance (throughput, latency) constraints are met.*

Problem 2 (software mapping): *By mapping each vertex (operation) of the DFG to a time (a clock cycle or control step) when it starts execution and to a functional unit (that will execute it) of an existing VSP processor (ie. VLIW processor), produce a schedule such that the performance constraints(throughput, latency), multiplexor constraints, I/O port constraints, register constraints, and register file constraints (to allow data transfers on busses and to/from register files according to specific processor architecture) are met.*

In problem 1 data will be transferred on the bus from register files to functional units, at an early time or as late as possible in order to minimize the number of busses required. By minimizing the number of busses one not only minimizes the interconnect complexity but also the number of register files required in the architecture. The extension of problem 1 for mapping to programmable hardware will also be discussed. In problem 2 the multiplexor, I/O port, register, and register file constraints in general are used to define the data transfer possibilities in the chosen processor. We have concentrated on VLIW processors and will present a model targeted to a specific VLIW processor.

Previous researchers[2,3,6,12] have examined problem 1 by mapping applications into registerfile architectures. In many cases the architectures[2,3] which use a register file per bus as opposed to a register file at each input to a functional unit[12] may require fewer total number of register files and therefore are further investigated in this paper. In both cases[2,3] the latched functional units receive data from busses and general data storage is performed by register files which receive/send data from/to buses. The mapping determined the number/type of functional units and attempted to minimize the number of bus connections using heuristic techniques. In SPAID[2] one registerfile per bus was used, whereas in STAR[3] each registerfile could send/receive data to/from one or more busses. An optimization approach to scheduling applications to minimize the number of busses was used[7] , however the model assumed that data was transferred onto the bus only when it was needed (as late as possible) and data could not be transferred in advance. STAR researchers have reported results on DCT from [9]. This model could take broadcast data into account, in other words only one bus is required to transfer data from one registerfile to two or more functional units. An integer linear programming (IP) approach[6] supported the transfer of data from register files onto busses and to functional units at any feasible time in order to minimize total number of busses. Unfortunately the IP model used required a very large number of variables and constraints and the cpu times were reported only for a small example.

Problem 2 is just now gaining interest[11,14]. Previous research into scheduling applications for VLIWs looked at general purpose computing applications, where a significant amount of effort looked at conditionals/loops support etc using trace scheduling [15]. Apart from heuristic approaches, such as list[11] and trace scheduling[15], which are all targeted towards specific architectures, there are no general techniques for solving problem 2. A large number of hardware VLSI chips for video compression have been researched [4]. Most VLSI chips do not use the fast DCT algorithms [4]. Many DCT processors are programmable for both DCT and IDCT [10]. A VLIW processor [17] was developed for executing the 8X8 2D DCT or IDCT No fast (I)DCT algorithms were used, and the application required 16 multiplications, 32 addition/subtractions on the 8 incoming data. The processor contained two adder subtractors, one multiplier and one rounder/limiter. The researchers claim that it is as efficient as a hardwired ASIC chip yet provides the flexibility of a microprogrammable VLIW processor. In comparison to ASICs designed for video compression computations, only a few researchers have used a software implementation [18]. For example a video signal processing system was researched which implemented DCT in software on DSP1616 processor [18] and on other commercially available video signal processors [10].

An integer programming approach for mapping video computations to hardware or software is presented. Two new IP models are introduced. The first maps schedules video computations to minimize cost (as a function of estimated area, including busses) for a full custom VLSI architectures and the second IP model specifically supports simultaneous scheduling and binding to map video computations to software on a previously researched VLIW processor[17]. This VLIW processor was chosen due to its support for parallelism and its VLIW structure, which some researchers believe is what future ASIPs will look like[19,11]. The mathematical optimization approach was chosen to perform the mapping because it is ideally suited for modeling the constraints of the architecture (such as bussing, multiplexors, reading/writing constraints for each register file, etc). This research breaks new ground by 1) providing industry with an optimized tool for mapping video computations into software and 2) synthesizing optimal registerfile architectures. The next section outlines the terminology and notation for the IP models.

3. The Hardware-Software Mapping Models

This section will present the mathematical models which perform the mapping of video computations into hardware or software. The following terminology will be used in this paper. The video computations can be represented by a data flow graph, DFG, which is a set of vertices and arcs, $DFG=(V,A)$. A vertex of the DFG, $v \varepsilon V$, represents an operation (such as addition or multiplication). Arc a is represented by $v_1 \rightarrow v_2$, where operation v_1 produces data for operation v_2. The term cstep (j) will be used to represent a clock cycle. Each operation is defined over a set of csteps defined by $R(v)$ ($j \varepsilon R(v)$), using as soon/late as possible scheduling[5]. For example if $a \rightarrow b$ and $R(a)=\{1,2,3\}$, then we define $R(b)=\{2,3,4\}$. When we sum over j in the models below, it is implied that we only sum over $j \varepsilon R(v)$. Each functional unit (such as an adder or multiplier) has a latency=C and an input latency=L associated with it. For example if the functional unit can execute in one cstep after receiving its data inputs then $C=1 L=1$. A two cycle pipelined multiplier would be defined as $C=2$ and $L=1$. The number of functional units of type i is represented by f_i, where $v \varepsilon F(i)$ means that operation v can be executed by functional unit i. The inverse of the throughput of a video computations will be referred to as input latency, IL, which is the number of csteps between successive data blocks. Modulo IL is used in the equations to represent pipelining of the application in order to meet throughput constraints.

3.1 Model 1 : Mapping to Hardware

In order to support the high throughput, and large data size requirements of video computations, the target architecture chosen in this paper is the register file architecture. Two port register files are used, where at most one register file per bus may be used unlike STAR[3]. The functional units have latched inputs and outputs so that the minimum clock period can be achieved, calculated as in STAR[3]. Each clock period has a read phase and a write phase. During the read phase data is read from the registerfile and latched into the local input latch at the functional unit. The output result produced by the functional unit is transferred onto the bus and written into the registerfile during teh write phase. An example of the targeted hardware architecture is given in figure 1.

Model 1 will simultaneously schedule operations of the video computations, determine how many of each type of functional units are required to meet throughput requirements, and finally it will minimize the number of busses in the architecture.

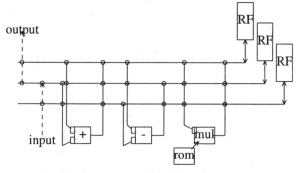

Figure 1. Example of a VLSI Architecture for Hardware Mapping. Synthesized VLSI architecture for DCT-II with *IL*=16, showing 3 busses (*B*), and 24 bus connections (*BC*=24).

The variables for this model are $x_{j,v}$, where $x_{j,v}=1$ means that operation v starts execution at time j. The variable *B* is the number of busses required in the hardware architecture. The variable $y_{s,j}$ is used to represent broadcasting of a data value on a bus to more than one operation. For example $s=(v1,v2)$ is used to represent a pair of operations $v1,v2$, such that there exists a vertex *v*, where $v \rightarrow v1, v \rightarrow v2$. Vertices of the DFG that represent addition or subtraction operations are represented by $vas \varepsilon V$, and multiplication operations are represented by $vmul \varepsilon V$. Vertices (operations) which do not share input data with other operations are represented by $vsingle \varepsilon V$. Similarly we define sets *sone* and *stwo*. For illustration purposes we will assume that the sets *stwo* broadcast two data values and sets *sone* broadcast only one data value. However we can support other types of data broadcast situations as well. For example in figure 2, based upon analysis of input data to the operations, we define sets *stwo*1=(*c,d*), *sone*1=(*f,g*), (where *stwo*=(*stwo*1), *sone*=(*sone*1)) and *vsingle*=(*a,b,e*). In figure 2 the arrows indicate that a data value is being transferred from a register file onto a bus and into a latch at the functional unit. The two columns formed by the circles indicate two functional units, and the circles represent an operation being executed by a functional unit.

Equation (1.1) ensures each operation is assigned to an execution time and equation (1.2) is the precedence constraint that ensures an operation will not start execution until both input data values are available. The basis of the precedence constraints, constraint (1.2), has been previously presented in [5]. These constraints generate a small search space and allow the IP model to be solved in reasonable cpu times as will be shown.

$$\sum_j x_{j,v} = 1, \quad \forall v. \qquad (1.1)$$

$$\sum_{j1, j1 \ge j-(C-1)} x_{j1,v} + \sum_{j2, j2 \le j} x_{j2,v1} \le 1, \forall v \rightarrow v1. \qquad (1.2)$$

Equations (1.3), and (1.4) define the *y* variables for the model. These variables indicate whether data can be broadcast to the sets *stwo* or *sone*. For example in figure 2 at time 2 the variable $y_{2,stwo1}=0$, where *stwo*1=(*c,d*), defined in equation (1.3). At time 3 the variable $y_{2,sone1}=1$, where *sone*1=(*f,g*), defined in equation (1.4). Equations (1.5), and (1.6) define the number of busses required for the video function, using the *y* and *x* variables. Equation (1.5) has not been previously presented and is further illustrated in figure 2. For example at time 2, the 1st,2nd and 3rd terms of equation (1.5) are 2 (operations *a* and *b* at time 1), 0 ($y_{2,stwo1}$ at time 2 representing operations *c* and *d*), and 0 (for *vsingle* operations at time 2). At time 3, the 1st,2nd and 3rd terms of equation (1.5) are 2 (operations *c* and *d* at time 2), 1 ($y_{3,sone1}$ at time 3 representing operations *f* and *g*), and 0 (for *vsingle* operations at time 3). At time 1, the 1st,2nd and 3rd terms of equation (1.5) are 1 (operations *e* at time 4), 0, and 2 (for *vsingle* operations *a* and *b* at time 1). The value of the left hand side of equation (1.5) for each *j* value is shown in figure 2 in the *B* column and refers also to the number of arrows at that time indicating use of a bus. The dashed line in figure 2 represents the storage of the data value at the input latch of a functional unit (ie. adder, subtractor or, multiplier). The dashed line starts at a time when the data value is transferred on the bus from a register file and it ends at a time when it is used by the operation (circle). The operations form a loop in this example. For example, one data input for operation *b* is transferred at time 4. Equation (1.6) allocates busses for the write phase.

$$\sum_{j1=j, j1=j+mod \, IL} (x_{j1,v1} - x_{j1,v2}) \le y_{j,stwo}, \qquad (1.3)$$

$$\forall j, v1, v2, stwo \mid stwo = (v1,v2).$$

$$\sum_{j1=j, j1=j+mod \, IL} (x_{j1,v1}) \le y_{j,sone}, \qquad (1.4)$$

$$\forall j, sone, v1 \mid v1 \varepsilon sone.$$

$$\sum_{j1=j, j1=j+mod \, IL} (\sum_{j2=j-1, j2=j-1+mod \, IL} (\sum_v x_{j2,v} + \qquad (1.5)$$

$$\sum_s y_{j1,s} + \sum_{vsingle} x_{j1,vsingle})) \le B, \forall j.$$

$$\sum_{v \mid j1+(C-1)=j} x_{j1,v} \le B, \forall j. \qquad (1.6)$$

Using an as late as possible scheduling scheme that previous research has employed the schedule in figure 1 would require four busses. Using our IP approach, which models early data transfers on the bus, the schedule in figure 1 only requires three busses (calculated by taking the maximum of all numbers at the left hand side of the figure in the B column) in the final architecture. Equation (1.7) determines the number of functional units such as adders, subtractors, etc. Finally the estimated area cost

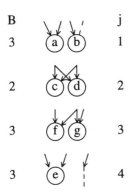

Figure 2. Illustration of constraint (1.5), where number at left shows the number of busses (B) required to transfer the data to the functional units at that time (j), where time increases from top to bottom.

function is given in equation (1.8).

$$\sum_{\substack{j\,l=j-Lv\in F(i) \\ j\,l=j}} x_{j1,v} \leq f_i, \forall j, i. \qquad (1.7)$$

$$\textit{Minimize Estimated Area}=(\sum_i area_i f_i)+area_b B \qquad (1.8)$$

Extension to Programmable Hardware

The model above can be extended to mapping a set of video computations to programmable hardware (ASIP). Assume we have a set of video computations S ={c1,c2,c3,...cn}, where each ci is described by a data flow graph. In order to determine the best architecture we use constraints above for each ci, where variables B_{ci} is the number of busses required for an architecture for video computations ci , etc. Then the following constraints are used to minimize the estimated area of the programmable hardware is : $B_{ci} \leq B, f_{ici} \leq f_i$

3.2 Model 2 : Mapping to Software

The VLIW chip used to illustrate the optimal mapping approach is taken from [17]. The chip contains two processors, processor A and processor B. Processor A is shown in figure 3. Processor B is the same as Processor A except it receives input from the output of the 64X12 register file (RF) and it produces output multiplexed from any of the four busses. The coefficient for the multiplications and the control signals for the registerfiles and the multiplexors are driven by values in the instruction register which controls both processors. We will map the DCT-II and IDCT-II to the VLIW chip to illustrate our optimization model. The input latency is limited to 16 csteps, since there are 16 multiplications in the (I)DCT-II and only one multiplier in the architecture.

From left to right in figure 3 we will refer to +/-1 as adder/subtractor 1 (fu=1) and it's register file as RF1, etc for +/-2,RF2,RF3,and mul as the multiplier. Registerfiles

RF1 and RF2 are 5 port memory with 2 write ports and 3 read ports. Each multiplexor will be referred to as MUX1,2,3,4 from left to right where MUX4 is multiplexor for output data. In one clock period the processor can support: two addition/subtractions, one multiplication whose result is written into RF1 or RF2 or out, reading data from RF1/2 and writing it to RF2/1/3 or OUT, or reading data form RF1/2/3 and writing it to OUT.

The variables for this model are $x_{j,v,fu,c}$, where $x_{j,v,fu,c}=1$ means that operation v starts execution at time j on functional unit fu. If c=2 then during the clock period after the functional unit (fui) writes the arc into RF_fui the data value will be read onto a bus and written into RF_fuj(where fuj≠fui). Otherwise if c=1 then the arc value is only used by functional unit fu, which produced the data value. When v is a multiplication then $x_{j,v,fu,c}=1$ means that the arc/data produced by the multiplier will be stored in RF_fu. For multiplications we always set c=1, since data is always stored in RF1 or RF2. The input/output data for the application is represented by INPUT, OUTPUT respectively.

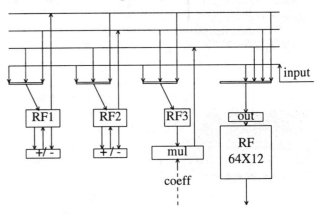

Figure 3. Part of the Target Architecture used for Software Mapping. Processor A of the VLIW chip [17] which shows adder/subtractors and multiplier along with four busses.

The integer programming model for mapping video computations to software on the VLIW is presented below. The solution of this IP model provides a schedule of operations and binding of operations to functional units and data values to register files. The microcode can be easily produced from this solution. Equation (2.1) ensures that each operation is assigned to exactly one functional unit, time, and c value. Equation (2.2) defines the fu parameter for multiplications (vmul) as the functional unit which receives the data it produces. Since a multiplication is performed in each cstep one multiplexor into the RF1 or RF2 will always be used. Therefore incoming data can only be read into one RF1 or RF2 register file. Therefore two operations which both use this data must be executed by the same functional unit.

Constraint (2.3) performs this function.

$$\sum_{j,fu,c} x_{j,v,fu,c} = 1, \ \forall \, v. \qquad (2.1)$$

$$\sum_{c,j} x_{j,vmul,fu,c} = \sum_{c,j} x_{j,v,fu,c}, \ \forall vmul \rightarrow v, fu. \qquad (2.2)$$

$$\sum_{c,j} x_{j,v1,fu,c} = \sum_{c,j} x_{j,v2,fu,c}, \ \forall INPUT \rightarrow (v1,v2),fu. \qquad (2.3)$$

Constraints (2.4) and (2.5) define the c parameter and define data precedence. These constraints have been described in [5], however they were not used for the problem of mapping applications to software.

$$\sum_{fu,j1,j1 \geq j-(C-1)} x_{j1,v,fu,1} + \sum_{fu,j2,j2 \geq j-1-(C-1)} x_{j2,v,fu,2} + \qquad (2.4)$$

$$\sum_{fu,c,j3,j3 \leq j} x_{j3,v1,fu,c} \leq 1, \ \forall v \rightarrow v1.$$

$$\sum_{j} x_{j,v,fu,1} + \sum_{j,c,fu} x_{j,v1,fu,c} \leq 1, \ \forall v \rightarrow v1. \qquad (2.5)$$

Multiplexor constraints (2.6) and (2.7) are new constraints that ensure only one data value can be sent over each bus through each multiplexor and written into a register file at a time. The precedence constraints and data transfer over the bus is illustrated in the scheduling example in figure 4. At cstep j=1 in figure 4 the data produced by the multiplier is transferred onto the bus and stored in registerfile RF2 (see solid line). At cstep j=2 the data is transferred onto the bus from registerfile RF1 to registerfile RF2 (see solid line). Constraint (2.6) is used for MUX1 and MUX2, constraint (2.7) is used for MUX3 and constraint (2.8) is used for MUX4. Output data can be set at a fixed rate or can be scheduled by the optimizer as shown in equation (2.8).

$$\sum_{j1=j,j1=j+modIL} \left(\sum_{vmul,c} x_{j1,vmul,fu,c} + \right. \qquad (2.6)$$

$$\left. \sum_{vas,fu1,fu1 \neq fu} x_{j1,vas,fu1,2} \right) \leq 1, \ \forall fu,j.$$

$$\sum_{j1=j,j1=j+modIL} \left(\sum_{vas \rightarrow vmul,fu} x_{j1,vas,fu,2} \right) \leq 1, \ \forall j. \qquad (2.7)$$

$$\sum_{v \rightarrow OUT,c,fu} x_{j,v,fu,c} \leq 1, \ \forall j. \qquad (2.8)$$

Constraint (2.9) ensures that when input data arrives it can be sent through a multiplexor and written into the proper register file,(ie. RF1), so that operations $(v \mid IN \rightarrow v)$, executed by an adder/subtractor (ie. +/-1) can use it. The incoming data can be scheduled to arrive at a fixed input rate, as shown below j_{io}, or can be buffered and allowed to be written according to the schedule. The first term of constraint (2.9) is the number of data values being transferred from other functional units going into the multiplexor at fu1 at the time of the input data arrival. This term should be zero if fu1 is the same functional unit that the input operations are bound to.

$$\sum_{j1=j_{io},j1=j_{io}+modIL} \left(\sum_{fu1 \neq fu,vas} x_{j1,vas,fu1,2} + \sum_{fu,vmul} x_{j1,vmul,fu,2} \right) \qquad (2.9)$$

$$+ \sum_{j2,c} x_{j2,v,fu,c} \leq 1, \ \forall IN \rightarrow v, fu, j_{io}$$

Figure 4. Illustration of precedence for operations in VLIW. The dotted arrow indicates when data is stored in a register file. A solid line indicates when the data is transferred on the bus. The arrows indicate that the data is being transferred from/to a registerfile to/from the functional unit. Time, j, is increasing from top to bottom. Circles represent the operations.

The number of registers per registerfile are also given by the architecture in constraint (2.11), where $R(RFi)$ is the number of registers in register file RFi. The operations head (or tail) refer to all operations which produce a data value that is stored in a register file (or all operations which receive data values). There is no objective function required since this is a satisfiability problem. Note that the number of instructions/microwords will be fixed by the throughput constraint.

$$\sum_{j1=j,j1=j+modIL} \left(\sum_{j2 \leq j1} x_{j2,head,fu,1} - \sum_{j2 > j1} x_{j2,head,fu,1} \right. \qquad (2.10)$$

$$+ \sum_{fu1 \neq fu,j2 \leq j1} x_{j2,head,fu1,2} - \sum_{fu1 \neq fu,j2 > j1} x_{j2,head,fu1,2} - \sum_{fu,c,j2 \leq j1} x_{j2,tail,fu,c}$$

$$\left. - \sum_{fu,c,j2 \leq j1} x_{j2,tail,fu,c} + \sum_{fu,c,j2 > j1} x_{j2,tail,fu,c} \right) \leq R(RFi), \forall j,fu.$$

4. Synthesizer Results

In order to illustrate the optimization approach (IP) to mapping video computations to hardware or software the (I)DCT-II video computation is chosen. The mapping of DCT-II[4,9] to hardware is compared with previous registerfile synthesis research. The input latency (IL, which is inversely proportional to throughput), the number of multipliers (*, which is two stage pipelined unless otherwise stated), and the number of adders (+) and subtractors (-) for each synthesized architecture are given in the tables. The number of registerfiles (RF) and busses (B) are also given. The bus connections BC is obtained from taking the solution from Model 1 and running it through model in [16] to complete the architecture. The IP problems solved are described by the number of integer variables (Var), the number of constraints (Eqn) and the number of nodes (Nodes) generated in each branch and bound tree using GAMS/LAMPS optimization software[20]. All cpu times (CPU) are obtained from solving the optimization problems on a IBM RS6000 workstation.

Table 1. Model 1 mapping compared with STAR[3].

Synth	*	+	-	IL	RF	B	BC
IP	1	1	1	16	3	3	24
STAR[3]	1	1	1	16	5	5	38
IP	2	1	1	13	4	4	29
STAR[3]	2	1	1	13	6	6	50
IP	2	2	2	8	6	6	48
STAR[3]	2	2	2	8	7	10	61
IP	2	2	2	10	5	5	43
STAR[3]	2	2	2	10	8	8	68
IP	2	2	2	12	4	4	41
STAR[3]	2	2	2	12	6	6	51

Table 1 illustrates the results of mapping the DCT-II to hardware using Model 1 (IP rows) in comparison with results from STAR[3] which also used DCT-II referenced from [9]. The B and RF columns show the number of busses and register files required in the architectures. Final architecture synthesized by the new model presented in this paper followed by binding stage performed by model in [16] are given in table 2 for complete synthesis cpu seconds. The architecture for row 1 of table 1 is given in figure 1. Input and output signals can either be read(written) from(to) the registerfiles (as assumed in table 1) or read(written) onto(from) the busses using external inputs(outputs) as shown in figure 1 (which requires four extra bus connections).

Table 2. CPU Times for Model 1

IL	Var	Eqn	CPU min	
			IP	STAR[3]†
16	530	961	1.1	2.5
13	720	1384	2.8	14.4
8	1112	2806	10.3	17.6
10	941	2391	4.1	17.5
12	770	980	2.8	7.3

† *reported for datapath refinement part only*

The DCT-II and IDCT-II were both mapped to the VLIW architecture [17], using the Model 2 presented in this paper. The cpu times are given table 3. The compression video computation (DCT-II)required 213 cpu seconds to be mapped onto the VLIW. The solution of the IP problem required searching a branch and bound tree of only 27 nodes. The IP problem had 1713 binary variables and 1159 constraints. Mapping the decompression computation (IDCT-II) onto the VLIW required the solution of an IP problem in 95 cpu seconds. A fixed input and output rate were used for data input/output. Further design exploration was performed using the model to see if the algorithms could be implemented on the VLIW with one adder and one subtractor instead of two adder/subtractors. This was possible however it would require an extra read port on RF1 and RF2 so that the input data could be read into the adder/subtractors in parallel with data being read from the bus.

Table 3. CPU Times for Model 2

IP Characteristics	DCT-II	IDCT-II
Var	1713	1041
Eqn	1159	1540
Nodes	27	23
CPU(sec)	213	94

5. Discussions and Conclusions

In this paper we have defined two optimization models, that support mapping of video computations onto software or hardware. For mapping video computations to VLSI hardware, the IP approach provided 50% to 66% fewer busses in the register file architectures than previous research[2,3] (see table 1) and when used in conjunction with the IP model from [16] the IP approach allocated the up to 24% to 72% fewer bus connections. This is in contrast to [6] that used a different IP model which could not minimize the number of bus connections. We attribute this improvement to the use of optimization. Optimal architectures which minimize interconnect costs have been synthesized in practical execution times. For mapping video computations to software, the IP approach mapped fast DCT compression computations (DCT-II and IDCT-II) to a VLIW processor[17] that had not previously been designed for these fast DCT algorithms. The ability to optimally map video computations to software has been demonstrated for one VLIW processor. This is important to support design specification changes or to explore the implementation of different types of algorithms, which for example may require lower power or have higher throughputs etc.

The optimization approach also provides us with a tool for exploring different types of architectures and tradeoffs in cost, performance, and programmability. For example the hardware-software analysis performed in this paper for the (I)DCT-II application showed that programmability can be gained by an increase in cost. Specifically we can compare figure 1 (the hardware mapping) to figure 3 (the VLIW software mapping). By using an extra bus, half the number of bus connections, and more expensive multiported registerfiles we can gain programmability (figure 3). Programmability may be important for many applications whose design specification may change late in the design cycle. However if the application is fully specified and unlikely to change then the VLSI architecture (which more likely has lower cost due to its smaller area) may be the desired implementation.

Although the worst case complexity is exponential (since we are solving several IP problems), we have found that many problems can be solved quickly to optimums. As input algorithms become larger we can partition the behavior or take advantage of the mathematical flexibility of the IP approach to model systems with hierarchy and regularity.

Although we are not limited to video computations, the optimization technique is particularly appropriate for this cost-sensitive video market since it provides optimal results in very efficient cpu times and can deal with high throughput and computation-intensive computations. These models are also not limited to mapping the video computations to the one VLIW processor taken from [17]. Other processor architectures can also be targeted due to the ability to support/model complex data transfer constraints which may arise due to the VSP processors architecture.

In summary this research for the first time maps video computations to optimal VLSI architectures in practical cpu times and maps video computations optimally to an previously researched VLIW video processor [17]. This is important for industry since these early decisions made during the mapping stage have the greatest impact on the final design. The mathematical basis of the approach provides the flexibility of modeling complex constraints such as data transfer restrictions in video processor architectures, or early data transfers for bus usage in mapping to hardware. Finally the methodology forms a DA tool that can be brought to market quickly since it based on highly reliable mathematical software. For the first time this research provides industry with a DA tool for mapping video computations to both hardware or software in an optimal manner. The authors would like to acknowledge the support of the WLU Research Office. This research is supported in part by grants from NSERC, and ITRC.

References

[1] B.Ackland,*Video Compression and VLSI*, IEEE Proc. of Custom Integrated Circuits Conf., p11.1.1-11.1.6, 1993.

[2] B. Haroun ,M. Elmasry ,"Architectural Synthesis for DSP Silicon Compilers" ,*IEEE Trans. on CAD*,CAD-8,N4,1989.

[3] F-S Tsai ,Y-C. Hsu ,"STAR: An Automatic Data Path Allocator", *IEEE Transactions on CAD*,V11,N9,1053-1064,1992.

[4] K.R.Rao,P.Yip,**Discrete Cosine Transform Algorithms, Advantages, Applications**, Academic Press, 1990.

[5] C.H. Gebotys ,"An Optimization Approach to the Synthesis of Multichip Architectures" *IEEE Trans. on VLSI Sys.* ,V 2 ,N 1 ,11-20 ,1994 .

[6] C.H. Gebotys ,R.J. Gebotys ,"Application-Specific Architectures for Field-Programmable VLSI Technologies",*Proc.of H.Int'l Conf on Sys Sci*,1994.

[7] C-T Hwang ,J-H. Lee ,Y-C. Hsu ,"A Formal Approach to the Scheduling Problem in High-Level Synthesis",*IEEE Trans on CAD*, V10,N4,464-475,1991.

[8] R. Gupta ,G. DeMicheli ,"Partitioning of Functional Modules of Synchronous Digital Systems" ,*Int'l Conf on CAD* ,1990.

[9] D.J.Mallon ,P.B.Denyer ,"A New Approach to Pipeline Optimization" ,*European DAC* ,83-88 ,1990.

[10] J.J.Bloomer,F.F.Yassa,A.A.Abdel-Malek, *Video Compression Options*, IEEE Proc. Custom Integrated Circuits Conf., p.26.1.1-26.1.7, 1992.

[11] P.Paulin,C.Liem,T.May,S.Sutarwala, *CodeSyn: A Retargetable Code Synthesis System* , Int'l Symposium on High-Level Synthesis, 1994.

[12] L.Claesen,F.Catthoor,D.Lanneer, G.Goossens,S.Note, J.VanMeergergen,H.DeMan, *Automatic Synthesis of Signal Processing Benchmark using the CATHEDRAL Silicon Compilers*, Intl Custom Integrated Circuits Conf., p14.7.1-14.7.4, 1988.

[13] M.R.Garey, D.S.Johnson, **Computers and Intractability**, Freeman, 1979.

[14] A.Kalavade,E.A.Lee, *A Methdology for Simulation and Synthesis of Mixed Hardware/Software Systems* , Int'l Symposium on High-Level Synthesis, 1994.

[15] J.R.Ellis, **Bulldog : A Compiler For VLIW Architectures**, MIT Press, 1986.

[16] C.Gebotys, "Synthesizing Optimal Register file Architectures for FPGA technology" Proc.Custom Intgd Circuits Conf , p11.1.1-11.1.4.,1994

[17] L.Matterne, D.Chong, B.McSweeney, R.Woudsma, *A Flexible High Performance 2-D Discrete Cosine Transform IC* , Intl Symp on Circuits and Systems, p618-621,1989.

[18] S.K.Azim,etal *A Low Cost Application Specific Video Codec for Consumer Video Phone*, Proc Intl Custom Integrated Circuits Conf, p6.7.1-6.7.4, 1994.

[19] Discussions with R.Hum, Cadence, May 1994.

[20] A.Brooke, D.Kendrick, A.Meeraus, *GAMS A Users Guide*, Scientific Press, 1988.

PERFORMANCE ANALYSIS OF RAID-5 DISK ARRAYS

Oleg A. Panfilov

NCR Corporation

Abstract

The impact of major I/O system parameters on the performance of RAID-5 disk array systems is described in this paper. It is shown that the system throughput is a nonlinear function of the number of disks per rank, number of ranks in the system, compounded data rate of SCSIs installed between a host and a controller, the size of a controller buffer, the way files are striped across individual disks, and the application dependent read/write ratio.

Introduction

Numerous disk and disk controller parameters as well as the way files are striped between different disks [1]-[4] define performance of a disk array system. The major disk parameters include seek time T_d, rotational latency T_r, and data transfer rate R. The major controller parameters depend on the controller implementation and may include command overhead T_0, size of the internal buffer S, data rate of the internal controller bus R_b, and a data rate of the interface to the host R_a. Correct selection of the major disk and array controller parameters is extremely important to achieve system performance goals. For example, inadequate selection of a controller buffer size will reduce the rate of writes. Insufficient rate of host SCSI will reduce the rate of reads. Inadequate controller bus bandwidth would restrict the system rating for both reads and writes by not allowing concurrent reads from multiple disks. It is important to remember that correctly selected parameters under one set of assumptions such as

a number of disks in a rank, number of ranks in the system and known average block size of data may be incorrect in other operating environments.

The process of selection of the disk and array controller parameters for a RAID-5 disk array system will be described in this paper.

A typical example of a RAID-5 system is shown in Fig 1. Each row has five disks (width of a rank N = 5). The data and parity information per sector are distributed across all five disks. The interface between a host and an array controller (further called as a host SCSI) has typically higher transfer rate than the interface between a controller and individual disks (disk SCSIs). The SCSI will be used as an interface in our analysis, although other types of interface devices are possible.

To understand relationships between different parameters of a disk array we have to review the operation of a system. As an example, we will consider one of possible implementations of a disk array system shown on Fig 1. Here a request from the host passes through a host SCSI to an array matrix controller. Within a controller the request passes through a controller bus to a controller microprocessor (MP). After the microprocessor completes translation of the logical address of requested data into a physical one, it tries to establish a connection with a disk through a disk SCSI. It takes a command overhead time T_0 to process an initial request for data and establish a data link through a disk SCSI to read the data. When a requested block of data is read from the disk, it passes through a controller bus for temporary storage in the buffer. A buffer can store data blocks from several disks permitting concurrent reads of data. The buffer also has to store a new and old data or parity blocks during the write operations.

In selecting the type of disk system to be implemented, fundamental questions concerning its performance have to be raised. These questions are:

- For a fixed number of disks in a rank, how many ranks can one controller support?

- How many read or write operations per second can the RAID-5 system sustain?

- How critical are parameters of the Host - Array controller interface and parameters of the controller for system performance?

- For the given microprocessor based hosts, generating requests to access data, how many hosts can be connected to one disk matrix?

The following performance analysis of disk arrays will give the answers to these questions.

Analysis of the requirements to the controller buffer size

The process of selection of the controller buffer size must be based on a thorough analysis of the read/write operation procedures in RAID-5. The following set of assumptions will be valid in the coming analysis.

ASSUMPTIONS:

1. Concurrent data transfers from 5 different disks through its own SCSIs to the controller buffer is possible due to sufficient bandwidth of the internal controller bus. (This feature benefits concurrent reads.)

2. Data writes have a Read - Modify - Write cycle, where read means read old data and parity blocks, modify old parity for the new one and write new data and parity blocks.

3. One write operation requires two separate read operations from the disks, three block-size space in the controller buffer, and five accesses to a controller bus.

4. Up to two concurrent writes for data blocks arriving asynchronously are possible for the disk array having five disks.

5. Insufficient controller buffer size penalizes performance of a disk controller by slowing down the rate of concurrent Read/Write operations.

6. Disk array controller software overhead is not taken into account.

7. Single host or disk SCSI is used;

8. Most numerical results are obtained under the chosen value of the SCSI command overhead of 0.67 ms.

Before we proceed with equations describing the disk array performance, the notations for some important system parameters have to be introduced.

MAJOR SYSTEM PARAMETERS

- N - number of disks in the array;

- N_a -number of disk arrays per controller;

- R_a - peak data rate of the host SCSI (Bps);

- R_d - peak data rate of the disk SCSI (Bps);

- L - data block size (Byte);

- C - array controller buffer size (Byte);

- M - number of concurrent writes in the disk array;

- P - portion of writes in the system I/Os;

- (1-P) - portion of reads in the system I/Os.

A *read* operation includes passing a request from a host through a host SCSI to a controller, decoding it, passing control information through a disk SCSI to a disk drive. The disk head has to be positioned to a requested cylinder (seek time), wait for the required data block come under a head (rotational latency) and transfer the data. Disk arrays, while positioning and waiting for the requested data block, can transfer data through the same disk SCSI from other disks belonging to other ranks using connect/disconnect procedures. That feature benefits the I/O throughput. The maximum read rate is limited only by the SCSI command overhead time and the amount of time a request has to wait before entering an array controller.

A *write* operation includes placing a new data block from a host to a controller buffer, reading the old data and parity blocks into a controller buffer, computing the XOR between old data and parity blocks and between new data and recomputed parity blocks. New data and parity blocks are written to the appropriate disk drives.

As we see, a controller buffer is used for storing incoming and outgoing blocks when a destination device is not available, and as an intermediate device to store old and new data and parity blocks.

A buffer will experience overflow if the number of incoming blocks exceed the buffer capacity C_m. When this happens new data blocks could not come into buffer until a necessary storage space will be available. This throttling effect can slow the overall system I/O rate. A buffer can be viewed as a single server of M/M/1 type. In a state of equilibrium, an average number of blocks in a buffer is constant and is a function of arrival V and departure W rates. It is described by a *birth-death* process of the M/M/1 type [5]. A state diagram for such case is shown on Fig 2. Assuming that all incoming blocks have the same length L (Bytes), the maximum departure rate, measured in (blocks/sec), can be found through the knowledge of the host SCSI parameters

$$W = \frac{R_{ae}}{L} \qquad (1)$$

The host SCSI effective data rate R_{ae}, measured in (Bps), depends on the burst (nominal) data rate R_a (Bps) and command overhead time T_0

$$R_{ae} = \frac{L}{\frac{L}{R_a} + T_0} \qquad (2)$$

The required buffer capacity, expressed as the number of messages (data blocks) it is capable of accommodating, may be estimated as

$$C_m = |\frac{C}{L}| + 1 \qquad (3)$$

where $|\frac{x}{y}|$ means the least integer of the quotient. Since new messages are coming into the buffer and other messages are leaving it, the number of messages in the buffer will be constantly fluctuating. The average number of messages in the buffer and the probability of its overflow may be found through the analysis of the state diagram for a single server buffer queueing system shown in Fig 2. The upper arcs show probabilities of transition from the state having fewer messages to the next one. The low arcs show probabilities of transition in the direction of reducing the number of messages in the buffer. Using the principle of detailed balancing [5] we may find the probability of being in the arbitrary k-th state

$$p_k = (1 - \frac{V}{W})(\frac{V}{W})^k \qquad (4)$$

The system utilization due to array controller buffer overflow U_c can be estimated as a sum of all probabilities being in states from 0 to C_m

$$U_c = \sum_{k=0}^{C_m} p_k \qquad (5)$$

After substituting Eq(4) into Eq(5) we obtain the analytical expression for the system utilization limited by buffer overflows

$$U_c = 1 - (\frac{V}{W})^{C_m+1} \qquad (6)$$

The number of messages which can be stored in the buffer has to be sufficient to provide M concurrent write operations (3M messages) plus a space sufficient to accommodate all concurrently executed read requests during waiting for access to the host SCSI. So, the value of C_m will be at least in tens. By substituting $C_m \gg 1$ into Eq(6) we can see that

$$U_c = \begin{cases} 1 & \text{if } W > V \\ 0 & \text{otherwise} \end{cases} \quad (7)$$

In practice, from the moment when the rate of incoming messages, V, is approaching the rate of outgoing messages, W, the throttling effect starts and reduces the rate of messages coming to the buffer. From that moment on, the internal feedback mechanism will start to reduce the rate of blocks entering the buffer. Since one write operation requires storage of three blocks, instead of only one for reads, we may expect that the most demanding requirements for the buffer space come from applications with a large number of writes. Correspondingly, the buffer size C_r may be defined for the extreme case of consecutive write operations

$$C_r = 6M \cdot L \quad (8)$$

The factor 6 in Eq (8) shows that we must have enough space to store three blocks per each concurrent write (new data, old data and parity blocks) plus have enough space if another write operation is under execution before the previous one is completed. Eqs(2), (5), and (7) allow to evaluate the impact of insufficient buffer size on system performance.

To prevent large waiting times to access a host SCSI the actual block arrival rate to the controller buffer has to be under 40 % of the estimated maximum departure rate W [5].

Analysis of the host SCSI requirements

The effective data rate of the host SCSI R_{ae} must be sufficient to transfer data blocks during Read/Write operations. The upper limit of the block arrival rate to the host SCSI is

$$V_{sa} = (1-p)NR_e + pMR_e \quad (9)$$

The first term in Eq(9) shows contribution of system reads to the traffic, and the second one is due to system writes. The weight coefficient p is the probability of having the write operations within system I/Os.

From the analysis of Eq(9) follows that since $N > M$, a system will experience the highest demand for the data transfer at the Host - Controller interface for the case of read operations exclusively (p=0).

The achievable data rate at the Host - Controller interface R_c is limited by insufficient buffer size (coefficient $U_c \le 1$), insufficient data rate of the host SCSI ($U_a \le 1$), or, even by a controller internal bus if an attached disk array is too wide ($U_b \le 1$)

$$R_c = V_{sa} \cdot U_c \cdot U_a \cdot U_b \quad (10)$$

The controller bus utilization U_b is the ratio of the packet transmission time T, in the case of successful packet delivery, to the total time T_{tt}, a packet spends in the bus (it includes the packet transmission time and waiting time for a bus access in the case of insufficient bus bandwidth)

$$U_b = \frac{T}{T_{tt}} \quad (11)$$

Effective controller I/O rate D_c, measured in (blocks/second), is a function of the write/read ratio and can be easily found from Eq (10)

$$D_c = \frac{R_c}{L} \quad (12)$$

For example, for the 40 MBps internal controller bus, only five 5 MBps disk transfers are possible without limiting the controller utilization. However, if the width of the disk array N will be increased, the additional drop in controller bus utilization will follow.

Now we have prepared an analytical foundation for the numerical results. The description of the numerical results will be the topic of the next section.

Numerical Results

The main bottleneck to the achievable throughput of the disk arrays, as it will be shown later, is caused by the insufficient data rate of the host SCSI (see Fig 1). Because of that, it is logical to start the performance analysis of disk arrays from consideration of the SCSI performance. Fig 3 shows the SCSI bus utilization vs. the block size for different SCSI nominal data rates. Utilization is defined as the ratio of the block transfer time to the total time a data block spends in the SCSI. Only the finite duration of the command overhead relative to the block transfer time prevents from the 100 percent SCSI utilization. The larger block size takes longer transfer time and constitutes a larger portion of the total time spent in a SCSI relative to a command overhead time. It leads to increasing of the SCSI utilization.

The values of the SCSI perceived (effective) data rate for small block sizes are dominated by the command overhead time as may be seen from Fig 3. The later is especially pronounced for the high data rates. Larger data blocks spend more time in the transfer state compared to the fixed command overhead. It leads to the rise of the SCSI utilization for larger data blocks. It may be seen from Fig 3 by comparing the 5 MBps SCSI solid curve with other plots of 10, 20 and 40 MBps SCSIs. The selection better models SCSIs with less command overhead time does not produce results directly proportional to the command overhead reduction. For example, the 30 % reduction of that parameter for the 20 MBps SCSI on Fig 3 produced only 12 % increase in the effective bandwidth during the transfer of 32 kB blocks. indent The lowest utilization is achieved by high data rate SCSIs since the command overhead and wait time constitute the largest fraction of total time being in the SCSI. Nevertheless, in absolute terms the high nominal data rate SCSIs still provide higher effective data rates as may be seen in Fig 4. The 32 bit wide 10MHz SCSI-2 with a nominal data rate of 40 MBps still can provide effective transfer rate of 16 MBps for 32 kB data blocks. The 0.7 ms connect/disconnect time SCSIs operating at the peak rate of 20 MBps provide higher absolute transfer rate for blocks below 12 kB compared to 40 MBps SCSIs having 1 ms disconnect time. indent The insufficient bandwidth of the SCSI is not the only reason for restriction of the disk array performance. The other source of such limitations is the limited size of the controller buffer. Fig 5 illustrates this. The number of ranks is not so important as soon as the host SCSI has relative sufficiency of bandwidth (for example, the curves for 12 kB data blocks for the case of one or four ranks are virtually identical). The prime importance is the size of data blocks. The quarter megabyte size of a buffer will be sufficient to accommodate traffic even for the future applications.

By tacit assumption that the size of the controller buffer is not less then 0.25 MB we can drop from our consideration restrictions of buffer size limitations.

The insufficient host SCSI bandwidth is difficult to overcome at the current state of technology. Fig 6 shows the relative read rate versus the host SCSI nominal data rate for different block sizes and different number of ranks in the system. The loss in the read rate is equal to 4 percent for the case of 5 MBps SCSI when 1 kB blocks are read concurrently by a disk array with four ranks. The loss increases to 32 percent for the case of 12 kB blocks and 4 ranks. The system based on the 10 MBps SCSIs using 12 kB data blocks for reads loses 18 percent of potential data rate. By going to the next generation of SCSIs with 40 MBps data rate we can increase read rate to 95 percent of it maximum rate from 90 percent for the case of 20 MBps SCSIs operating with 12 kB blocks.

The host SCSI data rate defines also the number of disk ranks the disk matrix can have. Fig 7 shows that for the 12 kB data blocks a RAID-5 system with the 5 MBps SCSIs can support about one rank of five disks. A system with the 10 MBps controller SCSI is capable to support on average slightly over two ranks. By replacing a 10 MBps SCSI by a 20 MBps counterpart the number of ranks supported is equal to four. For shorter data blocks (say 4 kB) the number of ranks supported is around 40 percent higher in the range of SCSI data rates between 10 and 20 MBps.

The I/O rate supported by the RAID-5 system is the integrated measure of its performance. That rate is shown on the Fig 8 as a function of the number of ranks in the system for the different write/read ratios, block sizes and controller SC-SIs data rates. The solid line with pluses is the number of read I/Os supported by a RAID controller for the ideal operating environment when no any bottlenecks exist in the system. Reading 12 kB data blocks by a four rank RAID-5 system will yield 450 Reads/s for a 20 MBps host SCSI, or only 340 Reads/s for a 10 MBps SCSI vs 620 Reads/s for the ideal case with no restrictions. A one rank RAID-5 provides about 130 Reads/s for the case of reading 12 kB data blocks. That number drops to about 100 IOps (I/Os per second) for the case of Write/Read ratio of 1:2.

The rate of IOps is strongly influenced by a Write/Read ratio, since for writes it is necessary to conduct two seeks of data blocks (data and parity) and additional full rotation time while a new parity is computed. Seeks partially can be executed concurrently. Without a queueing delay at the corresponding disks, two seeks will take on average 1.5 of average seek time. By executing more write operations concurrently, it is possible to counter performance degradation. Since two disks are involved in the execution of asynchronous writes, the number of concurrent writes must be half the number of disks in the array. A four data disk RAID-5 can provide only two concurrent writes. Fig 9 shows that a RAID-5 with a 10 MBps host SCSI provides 325 Reads/s while it drops to 150 IOps for the case of writes only. The use of 20 MBps SCSIs improves IOps rating to 440 and 180 for the cases of only reads or writes, respectfully.

It is interesting to know how the achievable IOps rating depends on the type of the host SCSI used. Fig 10 shows the variation of IO rate as a function of the compounded SCSI data rate for the 12 kB data blocks and different Write/Read ratios. It is assumed that two 5 MBps SCSI installed between Hosts and a Controller have comparable data rate of 10 MBps as one 10 MBps

SCSI. As it may be seen from Fig 10 that one rank RAID-5 system can not provide more than 160 Reads/s, while adding 4 ranks increases the Read rate to over 500. If one third of all IOs are writes, the maximum achievable IO rate is equal to 430. The increase of the portion of writes to two thirds drops the IO rate to 320. The IO rate for all writes is 200 IOps. The further increase in the host SCSI rate will not change the I/O rating while with other Read/Write ratios there is a possibility of improvements in the I/O rating.

The questions asked the most often by system architects is how many hosts one RAID-5 system can support. The answer depends on the type of the hosts and the RAID-5 system used. One controller having a compounded data rate between Hosts and Controllers of 10 MBps, and controlling on average two ranks of (4+1) disks as it can be seen from Fig 11, is capable to support one microprocessor based host. Correspondingly, a RAID-5 system with two controllers will be capable to support two hosts. The host rating improves only 20 percent by using the 10 MBps SCSIs. Doubling the rank width to 8 data disks and using 10 MBps SCSIs will give improvement near 100 percent relative to the first case. A system will be able to support four hosts.

Conclusions

A note of caution has to be exercised during reading the following conclusions and analyzing the described performance figures. These figures represent the performance estimates obtained under assumptions of negligible software overhead and 0.67 ms value of the SCSI command overhead. The large software overhead in some implementations or the other values of SCSI command overhead are capable of substantially changing the performance figures.

- Disk system (disk matrix) throughput is a nonlinear function of the individual disks and disk controller parameters such as: number of disks per rank, number of ranks in the system, compounded data rate of all SCSI buses installed between a host and a controller, the size of a controller buffer, the way files are striped across individual disks and the read/write ratio.

- Insufficient data transfer rate at the interface between a Host and a Controller may seriously affect the controller performance. A 5 MBps host SCSI may support on average 1.4 ranks consisting of four data and one parity drives. The 10 or 20 MBps Host - Controller interface can support 2.3 and 4 ranks correspondingly.

- Two 5Mbps host SCSIs have larger compounded transfer data rate as one 10 MBps host SCSI.

- Two microprocessor based hosts can be supported by a RAID-5 system with two controllers having access to four ranks of (4+1) disks in each. A replacement of both 5 MBps host SCSIs by the 10 MBps SCSI-2s will improve the supported number of hosts by only 20 per cent.

- To utilize the full potential of an array controller all its components have to be matched. That means that a compounded effective data rate at the Hosts-Controller interface and between disks belonging to the same rank and a controller should not exceed the effective transfer rate of the internal controller bus.

- 40 MBps internal controller bus can support only five disk ranks using 5 MBps disk SCSIs.

- Five disk ranks require a quarter of megabyte buffer size to eliminate the buffer overflow.

- To double the write rate, the number of data disks per rank has to be doubled too.

It will also require to double the controller internal bus bandwidth and the size of a controller buffer.

References

1. D. Patterson, G. Gibson, R. Katz "A Case for Redundant Arrays of Inexpensive Disks (RAID)", ACM SIGMOD Conference, Illinois, June 1-3, 1988

2. Jim Gray, Bob Horst, Mark Walker "Parity striping of Disk Arrays: Low Cost Reliable Storage with Acceptable Throughput," Proceedings of the 16th VLDB Conference, Brisbane, Australia 1990

3. Garth Gibson "Performance and Reliability in Redundant Arrays of Inexpensive Disks", CMG annual conference proceedings, December 1989, Reno, Nevada.

4. R. Muntz, J. Lui "Performance analysis of Disk Arrays Under Failure", Proceedings of the 16th VLDB Conference, Brisbane, Australia 1990

5. Kishor Trivedi "Probability and Statistics with Reliability, Queueing and Computer Science Applications", Prentice Hall, 1982.

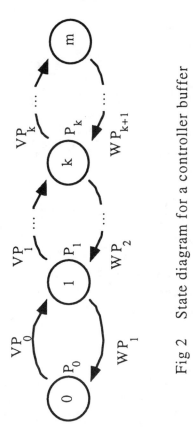

Fig 2   State diagram for a controller buffer

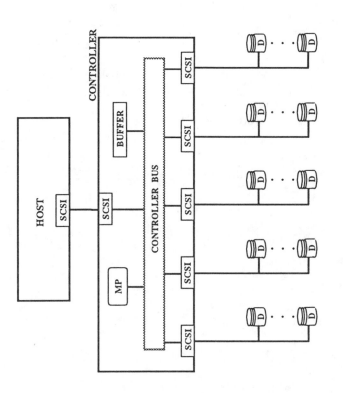

Fig 1   Block Diagram of the Disk Array

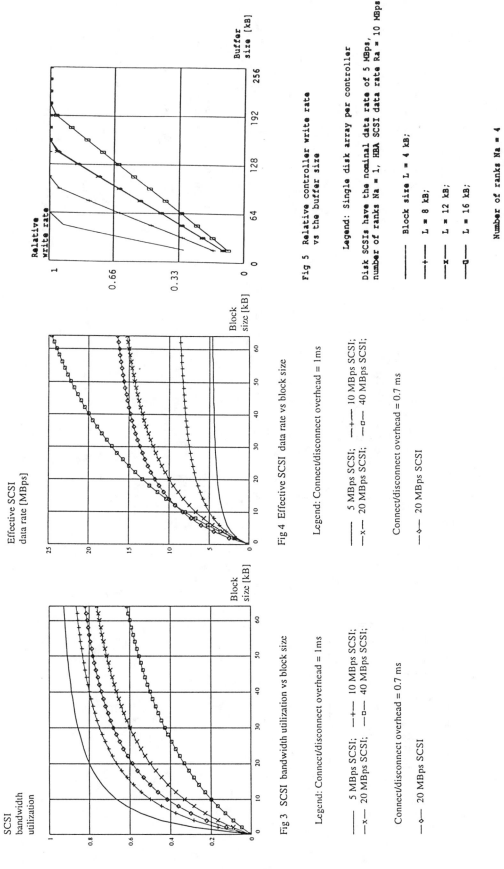

Fig 3 SCSI bandwidth utilization vs block size

Legend: Connect/disconnect overhead = 1ms

——— 5 MBps SCSI;   —+— 10 MBps SCSI;
—x— 20 MBps SCSI;   —□— 40 MBps SCSI;

Connect/disconnect overhead = 0.7 ms

—◇— 20 MBps SCSI

Fig 4 Effective SCSI data rate vs block size

Legend: Connect/disconnect overhead = 1ms

——— 5 MBps SCSI;   —+— 10 MBps SCSI;
—x— 20 MBps SCSI;   —□— 40 MBps SCSI;

Connect/disconnect overhead = 0.7 ms

—◇— 20 MBps SCSI

Fig 5 Relative controller write rate
        vs the buffer size

Legend: Single disk array per controller

Disk SCSIs have the nominal data rate of 5 MBps,
number of ranks Na = 1, HBA SCSI data rate Ra = 10 MBps

——— Block size L = 4 kB;

—+— L = 8 kB;
—x— L = 12 kB;
—□— L = 16 kB;

     Number of ranks Na = 4

—◇— L = 12 kB

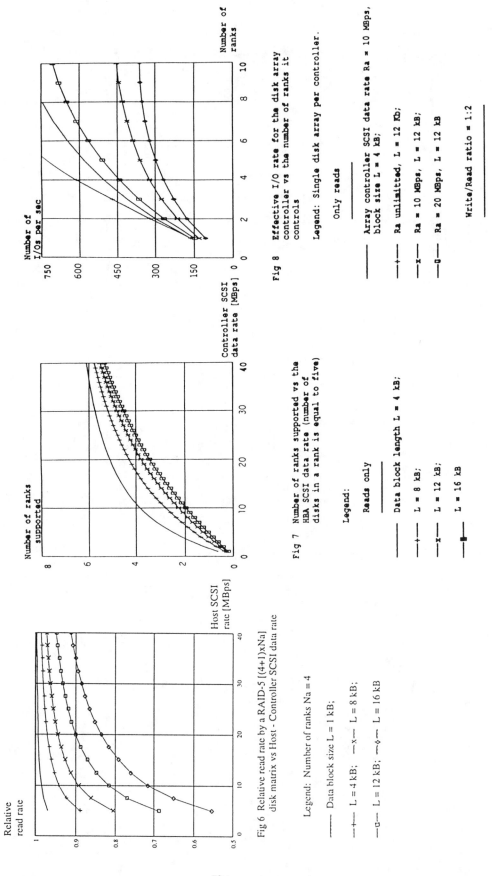

Fig 8 Effective I/O rate for the disk array controller vs the number of ranks it controls

Legend: Single disk array per controller.

Only reads

Array controller SCSI data rate Ra = 10 MBps, block size L = 4 kB:

—+— Ra unlimited, L = 12 Kb;
—x— Ra = 10 MBps, L = 12 kB;
—□— Ra = 20 MBps, L = 12 kB

Write/Read ratio = 1:2

—◇— Ra = 10 MBps, L = 12kB

Fig 7 Number of ranks supported vs the HBA SCSI data rate (number of disks in a rank is equal to five)

Legend:

Reads only

——— Data block length L = 4 kB;
—+— L = 8 kB;
—x— L = 12 kB;
—■— L = 16 kB

Fig 6 Relative read rate by a RAID-5 [(4+1)xNa] disk matrix vs Host - Controller SCSI data rate

Legend: Number of ranks Na = 4

——— Data block size L = 1 kB;
—+— L = 4 kB; —x— L = 8 kB;
—□— L = 12 kB; —◇— L = 16 kB

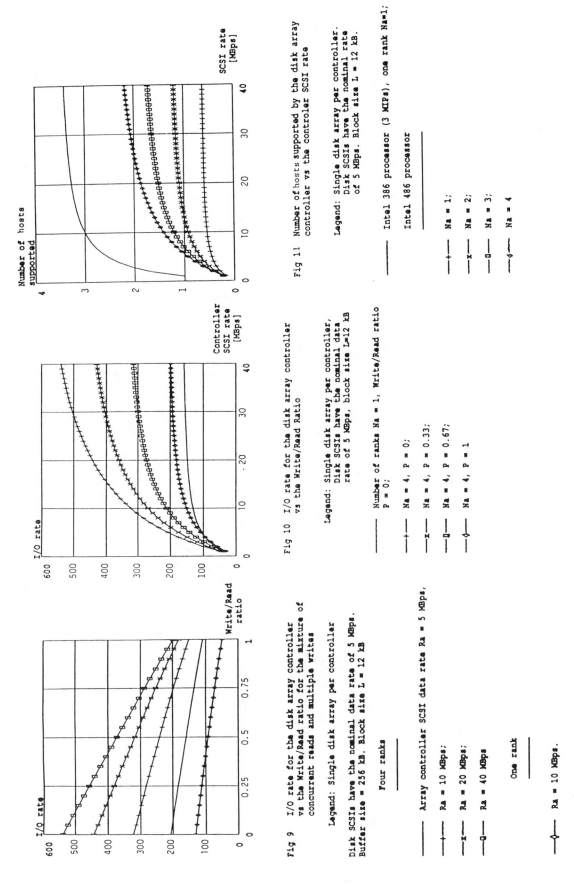

Fig 9   I/O rate for the disk array controller vs the Write/Read ratio for the mixture of concurrent reads and multiple writes

Legend: Single disk array per controller

Disk SCSIs have the nominal data rate of 5 MBps. Block size L = 12 kB Buffer size = 256 kB. Block size L = 12 kB

     Four ranks

———— Array controller SCSI data rate Ra = 5 MBps,

+———— Ra = 10 MBps;

x———— Ra = 20 MBps;

□———— Ra = 40 MBps

     One rank

◇———— Ra = 10 MBps.

Fig 10   I/O rate for the disk array controller vs the Write/Read Ratio

Legend: Single disk array per controller, Disk SCSIs have the nominal data rate of 5 MBps, block size L=12 kB

———— Number of ranks Na = 1, Write/Read ratio P = 0;

+———— Na = 4, P = 0;

x———— Na = 4, P = 0.33;

□———— Na = 4, P = 0.67;

◇———— Na = 4, P = 1

Fig 11   Number of hosts supported by the disk array controller vs the controler SCSI rate

Legend: Single disk array per controller. Disk SCSIs have the nominal rate of 5 MBps. Block size L = 12 kB.

———— Intel 386 processor (3 MIPs), one rank Na=1;

———— Intel 486 processor

+———— Na = 1;

x———— Na = 2;

□———— Na = 3;

◇———— Na = 4

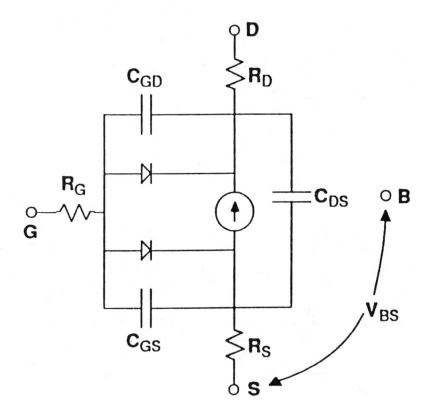

Correlation of the Paging Activity of Individual Node Programs in the SPMD Execution Mode

Kuei Yu Wang* and Dan C. Marinescu[†]

{kywang@cs.purdue.edu, dcm@cs.purdue.edu}
Computer Sciences Department
Purdue University
West Lafayette, IN 47907

Abstract

In this paper we introduce a methodology for the analysis of the paging activity of parallel programs running on massively parallel systems. The methodology includes parallel program monitoring and the analysis of the collected data. We study the correlation of the paging activities of individual node programs in the SPMD execution mode and its effect on scheduling.

1 Introduction

Massively parallel systems (MPPs) are viewed today as expensive scientific and engineering instruments. Their primary use is in the area of numeric simulation of complex physical phenomena. The performance/usability trade-offs of such systems are heavily tilted in favor of performance. Most distributed memory MIMD (DMIMD) systems have rather primitive operating systems with restricted functionality and rudimentary management of system resources. Only recently MPPs which run commodity operating systems in all Processing Elements (PEs) have been announced, e.g., IBM's, SP1 and SP2 (running AIX), and Intel Paragon (running OSF/1 under Mach). Such systems are easier to use but less efficient than their counterparts which run only communication kernels (e.g., SUNMOS, NX, etc.).

Virtual memory is a convenience function supported by operating systems, which allows users to design applications without an immediate concern for the amount of real memory available on a certain system. The operating system maps the virtual (user) address space into the real memory available. If the application exhibits a good locality of reference, then the performance penalty associated with virtual memory is low, even when the virtual address space is considerably larger than the real memory.

The support for demand paging is an important step towards making massively parallel systems more usable and more appealing for a broader class of applications [1]. Yet, existing distributed memory MIMD systems are unbalanced; their I/O and communication bandwidths are insufficient to sustain the request rates generated by powerful processors. There is a legitimate concern that the paging activity may lead to a significant performance penalty by increasing the I/O and the communication load.

The goal of our research is to observe and understand the paging activity of parallel programs. We want to answer questions like: (a) How to characterize the paging activity of a parallel program? (b) How is the paging activity affected by changes in the number of processing nodes and the size of the data space? How does it change when the system configuration changes, e.g. the placement and/or the number of I/O nodes, etc.? (c) How can the knowledge of the paging activity of an application be used to improve its performance? (d) How can the knowledge of the paging activity of several applications be used to improve the concurrent scheduling of these applications in different partitions of a large system? Such questions can only be answered by studying the paging activity of representative applications running on existing MPPs. Therefore our first objective is to develop a methodology for the study of paging activity which includes program monitoring and the analysis of the collected data. This paper discusses the development of an application paging profiler and a post-profiling tool.

In this paper we report on the paging activity of parallel programs running under OSF/1 on an Intel Paragon XP/S supercomputer. The parallel programs we have profiled and analyzed are structural biology programs used for the determination of the 3-D atomic structure of large macro-

---
*Work supported in part by CNPq Brazil

[†] Work supported in part by NSF under grants CCR-9119388 and BIR-9301210

molecules such as viruses [2],[6].

In §2.1 we discuss the relationship between paging and scheduling. In uniprocessor systems, context switching is used to hide the high latency associated with a page-in request. Parallel systems use gang scheduling, and context switching for hiding the latency of a page-in could only be used if all node programs of an application experience page faults leading to page-in requests precisely at the same time and if the overhead of a process group context switch is low. This motivates our studies of the correlation of the paging activities of all the node programs. Then we introduce a model of the paging activity (§2.3 and §2.2). In §2.4, the relevant paging statistical data collected during execution are discussed.

At the present time we are concentrating on a two prong data analysis. First, we study how similar/dissimilar is the paging activity of different node programs in SPMD, Same Program Multiple Data, execution mode by performing a "skyline analysis" of the data collected for different node programs. This analysis is done by determining the rate at which different events occur, by isolating the peaks of activity from the background and by correlating the time of occurrence and the amplitude of these peaks. The skyline analysis for the page faults, page-ins, copy-on-write, and page-outs, is presented in this paper. The second type of analysis is the "cumulative profile," used to determine the total load due to paging activity upon the communication and the I/O sub-system.

2 Characterization of the paging activity of parallel programs

A massively parallel system consists of compute nodes, I/O nodes, and service nodes connected by a high speed interconnection network. Network topologies used in existing systems are hypercubes (e.g., the Intel iPSC/860, the NCUBE), 2-D meshes (e.g., the Intel Paragon), 2-D tori (e.g., the Cray MPP), fat-trees (e.g., Thinking Machines CM5), or extra stage omega networks (e.g., IBM's SP1 and SP2).

Each compute node consists of one or more processors having a common memory, possibly co-processors (e.g., a message co-processor) and a network interface. In addition to the configuration mentioned above an I/O node has I/O interfaces for devices like disks, and/or computer networks. Space and cost considerations limit the number of I/O nodes, and therefore the I/O bandwidth of current systems.

MPPs are partitioned statically; a partition is allocated a number of compute nodes and shares with other partitions the set of I/O nodes. A parallel program runs in a partition

of a size determined by the needs of that application. A parallel program consists of a process group, a set of node programs, one for each PE.

2.1 Paging and scheduling

The paging behavior of a sequential program (process) is characterized by its *working set* defined as the collection of pages needed for process execution over a period of time.

The execution time in the presence of page faults, denoted by T_f is

$$T_f = T(1 + t^p \times \eta^p) = T(1 + a^p)$$

with

T — the execution time without any page fault
η^p — the actual page fault rate, the number of page faults per unit of time
t^p — the latency of a page fault
$a^p = t^p \times \eta^p$

The page fault rate depends upon the relationship between the size of the working set of the process and the amount of memory available. The page fault latency varies considerably depending upon the cause of the page fault. Page-ins require the longest time because they involve access to the swap file. In our simplified analysis we are primarily concerned with page faults due to page-ins and we will use the approximation $\eta^p \cong \eta_f$, with η_f the rate of page-ins and $t^p = t_f$ with t_f the latency of a page-in. In this case, $T_f = T(1 + a)$ with $a = t_f \times \eta_f$.

Let us now consider a parallel system with N_c compute nodes and N_{IO} I/O nodes and assume that every page fault requires an I/O operation. We expect the service time for a page fault to increase due to contention for shared resources like communication channels and I/O nodes. To obtain a very crude estimate of t_f^p, the time needed in this case for resolving a page fault leading to a page-in request, we consider a model of the system based upon a set of simplifying assumptions

(a) All compute nodes have identical page-in rates of η_f pages/second. The aggregate page-in rate of the parallel program consisting of N_c identical tasks running concurrently is $N_c \times \eta_f$.

(b) The page-ins are evenly distributed over the set of I/O nodes. Each I/O node runs a pager and has a request rate of $\eta_f^p = \frac{N_c}{N_{IO}} \eta_f$.

(c) Each I/O node can be modeled as an M/M/1 system with request rate of η_f^p and service rate of $1/t_f$. Then the time needed for a page-in is $t_f^p = \frac{t_f}{1 - t_f \times \eta_f^p}$.

The condition for the system to be stable is $t_f \times \eta_f^p = t_f \times \eta_f \times \frac{N_c}{N_{IO}} < 1$ or $\eta_f < \frac{N_{IO}}{N_c} \frac{1}{t_f}$.

(d) The communication delays can be neglected.

(e) We assume a linear speed-up; namely the parallel execution time in absence of page faults is $T^p = \frac{T}{N_c}$.

It follows that the parallel execution time in the presence of page faults is

$$T_f^p = T^p(1 + t_f^p \times \eta_f) = \frac{T}{N_c}\left(1 + \frac{t_f \times \eta_f}{1 - \frac{N_c}{N_{IO}} \times t_f \times \eta_f}\right)$$
$$= \frac{T}{N_c}\left(1 + \frac{a}{1 - a \times n_{IOC}}\right)$$

This approximate analysis shows that the support for virtual memory for the present generation of MPPs is a challenging task.

The overall load placed upon the shared resources (communication network and I/O nodes) is determined by the aggregate page fault rate which in turn is determined by the correlation of the paging activities of individual node programs. In our simplified analysis, we assume that the intervals at which page faults occur are exponentially distributed. Yet, in practice the SPMD paradigm discussed in §2.3 is often used. In this case, one could expect that different PEs generate page faults at about the same time, that page faults occur in bursts, and that the page fault service time increases dramatically.

The method used by traditional operating systems to hide the page fault latency, namely context switching at the time when a page fault leading to a page-in request occurs, is based upon the fact that the service time for a page fault is considerably larger than the time for context switching. Can the same approach be applied in case of MPPs? To answer this question, we need to examine briefly scheduling on MPPs. In all but a very few applications the individual processes of a process group need to communicate among themselves. To do so, they need to be active at the same time on different PEs. The scheduling strategy in which all processes in a process group are activated at the same time, then suspended at the same time, activated again at the same time and so on, is called *gang scheduling or co-scheduling*, [8]. Gang scheduling can be used to hide the latency of page faults if and only if different processes of a process group experience page faults at the same time and if the overhead for a process group context switch is low. Therefore, we need to study the correlation of the paging activity of individual processes of a process group.

To characterize the dynamics of paging for a sequential program we define the *page fault profile* as the number of page faults as a function of time. In a uniprocessing environment, the page fault profile of a process can be measured by having a cumulative counter of page faults and by sampling it periodically. In a parallel system we are interested in the dynamics of the total load placed upon the communication and I/O subsystems. To study this dynamics, we

define a "cumulative paging profile of a parallel program" by composing the individual paging profiles of individual node programs for all the relevant paging activities such as faults, copy-on-write, page-ins, and page-outs.

2.2 A model of parallel program execution.

In this section we are concerned with parallel programs for DMIMD systems. Such a parallel program consists of a set of tasks running concurrently, one task per node or possibly multiple tasks per node in case of multiprocessing nodes. Each task can be either active or suspended. Each active task can be in one of three possible states:

(a) *Compute*. The task executes its own code and issues system calls other than those related to I/O and communication.

(b) *I/O*. The task has invoked an I/O system call and might be waiting for its completion.

(c) *Communication*. The task has invoked a communication system call and might be waiting for its completion.

If we want to investigate a certain property of a parallel program, for example its paging behavior, a possible alternative is to study the dynamics of a set of parameters pertinent to that property.

The microscopic behavior of a parallel program consisting of N tasks, π_k, $k = 1, N$ each task going through a sequence of m_k states $S_{j,k}$ with $j = 1, m_k$, will be characterized by the average value $\lambda_{k,j}^{q_i}$ for each of the n parameters q_i with $i = 1, n$ relevant to the property of interest. For each parameter, for each task, and for each state we have a tuple $(t_{k,j-1}, t_{k,j}, \lambda_{k,j}^{q_i})$ with

$t_{k,j-1}$ — the time where task π_k performed its $(j-1)$ state transition, entering state $S_{j,k}$.

$t_{k,j}$ — the time where task π_k exited the state $S_{j,k}$.

$\lambda_{k,j}^{q_i}$ — the average rate of change of the global counter q_i given by

$$\lambda_{k,j}^{q_i} = \frac{q_i(t_{k,j}) - q_i(t_{k,j-1})}{t_{k,j} - t_{k,j-1}}$$

Several observations are in order. (a) The average rate of change of the parameter q_i is a good approximation of the temporal behavior of the task only if the lifetime of the corresponding state is short. (b) The model is amenable to performance monitoring. One could automatically detect the transition from one state to another, record the values of the parameters in the minimum set every time a state transition occurs, determine the lifetime of the state and

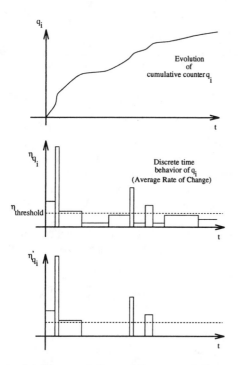

Figure 1: (a) The evolution of the cumulative counter q_i. (b) The discrete time behavior of q_i. The rate of q_i, η_{q_i} is plotted as function of time. $\eta_{threshold}$ indicates the threshold used to separate the peaks from the background. (c) The filtering out of the background and retention of the peaks of η_{q_i}.

compute the average rates. (c) This microscopic characterization is very costly in terms of the amount of information stored. (d) In some cases it will be difficult, if possible at all, to correlate events occurring different tasks. If different PEs have unsynchronized clocks, it is next to impossible to perform such a correlation.

The discrete time model introduced in this section can be used to reduce significantly the amount of data necessary to characterize the behavior of a sequential or parallel program by filtering the raw data obtained through monitoring. For example, assume that parameter q_i has the behavior illustrated in Figure 1a. Figure 1b shows the discrete event representation of η_{q_i} supported by our model. If we accept that values of η_{q_i} lower than a given threshold say $q_{threshold}$ can be neglected, then we can approximate η_{q_i} by a number of peaks rising above a background of level $q_{threshold}$. For example, when we want to correlate the paging activity of individual node programs, it seems reasonable to filter out the background and retain only the peaks of the page fault profile.

2.3 Modeling the paging behavior of SPMD programs

A commonly used paradigm for solving problems which require a considerable amount of computing time using parallel systems is to partition the data in some manner and to run the same program in all the PEs assigned to the user, with each PE executing the same program, but with different data, therefore the name SPMD. This execution mode is compatible with distributed and shared memory MIMD architectures.

In the SPMD mode, the sequence of instructions executed by different PEs is different due to data dependencies. Often, a special form of data dependency, the dependency of the identity of the PE, makes different PEs have a very different flow of control and allows the implementation of a worker-coordinator programming model. In this extended SPMD mode (ESPMD), the coordinator performs functions which are strictly sequential such as reading the problem description, computing some initial values and distributing them to all the workers, and then at the end of the computation, collecting statistical information from the workers. In the SPMD mode, one could reasonably expect similar, but not identical paging behavior for different PEs.

2.4 Virtual memory statistics

The implementation of a virtual memory system in the Paragon XP/S system is provided by the OSF/1 Mach 3 operating system [3],[4],[9]. The OSF/1 Mach maintains statistics on the use of virtual memory since the time the kernel was booted for the processor on which that kernel is executing in the *vm_statistic* structure. The pertinent information for the paging activity given in *vm_statistic* is provided by global counter such as:

- *page-ins* - the number of requests for pages from the kernel to the pager.

- *page-outs* - the number of pages that have been paged out.

- *faults* - the number of times page faults have been detected.

- *cow-faults* - the number of copy-on-write faults (deferred evaluation optimization) have occurred.

The data in the *vm_statistic* structure consists of *non-cumulative* and *cumulative counters*. Non-cumulative counters give the status of the paging queues when the *vm_statistic* is read. For example, *active count* reports the number of pages currently in use (in the active queue), *free count* the number of pages not holding any data, and so on. Cumulative counters keep the number of occurrences of an activity since the kernel was booted. For example, *faults* reports the number of page faults occurred since the boot time to the moment when the *vm_statistic* structure is read.

The type of statistic plays an important role in the form of processing its value. From a sequence of statistics collected from the system in different intervals, it makes sense to take the weighted (by interval) mean value of non-cumulative counters and take the weighted rate value of cumulative counters. The average rate of a certain indicator of the paging activity, e.g., page faults, page-ins, etc. is computed by taking the difference between two consecutive readings divided by the time elapsed between the two readings.

For our research purpose, the important measures of the paging activity are: *faults, page-ins, page-outs,* and *cow-faults.* Based on the behavior of these counters we are able to characterize the paging activity of the application under study. Other counters [4], such as *free, active, inactive* count, *lookup,* and *hits,* are mostly related to the status of the physical memory cache, which depend primary on the kernel.

3 Parallel program profiling

An event-driven *parallel profiling library* is provided to monitor and profile the execution of the parallel programs on the Paragon^{TM} XP/S System running the OSF/1 Mach Operating System. Following the Mach terminology we call a node program a *task*. During the execution of each task snapshots of paging statistics at each state transition are collected. The set of parameters related to paging activities in the OSF/1 Mach kernel is found in the *vm_statistic* structure, collected at the time a state transition occurs.

The steps for profiling a parallel program are:

1. *Instrumentation of the source code.* A pre-processor detects the points of state transition, such as I/O and communication system calls, and substitutes the corresponding system call by the counterpart profiler routine.

2. *Parallel program profiling.* During the profiling phase, each task of the parallel program generates trace records which are stored in a separate trace file. The trace records are collected according to the dynamics of the task execution path.

3. *Post-processing trace data analysis.* The trace data collected during the profiling phase are further processed to extract relevant information about the parallel program paging activities.

3.1 Parallel profiling library

The design of the parallel profiling library strives to guarantee accuracy of the collected data by minimizing the intrusion (see also §5.2).

The following steps are taken to ensure limited intrusion: (a) A compact format for the trace record; a minimum set of parameters relevant to the paging activities are collected in addition to the execution state and the time stamp. (b) Data collection frequency is limited to events of interest, such as task state transition. (c) I/O operation frequency, such as writing trace records into trace files, is reduced by using buffered I/O routines. (d) Off-line data analysis is adopted to avoid additional computation during the program profiling phase.

Trace data are collected when state transitions generated by I/O or communication system calls occur. To profile a parallel application, I/O and communication system calls are substituted by their counterpart profiler routines. A profiler routine generates two trace records in addition to the system call itself. Thus, during the execution of a profiler routine, one trace record is collected before the system call is executed and another right after its completion. The Paragon^{TM} XP/S System provides a global clock which allows the reconstruction of the global event sequence.

A trace record is a tuple (t_j, S_j, V_j) with

t_j – the time when the record for the event j is generated

S_j – the type of the event j. The event types are: *START_IO, END_IO, START_MSG,* and *END_MSG*.

V_j – the set of values of global counters, q^i with $i = 1, n$, at t_j.

Figure 2 illustrates the functioning of the profiling library. In this example, a task executing *Ps_csend* generates two consecutive trace records: $(t_{j-1}, START\_MSG, V_{j-1})$ and (t_j, END_MSG, V_j). These two trace records provide the following information: (1) A *compute* state ended at t_{j-1}. (2) A *communication* state started at t_{j-1} (START_MSG) and ended at t_j (END_MSG). The average rate of change of the parameters is calculated based on values recorded for V_{j-1} and V_j. (3) A *compute* state started at t_j. This *compute* state ends when a new trace record is issued, i.e. when the following communication or I/O event occurs.

3.2 Profiling library user interface

The profiling library consists of profiler routines for I/O and communication system calls, and a few routines providing the user with profiling flow control. Table 1 summarizes the profiling library user interface. The user can turn the profiling on and off, may generate additional trace records using the *Ps_profile_trace* call and other event control primitives in Table 1.

One of the problems with the event-driven profiling approach is the variable duration of a state. Since the trace records are collected at points of state switching, a long

Original Source Code	Profiled Source Code	Execution State
. . . .	. . . .	
a = 1234;	a = 1234;	
b = my_computation(a);	b = my_computation(a);	Compute
x[i] = b;	x[i] = b;	
csend(O_data, o_array, o_size);	**Ps_csend**(O_data, o_array, o_size);	Communication
a = a * arcsin(x[i]);	a = a * arcsin(x[i]);	
b = my_computation(b);	b = my_computation(b);	Compute
x[i] = b;	x[i] = b;	
crecv(I_data, i_array, i_size);	**Ps_crecv**(I_data, i_array, i_size);	Communication
. . . .	. . . .	Compute

Figure 2: Profiling parallel programs: an example

Communication		Global Ops	I/O		Event Control
Msg Passing		Global Ops	I/O		Event Control
Ps_csend	Ps_crecv	Ps_gsync	Ps_cread	Ps_open	Ps_init
Ps_csendrecv		Ps_gdsum	Ps_cwrite	Ps_close	Ps_printstat
Ps_isend	Ps_irecv	Ps_gisum	Ps_iread	Ps_stat	Ps_sleep
Ps_isendrecv		Ps_gssum	Ps_iwrite	Ps_lseek	
Ps_msgdone	Ps_msgwait		Ps_iodone	Ps_eseek	Ps_profile_label
Ps_hsend	Ps_hrecv		Ps_iowait		Ps_profile_trace
Ps_hsendx	Ps_hrecvx				
Ps_hsendrecv	Ps_gsendx				

Table 1: The Profiling Library User Interface

state is described the same as a short state is. It is possible that an application stays in a state (e.g. *compute*) for a long period of time or that an application presents a very small number of state switches. In those applications a very small number of trace records are generated for a long period of time. The user may insert *Ps_profile_trace* calls in the source code, and at execution time each call to *Ps_profile_trace* generates a trace record containing the snapshots of paging parameters. Because of the intrusion and overhead to the program execution, this routine should be used only it is necessary; the indiscriminate use of it can alter the behavior of the program.

4 Data reduction and peak selection

In this section we study the correlation of the paging activities of individual node programs in the SPMD execution mode and introduce a methodology for reduction, interpretation, and analysis of the paging activities called "skyline analysis."

4.1 Data reduction

For most of the parallel applications studied, the profiles for different paging activity indicators show transients of high paging activity intermixed with longer periods of low activity.

The objectives of data reduction are (a) to expedite the identification of paging activity bursts and observe the system response under heavy paging work load, and (b) to reduce the amount of data needed to describe the parallel program paging behavior.

The data reduction is composed of the following three elements: peak selection, background filtering, and skyline representation.

• Peak selection

During the execution of an SPMD parallel program, there are usually several bursts of paging activity, called "*peaks*", at certain periods intermixed with other low activity periods, called "*background.*"

To compose the paging profile of parameter q_i for a node k, we select the N_k largest peaks occurring during the execution in node k. The number N_k may vary for each node according to the following selection criterion (see §4.2):

$$N_k = \min(\text{all peaks within the selection range}, N_{max})$$

The *selection range* is upper bounded by the maximum value across all nodes of the rate of parameter q_i, η_{q_i}, and lower bounded by a *background cut-off* value $\eta_{threshold}$. N_{max} is the maximum number of selected peaks.

● **Background filtering**

The selected peaks are sparse in time; the interval between two successive peaks is populated with a number of trace records with small amplitudes, called a *background region*. The trace records in a background region are reduced to one "background record" $B_j : (t_s, t_e, \lambda_{B_j}^{q_i})$ representing the interval of the background and the weighted average value of the parameter q_i of all records previously within the background region.

● **Skyline representation**

The paging profile is reduced to a much more compact discrete time representation composed of peaks and background regions, each one represented by a tuple $(t_s, t_e, \lambda^{q_i})$ as described in §2.2. The graphical representation of the model is a *"skyline"* representing the overall paging behavior of a node.

Several graphic visualization tools are provided to expedite the understanding of the paging behavior, such as the time line of a parameter collected in the trace records before filtering – *raw trace data*, the time line of the compact paging profile of the same parameter – *skyline representation*, along with other graphic tools used during the peak selection process and the data analysis after the filtering process.

4.2 Peak selection criterion

To examine the paging parameter q_i based on the collected trace data, the peak selection procedure uses two counterbalanced parameters: the constant value N_{max} and the background cut-off value $\eta_{threshold}$.

Depending on the purpose of the data processing, more weight is given to one or other parameter. A small N_{max} significantly reduces the amount of trace data because only the few higher peaks (N_{max}) are selected, and all others are neglected and merged with the background regions. This indiscriminate data filtering process creates a paging behavior description which is not accurate with the profiled program's behavior. Since our primary purpose is to provide a simplified but accurate description of the profiled program's behavior, the *background cut-off level* is the most important parameter in the selection criterion.

Two graphs, one showing the total number of selected peaks, and the other the number of peaks selected in each node, both for different cut-off levels, are provided to help in defining an adequate background cut-off value for the purpose of trace data analysis. A compact data set (one with fewer peaks) facilitates the first rough analysis, but a detailed data set more accurately describes the program behavior.

The cut-off value for the peak selection is chosen by the user depending upon the level of detail needed and the parameter under examination.

5 Case studies

In this section we discuss the applications we have monitored, and present and analyze the data we have collected. The conclusions drawn from our analysis of a few programs have to be confirmed by additional data before they can be used to improve the design of massively parallel systems and the mechanisms for resource sharing in such systems.

5.1 The applications

We have concentrated our attention on a few applications in the area of computational biology which we helped develop over the past few years [2],[6]. The programs we have studied are used for the 3-D atomic structure determination of large macromolecules such as viruses. These programs are: (a) The Envelope program used for real space electron density averaging. (b) The FFTsynth, a program used for transformation from reciprocal to real space by means of 3-D FFT. (c) The Recip program used to correlate calculated structure factors with observed ones. A brief outline of the computations and the algorithms used by the Envelope program follows. The algorithms and profiling results of the FFTsynth program and the Recip program are presented in [11].

The Envelope program

The input for this program is a 3-D lattice with $nx \times ny \times nz$ points. Every grid point with coordinates (x_0, y_0, z_0) has an electron density ρ_{x_0,y_0,z_0}. Symmetry operators: π_1, $\pi_2, \ldots, \pi_n$ allow us to associate to every grid point (x_0, y_0, z_0) n other points, (x_1, y_1, z_1), $(x_2, y_2, z_2) \ldots (x_n, y_n, z_n)$, related to it by non-crystallographic symmetry. The electron density at every grid point is replaced by the average value of the electron density of all the points related by non-crystallographic symmetry.

The parallel algorithm used for averaging is based on a partition of the 3-D lattice into small volumes (bricks). Each PE is assigned a number of bricks to transform, but it needs access to the entire data space (the entire lattice) because points related by the non-crystallographic symmetry are scattered throughout the lattice. The program implements a shared virtual memory and it is capable to operate in several modes: (a) the disk mode (DFS), (b) the data caching in the nodes mode (DAN), and (c) data server mode (DS).

The memory maps of each mode differ in the following way. In the DFS mode each processor fetches bricks on demand from the disk file into the dynamic brick memory area. In the DAN mode the bricks are cached in the static brick memory area of all nodes. When a processor needs a brick not available locally, it uses interrupt driven communication to fetch it from another processor's memory. In the DS mode few fat nodes are used to cache the entire data space.

5.2 The environment

The measurements were performed on a Paragon XP/S system with 66 compute nodes, two I/O nodes and three service nodes with 32 Mbytes of memory per node. The system was running Paragon OSF/1, Release 1.0.4, Patch R1.1.6.

We discuss briefly the intrusion due to our monitoring [7]. Comparing the size of the original load module and of the load module of the instrumented programs, we noted that the instrumented code is 5-11% larger than the original code. The effects of instrumentation upon the execution are visible in the execution time of instrumented code of FFTsynth program which takes about 15-25% more time (see [11] for more details).

Yet another form of intrusion which affects the data obtained through monitoring, is caused by interactions of the program being monitored with programs running concurrently in other partitions of the system. This type of interaction is due to contention for the I/O and communication resources, and always leads to an increase of the execution time. Even when a program is not instrumented, its execution time may vary by a significant amount for the same input data depending upon the activities of its competitors. In our monitoring process, the correlation of the peaks of activity in time is affected by this type of intrusion.

While the first type of intrusion, the one due to our measurements *cannot* be eliminated, there are costly ways to eliminate the second type by using the machine in an exclusive fashion.

5.3 Event and state information

Our methodology for monitoring the paging activity of a parallel program is based upon detecting transitions from one state of the task to another and recording the paging activity data collected by the kernel at the time of the transition. A parallel program can be in one of the following states: compute, I/O and communication.

In this section we present synthetic data closely related to our model, namely (a) the total number of events recorded during the execution of the program, (b) the average number of events per node, (c) the total time spent by a program in each state, and (d) the average duration of an event for all the programs we have monitored. Figures 3 and 4 present these data for the Envelope program in the DFS and DAN mode.

The data we collect to study the paging activity of parallel programs are extremely useful for understanding the behavior of a parallel program, the way it uses the resources

of the parallel system and for determining means for improving the performance of the parallel program.

For example, Figures 3a and 3b show that the Envelope program in DFS mode performs a large number of I/O operations and that there are virtually no communication events. Figure 3c shows that the I/O bandwidth of the system is insufficient. As a result there is no gain in using 64 PEs; the execution time with 64 PEs is essentially the same as the one with 32 PEs, about 1,300 seconds. While in the case of 16 nodes, the time spent in the I/O state is less than 10% of the total execution time (200 seconds for a 2200 seconds execution time), it represents more than 60% when 64 PEs are used (about 1,000 seconds out of 1,300 seconds total execution time). Figure 3d provides additional arguments that the I/O is the bottleneck: the average duration of an I/O event increases from about 0.08 seconds for 16 PEs to about 0.2 seconds for 32 PEs and about 0.5 seconds for the 64 PEs.

This analysis justifies our approach used in the DAN execution mode of the Envelope program to cache data across nodes. Figures 4a-d present this mode of execution using 16 PEs in two different experiments called A and B, and 32 PEs. As expected, the number of I/O events is considerably lower, but there are many more communication events compared with the DFS mode. The total execution time is reduced, about 1,600 seconds (versus 2,200 seconds) with 16 PEs, and about 800 seconds (versus 1,300 seconds) with 32 PEs. Figure 4c also shows that the total time spent in the compute state is a fairly large fraction of the total time (more than 90% for the 32 PE case) and that the fraction of time spent in the I/O state is insignificant. Figure 4d illustrates that the execution time of a program is influenced by the other program running concurrently in other partitions of the system. In the case of experiment A the average duration of an I/O event is larger than that of experiment B, because for A, other programs requesting I/O were running concurrently.

5.4 The amplitude and time correlation of the paging activities of the individual node programs

The methodology used to study the correlation of the paging activities of individual PEs is to isolate the peaks of activity and to study how their amplitude and time of occurrence relate to each other. For example, Figure 5 shows the page fault data obtained for the Envelope program running in 16 nodes in DFS mode. Figures 5a and 5b show the amplitude correlation in the compute and I/O state, while Figures 5d and 5e show the same data for the time correlation. From Figure 5a, we see that in the compute state, we have isolated 16 peaks. Peaks 1, 2 and 5 exhibit the most dissimilar behavior. For example, among the 16 PEs, the lowest rate of page fault for the first peak of

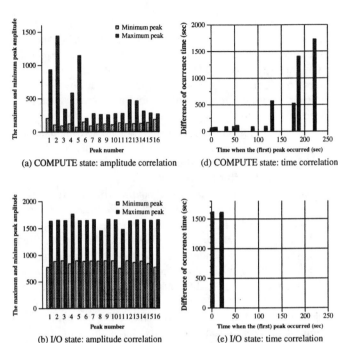

(a) COMPUTE state: amplitude correlation

(d) COMPUTE state: time correlation

(b) I/O state: amplitude correlation

(e) I/O state: time correlation

Figure 5: The page fault analysis. The correlation of amplitude and time of occurrence for the peaks of page fault activity for the Envelope (DFS mode) program running in 16 nodes.

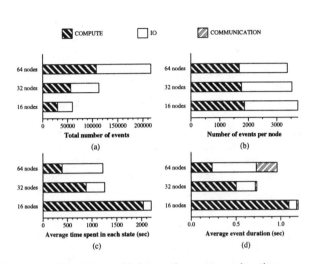

Figure 3: Summary of information concerning the number of events, the average lifetime of a state and the average lifetime of an event for the Envelope program running in DFS mode.

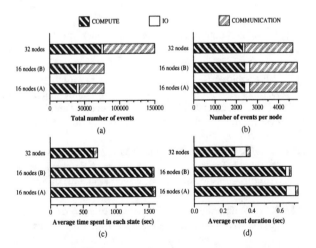

Figure 4: Summary of information concerning the number of events, the average lifetime of a state and the average lifetime of an event for the Envelope program running in DAN mode.

activity is slightly lower than 250 faults/sec and the highest rate observed is slightly lower than 950 page faults/second. Figure 5d shows that the first seven peaks of the page-fault activity occurred within the first 10-15 seconds and the time elapsed between the first and the last occurrence of a certain peak is less than 50 seconds. We see that the time elapsed between the first and the last occurrence of a certain peak increases as the peak id increases. For example, the 15-th peak occurred first after about 220 seconds and the last PE experienced this peak some 1700 seconds later.

The complete set of results is presented in [11]. For each run we presented the page fault, page-in, copy-on-write and page-out paging activity indicators.

6 Conclusions

An accurate analysis of the paging activity of a parallel program can only be done if there is enough hardware and kernel support for monitoring the execution of the program. The minimal hardware support requires the existence of synchronized clocks for all PEs. The kernel should support creation of a trace record for every paging event to identify the time when the event occurs, the type of fault and possibly other information. Such an accurate monitoring activity is very costly and very intrusive.

We have opted for a less accurate, yet less intrusive and

less costly approach, based upon sampling of the event counters maintained by the kernel. The sampling is done at the time of a state transition or as an explicit user request. The time spent by a node program in a state varies widely; therefore, our sampling of the paging activity counter occurs at irregular intervals and we are forced to use average rates to measure the paging activity.

It is difficult and risky to derive general conclusions from a few experiments and we will stress only those observations which are confirmed by all our measurements and have a plausible explanation.

All our measurements carried out for different programs running on a different number of PEs show that *in the paging activity, there is a substantial dissimilarity among the node programs even for SPMD programs*. This is plausible because of data dependencies, but it is still very surprising to see that one PE experiences an average rate of 1000 page-in/second and another one close to 200 (Figure 5a, the first peak in the COMPUTE state). Yet such discrepancies are rather common for all parameters. The correlation in time of different peaks of activity shows the same trend. For programs which use asynchronous algorithms, such as the Envelope, in which each node works independently, the difference in time of occurrence from the first PE to the last PE increases with the peak id.

This observation has a profound impact upon scheduling on MPPs which use gang scheduling of all tasks in a partition to allow them to communicate with one another. The high latency of a page-in request cannot be hidden by context switching as in the case of traditional operating systems. Even moderate rates of page-ins may lead to a substantial increase of the execution time of a parallel program and to fairly poor utilization of resources of the system, due to communication among tasks.

There are two possible solutions to this problem. The first is to attempt to reduce the number of page-ins by increasing the amount of real memory available or by anticipating the faults and bringing in pages before they are actually needed. There are no general solutions we are aware of for this last approach. The second possible solution of this problem is to reduce the latency of a page-in by having dedicated nodes with a fairly large memory acting as swap devices.

Unfortunately, we are unable to answer an important question related to the paging activity of parallel programs. Given the data characterizing the paging activity of a program running with n PEs, we cannot predict the paging activity when running with m PEs.

Acknowledgements

The authors want to express their thanks to Dr. Denise Ecklund from the Supercomputer Systems Division of Intel for many insightful discussions which have helped clarify many aspects of our work. Many thanks to Dr. Zhongyun Zhang who has helped us install the parallel programs on the system used for testing.

References

[1] D.C.Burger, R.S.Hyder, B.P.Miller, and D.A.Wood. "Paging Tradeoffs in Distributed-Shared-Memory Multiprocessors." In: *Proceedings of Supercomputing '94*, to appear, Nov. 1994.

[2] M.A. Cornea-Hasegan, D.C. Marinescu, and Z. Zhang, "Data Management for a Class of Iterative Computations on Distributed Memory MIMD Systems," *Concurrency: Practice and Experience*, vol 6(3), pp. 205–229, 1994.

[3] Intel Corporation, Paragon^{TM} OSF/1 User's Guide, Inter Supercomputer Systems Division, Beaverton, Oregon, 1993.

[4] K. Loepere. "Mach 3 Kernel Interfaces." In: *Open Software Foundation*, Carnegie Mellon University, 1992.

[5] A.D. Malony, D.A. Reed, and D.C. Rudolph, "Integrating Performance, Data Collection, Analysis and Visualization." In: *Performance Instrumentation and Visualization*, (M. Simmons, R. Koskela, eds.), Addison Wesley, 289 pages, 1990.

[6] D.C. Marinescu, J.R. Rice, M.A. Cornea-Hasegan, R.E. Lynch, and M.G. Rossmann, "Macromolecular Electron Density Averaging on Distributed Memory MIMD Systems." *Concurrency: Practice and Experience*, vol 5(8), 1993. pp. 635–657.

[7] D.C. Marinescu, J.E. Lumpp, T.L. Casavant, and H.J. Siegel, "Models for Monitoring and Debugging Tools for Parallel and Distributed Software." *Journal of Parallel and Distributed Computing*, vol 9, 1990, pp. 171–184.

[8] J.K.Ousterhout. "Scheduling Techniques for Concurrent Systems." In *Proceedings of the 3rd Distributed Computing Systems Conference*. pp. 22-30, October 1982.

[9] R.F. Rashid, A. Tevanian, Jr., M. Young, D. Golub, R. Baron, D. Black, W.J. Bolosky, and J. Chew, "Machine-independent Virtual Management for Paged Uniprocessor and Multiprocessor Architectures," *IEEE Transactions on Computers*. v.37, n.8, pp. 896–908, 1988.

[10] D. Wybranietz and D. Haban, "Monitoring and Measuring Distributed Systems." In: *Performance Instrumentation and Visualization*, (M. Simmons, R. Koskela, eds.), 289 pages, 1990.

[11] K. Y. Wang and D. C. Marinescu. *"An analysis of the paging activity of parallel programs. Part I: Correlation of the paging activity of individual node programs in the SPMD execution mode."* Technical Report CSD-TR-94-042, Purdue University, Department of Computer Sciences, June 1994.

[12] M. Young, A. Tevanian, R. Rashid, D. Golub, J. Eppinger, J. Chew, W. Bolosky, D. Black, and R. Baron, "The Duality of Memory and Communication in the Implementation of a Multiprocessor Operating System," *Proceedings of the 11th Symposium on Operating Systems Principles*, pp. 63–76, 1987.

REFLECTIVE MEMORY AND DISTRIBUTED MEMORY ARCHITECTURES FOR OLTP

Minitrack Coordinator:

Ilya Gertner

Reflective Memory and Distributed Shared Memory Architectures for OLTP

Computer Architecture Track
Introduction to Minitrack

Ilya Gertner

Encore Computer Corporation

300 Nickerson Rd, Marlborough MA 01752

OLTP requirements are straightforward- scalability and fault-tolerance. Large OLTP systems are comprised of thousands of terminals and PC networks. A typical system that needs to support a few thousand transactions per second may consists of 0.5-2 Terabytes of disk storage, 40-60 RISC processors, 1-2 Gigabytes of private memory on all processors, 512 Megabytes of total shared memory allocated for data caches and control information.

For such large systems, scalability means always achieving user-response time requirements by scaling the system. Computational bottlenecks are eliminated by adding new processors; I/O bottlenecks are eliminated by either adding new disks and controllers or re-organizing data; inter-processor communications bottlenecks are eliminating by adding more memory. Requirements for new users can be easily accommodated by adding new hardware.

Fault-tolerance in such systems means that the entire systems as a whole never comes down. This does not mean that all system components must stay up at all times. Some components may fail. For example a node may come down because of a hardware failure or transient software failure, or software upgrade; a disk may actually suffer a hardware failure.

Large OLTP systems are prepared to deal with such failures by reconfiguring at run-time without bringing the entire system down. Some users may experience temporary delays; other users may continue working without interruptions on portions (of the undamaged) database. Better managed OLTP systems may be prepared to deal with such failures by having some critical data files replicated on a pair of mirrored disks or RAIDs. Other sites, which must deal with disaster recovery may replicate data in different buildings or even cities. The important fact remains the same- the database and its associated query engines are always available.

Users of large OLTP systems may also want to take advantage of "open systems" and off-the-shelf components. This is a very important point because many existing fault-tolerant systems achieve even greater fault-tolerance at the cost of custom hardware that lags behind the RISC processor technology curve.

This minitrack focuses on the implementation and use of reflective memory to provide the shared-memory abstraction of SMP computers and still support the properties of scalability and fault-tolerance which are normally available only in MPP computers. Reflective memory can also be thought as a convenient medium to "rack & stack" off-the-shelf components. Although reflected memory has its origins in real-time computing, this minitrack focuses primarily on OLTP applications.

The survey paper on distributed shared memory systems provides a framework for evaluating reflected memory systems. There, reflective memory could be thought of as hardware-supported replicated shared memory.

The reflective memory multiprocessor paper provides an interesting perspective of the mechanisms in software with some support in hardware for the memory semantics necessary to implement a multiprocessor. Of particular interest are the sections on spinlocks and memory recovery. Spinlocks in reflective memory are presented as a version of a swap & test instruction which is emulated by enabling reflection to two addresses. An atomic test operation ascertains that no other node has attempted to obtain the same lock at the same time. Memory recovery or reflective memory refresh allows disaster recovery even in the case of physical destruction of one of the nodes. Hardware repair and OS reboot is controlled by a heart-beat that ensures consistency of all on-line nodes.

The Pentium architecture paper describes a shared-memory MPP board that packs 8 Pentium chips on a board coupled with 2 Gigabytes of memory. This board can be used in reflective memory systems described in the earlier paper. Similar OS structures are used in both on-board shared memory and across the cabinet reflective-memory supported shared memory.

The fault-tolerant paper puts it all together in a disk storage and file system server. Both services have been implemented and used to support fault-tolerant disk storage for Oracle database and IBM DASD storage. The salient features of RMS and ease of shared-memory programming are demonstrated in this fairly complex yet very flexible implementation that supports such widely differing requirements. In particular, the implementation of the logging algorithms and the low-overhead of mirroring operations are interesting examples of the reflective memory usage.

The paper on checkpoint in Mach advances the state-of-the-art in fault-tolerant computing. It shows excellent performance results in taking a snapshot and checkpoint recovery. It also shows an example of what one can achieve (when compared with the previous paper) when one is not constrained with backward compatibility and other "mundane/industrial" constraints.

The paper on MPP Unix enhancements moves up above the file system layer and describes experiences in porting CICS, a mainframe OLTP applications, to a multi-computer/multi-UNIX system. Reflective memory plays a major role in providing efficient support for UNIX primitives that are required for the porting effort. Interesting experiences are described in implementation tradeoffs- when to implement precise UNIX semantics and when to modify applications in order to ease the implementation effort.

The following two papers describe experiences and performance results in porting Oracle Parallel Server to two MPP platforms: nCUBE, a distributed memory massively parallel computer, and Infinity, a reflective memory based computer.

The last paper describes hardware design tradeoffs in implementing reflective memory boards. It proposes an interesting combination of compile-time and run-time enhancements that significantly reduce the latency of short messages.

A Survey of Distributed Shared Memory Systems

Jelica Protić   **Milo Tomašević***   **Veljko Milutinović**

Department of Computer Engineering
School of Electrical Engineering
University of Belgrade
POB 816
11000 Belgrade, Yugoslavia

(*)Department of Computer Engineering
Institute Mihajlo Pupin
University of Belgrade
POB 15
11000 Belgrade, Yugoslavia

e-mail: { eproticj, etomasev, emilutiv }@ubbg.etf.bg.ac.yu

Abstract

Distributed shared memory (DSM) systems have attracted considerable research efforts recently, since they combine the advantages of two different computer classes: shared memory multiprocessors and distributed systems. The most important one is the use of shared memory programming paradigm on physically distributed memories. In the first part of this paper, one possible classification taxonomy, which includes two basic criteria and a number of related characteristic, is proposed and described. According to the basic classification criteria—implementation level of DSM mechanism—systems are organized into three groups: hardware, software, and hybrid DSM implementations. The second part of the paper represents an almost exhaustive survey of the existing solutions in an uniform manner, presenting their DSM mechanisms and issues of importance for various DSM systems and approaches.

1. Introduction

A large progress was recently made in the research and development of systems with multiple processors, capable of delivering high computing power in order to satisfy the constantly increasing demands of typical applications.

A relatively new and promising concept—distributed shared memory (DSM) tries to combine the advantages of two classes of systems: *shared memory systems*, having a single global physical memory, equally accessible to all processors, and *distributed memory systems*, that consist of multiple processing nodes communicating by means of message passing. A DSM system logically implements the shared memory model on a physically distributed memory system. The DSM system, implemented in hardware and/or software, hides the remote communication mechanism from the application writer, so the ease of program-

ming and the portability typical of shared memory systems, as well as the scalability and cost-effectiveness of distributed memory systems are both inherited.

The DSM research area is strongly affected by issues and results generated in a number of closely related disciplines of computer engineering (Figure 1). One of the main objectives of DSM studies was to develop algorithms that minimize the average access time to the shared data, while keeping the data consistent. Some solutions were reached by implementing a specific software layer on the top of message passing system, and the others extended strategies applied in shared memory multiprocessors with private caches, described in [TOMAS93], to multilevel memory systems.

Figure 1. DSM and related disciplines

The goal of this paper is to give a comprehensive insight into the increasingly important area of DSM. To this end, it covers general DSM concepts, and tries to bring an extensive and up-to-date information on the DSM systems. A taxonomy that defines possible classification criteria and parameters is proposed, and various outcomes and design choices are discussed.

This research was partially sponsored by the FNRS.

Proceedings of the 28th IEEE/ACM Hawaii International Conference on System Sciences, Maui, HA, January 3-6, 1995.

2. DSM Classification

In order to provide a wide and extensive overview in the field of DSM, possible platforms for classification and a set of relevant parameters that must be considered in DSM design are proposed. The selection of classification criteria can be taken conditionally, since some of the parameters could also be adopted as the platform for classification. Our choice of classification criteria relies on the possibility to classify all existing systems into the appropriate non-overlapping subsets of systems with common general advantages and drawbacks.

- *The first criterion: DSM implementation level*
  Types:
  1. Hardware
  2. Software
  > *2.1. Operating system*
  >> *2.1.1. Inside the kernel*
  >> *2.1.2. Outside the kernel*
  > *2.2. Runtime library routines*
  > *2.3. Compiler-inserted primitives*
  3. Hardware/software combination

The level of DSM implementation affects both the programming model and the overall system performance. While the hardware solutions bring the total transparency to the programmer, and achieve very low access latencies, software solutions can better exploit the application behavior and represent the ideal polygon to experiment with new concepts and algorithms. As the consequence, the number of software DSM systems presented in the open literature is considerably higher, but the systems intending to become commercial products and standards are mostly hardware-oriented.

- *Parameters closely related to the DSM implementation level*

Some important characteristics of the system are often (but not necessarily) closely related, or even determined by this criterion.

Architectural configuration of the system affects the system performance, since it can offer or restrict a good potential for parallel processing of requests related to the DSM management. It also strongly affects the scalability. Since a system applying a DSM mechanism is usually organized as a set of clusters connected by an interconnection network, architectural parameters include:

a) **Cluster configuration** (*single/multiple processors, with/without, shared/private, single/multiple level caches, etc.*)

b) **Interconnection network** (*bus hierarchy, ring, mesh, hypercube, specific LAN, etc.*)

Cluster configuration is usually very important for the hardware-oriented proposals that integrate the mechanisms of cache coherence on the lower level with the DSM mechanisms on the higher level of the system organization, or even store all shared data in large caches. Cluster configuration is mostly transparent for software solutions. It includes the memory organization and the placement of directory, as well.

Almost all types of interconnection networks found in multiprocessors and distributed systems have also been used in DSM systems. The majority of software-oriented DSM systems were actually build on the top of Ethernet, although some of the solutions tend to be architecture independent and portable to various platforms. On the other hand, topologies such as bus hierarchy or mesh are typical for hardware solutions. The choice of topology can be also very important for the implementation of DSM algorithm, since it affects the possibility and cost of broadcast and multicast transactions.

Shared data organization represents the global layout of shared address space, as well as the size and organization of data items in it, and can be distinguished as:

a) **Structure of shared data** (*non structured or structured into objects, language types, etc.*)

b) **Granularity of coherence unit** (*word, cache block, page, complex data structure, etc.*)

The impact of this organization to the overall system performance is closely related to the locality of data access. Hardware solutions always deal with non-structured data objects (typically cache blocks), while many software implementations tend to use data items that represent logical entities, in order to take advantage of the locality naturally expressed by the application. On the other hand, some software solutions, based on virtual memory mechanisms, organize data in larger physical blocks (pages), counting on the coarse-grain sharing.

- *The second criterion: DSM algorithm*
  Types:
  > *1. SRSW (Single Reader/Single Writer)*
  >> *1.1. Without migration*
  >> *1.2. With migration*
  > *2. MRSW (Multiple Reader/Single Writer)*
  > *3. MRMW (Multiple Reader/Multiple Writer)*

This classification is based on the possible existence of multiple copies of a data item, also considering access rights of those copies. The complexity of coherence maintenance is strongly dependent on the introduced classes. In order to explore the properties of application behavior, including typical read/write patterns, while keeping the acceptable complexity of the algorithm, many solutions were proposed, among which MRSW algorithms represent the majority.

- *Parameters closely related to the DSM algorithm*
  a) **Responsibility for the DSM management** (*centralized, distributed/fixed, distributed/dynamic*)
  b) **Consistency model** (*strict, sequential, processor, weak, release, lazy release, entry, etc.*)
  c) **Coherence policy** (*write-invalidate, write-update, type-specific, etc.*)

Responsibility for DSM management can be centralized or distributed, and it determines which site has to handle actions related to the consistency maintenance in the system. Centralized management is easier to implement, but suffers from the lack of fault tolerance, while the distributed management can be defined statically or dynamically, eliminating bottlenecks and providing scalability. Distribution of responsibility for DSM management is closely related to the distribution of directory information, that can be organized in the form of linked lists or trees.

Memory consistency model defines the legal ordering of memory references issued by some processor and observed by other processors. Stronger forms of consistency typically increase the memory access latency and the bandwidth requirements, and simplify the programming. More relaxed models result in better performance, at the expense of a higher involvement of the programmer in synchronizing the accesses to shared data. In strive to achieve an optimal behavior, systems with multiple consistency models adaptively applied to appropriate data types have been recently proposed.

Coherence policy determines whether the existing copies of the data item being written to at one site will be immediately updated, or just invalidated on the other sites. The choice of coherence policy is related to the granularity of shared data. For very fine grain data items, the cost of update message is approximately the same as the cost of invalidation message. Therefore, update policy is typical for systems with word-based coherence maintenance, and invalidation is used in coarse-grain systems. The efficiency of an invalidation approach is increased when the sequences of read and write to the same data item by various processors are not highly interleaved.

3. Hardware Level DSM Implementations

Hardware implementations of the DSM concept usually extend the principles found in traditional cache coherence schemes of scalable shared-memory architectures. Therefore, the unit of sharing is smaller—typically cache line size. Communication latency is considerably reduced, based on the advantage of fine-grain sharing, that also minimizes the effects of false sharing and thrashing. Searching and directory functions are much faster, compared to the software level implementations, as well. According to the general properties of memory system architecture, three groups of hardware DSM systems are regarded as especially interesting:

- CC-NUMA (Cache Coherent Non-Uniform Memory Architecture)
- COMA (Cache-Only Memory Architecture)
- RMS (Reflective Memory System architecture)

In a CC-NUMA system, the shared virtual address space is statically distributed across local memory modules of clusters. It is accessible by the local processors and by processors from other clusters, with quite different access latencies. The DSM mechanism relies on directories with organizations varying from a full-map storage to different dynamic organizations, such as single or double linked lists and fat trees. In order to minimize latency, static partitioning of data should be done with extreme care, in order to maximize the frequency of local access. The invalidation mechanism is typically applied, while some relaxed memory consistency model can be used as a source of performance improvement. Typical representatives of this type of DSM approach are Dash and SCI.

COMA architecture provides the dynamic partitioning of data in the form of distributed memories, organized as large second-level caches (attraction memories). There is no physical memory home location predetermined for particular data item, which can be simultaneously replicated in multiple caches. The existing COMA architectures are characterized by hierarchical network topologies that simplify two main problems in this type of systems: finding an item and replacement of a cache block. In COMA architectures, the distribution of data across attraction memories is dynamically adaptable to the application behavior; therefore, they are less sensitive to static distribution of data than the NUMA architectures. Increased storage overhead for keeping the information typical for cache memory is inherent to the COMA architecture. However, some findings pointed out that this approach means an acceptably low amount of the overall system memory. Two most relevant representatives of COMA systems are DDM and KSR1.

Reflective memory systems are characterized with hardware-implemented update mechanism on the low level of data granularity. Some parts of local memory in each cluster can be declared as shared, and appropriately mapped into the common virtual space. Coherence maintenance of shared regions in these systems is based on full-replication algorithm. Following the assumption that all data written will be soon read by other sharing processors, those systems immediately propagate every change to all sharing sites, using a broadcast or multicast mechanism. Because of the property of "reflection," this kind of memory is also called "mirror memory." It results in high cost of write operations, especially when multiple writes to the same location occur; consequently, this architecture is the most convenient for the applications with a lower write frequency. Typical reflective memory systems are the Encore's RMS and Merlin.

3.1. Memnet

Delp, et al., in [DELP91] present the Memnet (Memory as Network Abstraction) system that provides an abstraction of shared memory and the strict coherence semantics. This system was developed at the University of Delaware.

Memnet system connects a number of nodes with the insertion-modification token ring (Figure 2). Memnet device serves as a dual port memory controller on its local bus, and an interface from the node to the ring. When some access to the DSM area can not be satisfied locally, interface sends an appropriate message on the ring, and blocks the processor. Ring message is inspected by other interfaces and forwarded as long as no action is imposed in the particular node for this piece of data. When an interface must act on a request, the response is sent by modifying the same request and inserting the requested data. Finally, the message sinks into the interface of the node by which it was generated, so the waiting processor is released in a predictable time.

DSM mechanism. The entire address space of the Memnet is mapped onto the local memories of each node, and divided into 32 byte chunks. The consistency protocol is of the invalidation type, similar to snooping cache protocols. The read request on the ring is satisfied by the nearest node which possesses a valid copy. The write requst to a non-exclusive copy is followed by an invalidation request. In the case of the eviction of a chunk from local cache, its updated version is saved into a specific area reserved for this chunk in one of the Memnet devices.

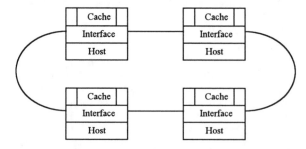

Figure 2. The ring-based Memnet system

Issues of importance. The token ring architecture provides several advantages over bus-based systems. Ring ensures an absolute upper bound on the time of network access and its bandwidth does not decrease as more nodes are added. Since the packets arrive at each interface in the same order, the tags used to manage the consistency protocol are themselves kept consistent, and their maintenance is simplified. The major inhibition of Memnet is its limited scalability, since the storage for cache directories grows at the rate O(NxN).

3.2 DASH

Lenoski, et al., in [LENOS92] describe the DASH (Directory Architecture for Shared Memory), a scalable multiprocessor architecture with a four-level memory hierarchy, using a directory based hardware DSM approach. The research was conducted at the Stanford University.

The basic component of DASH system is a cluster that contains an equal part of the overall system's shared memory (home property). Clusters are interconnected by a pair (request/reply) wormhole routed meshes. The directory controller preserves the coherence across the nodes, and serves as an interface to the interconnection network.

DSM mechanism. The memory hierarchy of DASH is split in four levels: 1) processor cache, 2) caches of other processors in the local cluster, 3) home cluster (cluster that contains directory and physical memory for a given memory block), 4) remote cluster (cluster marked by the directory of the cluster as holding the copy of the block). The coherence maintenance is based on a full-map distributed directory protocol. A memory block can be in one of three states: UNCACHED (not cached outside home cluster), CACHED (one or more unmodified copies in remote clusters), and DIRTY (modified in some remote cluster).

In most of the cases, due to the property of locality, references can be satisfied inside the local cluster. Otherwise, a request is sent to the home cluster for the involved block which takes some action according to the state found in its directory. Read request for uncached or shared block is satisfied by the home cluster. For a block in the dirty state, the request is forwarded to remote cluster which directly supplies data to the requester and also sends a write-back message to the home cluster for an update. On occasion of write to shared copy, the home cluster sends point-to-point messages to known locations in order to invalidate the shared copies. DASH supports a relaxed memory consistency model - the release consistency.

Issues of importance. DASH offers a good potential for scalability due to its directory-based cache coherence protocol, distributed memories and directories, and a scalable interconnection network. Techniques for reducing memory latency, such as software-controlled prefetching, update and deliver operations, are shown to be effective, but the advanced techniques used for coherence maintenance and latency reduction make the design very complex and hard for verification. For a larger number of processors, the amount of directory storage grows unacceptably, and some space saving techniques (e.g., limited number of pointers) are considered.

3.3. SCI - Scalable Coherent Interface

Gustavson in [GUSTA92] and James in [JAMES94] present the IEEE P1596 Scalable Coherent Interface (SCI) — an interface standard, rather than a complete system design. Among other issues, the standard defines the cache coherence protocols in a distributed shared memory multiprocessor, based on distributed directories in the form of chained lists.

The SCI (Scalable Coherent Interface) standard provides a very large communication bandwidth of up to 1Gbyte/s, using point-to-point unidirectional links. The low-cost SCI systems typically use a ring connection, while the intermediate-level SCI systems may use a combination of switch and ring, employing paired SCI interfaces as a simple bridge that connects two rings.

DSM mechanism. Instead of centralizing the coherence directory, SCI distributes it among those cache controllers that are sharing the data. The directory is organized in the form of a distributed, doubly linked lists of caches, one for each cache block, in which the copies of the same block currently reside. The directory entry is a shared data structure that may be concurrently accessed by multiple processors. The home memory controller keeps a pointer to the head of the list and a few status bits for each cache block, while the local cache controllers have to store the forward and backward pointers, and the cache status bits. This approach makes the replacement of a cache line easy, since one can remove itself from the list by directing its neighbors to point to each other. Read request is always sent to the home memory. Memory controller uses the requester identifier from the request packet, to point to the new head of the list. The old head pointer is sent back to the requester along with the data block (if available). It is used by the requester to chain itself as the head of the list, and to request the data from the old head (if not supplied by the home node). In the case of write to a non-exclusive block, the request for the ownership is also sent to the home memory. All copies in the system are invalidated by forwarding an invalidation message from the head down the list, and the requester becomes the new head of the list.

Issues of importance. SCI scheme provides that the amount of directory pointer storage grows naturally with system size, achieving its main design goal — scalability. Another desirable kind of scaling behavior is that the cache controller acknowledges the arrival of the packet and checks it when it is convenient. Consequently, the impact of particularly slow caches in the system on those with higher performance is minimized. However, the distribution of individual directory entries increases the latency and complexity of the memory references, since the additional directory-update messages must be sent between processor caches. To reduce the latency and to support additional functions, the SCI working committee has proposed some enhancements such as: converting sharing lists to sharing trees, request combining, use of clean cached state, and support for queue-based locks.

3.4. KSR1

Frank, et al., describe in [FRANK93] and [KSR92] a COMA architecture — the KSR family of computer systems. The KSR is patented by the Kendall Square Research Corporation, and up to now this is one of the rare commercially available DSM systems.

KSR1 system consists of hierarchically organized ring-based nodes. There is no fixed physical location for an address within the ALLCACHE memory system, and the main memory is physically eliminated. The unit of allocation in local caches is a 16-KByte page, while the unit of transfer and sharing in local caches is a 128-byte subpage. The dedicated hardware responsible for maintaining consistency, finding and copying subpages stored in local caches is called the ALLCACHE engine.

The ALLCACHE engines are organized in a hierarchy (Figure 3). At the lowest level are ALLCACHE Group:0s, each of which is a combination of ALLCACHE Engine:0s and the complete set of local caches associated with them. An ALLCACHE Engine:0 includes the directory that maps addresses into the set of local caches of processors within its group. An ALLCACHE Engine:1 includes the directory which maps addresses into its constituent set of ALLCACHE Group:0s. Higher level ALLCACHE groups are hierarchically constructed in the same manner. The ALLCACHE engine hierarchy is constructed with a fat-tree topology, so that bandwidth increases at each level of ALLCACHE engine. The ALLCACHE engine uses internal ring topology, that allows ordering to be maintained.

DSM mechanism. The coherence protocol in ALLCACHE is invalidation-based. Possible states specific to the physical instance of a subpage within a particular local cache are: EXCLUSIVE (only valid copy), NON-EXCLUSIVE (owner; multiple copies exist), COPY (non-owner; valid copy), and INVALID (not valid, but allocated subpage). KSR1 implements a sequentially consistent shared address space programming model.

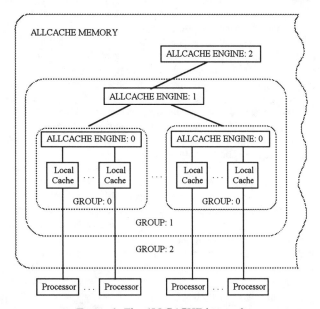

ALLCACHE MEMORY

Figure 3. The ALLCACHE hierarchy

Issues of importance. ALLCACHE takes the advantage of the serial locality, just like all other systems that store data in caches. However, the unique feature of ALLCACHE is that it exploits parallel locality — the phenomenon of common reference patterns for related threads. On the other hand, hierarchical directories are responsible for longer latencies. As the ALLCACHE architecture combines the internal ring and the global fat-tree topology, the overall latency grows as $O(\log_T n)$. The ALLCACHE design is very complex, and it is completely implemented in hardware. Some kind of partly centralized and software implemented approach could be a source of possible improvements.

3.5. DDM

Hagersten, et al., in [HAGER92] give an overview of another COMA multiprocessor —DDM (Data Diffusion Machine) — developed at the Swedish Institute of Computer Science.

The DDM prototype is made of clusters that consist of up to four Motorola MC88100 processors. All global memory is distributed among the large second-level caches — attraction memories, organized in 16-byte *items*, comparable to cache lines, that contain both the state information and the data. It is managed by the controller that handles the snooping protocol (oriented to the snooping bus) called *memory above protocol*, as well as the interface between the processor and the attraction memory, according to the *memory below protocol*. The smallest instance of the DDM architecture, which can be independent, or just a subsystem of a large COMA, uses an asynchronous split-transaction bus. Attaching a directory on the top of the local DDM bus, in order to enable its communication with a higher level bus of the same type is the way to build a large DDM system with directories/buses based hierarchy. Directory is a set-associative memory that stores the state information for all items in attraction memories below it, but without data.

DSM mechanism. The utilized single-bus coherence protocol is of the snoopy write-invalidate type, which handles the attraction of data on read, erases the replicated data on write, and manages the replacement when a set in an attraction memory is full. An item can be in seven states; tree of them correspond to Invalid, Exclusive and Valid, typical for the snoopy protocols, while the state Dirty is (in DDM) replaced with a set of four transient states needed to remember the outstanding requests on the split-transaction bus. DDM provides a sequential consistency model to the programmer, since all writes have to wait for the acknowledgment before being performed.

Issues of importance. Being of the COMA type, DDM is suitable for applications with dynamic and semidynamic scheduling. It obviates the need for static data partitioning, and achieves a dynamic distribution adapted to actual program demands. In order to cut down the number of system transactions and reduce latency, acknowledgments are sent by the topmost node in the subsystem containing all relevant copies instead of being sent by a particular attraction memory that has a copy of data. Instead of the sequential consistency, looser forms of consistency are also supported, such as processor consistency or a specific form of the processor consistency combined with the adaptive write update strategy.

3.6. RMS

Technical description of the Reflective Memory System (RMS) is provided in [ENCOR92]. Several systems with the reflected memory approach (found in early Gould systems) are designed and implemented at the Encore Computer Corporation, Fort Lauderdale, Florida.

The RMS has a special link for maintaining the coherence of shared memory regions. This linkage is realized through the Reflected Memory Bus. The nodes in a system have local/shared memory, where a local copy of global data structures is maintained. Address mapping of the private/shared window regions, for transmitting to and receiving from the RM bus, is enabled by means of translation RAMs. The design is modularized into two parts: the standard transition module interface to the RM bus and the host-specific interface board with on-the-board memory.

DSM mechanism. In this system, all writes to shared regions of local memory are broadcast over the RM bus, while write controllers of other nodes sense the write operation on the bus. Therefore, if the address of the distributed write falls within a region mapped as shared on the receiving side, the corresponding location in local memory is updated. The write sensing is the task of the write controller.

Issues of importance. The RMS provides advantages of the symmetric shared memory models, without incurring the usual access latencies. However, this mechanism is not sequentially consistent and an explicit synchronization is needed. The parts of address space which are configured as the reflected memory have to be disabled for placing in the cache. If the writes to this range (on the RM port) can be sensed on the host and the local bus, the caching of global data would be feasible, and the access to them would be faster.

3.7. Merlin

Another approach to dynamically mapped reflective memory is proposed by Maples and Wittie in their paper [MAPLE90]. Merlin (MEmory Routed, Logical Interconnection Network) uses flexible, extensible interconnection system, and intends to be a convenient solution for heterogeneous computing. It was developed at the Sandia National Laboratories and SUNY at Stony Brook.

Merlin interfaces in the host backplanes monitor all memory changes, and make a temporary copy of the address and the value of each word written into the local physical memory, in order to pass it via network links, if preselected to be shared. In such a system, only static information about data sharing is needed, and fast memories for address translation and word routing are initialized by system software.

DSM mechanism. The operation of Merlin is not based on demand. It works as an anticipatory system, which means that all data changes are immediately sent to sharing sites in individual word packets that contain data and address. The routing information is not a part of the word packet, but is associated with it because it is lost in the next stage. All read operations are performed from the processor local memory, which contains the replicated shared regions. Possible inconsistency can be avoided using efficient lock operations, supported on the level of page.

Issues of importance. Merlin is a simple and efficient solution for DSM. Only about 10% of Merlin interface is processor-specific, so it can be implemented for a wide variety of commercially available processors. In most cases, communications overlap computation, since all copied words are routed by interface without any host cycle. Although intended to provide the shared memory paradigm in heterogeneous environments, Merlin does not resolve the problem of format conversions for different representations of data, and it exclusively uses static information about data sharing, independently to dynamic application behavior.

4. Software level DSM Implementations

The basic principle of the first software-implemented DSM mechanisms was quite alike to that of the virtual memory management, except that on page fault the data are supplied from local memory of the remote cluster instead from the local secondary storage. Software implementations of the DSM concept are usually built as a separate layer on the top of message passing model. According to the implementation level, several types of software-oriented DSM approaches can be recognized:

1. *Compiler implementations.* In the cases where the DSM paradigm is applied at the level of parallel programming language, the shared address space is usually structured into logical units of sharing. Therefore, shared data have to be declared as a specific type in the source program. In this approach, accesses to shared data are automatically converted into synchronization and coherence primitives. Language implementation can be portable between various systems, and recompiled if appropriate run-time primitives are available. Linda is an example of this software approach to DSM implementation.

2. *User-level runtime packages.* The DSM mechanism is implemented by virtue of the run-time library routines, which are to be linked with an application program that uses the shared virtual address space. This approach is not only convenient for experimenting, but also flexible and easy to implement. IVY and Mermaid systems are based on run-time library routines.

3.1. *Operating system level (inside the kernel).* The interaction of scheduling, interrupt processing, and the application behavior can be efficiently examined if the DSM model is incorporated into the operating system kernel. The advantage of this approach is that the semantics of the underlying OS architecture can be preserved; hence, the applications can be ported from the local environment to the distributed system without being recompiled. Mirage is an example of system built according to this method.

3.2. *Operating system level (outside the kernel).* The DSM mechanism is incorporated in the specialized software controller, that can be (with minor modifications) used by different kernels. The same DSM mechanism can be used both by user and by the operating system kernel objects. One of the systems that follow this implementation level is Clouds.

The above classification should be taken conditionally, since all programming language implementations require some operating system support. Also, some programmer's hints, at the level of the language, can help the run-time implementation to become more efficient. Software implemetations are clearly inferior in performance to hardware implementations, but they are less expensive, can be suitable for a variety of underlying architectures, and can better take the advantage of the application characteristics. Problem-oriented shared memory, DSM in heterogeneous environments, and various sophisticated consistency mechanisms are mostly implemented in software.

4.1 Munin

Bennet, Carter, and Zwaenepoel in [BENN90a, BENN90b] describe Munin — a DSM system that implements several schemes of memory coherence, which are dependent on the object type declared by the programmer. The system was built on the top of an Ethernet network of SUN workstations. The Munin DSM server is implemented as a user-level process. It was developed at the Rice University, Houston, Texas.

DSM mechanism. The sort of memory coherence in Munin is referred to as type-specific memory coherence, and can be regarded as an adaptive management method. The shared data objects in Munin are classified into several types (Figure 4). For each of these shared data types, an adequate consistency preserving mechanism is applied in order to minimize the coherence overhead.

In the Munin prototype, a preprocessor converts the program annotations into a format suitable for use by the run-time system and the modified linker creates a shared memory segment. A collection of library routines, that should be linked into each Munin program and the operating system support for page handling and page table manipulation, are also provided.

Data object type	Coherence mechanism
private	none
write-once	replication
results	delayed update
synchronization	distributed locks
migratory	migration
producer-consumer	eager object movement
read-mostly	broadcast
general read-write	ownership

Figure 4. Munin's type-specific memory coherence.

Issues of importance. Programmer has to provide all the semantic information needed by Munin. Some of this should be implemented in a more powerful compiler to ease the responsibility imposed on the programmer. Another source of improvement would be the possibility of the run-time system to dynamically determine the type of object according to the observed data use. Also, it has to be examined how the additional hardware support could improve the performance.

4.2. IVY

Li and Hudak in [LIHUD89] present the IVY (Integrated shared Virtual memory at Yale), a prototype multiprocessor with DSM that implements strict coherence semantics on 1-Kbyte pages, using several MRSW algorithms based on the write invalidation. The system is based on an Ethernet network of Apollo workstations and a modified operating system Aegis. IVY was developed at Yale University, New Haven, Rhode Island.

DSM mechanism. Global memory in IVY is distributed across processor nodes, and a mapping mechanism provides the single address space. The shared memory is partitioned into pages. The pages with read-only permission can be replicated on several nodes, whereas the pages allowed for writing can reside only on one node — the page owner. Apart from providing the mapping function, mapping managers handle also the problem of memory coherence. IVY can support several memory coherence algorithms based on an invalidation protocol for page synchronization and dynamic page ownership: centralized manager, fixed distributed manager, and dynamically distributed manager.

Centralized manager resides on a single processor. Its task is to maintain the necessary information regarding the ownership for all shared pages. This information is placed in data structures contained by the owner: copy set and lock fields for each page. The owner field holds the identification of the processor that owns the page. The copy set field holds a list of all processors having the local copy of the page. The lock field is used for synchronization of the requests. All processors have a table for storing the information about the accessibility of the pages that reside in their local memories. Fixed distributed manager is implemented by giving each processor a predetermined list of pages that it should manage. The list of pages is determined by the mapping function. Dynamic distributed managing of pages means that each processor manages only those pages that it owns. All processors have a data structure for holding the ownership information. The fields are the same as in the centralized manager, except that the owner field is substituted by the probable owner field. The requests are always forwarded to the processor whose identity is stored in this field.

Issues of importance. The dynamic distributed manager approach, especially with some refinements, offers the potentials for good performance and implementation in large-scale multiprocessor system. In the centralized approach, there is only one manager in the system, which represents the performance bottleneck by its nature. This problem is alleviated in the fixed distributed manager approach; however, more than one message is needed to find the owner.

4.3. Linda

Ahuja, et al., in [AHUJA86] present LINDA, an architecture-independent language concept for explicitly parallel programming. In order to improve the efficiency of the software implementation of LINDA, various hardware coprocessors, such as LINDA Machine described in [BORRM89] by Borrman and Herdieckerhoff, were also proposed. LINDA is developed at the Department of Computer Science at Yale University, New Haven, Rhode Island.

DSM mechanism. The DSM paradigm in Linda is implemented as a logically shared associative memory accessible to all nodes. In the Linda multiprocessor system, shared memory is referred to as *tuple* space. A tuple is similar to a record in Pascal, and represents an ordered set of values. Tuples can be accessed by their logical names, where the name stands for any selection of its values. It is not possible to update a tuple directly. In order to change its value, a tuple must be physically removed, updated, and then reinserted in the tuple space. Using this technique, the possibility of consistency corruption is avoided.

Shared memory space in Linda is distributed among the nodes. Tuples are accessible through their values, thus making the memory associative (e.g., addressable by contents). The manipulation of the tuple space can be done using three atomic operations *out*, *in*, and *read*. The whole concept of naming in Linda introduced by those operations is similar to that applied in relational databases.

Issues of importance. Linda is a general parallel programming concept, so it can provide portability between various machines, while only a recompilation is required. This is an entirely software approach, and the tuple space implementation may involve a substantial overhead. When the probability of writes is increased, the broadcast mechanism used in its implementation can be inappropriate and time consuming.

4.4. Mirage

Fleisch and Popek in [FLEIS89] describe Mirage, a kernel level implementation of DSM. Mirage applies the strict coherence semantics using a write-invalidate protocol, and introduces a tunable parameter — time window Δ. Mirage was developed at the University of California, Los Angeles.

DSM mechanism. Mirage provides a form of network transparency to make the network boundaries invisible for shared memory. It is implemented in the kernel of an existing operating system Locus. Both files and programs can be moved in Locus, and process creation and migration are fully supported.

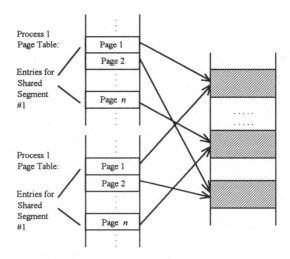

Figure 5. Paged segmentation in Mirage

The model is based on the paged-segmentation technique. Segments may be attached into the address space of a process with the read-only or the read/write protection. Segments are partitioned into 512-byte pages, because of their fixed size and suitability for the underlying hardware. Each segment has a unique library site (the site that creates the segment) — the controller for the pages of that segment, and a clock site (e.g., a writer of the page) — the site that has the most recent copy of a page. All requests for the DSM page are queued at the library. Write requests are sequentially processed, while the read requests are batched together. Page fault mechanisms are incorporated into the Locus interrupt handlers. During a user-level interrupt fault, the faulting process waits the library's request processing. Before a write to a page, all readable copies of the page must be invalidated. Invalidation unmaps and discards the page for all processes at all sites. General view of the address space is presented by Figure 5.

Issues of importance. A unique feature of Mirage is the time window Δ mechanism intended to reduce the trashing. This is a dynamically tunable parameter which determines the minimum amount of time that the page will be available at the node. Performed measurements showed that the performances highly depend on the appropriate choice of Δ.

4.5. Clouds

Ramachandran and Khalidi in [RAMAC89] present Clouds, an object-oriented operating system based on the virtual address space of objects that constitute DSM. The implementation was done on Sun 3 workstations connected by an Ethernet network. Clouds was developed at the Georgia Institute of Technology, Atlanta, Georgia.

DSM mechanism. In order to achieve the DSM programming model in Clouds, a set of primitives is built either on the top of Unix, or in the context of object-based operating system kernel Ra. Distributed shared memory constituted of segments is organized into objects. Segments have access attributes: read-only, read-write, weak-read, or none. Fetching of segments is based on *get* and *discard* operations provided by the software-implemented distributed shared memory controller (DSMC), that also provides P and V semaphore primitives as separate operations. The DSMC is a part of the Clouds operating system, implemented outside its kernel Ra. The DSMC is invoked by DSM partition, that handles segment requests from both Ra and user objects, and determines should the request for segment be satisfied locally, by disk partition, or remotely, by distributed shared memory controller. The DSMC requires simple and reliable request/response messages, so it uses Tal/RaTP protocol, tailored to satisfy requirements of DSMC implementation. DSMC and DSM partitions are also implemented on the top of Unix, that offers good environment for testing and verification.

Issues of importance. The Clouds project is among the first ones that implemented distributed shared memory in order to support object relocation. Various modes of the segment enable an efficient combination of coherence strategy with synchronization primitives, in order to get better performance; namely, the lock can be acquired when the object is invoked and released when it is finished. Since the segment must be discarded when unlocked, the need for later invalidations, when accessing the segment for write, is avoided.

One of the future goals is also to provide full interoperability between Unix and Clouds. In this way, the strength of Unix in rich development environments can be explored.

4.6. Orca

Bal and Tanenbaum in [BAL88] introduce a new concept called the shared data-object model and its implementation incorporated in the design of a simple, general purpose programming language Orca. It was developed at the Vrije Universiteit, Amsterdam, Netherlands.

DSM mechanism. Shared data-object represents a communication channel between processes. Shared data are encapsulated in passive objects, and all data in objects can be only accessed by a set of indivisible operations defined by the object's type. Dynamic creation of multiple sequential processes is assumed. When a process spawns a child process, it can pass its object as a shared parameter to it. Replication of shared objects is based on the frequency of read/write operations that can be determined by the runtime system. Consistency maintenance is based on an update mechanism. Shared-data model algorithms are described for three cases depending on the available network services. The first case is based on reliable point-to-point messages, and represents a two-phase update protocol. The other cases of the implementation of the protocol use either reliable or unreliable multicast messages.

Issues of importance. Shared data-object model can be suited to various network interconnections. Update mechanism is a good solution when an object to be changed is small, and sending a new value is just as expensive as sending an invalidation message. In the case of unreliable multicast, updates are broadcast to all sites. Because of that, the message has to be processed even in those sites that do not actually use the involved data. A combination of update and invalidate mechanism, when updates are performed only when cost-effective, is one of the possible sources for improvement. Later implementations also introduce a role of sequencer that ensures a reliable broadcast.

4.7. Midway

Bershad, Zekauskas and Sawdon in their paper [BERSH93] describe Midway, a DSM system that introduces a new consistency model — entry consistency. This is a software system intended to be used on medium-scale multicomputers, and it is operational on a cluster of MIPS R3000-based DEC stations, under the Mach operating system. Midway was developed at Carnegie Mellon University, Pittsburgh, Pennsylvania.

DSM mechanism. Midway supports multiple consistency models used in the same program: processor consistency, release consistency, and an original model named entry consistency. For all three consistency models, Midway uses an update mechanism. Entry consistency is such a model where data is guaranteed to be consistent only on an acquiring synchronization operation. Consistency is applied only to data guarded by the acquired object, and the view of shared address space includes most recent updates only when processor enters a critical section. Accesses related to synchronization objects must be sequentially consistent. At the level of programming language, all shared data must be declared and explicitly associated with at least one synchronization object, also declared as an instance of one of Midway's data types, that include locks and barriers. If the necessary labeling information is included, and all accesses to shared data done with appropriate explicit synchronization accesses, sequential consistency can be also achieved. Midway consists of three components: a set of keywords and function calls used to annotate a parallel program, a compiler that generates code that marks shared data as dirty when written to, and a runtime system that implements several consistency models. Runtime system procedure calls associate synchronization objects to runtime data. The control of versions of synchronization objects is done using the associated timestamps, which are reset when data is modified.

Issues of importance. Multiple consistency models that can be dynamically changed may be very convenient for some applications with specialized requirements for consistency semantics closely related to particular algorithm. Anyway, entry consistency may be hard to use, and it can be very complicated to port programs with this model, since consistency requirements should be well understood and made explicate by the programmer.

4.8. Agora

Bisiani and Forin in their paper [BISIA88] describe Agora, a DSM system that allows processes written in different languages and executing on heterogeneous machines to communicate using a DSM approach. Agora was developed at the Carnegie Mellon University, Pittsburgh, Pennsylvania.

DSM mechanism. In Agora, sharing is performed at the level of user-defined structures, that have to be described using data definitions and access-function definitions, written in a simple language with a Lisp-like syntax. Compiler for this specification language generates code for the Agora run-time system, as well as the code for supported programming languages (such as C, C++, CommonLisp). At runtime, data elements can be stored or retrieved using addresses, that can be integers or strings. Address translation is performed using multiple maps. Once the data is written, it can not be changed, but the new element must be added in shared memory and then remapped. In order to reuse the memory space, garbage collection must be performed. Data is replicated in all the machines that use it, so read operations can be done with no messages. Write operations are sent to the master copy, which resides at the machine of the process that created the data structure. All network operations are handled by special process called AgoraServer.

Issues of importance. Although Agora supports various programming languages and architectures, and provides mechanisms for data format conversion, its implementation is limited to the single operating system Mach. Data structuring according to the user-defined types reduce the possibility of false sharing, but the fact that data is replicated at all sites that use it, instead of being dynamically fetched when needed, can result in an unnecessary storage overhead.

4.9. Mermaid

Zhou, Stumm, and McInerney in [ZHOU90] describe Mermaid, a prototype DSM system with the main goal to extend the DSM concept to heterogeneous environments. It runs on Sun/UNIX and DEC Firefly/Topaz multiprocessor workstations connected by Ethernet. The system was designed at the University of Toronto, Canada.

DSM mechanism. The main objective of Mermaid was to implement DSM algorithms originally introduced by Li for the IVY system, and to make them run in a heterogeneous environment. Although the two systems have different data representations, page sizes and operating systems, they were integrated in order to cooperate in executing the parallel applications.

Mermaid is implemented as a library package to be linked into application programs using DSM. The overall system consists of the thread management module, the shared memory module, and the remote operations module. Write invalidate protocol with multicast capabilities is employed. Thread management package enables creation of threads on remote host, as well as their migration from host to host.

Issues of importance. Carefully designed DSM system for heterogeneous environment makes it possible for programmers to take advantages of multiple different architectures, in order to gain better performance of their applications. However, the Mermaid prototype imposes some restrictions. Every page may contain data of only one type and an entire page must be converted when transferred, including data that could never be accessed. Numerical accuracy may be corrupted by multiple migrations causing the conversion of floating-point numbers. The size of each data type must be the same at each site. Users must specify conversion routines for user-defined data types in the original implementation, although automatic generation of conversion routines can be realized in a preprocessor.

5. Hybrid DSM Implementations

The integration of software and hardware methods, competitive management of DSM, and various consistency models, seem to be the most promising approach in the future of DSM.

The idea to implement a combination of hardware and software is explored in the efforts to achieve scalability, limited in directory based schemes, that use the full-map hardware directories. Based on the observation that only a few simultaneously shared copies of the same shared data exist on average, the solution was found in which only a limited number of pointers for each directory entry are implemented in hardware. When more directory storage is needed, it is managed by software. This principle is implemented in the MIT Alewife system.

In order to gain better performance of DSM systems, researchers experiment lately with the use of multiple protocols within the same system, and even integrate message passing with the DSM mechanism. Innovative consistency models are also being implemented, requiring additional activities of the programmer to suit the needs of application. In order to handle complexity of those, basically software solutions, special programmable protocol processors are added to the system, as it was done in the Stanford FLASH system.

5.1. PLUS

Bisiani and Ravishankar in [BISIA90] propose PLUS, a DSM system designed for efficient execution of a single multithreaded process, with processor coherence semantics and a non-demand write-update protocol. PLUS was developed at the Carnegie Mellon University, Pittsburgh, Pennsylvania.

DSM mechanism. Global memory mapping, coherence management, and atomic operations in PLUS are implemented in hardware, while pages, that reside in shared virtual address space, can be replicated and migrated under software control, maintained by the operating system. When write operation is performed in PLUS, updating data in the same order guarantees the general coherence. If the strict ordering is necessary, writes are performed by the *fence* operation. During these writes, the processor is blocked until the write is completed. Since data in local memories can be cached, the write-through policy is employed to preserve consistency. Snoopy mechanisms ensure consistency when data is being updated.

Issues of importance. There is no overhead in referencing the remote memory locations. The memory consistency protocol is carried out independently, since it is implemented in hardware. Performance evaluation shows that the concept of replicated data (as a consequence of write-update mechanism) increases the processor utilization substantially, due to the decrease in read latency. For a higher level of replication, the system can get saturated with frequent updates, slowing down the useful computation.

5.2. Alewife

Agarwal, et al. in [AGARW90, CHAIK91] give an overview of Alewife, the DSM system developed at the MIT, Cambridge, Massachusetts.

DSM mechanism. Alewife provides the strongly consistent DSM mechanism — the LimitLESS protocol — which represents a hardware-based coherence method supported with a software mechanism (fast trap). Alewife manages a limited directory in hardware, and emulates the full-directory in an interrupt-based software.

Issues of importance. The main advantage of this approach is that the applied directory coherence protocol is storage efficient, while performing about as well as the full-map directory protocol. On the other side, processor utilization is limited by the available network bandwidth.

5.3. Lynx/Galactica Net

Wilson, et al. in [WILSO92] present the Lynx/Galactica Net, the multiprocessor system developed at the Institute for High Performance Computing, Worchester Polytechnic Institute, Marlborough, Massachusetts.

DSM mechanism. Main memory on each node in the Lynx system is used as a cache space for the global shared memory. This is achieved through virtual memory software, implemented in the Mach operating system. There is a hardware support for virtual memory mechanism, realized through a block transfer engine. When writes to a certain memory address are infrequent, the invalidation strategy is used. In the case of frequent writes, the operating system uses the update-based protocol. A page can be in one of three states: read-only, private, or update. The idea of hardware and software cooperation is that the operating system can put the page in the update mode, and initialize tables that contain information about the node that have a copy. Then, write references to update mode pages are detected by hardware and propagated according to the table. Those hardware assisted updates significantly improve the performance of the system.

The cache coherence among processors on the same board is maintained by the Motorola defined protocol. All writes made to shared memory (via the local bus) are sensed by the network interface module, which then sends them on the network. Any request that a processor issues goes to local memory. In the case of a page fault, the operating system initiates the page transfer; and the request can be serviced locally.

Issues of importance. Since the unit of sharing is the page, the only special hardware required on the node is the standard memory management hardware. Because of the update mechanism, for some applications, broadcast of excessive updates can produce a large amount of traffic in the system.

5.4. FLASH

Kuskin et al. in [KUSKI94] present the FLASH multiprocessor, that implements the message passing, as well as the DSM paradigm. The FLASH multiprocessor system is developed at the Stanford University, Palo Alto, California.

DSM mechanism. The basic idea behind FLASH is to implement the memory coherence protocol in software, but to take the burden of its execution from the main processor of the node, by adding a specific protocol processor incorporated in a custom node controller — MAGIC (Memory and General Interconnection Controller). It consists of memory controller, I/O controller, network interface, and a programmable protocol processor, having a 64-bit superscalar core.

FLASH uses dynamic pointer allocation for a scalable directory structure, managed by a set of handlers. Each cache line-sized block consists of 128 bytes. It is associated with an 8-byte state word called a directory header. A link field that points to a list of sharers is stored in the directory header, together with some necessary flags. The space for the list of sharers is dynamically allocated from the pointer/link store, and a free list is used to track the available entries. Coherence protocol applied in FLASH is very similar to that of Dash, with some elements that help in deadlock avoidance.

Issues of importance. The FLASH system design has potential for scalability, as the overall directory occupies only 7% to 9% of the main memory, depending on the system configuration. Preliminary performance measurements show that the sustained rate at which MAGIC can supply data will depend on the memory system, and that the flexible protocol processing is not the limiting factor of the MAGIC's performance.

5.5. Paradigm

Cheriton, et al., in [CHERI91] present a concept of parallel distributed global memory architecture in the Paradigm system. A new multiprocessor is based on several previous projects with V software and VMP hardware. Paradigm is being developed at the Stanford University, Palo Alto, California.

DSM mechanism. Paradigm combines the operating system, hardware, and firmware-like components, in order to achieve low cost, high performance, and scalability. Paradigm clusters the processors in nodes organized as an optimized high-speed shared bus/cache hierarchy. An ownership-based, hierarchical directory coherence protocol based on hardware inconsistency detection and software cache management routines is employed. Directory entries are normally modified as a side effect of bus operations. Protocol is invalidation-based, and it can choose to broadcast the invalidations, or to send them just to those modules that have a copy of the block. Further optimizations include a memory-based message exchange protocol and efficient locking, as a part of the consistency mechanism.

Issues of importance. The strategy of application structuring, in order to explore locality and make a good use of a deep shared cache/bus hierarchy of the system, seems to be very important for this solution.

6. Conclusion

The intention of this survey was to provide an extensive coverage of all relevant topics in an increasingly important area — distributed shared memory computing. A special attempt has been made to give the broadest overview of the proposed and existing approaches, in a uniform organizational manner. Because of the combined advantages of the shared memory and distributed systems, DSM solutions appear to be the most appropriate way toward large-scale high-performance systems with a reduced cost of parallel software development. In spite of that, building of successful commercial systems that follows the DSM paradigm is still in its infancy; consequently, experimental and research efforts prevail. Therefore, the DSM field remains a very active research area. Some of the promising research directions can be: improving the DSM algorithms and mechanisms, and adapting them to the characteristics of typical applications and system configurations, synergistic combining of hardware and software implementations of the DSM concept, integrating of the shared memory and message passing programming paradigms, innovative system architecture (especially memory system), comparative performance evaluation, etc. From this point of view, further investment in exploring, developing, and implementing DSM systems seems to be quite justified and promising.

7. References

[AHUJA86]   Ahuja, S., Carriero, N., Gelernter, D.,"Linda and Friends," *IEEE Computer*, Vol. 19, No. 8, May 1986, pp. 110-129.

[AGARW90]   Agarwal, A., Lim, B., Kranz, D., Kubiatowicz, J., "APRIL: A Processor Architecture for Multiprocessing," *Proceedings of the 17th Annual International Symposium on Computer Architecture*, 1990, pp. 104-114.

[BAL88]   Bal, H., E., Tanenbaum, A., S., "Distributed programming with shared data," *International Conferance on Computer Languages '88*, October 1988, pp. 82-91.

[BENN90a]   Bennet, J. K., Carter, J. B., Zwaenepoel, W., "Munin: Distributed Shared Memory Based on Type-Specific Memory Coherence," *Proceedings of the 1990 Conference on Principles and Practice of Parallel Programming*, March 1990, pp. 168-176.

[BENN90b]   Bennet, J., Carter, J., Zwaenepoel, W., "Adaptive Software cache Management for Distributed Shared memory Architectures," *Proceedings of the 17th Annual International Symposium on Computer Architecture*, June 1990, pp. 125-134.

[BERSH93]   Bershad, B., N, Zekauskas M., J., Sawdon, W., A., "The Midway Distributed Shared Memory System," *COMPCON 93*, February 1993, pp. 524-533.

[BISIA88]   Bisiani, R., Forin, A., "Multilanguage Parallel Programming of Heterogeneous Machines," *IEEE Transactions on Computers*, Vol. 37, No. 8, August 1988, pp. 930-945.

[BISIA90]   Bisani R., Ravishankar M., "PLUS: A Distributed Shared-Memory System," *Proceedings of the 17th Annual International Symposium on Computer Architecture*, Vol. 18, No. 2, May 1990, pp. 115-124.

[BORRM89]   Borrmann L., Herdieckerhoff M., "Parallel Processing Performance in a Linda System," *Proceedings of the 1989 International Conference on Parallel Processing*, pp. I-51 - I-58.

[CHAIK91]   Chaiken, D., et al, "LimitLESS Directories: A Scalable Cache Coherence Scheme," *Proceedings of the 4th International Conference on Architectural Support for Programming Languages and Operating Systems*, April 1991, pp. 224-234.

[CHERI91]   Cheriton, D. A., Goosen, H. A., Boyle, P. D., "Paradigm: A Highly Scalable Shared-Memory Multicomputer Architecture," *IEEE Computer*, Vol. 24, No. 2, February 1991, pp. 33-46.

[DELP91]   Delp, G., Farber, D., Minnich, R., " Memory as a Network Abstraction," *IEEE Network*, July 1991.

[ENCOR92]   *RMS Functional Specification*, Encore Computer Corporation, Ft. Landerdale, Florida, U.S.A., 1992.

[FLEIS87]   Fleisch, B., D., "Distributed Shared Memory in a Loosely Coupled Distributed System," *Proceedings of ACM SIGCOMM '87 Workshop*, 1987, pp. 317-327.

[FLEIS89]   Fleisch, B., Popek, G., "Mirage: A Coherent Distributed Shared Memory Design," *Proceedings of the 14th ACM Symposium on Operating System Principles*, ACM, New York, 1989, pp. 211-223.

[FRANK93]   Frank, S., Burkhardt III, Rothnie, J.,"The KSR1: Bridging the Gap Between Shared Memory and MPPs," *COMPCON 93*, February 1993, pp. 285-294)

[GUSTA92]   Gustavson, D., "The Scalable Coherent Interface and Related Standards Projects," *IEEE Micro*, February 1992, pp. 10-22.

[HAGER92]   Hagersten, E., Landin, A., Haridi, S., " DDM - A Cache-Only Memory Architecture," *IEEE Computer*, Vol. 25, No. 9, September 1992, pp. 44-54.

[KSR92]   *Kendall Square Research Technical Summary*, KSR Corporation, Waltham, Massachusetts, U.S.A., 1992.

[KUSKI94]   Kuskin, J., Ofelt, D., Heinrich, M., Heinlein, J., Simoni, R., Gharachorloo, K., Chapin, J., Nakahira, D., Baxter, J., Horowitz, M., Gupta, A., Rosenblum, M., Hennessy, J., "The Stanford FLASH Multiprocessor," *Proceedings of the 21th Annual International Symposium on Computer Architecture*, April 1994, pp. 302-313.

[JAMES94]   James, D. V, "The Scalable Coherent Interface: Scaling to High-Performance Systems," *COMPCON `94: Digest of papers*, March 1994, pp.64-71.

[LENOS92]   Lenoski , D., Laudon, J., et al., "The Stanford DASH Multiprocessor," *IEEE Computer*, Vol. 25, No. 3, March 1992, pp. 63-79.

[LIHUD89]   Li, K., Hudak, P., "Memory Coherence in Shared Virtual Memory Systems," *ACM Transactions on Computer Systems*, Vol. 7, No. 4, November 1989, pp. 321-359.

[MAPLE90]   Maples, C., Wittie, L., "Merlin: A Superglue for Multicomputer Systems," 930-945.*COMPCON '90*, pp.73-81.

[RAMAC89]   Ramachandran, U., Khalidi, M., Y., A., "An Implementation of Distributed Shared Memory," *First Workshop Experiences with Building Distributed and Multiprocessor Systems*, USENIX Association, 1989, pp. 21-38.

[TAM__90]   Tam, M., C., Smith, J, M, Farber, D., J., "A Taxonomy-Based Comparison of Several Distributed Shared Memory Systems," *ACM Operating Systems Review*, Vol. 24, No. 3, July 1990, pp. 40-67.

[TOMAS93]   Tomašević, M., Milutinović, V., *Cache Coherence Problem in Shared Memory Multiprocessors: Hardware Solutions* , IEEE Computer Society Press, 1993.

[WILSO92]   Wilson, A., Teller, M., Probert, T., Le, D., LaRowe, R., "Lynx/Galactica Net: A Distributed, Cache Coherent Multiprocessing System," *Proceedings of the 25th Annual Hawaii International Conference on System Sciences*, 1992, pp. 416-426.

[WITTI89]   Wittie L., Maples C., "Merlin: Massively Parallel Heterogeneous Computing," *Proceedings of the 1989 International Conference on Parallel Processing*, pp. I-142 - I-150.

[ZHOU90]   Zhou, S., Stumm, M., McInerney, T., "Extending Distributed Shared Memory to Heterogeneous Environments," *Proceedings of the 10th International Conference on Distributed Computing Systems*, May-June 1990. pp. 30-37.

Reflective-Memory Multiprocessor

Stephen Lucci, Izidor Gertner
Computer Science Department
City College, City University of New York
Convent Avenue and 138 Street
New York, New York 10031
and
Anil Gupta, and Uday Hegde
Encore Computer Corporation
6901 W.Sunrise Blvd
Ft.Lauderdale, FL 33313

Abstract

Reflective memory may be thought of as hardware-supported replication of data on multiple computers.This simple mechanism has been extended further, in software, to support memory semantics required by multiprocessors. This paper describes the reflective memory implementation of the Encore Infinity - a distributed shared memory multiprocessor. A brief overview of the system is provided and comparisons are made with other cached architectures. Spinlocks are employed in this system to manage the herculean cache coherency problems which are a natural result of any system which employs massive replication. A Brief introduction to the recovery procedure used to return crashed nodes to normal operation is also described.

1. Introduction - Distributed Shared Memory Fundamentals

This paper describes Infinity, the Encore Reflective-Memory Multiprocessor. It is a Distributed Shared Memory Multiprocessor which is ideal for On-Line Transaction Processing Systems. A brief overview of the architecture, details of the software infrastructure, and some discussion of applications is provided. There is also an appendix which lists spinlock code employed for synchronization purposes.

It is quite customary for many people to access a data-base system simultaneously. And it is also customary for databases to be subject to failures - caused by either system software bugs or hardware crashes. An on-line transaction processing system [OLTP] allows users to ignore these "inconveniences". That is, "transaction processing systems let each user think of himself or herself as the sole user of an idealized, failure-free database system."[1]

Maintaining these criteria in systems which may be distributed, autonomous and even heterogeneous is still a subject of current research.[2] At the heart of these so called on-line transaction processing systems must be a high-level communication system and huge amounts of computational prowess. OLTP systems require greater computational speeds than that offered by traditional mainframes. Most Computer Scientists believe that any subsequent increases in processing speeds will depend upon the incorporation of parallel techniques.

Two approaches to parallelism that have obtained widespread acceptance are distributed memory multiprocessors and tightly coupled shared-memory multiprocessors. A distributed memory multiprocessor is comprised of a collection of independent computers connected by an interconnection network. Communication between processors may employ message passing - often under programmer control - making programming a difficult task. NCube and Intel are successful vendors for this genre of parallel machines. These machines often find their niche in scientific and engineering research environments. Tightly coupled shared-memory multiprocessors, on the other hand, are comprised of multiple CPUs and a single memory which is referenced globally. This model is easier to program.

Commercially successful shared-memory machines are manufactured by Encore, Concurrent, Convex, and others. "It is no great step to move from a computer whose operating system gives each user the illusion of having his or her own independent processor, to one which actually provides such processors, along with an operating system which knows how to use them." [3, p.55] A Distributed Shared Memory (DSM) system must automatically transform shared-memory accesses into interprocess communication. Algorithms are required to locate and access shared data, maintain coherence and replace data when necessary. To accomplish these tasks, a designer of a DSM system must address several key issues. The first of these is probably - how is the DSM to be implemented? A hardware-based implementation would use caching methodologies, while a software-based approach could rely upon the operating system or compiler. If the operating system is responsible for the DSM - then virtual memory management strategies (e.g., page swapping and logical to physical address translation) would be employed. A compiler-based approach would generate synchronization and coherence primitives as needed. Some combination of these strategies may be evident in a particular system.

Another major concern in DSM systems is coherence semantics. How are parallel memory updates to be propagated throughout the system? If shared data is not replicated - then enforcing coherence is trivial. Replication of data, however, can dramatically decrease memory access times; the price tag for this enhanced performance is the need for sophisticated read and write protocols (refer to section 3 for a glimpse of the complexity involved). When coherence semantics are relaxed - more efficient shared access may result and a marked decrease in synchronization overhead will be apparent. Of course, some types of programs may not execute correctly under these conditions.

A large advantage of shared-memory multi-processors is that they tend to scale better than message passing-based systems. That is, as the number of processes increases in a DSM computer, system reliability and performance undergo a similar increase. However, there are limits to this scalability. These are due in large measure to two problems: 1) central bottlenecks - such as saturation of the bus line by heavy traffic, and 2) the proliferation of global common knowledge operations involved in memory maintenance - e.g., message broadcasting.

Due to the relative ease in programming, however, DSM systems have gained a strong foothold in the commercial marketplace. The drawback to these systems is that accessing data and maintaining cache coherence entails huge communication overhead. A successful design must possess a network or bus with phenomenal bandwidth as well as strategies for keeping I/O traffic below gridlock levels. This paper will describe Infinity - Encore's Shared Memory multiprocessor. At the heart of this machine is a Reflective Memory System (RMS). This paper will explain how the RMS system creates the illusion of a seamless shared memory.

2. Reflective Memory System (RMS)

2.1 Infinity's Architectural Overview

The internal structure of a computational node involves one to four identical RISC processors, each having a peak performance of 40 MFLOPS.

The expansion memory module provides an additional 256 MBytes. Communication within the node is handled by a 100 Mbytes/sec Local Bus. The local system disk and one to four Memory Channel Adaptor Modules each of 128/256/512 Mbytes are also attached to the Local Bus.

All processing elements have full addressability over the entire addressing range of the node. They get service from memory and extended memory modules at effectively the same rate. A single operating system is responsible for all resources. Asynchronous and ethernet ports provide access using any standard protocols.

The Reflective Memory System Architecture provides efficient coupling of multiple processor nodes to shared data in a distributed computing environment. The physical use of the RMS system is essentially as a memory I/O channel. I/O operations between different nodes are actually memory-to-memory transfers.

Figure 1 presents an example of a processing node.

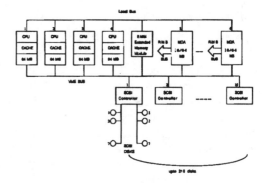

Figure 1. Infinity Node.

The Reflective Memory system has the following features:

- Allows up to 9 MCA (memory channel adaptors) connected in a single Reflective Memory bus string.

- Bus arbitration and transfer latencies are on the order of 40 ns.

- Each MCA has up to 512 MB of physical memory, broken up into units of 4096 byte pages.

- Each unit or page of the MCA memory can be programmed to be enabled to transmit/receive on the RM bus.

- Shared data is replicated in the respective MCA's.

- The memory is tri-ported on Local, VME and RM bus for greater usage flexibility.

- The MCA provides up to 128K transmit and 256K receive "windows" that provide a passage for each physical page onto the RM bus.

Each window address is termed an "RM network address" and is the address that is sent on the RM bus along with the data. Any MCA that has this "RM network address" window enabled for receiving, captures the data on the bus and directs it to the previously programmed physical page. Thus the data that is written to a physical page on one node could make a traversal on the RM bus and be replicated in several other memory modules.

The salient feature of this replicated shared memory concept is that while each computer physically has its own local memory, the results are the same as if all the computers were attached to a large common memory. The computer system appears at all times as a large virtual multiprocessor because all the interprocessor communications occur at memory speeds. A more detailed account of RMS hardware organization may be found in [4]. The rest of this section will concentrate on the software implementation of RMS.

Figure 2 depicts a configuration of 12 processing nodes and 4 storage nodes. The internode communication is via RMS.

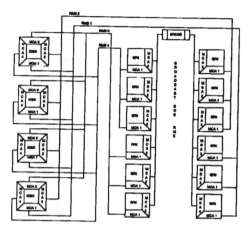

Figure 2.   16 Node Infinity.

2.2 Comparison of the RMS Multiprocessor with other Cached Architectures

From the computer architecture point of view, RMS is just uncached shared-memory that is available in addition to each processor's private memory. However, RMS is replicated on each computer node(which may include multiple processors). From the node point of view, RMS may be thought of as cache that is maintained by hardware.   A brief overview of existing cache architectures may provide a better perspective on where to place the RMS.

Convenitional CPU snoopy caches work like this: In order to reduce the traffic on the bus, each processor has a fast local cache which contains a copy of some of the data in shared memory. Whenever the processor would issue a read, the cache is checked, and then if a cache miss occurred, the cache retrieves a block of data from the   shared data [5]. On the other hand, a cache miss would be forced on the next access to that cache .

Other CPU cache coherence maintenance solutions include continuously updatable caches which would watch the traffic on the bus and then update as needed [6].

RMS is very similar to this continuously updated

write-back cache system. However, there are several differences worth noting.

The Reflective Memory architecture is not based on a single large shared memory unit as described above, wherein multiple processors connect to memory over a bus.

Instead, RM could be succinctly described as a "replicated distributed memory". The Reflective Memory bus can be viewed as a WRITE-only bus, unlike a bus that is connected to a single shared memory which could have read requests on cache misses, and write requests on cache write-throughs or write-back operations. The RM architecture allows nodes to selectively share their reflective memory with the other participating nodes. A write by one processor/node to its Reflective Memory could result in an RM-bus transaction, which may update the Reflective Memory of other processors/nodes as well. Read requests to memory do not result in an RM-bus transaction. (There is no concept of cache read miss, since a processor's/node's Reflective Memory is not a cache. It is a copy of the shared memory relevant to that processor/node.)

The fact that RMS has an additional copy of RAM, makes it extremely well suited for a high availability, or fault tolerant architecture.

There are other differences worth noting: for one, the RM can do simultaneous reads and writes. What is in one local processor's memory is in ALL the processors' memories at the same time, hence there is no contention for accesses to the common shared memory, because every processor has its own local copy. RM can be used as an ultra-high speed network with no network protocol overhead. RM can connect many systems in the same room or over much larger distances via a fiber interface in real-time.

The RM architecture allows nodes to selectively share their Reflective Memory with other participating nodes. A write by one processor/node to its Reflective Memory *could* result in a RM-bus transaction, and that *might* result in the update as noted earlier of other processor/node Reflective Memories. There are reasons for this hedging (i.e., the "could" and "might"). Suppose one has an 8MB dual-ported memory module in the Reflective Memory of a local node. One could choose to only share (reflect) 4MBs of it and not the full eight. That way one can use the other 4MB as private memory.

Of course, if the "cache" is as large as the shared memory unit, then the shared memory unit could reasonably be ditched. There is no such thing as a cache read miss,

since everything is present.

The RM-architecture provides for a programmable dynamic-reflection of memory. The memory is broken up into smaller units (pages) and each of these pages can be programmed for reflection. An RM page could be programmed to transmit writes to the page onto the RM bus and/or receive updates to the page from the RM bus. The page could also be disabled for reflection.

Moreover, the reflections could be set up such that a certain RM-page on node A could reflect to a different page on nodes B and C, and none of the pages on nodes D, E, etc.

This allows each node's memory to be programmed so that a part of the Reflective Memory may be used to participate in "global-shared-memory". Portions of memory can be used as memory which is private to the node. The rest of the memory can be used for dynamically enabling and disabling reflection for selective communication as required.

One would not normally wish to keep all of the copies updated whenever there was a write. The reason one may not wish to share all the memory is to make more effective use of RM memory on each node. If 2 or more nodes are participating in some shared-memory communication, and the rest of the nodes in the cluster are not participants in this transaction, then they need not reserve physical RM pages for this particular communication. These other nodes could employ their RM-pages for more worthwhile endeavors.

The RMS protocol is very different from the cache directory mechanisms that were used to keep track of block ownership in write-back protocols. [7]

When compared with directory-based architectures, the RM framework manifests marked similarities to a snooped cache mechanism. There are no global/distributed cache directories to specify block ownerships. The RM-module on each node in the multiprocessor keeps track of its own mappings; i.e., how each block of RM memory on that node is mapped on to the RM-bus. The mappings for each block could be in one of 4 states: Receive Only, Receive and Transmit, Transmit Only and Unmapped. There is an attempt here to draw an analogy with caching schemes: The first 2 states are analogous to a cache block in either Read-only or Read-Write mode, respectively. The next 2 states could be described as Allow-Writes-Inhibit-Updates and Local-Uncached-Block, which may not carry much meaning in a caching scheme.

The RM-module on each node "listens" on the RM bus. If it finds an address on the bus that is enabled to be received on that node, it lets the data in, and then routes this data to the correct local memory block. The address and data make a trip on the RM-bus with the sole intention that any other RM-module which has its address enabled for receiving, may also have an opportunity to clock this data in.

The RM architecture gives full control to software in regard to how the multiprocessor-wide memory is to be configured and utilized.

This allows each node's memory to be programmed, so that a part of the Reflective Memory is used to participate in "global-shared-memory". And part of the memory can be used as memory which is private to the node. The rest of memory can then be used for dynamically enabling and disabling reflection for selective communications as required. The processing element at a given node is responsible for deciding whether or not a given write is to be reflected.

2.3 RMS Dynamic Allocation for an Efficient File System

For a communication link between 2 machines that is temporary (for example, RPC requests), it is required that a means be present by which a physical page on each node participating in the communication be tied to a single RM window to enable the communication.

For this reason, each node is allocated ownership over a set of RMS windows (network addresses) which can be allocated and passes as a token to set up a communication link. Below is an example of how the dynamic RMS management is used for efficient file system operations.

A user program on a client, initiates a read with a standard system call. In the kernel the system call is intercepted and prepared for the RMS protocol. As part of the protocol, the client sends the read RPC request:

- allocates the RMS network address,
- allocates a local RMS (unmapped memory) buffer,
- binds the RMS network address to a local buffer address,
- initializes read-only reflection on the RM network address,
- sends an RPC to the server node; the RPC carries the command (i.e. read) and the RMS network address.

The server receives the RPC request and does the following:

- allocates a server RMS buffer,
- binds the requested RMS network address to the server RMS buffer,
- starts a disk I/O operation into the server RMS buffer,
- once I/O completes, the server
  - disconnects the RMS network address binding to the server buffer (so it can reuse the buffer for other requests)
  - sends an RPC back to the client.

The client receives the reply and proceeds to:

- disconnect the RMS network binding to the client buffer,
- update the user program's VM table by removing the old RMS buffer (i.e. returning it to a free buffer pool) and inserting the new RMS page with data which was recently read.

This algorithm uses no CPU-based memory copying; instead VM has been modified to take advantage of the RMS dynamic buffer management capability. The result is a file-system that can provide a total throughput at full RMS capacity (up to 100 MB/sec) which may even exceed the local bus capacity.

3. RMS Spinlocks

Previous implementations of RMS spinlocks have relied upon Ethernet-like retransmission algorithms - wherein one obtains a lock, if a conflict occurs, then just retries after some random interval. Clearly, this approach fails to scale for large configurations. This section describes an RMS enhancement that allows for an elegant hardware-support SWAP-AND-TEST primitive which supports lock operations, requiring on the order of a few micro-seconds.

RMS spinlocks are based on SWAP & TEST.

An example of spinlock operation follows.

First establish a reflection:

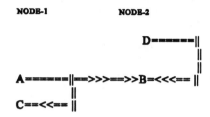

Now, variables A and C are initialized to identical values (say zero). Also, reflection is set up from A to each of C and B, and also from B to C (but not to A). NODE-1 sets its variable to a new value (say 1) and spins on variable C, waiting for (1) to show up.

Now node-1 writes to variable A and is allowed to proceed but the value (1) is queued, waiting for the RMS arbitrator so that (1) may be posted on the bus, at which time, the new value(1) is delivered to both (B) on node (2) and (C) on node (1). In other words, Node 1, when it sees (1) in C, is absolutely certain that Node-2 has also seen (1) in (B). Now, we are going to resolve arbitration among several nodes, using the method above. However, we will set and test only one byte for each node.

Variables A, B, and C are 64 bit integers. Each node (in an 8 node multiprocessor) is assigned an index (which is the node number) into a byte.

The algorithm is based on the fact that one can write atomically 1 byte to the RMS, however one can read atomically 64 bits thereby enabling each node to know whether or not there has been a conflict. A small example may help to clarify matters. Below are three variables A, B, and C. Following each variable is a list of the value that this variable contains in any of 6 nodes.

A = | n1 | n2 | n3 | n4 | n5 | n6|

B = | n1 | n2 | n3 | n4 | n5 | n6|

C = | n1 | n2 | n3 | n4 | n5 | n6|

To start, suppose initialization sets all variables to zero (0). We have:

A = | 0 | 0 | 0 | 0 | 0 | 0 | 0 | 0 |

B = | 0 | 0 | 0 | 0 | 0 | 0 | 0 | 0 |

C = | 0 | 0 | 0 | 0 | 0 | 0 | 0 | 0 |

Next, suppose node 1 attempts to get a spinlock.

The node will set:

A = | 1 | 0 | 0 | 0 | 0 | 0 | 0 | 0 |

and will wait for (A == B). There are three possibilities.

Case I.

B = | 0 | 0 | 0 | 0 | 0 | 0 | 0 | 0 |

C = | 0 | 0 | 0 | 0 | 0 | 0 | 0 | 0 |

Here, the setting of A is still in progress, it is being queued for the RMS bus.

Case II.

B = | 1 | 0 | 0 | 0 | 0 | 0 | 0 | 0 |

C = | 1 | 0 | 0 | 0 | 0 | 0 | 0 | 0 |

The set of A[1] got onto the bus and both B and C were set. Note, that if B gets updated, we are absolutely sure that C was also updated. And finally,

Case III.

D = | 0 | 1 | 0 | 0 | 0 | 0 | 0 | 0 |

B = | 1 | 1 | 0 | 0 | 0 | 0 | 0 | 0 |

C = | 1 | 1 | 0 | 0 | 0 | 0 | 0 | 0 |

Note, here both Node-1 and Node-2 have tried to obtain the same spinlock.

If, after a certain period of time (A != B) but (A[1] == B[1]).

Note, also that the Node-2 attempt fails, i.e., (D != C) but D[1] == C[1].

So both nodes have failed to obtain a spinlock and hence must back out.

In RMS, obtaining a spinlock requires the enforcement of relative time-alignment of RMS node(s), write transfers, and the echoing (reflecting) of results to all local nodes. The solution to this requirement, is to employ a doubleword data structure (64 bits), with a specific byte dedicated to each of the 8 nodes. More specifically, a node is associated to a byte, by the node's id (ie. node 0 owns byte 0, node 1 owns byte 1, etc.).

A spinlock's memory address is defined by its RM bus receive window address, and not by its local bus (transmit window) address. The transmit and receive addresses must always be different, to insure that a local bus (memory) write cannot directly modify the spinlock location, furthermore only the RM bus (reflected) writes can modify a spinlock.

By convention, after a spinlock has been initialized (set to zero) a node must only write to its assigned byte using the spinlock procedures.

To acquire a lock, a node must follow the following process.

1. Read the spinlock location.
If the spinlock is non-zero (any or all bytes) then another node either owns the spinlock, or is arbitrating for the barrier. In this case, the node should continue to monitor the spinlock and wait for it to become zero.
If the spinlock is zero (all bytes), then the node can attempt to acquire the spinlock.

2. A node acquires or arbitrates for the spinlock by writing a non-zero byte to its assigned byte position within the spinlock.
The content of the byte is arbitrary, but it could contain a bit flag to indicate the arbitration process and the node's id (a 4-bit field). The write must be accomplished by executing a store byte to the transmit window address of the spinlock.

3. After the write (store byte), the node should read the spinlock location by executing a load doubleword.
If the spinlock is zero, the read must be repeated.
If the spinlock is non-zero, the process may continue.

4. When the content of the spinlock is non-zero, the node must examine all bytes of the spinlock other than its own.
If the other bytes of the spinlock are non-zero, then other nodes are competing for the spinlock and may have won. This node should remove itself from contention, by writing zeros to its byte position within the spinlock transmit window address.

When a node writes a zero byte to remove itself from contention, it should monitor the spinlock location. When the node sees its byte go to zero and if in addition, all other bytes are zero, then no node has won/acquired the spinlock.
If the entire spinlock goes to zero, then a fall-back software strategy should be used to arbitrate for the spinlock or lock.
If one byte of the spinlock remains non-zero, then the corresponding node has won the spinlock.
If all other bytes of the spinlock are zero, and the node's byte is as written, then the node may assume it has won the spinlock, and no errors have occurred.
If all other bytes of the spinlock are zero, and the node's byte is not as written, then some type of error has occurred and the node's software must recover from this situation.

5. When a node recognizes that one byte, and only one byte, has gone to a non-zero value, the corresponding node has won/acquired the spinlock, and that node is free to proceed with exclusive data modification related to the spinlock.

To release a spinlock, a node must follow this process:

1. Write zeros to its byte position within the spinlock and at its transmit window address.

2. Monitor the spinlock, and when its byte has returned to zero, the spinlock has been released. In theory, the entire barrier should be zero when the spinlock is released.

3. In actual practice, it is possible for a node to release a spinlock, and for a second node to see that release and acquire it, before the releasing node can verify that the spinlock is totally released (all zeros).

Hardware implementation of the spinlock is quite simple. It simply depends upon a node being capable of receiving its own transmission, and it is required that a byte write (store) address is different from the receive (spinlock) address. With this form of implementation, the local bus store goes to one address and the reflected store goes to a different address within the local memory. The reflected address is the address of the spinlock for reading, and the local bus address is the address for writing. The RM bus becomes a single point through which byte-writes to a spinlock are time aligned.

It should be noted that the writes are time aligned on the RM bus and into the nodes' receive FIFOs. The actual reflected memory changes may not occur simultaneously due to differences in the receive FIFO depths, and the rate at which the receive FIFOs are serviced by the local buses and memories; however, the writes retain their time alignment, which is the main requirement for this Implementation.

4. RMS Recovery

RMS could be thought of as a shared-memory, where all participating systems are up and running and have RMS windows enabled for reflection. In normal operation of the system, each node maintains a copy of its own reflected memory.

The situation where identical RMS copies change when a node goes down, due to either hardware or software problems is now considered. The repair may involve upgrading software or hardware, changing boards and even replacing the RMS board of the faulty-node. None of these operations affect the functioning of the remaining nodes connected via the RMS bus. Once the repair is completed, the node is rebooted. At this point the RMS memory refresh problem begins.

While the faulty-node was down, other nodes were still running and updating their shared RMS regions. Once the faulty node is repaired and being brought on line, its RMS memory context is out of sync. The problem one has, is to atomically update the RMS memory of the new node, and then add it to the already functioning system of nodes.

Shared memory area consistency:

In a "distributed-shared-memory" architecture, as provided by RMS, MCS, etc., provisions exist to share globally a portion (or all) of memory among all the nodes that form the multiprocessor. Partial sharing (i.e., sharing a portion of memory among a subset of nodes is also possible, but is not of interest here).

The RMS shared memory is not a centralized unit. The global shared memory actually consists of physically backed memory on each of the individual nodes, the memory holding a copy of the shared global information. Only writes to the shared area go out on the RM bus to update each node's private copy, and reads happen locally on each node.

In such an architecture, it is required to make sure that all copies of the information are consistent. Under normal circumstances, this is taken care of by the reflective property of the memory. The exceptional situations occur when a new node wants to join the multiprocessor. The underlying architecture ensures that the new node gets all future updates, but it must be emphasized that the node starts with a clean slate and does not hold a copy of the global shared information. The functionality of determining the state of the reflective memory system across a multiprocessor of nodes is implemented by a subsystem called the Health Monitor.

Goals of the health-monitor:
1) The primary goal of the health monitor is to update the status of its node.
2) Detect node failures in the multiprocessor
3) Detect new nodes which are joining the multiprocessor
4) Present a consistent multiprocessor-wide view of the shared data.

Implementation:

The goals of HM are accomplished as follows.

Each node in the multiprocessor executes a health-monitoring daemon. A node announces its existence by updating a value, which is called its HeartBeat, in RMS at fixed intervals of time, (this could be implemented as a function of the clock interrupt for accurate determinism). The health monitor (HM) on each node monitors the HeartBeat values of all nodes in the multiprocessor.

A change in the HeartBeat value of an inactive node indicates that this particular node has joined the multiprocessor. A node's heart-beat value that has just stopped changing does not, however, mean that the node has dropped out of the multiprocessor. This is due to the inherent asynchrony between the inter-node communications of the health-value. For this reason, a threshold value is set up for state transitions from the operational to the inactive status of a node. Each time a scan indicates that a node has not updated its Healthvalue, the threshold is decremented until it reaches 0, at which point the node in question is finally marked as non-operational. At any point during this sequence, if the node updates its health value, the threshold is restored to its original value.

Memory Recovery:

The basic health monitoring could be described by the following finite state machine:

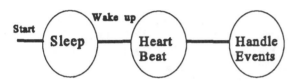

Figure 3. Memory Recovery States.

Under ordinary circumstances, the HM is in the *Sleep* state. The HM is woken up after a pre-programmed timeout value. In the *Heart Beat* state, the HM updates a global per-node counter in RMS, which indicates whether the node upon which the HM is running is alive or not. The *Handle Event* state contends with exceptional circumstances in which the HM should start up a thread of execution to handle some event. Typical events are a request to repair a state of memory, or to recognize the fact that some node has not updated its heart beat long enough to have it acknowledged by the system so that resources held by that node could be freed.

The HM provides the update functionality under the above exceptional conditions as follows:

"The Request":

When a node wishes to join a multiprocessor, that node's HM starts updating the HeartBeat value, thus broadcasting the fact that the node is now alive on the multiprocessor. At the same time, it scans the heart-beat values of other nodes in the shared memory and comes to a determination as to which nodes are alive on the multiprocessor.

The new node's HM then sets up a scheduling flag which instructs the scheduler that all processes which have attached, or are attempting to attach, to the global shared memory are not to be scheduled. This prevents a process from inadvertently using and/or updating a value in the shared global area, which is inconsistent with that node's point of view in the first place.

The HM then picks an arbitrary "suitor" node, among those alive on the multiprocessor, and marks a request in the "shared memory refresh" slot of the suitor node. (This slot is also allocated in the shared global area of the multiprocessor, and is allocated in the area which is reserved for health monitoring.)

The suitor node's HM, when scheduled, scans through its slots and finds a request pending for shared memory refresh. It checks if any other HM process in the multiprocessor has marked that the bus is in use. If not, it goes into an arbitration state, arbitrating for use of the bus. The arbitration mechanism could be simply to mark its status in RMS and wait for that status to loop back to the node. If no other node has requested use of the bus in the meanwhile, it is guaranteed that the bus can be acquired by the requesting node. If not, the HM passes through some back-off iterations. This process of arbitration by the HM process is done asynchronously; i.e., health-monitor may perform other work such as scanning for other requests, checking multiprocessor status, and yielding the cpu after having set up a timeout after which time it should be rescheduled.

The health-monitor traverses through a state machine for each request, and each time it is scheduled, it attempts to process any pending request from that request's current state. When the HM determines that it has won the arbitration process for the bus among the other node's HM, it sets up the scheduling flag to deschedule all processes that have attached, or are in the process of attaching to the shared global region.

The HM also sends a "freeze" request to each of the other nodes it knows are alive on the multiprocessor, and then moves to a state of "shared-memory-freeze-requested". When the other nodes HM see that a freeze request is pending, they set the scheduling flag to deschedule all processes on their node which have attached, or are in the process of attaching to the shared global region. After the deschedule is complete, each of the HMs mark a "freeze-done" state in the HM global area.

The original "master" node's HM monitors the "freeze-done" flag of all the nodes to which it has requested a "freeze". All this happens over multiple schedules of the HM, and the HM does not spin while waiting for the state transitions.

Once all nodes have marked that they are "frozen", the health-monitor reads the shared-global-memory data and writes it back. The global freeze of all processes that use the RM ensures that no updates may occur while a shared-global-area update is still in progress.

When an update is done, the HM notifies every node that the update is completed and the node can "de-freeze", whereupon each node resets the scheduling flag which enables processes to use the shared-global-area normally.

The entire process of "update-request" to "request-complete" could take several passes through the health-monitor. Timeouts or thresholds are set up at each state of the Finite state machine, to make sure that any request will not be stuck in the same state forever.

Nodes leaving or re-joining the multiprocessor while the health-monitoring is in progress and doing updates, may be treated in essentially the same manner as nodes going up and down under normal circumstances.

5. Summary

This paper has described the architecture and software underpinnings of the Encore Infinity computer. This machine is a Distributed Shared Memory processor in which Memory Replication is gainfully employed to provide an almost seamless shared memory. A Memory Channel Adaptor (MCA) implements Reflected Memory Technology which facilitates the sharing of code/data segments between processors. RMS buses can be added as the number of General Computing Nodes increases, increasing bandwidth and enabling high scalability. Spinlocks are employed to maintain cache coherency. And a discussion explained how nodes which have crashed may be brought back into the system by the use of a Health Monitor which is a diagnostic system for this DSM machine.

Acknowledgments: The authors wish to thank Ms. Yoon Kimn - a recent CCNY Computer Science graduate. for her tireless efforts in the preparation of this manuscript.

6. References

[1] A. Leff and C. Pu, "A classification of Transaction Processing Systems", IEEE Computer, Aug. 1991.
[2] M. T. Ozsu and P. Valduriez, "Distributed Database Systems: Where Are We Now?" IEEE Computer, Aug. 1991.
[3]A. Trew and G. Wilson, *Past, Present, Parallel A Survey of Available Parallel Computing Systems*, Springer-Verlag, 1991.
[4] I. Gertner, S. Lucci, "Infinity-Encore's Shared-Memory Multiprocessors",Encore Computer Corporation Technical Report, 1993.
[5] B. Nitzberg and V. Lo, "Distributed Shared Memory: A Survey of Issues and Algorithms", IEEE Computer, Aug. 1991, pp. 52-60 .
[6] S.Thakkar, M. Dubois and A. Laundrie, "Scalable Shared-Memory Multiprocessor Architectures"Computer, June 1990, pp.71-74
[7] J. Hennessy et.al. , "The Stanford DASH Multiprocessor", IEEE Computer Magazine, vol. 25, No. 3, pp. 63-79, March 1992.
[8] D. James, A. Laundrie, S.Gjessing,G. Sohi, "Scalable Coherent Interface" IEEE Computer Magazine, June 1990, pp.74-77.

PENTIUM MPP FOR OLTP APPLICATIONS

Mark Natale, Mark Baker, Roger Collins, David Wilson
Encore Computer Corporation
6901 W.Sunrise Blvd
Ft.Lauderdale, FL 33313
and
Stephen Lucci, Izidor Gertner
Computer Science Department
City College, City University of New York
Convent Avenue and 138 Street
New York, New York 10031

Abstract

This paper describes a multi-Pentium architecture with a hierarchical memory and an I/O bus subsystem. On a board-level, this architecture achieves a very high-level of integration, by accommodating 8 Pentium processors with up to 2 Gigabytes of RAM. This hierarchical architecture has been extended to support multiple boards in a single cabinet as well as multiple cabinets connected via reflective memory.

1. INTRODUCTION

1.1 Motivation

Shared-memory multiprocessors are known for their relative ease of programming and their difficulty in scaling; distributed memory multiprocessors, on the other hand, are known for their ease in scaling and difficulty in programming. However, shared memory multiprocessors have problems in achieving high performance, due primarily to contention in accessing shared resources. Implementations of multiprocessors which are based on single or multiple buses do not scale well to large systems. The only practical way to implement a memory shared among a substantial number of CPUs is to split the memory up into numerous modules and provide multiple paths between the CPUs and the memories. This arrangement not only provides more bandwidth, but it also allows multiple requests to be handled in parallel.

During the 1980's companies were formed with charters to develop commercial shared -memory multiprocessors. At that time very few had the digital wherewithal to support an SMP architecture. Standard CPUs were used to build SMP systems.

On the other hand, parallelizing compilers and programming techniques were developed to take advantage of SMP systems. However, most programs could not gainfully employ parallel processing primitives since many programs (especially those written in Fortran) were hand optimized. The operating system could schedule user processes over multiple processors and manage all system resources by load balancing. Good programming practice was to minimize the use of shared variables, so as to achieve better performance.

The landscape today is very different. There is greater computational prowess in a present day processor than there was in an entire SMP system of just a few short years ago. Parallelizing several processors will quickly strain bus bandwidth and any gains from large scale SMP would soon be lost due to system overhead, and of course, bus and memory saturation. Hence gigabyte bus structures to handle this traffic from high powered CPUs becomes a necessity.

Today's SMP systems are supported on the chip level. The advent of a new Pentium processor completely changes multiprocessor system design. The Pentium has its own private cache and memory bus, which can sustain high data rates. The bus is decoupled from the I/O bus so that memory bandwidth suffers no degradation from other CPUs in the system.

To efficiently support large OLTP applications, SMP systems require modification [1]. The issue is that OLTP applications are heavy-weight processes with a large working set site which are extremely inefficient in process switching. (This is because it takes a long time to load CPU caches to run an OLTP program). On SMP systems, these limitations have been side stepped by implementing and using Process affinity. Process affinity binds a process to a specified CPU. This allows heavy-weight OLTP processes to run efficiently the next time they are scheduled to run on the same CPU.

On the other hand, process affinity appears to be a paradox on SMP systems which have been designed for symmetric process scheduling.

The Pentium-architecture described in this paper attempts to capitalize on the requirement of supporting process affinity. It goes one step further by providing multiple computers and operating systems to support individual OLTP processes that are permanently bound to the same CPU. Inter-process communication facilities which are required by OLTP applications are implemented as an additional package, which runs on top of shared memory. This provides a programmer with additional motivation to explicitly manage shared memory. Some memory, for example, the program stack, is allocated on a CPU private memory that is cached; while other memory pools such as the inter-process communication mechanism is allocated in shared non-cached memory. (As opposed to SMP machines which share everything. This sometimes results in a long sequence of CPU cache flushes for the purpose of synchronization).

1.2 Related Work

There are numerous ongoing research projects whose goal is to bridge this gap, and produce a large scalable general-purpose multiprocessor which at the same time is easy to program. One approach employed in DASH - a Stanford-based project is to use a directory to provide scalable services on a shared-memory multiprocessor; another approach - the one taken by NCUBE - is to provide better programming support on distributed memory multiprocessors. The DASH experimental system (directory architecture for shared memory), is being built at Stanford in which memory is distributed among processor nodes, and a scalable bandwidth network is used to communicate between them.

The goal of developing a scalable shared-memory multiprocessor has also sparked interest in industry. There have been several commercial machines such as the Kendall Square Research KSR-1, the Cray T3D, the Convex SPP, and Encore's Gigamax. These machines could all be classified as hardware-intensive approaches to building scalable shared-memory multiprocessors. Experience with these systems shows that it's exceedingly difficult to demonstrate the benefits of a massively parallel system that employs advanced CPU technology. (Advances in CPU technology are made every few months, whereas it takes much longer than this to design a scalable bus.)

Encore has accepted this challenge. It has attempted to design an "open" system, one which can take advantage of the latest CPU, memory, and cache technology advances, and still provides a massively parallel computer. The multi-Pentium computer described in this paper is the 2-nd generation of Encore's Infinity family of computers which all take advantage of a Reflective Memory Subsystem (RMS).

2. Pentium-MPP

2.1. Infinity System Overview

In this paper we describe Infinity, a Reflective Memory Based multiprocessor that has been configured to provide scalable on-line transaction processing and file system services. Only those services which are absolutely essential to provide efficient shared data access services are supported in hardware. Other system services - those that do not require shared-access, employ the distributed memory model. In the Infinity, in particular, Reflective Memory is used to store control and data buffers which are shared by all of the users and storage devices in the system. This shared-view is preserved, despite the ever increasing demand for more users and more disk storage. This is made possible by carefully configuring a special system, and by utilizing n-dimensional buses to support the increased demand for bandwidth.

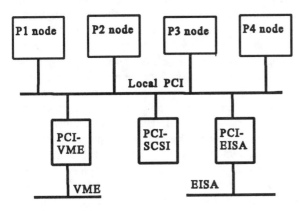

Figure 1. Multi-Pentium Board.

Three-ported memory modules at each CPU node are instrumental to the implementation of a Reflected Memory System. Memory Channels are used to communicate between these memory modules. The Memory Channel Adaptor (MCA) serves as a mediator for intercluster communication. Remote data is accessed in remote write-through caches and is handled automatically without CPU intervention. MCAs serve as "deep buffers" to disk units, so that disk reads and writes are handled at almost memory-to-memory transfer rates.

Infinity is a new shared memory scalable multiprocessor. It consists of a set of multiple General Purpose Computing Nodes (GPC) and Storage Nodes, which are connected by Memory Channels and treated as a single computing system. It is designed to satisfy intensive On-Line-Transaction-Processing (OLTP) and general purpose computing as well .

The heightened scalability and performance is achieved by having several Memory Channels, which are based on Reflected Memory Technology, and are used to communicate between GPC and Intelligent Storage Nodes. The Infinity system provides a broad scalability range - from just a few nodes up to a thousand or more. This is made possible by multiple high speed Memory Channels associated with each node. The operation rate of each Memory Channel is comparable to that of regular

memory logic, and therefore transfers to/from memory or Memory Channels are at memory speeds.

2.2. Pentium Board Description

The main CPU consists of a 9U VME board with four Pentium processor sockets per board. Each of the processors uses the Intel Peripheral Component Interconnect (PCI) chipset which provides three hierarchical levels of buses:

1. Host Bus as an execution bus:

    a. 64-bit data path

    b. 32-bit address bus with address pipelining

    c. both first and second level caches

    d. supports concurrency with the PCI and memory subsystems

2. PCI bus as a primary I/O bus

    a. 32 bit address/data path

    b. 132 Mbytes/sec bandwidth

3. EISA bus as a secondary I/O bus

    a. 32-bit addressing with 32-bit data path

    b. 33 Mbytes/sec bandwidth

This bus hierarchy supports concurrency for simultaneous operations on all three buses. Extensive data buffering for Host-to-PCI, PCI-to-main memory, Host-to- main memory, and PCI-to-EISA communications permits concurrency of operations on all three system buses.

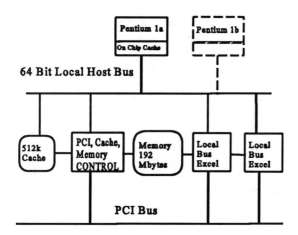

Figure 2. Pentium Node Architecture

There are two separate caches in the Host system. The Pentium processor contains on its chip, first level cache, and external to it is a 512Kbyte secondary cache. The snooping mechanism in the controller ensures data consistency between first and second level caches, and main memory. The snoop mechanism guarantees data consistency between the Host CPU and the PCI.

Local main memory of 192Mbytes and a secondary cache are located on the Host bus. Thus, each processor uses its private Host Bus to communicate between its memory, secondary cache, and PCI interface.

To increase the computational power, Dual Pentium Processor Modules can be used in each processor socket, resulting in an eight Pentium System board. In this case, each processor pair has a 512k shared cache, and 512 Mbytes of local memory.

This configuration enables the system, if desired, to run four independent operating systems. The four processors communicate via the on-board, local PCI bus. The corresponding bridges from this local bus provide the interface to the EISA Bus, VME64, PCI Backplane, and SCSI/E-net. Thus I/O is independent of the main processors' operations.

3. Memory Organization

Each processor is equipped with primary on the chip and secondary caches as well. These caches maintain full coherency between themselves, the processor and local memory. In the two processor implementations which are used, secondary cache and local main memory are shared . This is the only type of memory coherence

maintained in the system. The second level cache is configured for a write-through caching policy. If the write cycle hits the cache, both the cache and main memory are updated. Upon a cache miss, only main memory is updated. A new cache line is not allocated for cache misses. In the case of a cache read, upon a cache hit, data is transferred from cache. If the read cycle causes a cache miss, the line containing the requested data is transferred from the main memory to the processor and to the cache. Only the local processor is allowed to snoop the Host bus, it is not snooped by a remote processor. There is no caching for any remote memory, i.e., all four processor nodes use a remotely non-cached memory. Therefore, a traditional symmetric multiprocessor OS is impractical, as attempts to use primarily local pages by each remote processor, makes process migration expensive, and does not expedite access to shared kernel data structures. In spite of this drawback, such an architecture has no cache traffic overhead on the local PCI bus. The architecture rewards locality, and penalizes excessive remote memory accesses. To capitailize on this, a separate copy of the OS for each processor or a pair of processors is used. The only local PCI bus traffic comes from high-level communication and synchronization primitives.

So far we have discussed how memory is allocated for each processor. In fact all system memory could be viewed as divided into 4 parts, and each assigned to a different computer. However, the same memory is accessible globally via the PCI bus as well. On each computer, part of memory is allocated to provide consistent access to non-cached shared memory. The implementation is described below. Processors accessing remote memory must store the id of the remote processor in the leading nibble of the requested address. When the request is passed to the remote processor's Host bus, the leading nibble is cleared and the request is made, as though it were local to that processor's memory. Accesses to local memory must be made with the leading nibble cleared.

The hardware requirement that processors making a remote memory access, must include the id of the remote processor, has some high-level implications. Due to this constraint, the processors cannot share a common set of page tables, as the local processor has a different view of its local memory than a remote processor. In addition, a remote processor cannot dereference pointers within remote memory, since they would resolve to local, rather than remote addresses. The solution is to designate a portion of local memory to be shared. All processors mark this area as cache disabled, and all of them map it in at the same virtual address. Although the page tables for the shared area will differ between local and remote processors, dereferencing of pointers within the shared area *will* be correct. This allows processors to share complex data structures within the shared memory.

4. UNIX Enhancements

This section describes UNIX enhancements that have been implemented to support the multiple Pentium architecture.

This section consists of three parts: the first of which describes low-level support for booting and running a multi-computer/multi-UNIX system; the second part describes the shared-memory extensions to the multi-computer model; and the third section describes UNIX service extensions that are based on the shared memory model. These extensions include an extremely efficient RPC service that is used to build fault-tolerant and scalable file system and communication system services.

We also describe how these shared-memory extensions are used to provide other services that make the system appear to the user as a single UNIX system. due to the distributed nature of the architecture, we use the term "nodes" and "processors" interchangeably.

4.1 Low-Level Support

While it is convenient to boot a separate UNIX copy on each processor, doing so, over the same console port presents a problem. The solution was to provide two serial ports. The first port is shared for all the CPUs on a single board, while the second one is used for debugging. The shared console is implemented for two modes of operation: ROM monitor level and OS level. At the ROM level, multiprocessing is not required. The ROM-level console uses a simple design which passes a token between processors. The processor holding the token controls the serial port; all other processors spin. The token is passed by a command sequence on the console keyboard.

At the OS-level, a new STREAMS module is pushed onto the console stream head. This module directs console I/O to/from a network console port. If the processor has the serial console token (same token used by the ROM level), the module also directs console I/O to/from the serial port. Use of the serial console token allows processors to coexist while

running either the ROM monitor or the OS. This architecture had produced another problem of bootstrapping distributed OS's on a single board. The root disk is controlled by one processor, the root server. This root server is bootstrapped by the ROM monitor. Then a user level boot program on the root server uses /dev/mem to load the OS images for the client processors and to clear a flag for each processor which notifies each to start booting.

4.2 Shared Memory and Global Processes

This subsection describes support for shared-memory and global processes that provide inter-processor communication primitives on the board. These primitives provide conventional UNIX system calls that have been extended with the global memory and process identifiers. A key aspect of the multi-Pentium architecture is its flexible configuration of shared memory. All processors on a board can access all memory on the board, cached or uncached. One portion of this memory is mapped in broadcast mode (which can also be used for reflective memory), by all processors, at the same kernel virtual address range. This region is mapped uncached to provide a consistent shared memory between all processors.

Each distributed service is allocated its portion of this broadcast memory. Such services include system services like the RPC facility, the health monitor (for failover/recovery of redundant services), file system (IFS), networking, global processes, and application-specific services like Oracle Distributed Lock Manager (DLM). Appendix A contains a sample memory configuration file (/etc/memcf). This file statically maps regions of broadcast memory for distributed services, and specifies permissions for each region.

4.2.1 System V IPC Shared-Memory Primitives

The goal of this service is to achieve the semantics of UNIX shared memory calls on the multi-Pentium. A fixed number of the system wide shared memory identifiers is reserved for the global shared memory. The system file specifies the maximum number of allowed global shared memory identifiers. The Shared_Memory_Get system call sets a flag that requests a Shared Memory Id. The node that initially requests allocation of a global shared memory block is called an "initiator". If the global shared memory for the amount requested is available, the node gets the first unused global shared memory structure and sets up all the permissions. The global shared memory is allocated and setup for the allocated region. The "initiator" is an important entity. For multiple nodes to communicate using a shared memory page, the nodes have to negotiate on an address and map that page to this address. For shared memory, each of the addresses needed for each page is allocated from the initiator's pool. Each global shared memory structure has a page (also in the BROADCAST area) where the addresses are stored. For example, a shared memory page can hold 2048 addresses which can be used for up to (2048 * 8k) = 16 Megabytes. This is not a hard limit , since we can increase the storage space to more than two pages. This is different from the regular `shared memory get` which only allocates the region and waits until the first shared memory attaches to actually allocate virtual memory. In the multi-Pentium architecture, we need to be sure that we have memory to back a shared memory segment. So, we back the region with physical pages during the shmget call. When a node performs get global shared memory on an existing key, a new region is allocated (if it has not already been allocated for the node) if there is sufficient memory for the size required. A node could also do an attach global shared memory call on a global shared memory ID, passed on from a different node, and the new region and memory gets allocated in the shmat call in this case.

4.2.2 Global Processes

The goal of global process IDs (global pids) is to allow system functions like kill (send a signal to a process) and ps (list processes) to work system-wide. In both the Encore 91 Series and the new multi-Pentium, the same approach is taken. Each processor is configured with a subsystem ID. That ID is encoded in the high order 16 bits of the 32 bit process id. The `fork()` system call, assures that process ids conform to this convention. The design of the `kill()` system call is straight-forward. If the target process id's node id matches the local processor, do a normal `kill()`. If the process id is remote, send a synchronous RPC to execute the normal `kill()` on the remote processor. The `ps` command, lists all processes system wide by default. A new option (-X) presents the pid in hex so the node id is obvious. The Infinity architecture takes a minimalist approach to process migration. One system call, `rexec()`, is provided to execute an image on a different node.

In the UNIX kernel, the global process IDs are interpreted internally by the following structure:

```
typedef int pid_t;

union process_id {
  struct global_pid {
    short systemid;
    ushort local_pid;
  } gpid;
  pid_t pid;
}
```

The running processes see a unique pid (of type pid_t) on all UNIX kernels. However, any action on the processes are intercepted such that if

```
if(process_id.gpid.systemid!=LocalID)
```

then an RPC is sent to the appropriate systemid with the RPC specifying the action to be executed on the remote node.

The `user_id` and `group_id` of the process attempting to communicate with the remote process is also packaged into the RPC. The server on the destination node picks up the RPC, determines if the function to be executed on he target process is valid (for example permissions, etc), and then executes the function on the remote node on behalf of the original process.

4.3 UNIX High-Level Services

This subsection describes Remote Procedure Calls (RPC), file system. networking and single system view administration services, all of which are built on top of the shared-memory and global process model.

4.3.1 Remote Procedure Calls

This section briefly describes a very efficient, memory-based remote procedure call (RPC) mechanism that has been used to support file system and other system services.

On the client, an RPC structure is set with the call identifier, arguments, and other system information (e.g., credentials). The RPC is then "sent" by being placed on a client to the server queue. On the server, an RPC daemon executes the remote procedure call. The server does not remove the RPC from the queue. It simply marks in memory, that the call is complete so the client can garbage collect the RPCs without taking global locks. If a reply is requested (the usual case), the server sends it in much the same way as it received the request.

The RPC implementation philosophy is flexibile - provide the programmer with an array of options in buffer management and process scheduling. In buffer management, the programmer has the option of either coping a large buffer (i.e. greater than 128 bytes) or of refering to the identifier of the buffer stored in shared memory. For example, in the case where the buffer is accessed often by a remote procedure, the remote procedure might then copy it to cached memory. In other cases , it is better to use the buffer in uncached memory (e.g., data that is just being routed to some I/O controller).

In process scheduling, the programmer is given the option of spinning (flag=RPC_SPIN) for short requests (typically under 100 microseconds) or invoking the UNIX scheduler to sleep until a reply is issued. Another option is to not wait for a reply (flag=RPC_ASYNC). This shared memory which is based on the RPC mechanism, is very efficient and has been measured to produce 20,000 RPC/sec ,each carrying 1K of data. Based on this very efficient RPC mechanism, the philosophy for high-level services is to offload client computations to the server. Since it takes less time to offload the work, than to actually do it on the client, scalability is achieved.

4.3.2 File System

The file system is the Infinity File System (IFS), a shared-memory based, distributed file system. IFS has been used on various Encore architectures, under UNIX System V Release 3, UNIX SVR4.2 and OSF/1. The virtual file system interface of SVR4.2, and the shared-memory RPC facility make porting of IFS a straight-forward task. Each vnode operation uses an RPC to execute the same operation on the appropriate file server processor.

An important property of this file system is cache consistency. Unlike many distributed file systems , for example, NFS, IFS caches only on the server. This approach is feasible because of the very efficient RPC mechanism. Because RPCs communicate at near memory speeds, server cache hits provide almost the same advantage as client cache hits. In addition, database programs such as Oracle already implement their own caching and do not need (in fact cannot work correctly to support transactions) yet another level of cache on the same node.

4.3.3 Networking

The multi-Pentium architecture also uses a client/server model to distribute network controller services. The multi-Pentium uses Ethernet for its networking, with either an EISA or VME controller, or an onboard Ethernet chip.

Shared Ethernet is implemented via distributed streams. Outgoing packets from the server processor travel down the stream to the network controller in normal fashion. Outgoing packets from client processors are sent to the server via RPC, and passed down to the controller. As processors establish connections, they are issued dynamically allocated IP port numbers. This allows a packet received by the server to be routed to the correct processor. When a packet is received, the IP module on the server, checks the destination port number. If the packet is intended for the server, the packet is passed up the stream. If the packet is meant for a client, then the packet is sent to the correct processor via an RPC. The client receives the packet in its IP module and passes it up the stream.

5. Conclusions

Infinity is a hybrid multiprocessor that combines properties of both distributed and shared memory multiprocessors. A separate copy of the UNIX kernel is running on each node as in a distributed-memory multiprocessor, whereas a portion of the OS primitives is shared among all nodes as in a shared-memory multiprocessor. The shared OS primitives include inter-process communication mechanisms, a shared file system, and other shared system resources. Implementation of these shared OS primitives relies on shared data structures that must be consistently reflected on all nodes. Software guarantees consistency of the data structures which are based on hardware-supported shared memory reflections.

Acknowledgments: The authors wish to thank Ms. Yoon Kimn - a recent CCNY Computer Science graduate. for her tireless efforts in the preparation of this manuscript.

6. References

[1] Goetz Graefe and Shreekant Thakkar.
"Tuning a Parallel Database Algorithm on a
Shared-Memory Multiprocessor", Software-Practice
and Experience, Vol.2(7), July, 1992.

[2] Gray and A. Reuter.
"Transaction Processing Concepts and Techniques",
Morgan Kaufman Publishers, Inc. 1993.

[3] Zajcew, O.Roy, D. Black and et. al.
"An OSF/1 UNIX for Massively Parallel
Multicomputer", 1993 Winter USENIX,
Jan 25-29, 1993, San Diego, CA.

[4] "Transaction Processing Performance Council",
TPC Quarterly, p.1112, San Jose, CA.

[5] A.W. Wilson Jr.
"Hierarchical cache/bus architecture for shared memory
multiprocessors",
Proceedings of the 14th Annual International
Symposium on Computer Architecture, June, 1987.

[6] J. Hennessey.
"The directory-based cache coherence protocol for the
DASH multiprocessor",
Proceedings of the 17th Annual International
Symposium on Computer architecture, pp.148-159,
May 1990.

[7] D. Cheriton, H. Goosem, and P.Boyle.
"Paradigm:A Highly Scalable Shared-Memory
Multicomputer Architecture", IEEE Computer, 24(2),
pp.33-46, February,1991.

Appendix A

Excerpt from an `/etc/memcf` file which specifies broadcast memory regions for distributed services.

#	start windows	perms	net	owner	group	usage
0	1	0000	0	root	sys	mbox–interrupt
1	1	0644	0	oracle	sys	scnd
2	1	0644	0	root	sys	health monitor
3	25	0644	0	root	sys	kernel
28	256	0644	0	root	sys	ifs_rpc
284	65	0666	0	root	sys	dali
349	2	0666	0	root	sys	loopback
351	600	0640	1	oracle	dba	dlm

mailbox–interrupts are used for exceptional conditions
scnd– system commit number for Oracle– monotonically
increasing transcation id. health–monitor– heart beat data
structures for monitoring the wealness of system
kernel– UNIX shmat control, preallocated shared–memory
identifiers ifs_rpc– static area for RPCs.
dali– shared data structures for UniKix. loopback– control
structures to hold spinlocks dlm– Distributed Lock Manager;
note a different network.

Fault-Tolerant Disk Storage and File Systems Using Reflective Memory

Nicos Vekiarides
Department of Electrical and Computer Engineering[1]
Carnegie Mellon University
Pittsburgh, PA 15213

Abstract

Most replicated storage and file systems either take a specialized hardware approach or a software-oriented approach to fault tolerance. This paper describes a fault-tolerant disk storage and file system that falls in between the hardware and software categories. The system uses Reflective Memory to interconnect an array of standard computers comprising a massively parallel system. This architecture provides the basis for high-availability replicated file and storage systems with the performance and low overhead expected from specialized hardware while offering the modularity and scalability of a distributed system. In this paper, we describe the implementation of the fault-tolerant file and storage system to run large scale I/O-intensive applications, such as emulation of a stable storage DASD subsystem. Preliminary performance measurements indicate that selectively broadcasting regions of Reflective Memory allows for virtually no overhead over conventional systems for supporting replicated, distributed storage and file services.

1. Introduction

Most existing fault tolerant systems may be categorized as either hardware solutions that rely on redundant logic, lock stepped hardware, and specialized power supplies, or software solutions that rely on standard network protocols or clustering techniques. Both approaches have their shortcomings: the hardware approaches tend to fall behind the technology curve and become obsolete very quickly; software approaches tend to incur high overhead and are often limited by the speed of the network interconnect. Often, neither approach is able to offer high performance for I/O-intensive applications such as on-line transaction processing (OLTP).

Studies indicate that hardware faults are a minor cause of down time in OLTP systems [6]. Much of the time spent off-line can be attributed to other reasons such as:

- Power or other environment-related failures
- Software failures, upgrades or repairs
- Data reorganization
- Failures due to operator error

Most solutions are not sufficient to address all of these issues and provide adequate performance for OLTP applications. While power failures can be addressed through specialized power supplies, they do not provide disaster recovery. Hardware or software upgrades and repairs require a modularity allowing some hardware or software subsystems to be taken off-line, upgraded and brought back on-line transparently. Data reorganization, which involves redistributing data among storage devices or migrating data to new devices, has been supported by proprietary mainframes for many years [4]. Yet this capability is lacking from many of today's open systems. Failures due to operator error are difficult to address through hardware and software fault-tolerance, since such errors are not always possible to detect. Yet the prevention of and recovery from operator error are essential to any mission-critical system.

1.1 Motivation

The goal of the Reflective Memory approach described in this paper is to provide a high performance alternative to current fault-tolerant systems that is able to address the common causes of down time in OLTP system. Architecturally, this approach falls somewhere between the hardware and software categories: rather than specialized hardware, it uses standard hardware and software components to implement individual subsystems of an massively parallel processor (MPP); for performance and throughput, it uses a high-bandwidth Reflective Memory bus to interconnect the subsystems; for ease of integration, it uses standard memory interface as the basic communication mechanism.

Reflective Memory allows selected memory regions to be reflected or shadowed between two or more subsys-

---

[1] This research has been supported by Encore Computer Corporation, 6901 W. Sunrise Blvd, Ft. Lauderdale, FL 33313.

tems comprising the MPP. This hardware-assisted memory reflection provides a fault-tolerant and persistent global shared memory mechanism; a subsystem can be individually removed or added while maintaining a globally consistent view of the shared-memory region and without disrupting memory accesses and updates already in progress from other subsystems.

The capability to dynamically remove, repair, and return subsystems of an MPP to service transparently, combined with the advantages of standard software that uses shared-memory as a basic communication mechanism has helped to implement a fault-tolerant file and storage system with very promising features:

- virtually no performance overhead for maintaining replicated storage and file systems

- on-line maintenance and software upgrades, where individual MPP subsystems can be removed or added without disrupting the remainder of the system

- disaster recovery capability allowing a single configuration to span several buildings

- on-line data reorganization and migration to maintain high utilization and efficiency

- efficient switchover between failed nodes (less than 1 second for detection and failover)

- on-line automated recovery and reconfiguration to reduce the possibility of operator error

These features have been implemented on the Encore Infinity 90 and have been used to run a non-stop IBM DASD [7] emulation application [13]. Preliminary experience and performance measurements indicate that Reflective Memory is a very efficient interconnect for building massively parallel fault-tolerant systems.

In the remainder of the paper, we compare Infinity to other fault-tolerant systems, highlight key design decisions and describe the user interface, enumerating the different configuration alternatives. We continue by describing the design, presenting an analysis of the algorithms used to implement mirroring services. Finally, we summarize our experiences with DASD emulation that has been shown to survive node failures and utilize on-line recovery in a manner transparent to the end user.

1.2 Overview

This paper describes a fault-tolerant disk storage and file system on the Infinity, a Reflective Memory-based MPP. Infinity is built from "off-the-shelf" nodes, each an independent computer with its own memory and power-supply, interconnected via the Reflective Mem-

ory System. Following an installation, certain memory areas are maintained consistent across all nodes. In these areas, an update by one subsystem is immediately visible across the entire MPP.

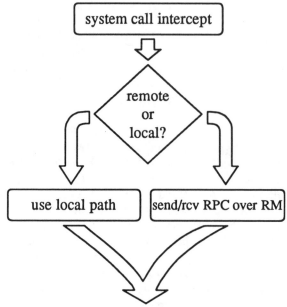

Figure 1: System Call Intercept

Fault-tolerance is based on the full or selective replication of a file system on at least two distinct subsystems called Input/Output Caching Controllers that, in conjunction with transaction processing systems, provide both a hardware and software fault-tolerant environment (transaction processing using system pairs results in software fault-tolerance [5]). Input/Output controllers run a standard UNIX operating system and provide cached file system or disk services on top of a massive array of disk controllers, drives and tape backup devices. User programs run on a distinct set of computing subsystems or a mainframe. These computing subsystems or nodes may also run a standard UNIX operating system and, although they may support a local file system, they maintain little state and offload most of the file-system work to the Input/Output controller. The computing node essentially performs only a routing function: as illustrated in Figure 1, it intercepts a system call, determines its destination, forwards the call to the appropriate controller which executes the file system task and returns the result.

Differently from network operating systems that may incur overhead in handling client/server protocols and associated data copying, Infinity relies on the "zero-protocol", shared memory-based communication that adds virtually no overhead to file system calls performed on the Input/Output controller. More importantly, it avoids data copying, a typical bottleneck in many UNIX file system implementations, by utilizing memory mapping: a dynamic configuration capability allowing blocks of memory to be either in private mode (mapped into a single program's address space) or in reflective mode (mapped into the network shared memory space). Combining the dynamic mapping capability with extremely efficient Remote Procedure Call (RPC) mechanism, the controllers act as an intelligent DMA engine capable of executing disk transfers directly into the user address space, without intervention from the operating system or user program. Figure 2 illustrates this memory-mapped I/O.

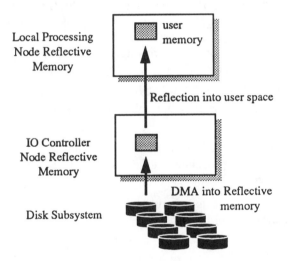

Figure 2: Memory-mapped I/O

The dynamic memory management capability has been used to implement a mirrored, almost no overhead fault-tolerant file and storage system that is the subject of this paper. Dependent upon configuration, a file system call may be forwarded to either one I/O controller or pair of replicated controllers. It is transparent to the end user program whether a write request is issued to one or two I/O controllers.

The controller replication is enabled by a mount command option that can be individually selected by the system administrator: some critical file systems may be replicated; others, to save memory and/or disk space, are not replicated. The flexibility to configure mirroring at mount time allows the same set of controllers to be used for both load balancing and replication. It is the decision of the system administrator whether or not to specify mirroring when installing a new file system.

In this paper we describe the implementation and experiences using the fault-tolerant file system to run large scale I/O-intensive applications. Since the fault tolerance is application transparent, no modifications were made to the applications. The overhead for maintaining fully replicated disk services has been measured to be less than 5%. The overhead of maintaining replicated caching for dual-hosted disk subsystems has been measured to be negligible due to the broadcast capability of Reflective Memory. The delay in switchover, in case of a controller failure, is unnoticeable (less than 1 second). On-line repair times depend on the type of failure. In the case of a disk media failure, replacing a disk and resynchronizing takes about 30 minutes depending on the disk capacity and bandwidth. In the case of a controller failure, recovery is proportional to the amount of time a controller has been out of service and the amount of updates occurring in that time period. The ceiling on this recovery time corresponds to the amount of time required to replicate all of the data on all of the disks using efficient parallel recovery algorithms.

1.3 Related Work

There is a wide spectrum of design alternatives in building fault-tolerant systems. At one extreme, hardware-oriented approaches are based on special-purpose, lock-stepped replicated hardware; at the other extreme, software approaches rely on routing and replication across a network to provide high-availability service to users. Infinity's architecture does not strictly follow either of the above categories.

Infinity is also different from the existing massively parallel computers, such as nCUBE [4] or Paragon [8], that support multiprocessing but fail to provide the shared-memory abstraction for their interconnects. In addition, many of those systems lack even rudimentary support for nodes being able to enter or exit the configuration without taking the entire system off line [17]. In contrast, Infinity's hardware and software allow any node to enter or exit the configuration without rebooting, atomically updating an entering node's state in Reflective Memory.

Infinity is not an "ultracomputer" in the quest for the Teraflops Supercomputer [3]. Instead, Infinity strives towards scaleable, fault-tolerant and massively parallel input/output processing [1] [12] [16]. From the user perspective, Infinity appears similar to the emerging "open-cluster" computers that are used for on-line transaction processing [13] [14].

Many of the "open cluster" computers use RAIDs [11] and dual-hosted or multi-hosted disk storage systems to increase reliability. IBM's AIX High Availability 6000 clusters utilize disk sharing between clustered workstations to provide higher availability [2]. Similarly, Infinity utilizes RAID technology and dual-hosted disks. Most such clustered systems, however, rely on sophisticated lock managers to coordinate file access between nodes. Unlike these systems, Infinity does not require a distributed lock manager because it runs only one file system that is accessible from multiple nodes. It also goes a step further than RAID in disaster recovery by offering remote disk replication over a fiber optic Reflective Memory link allowing replicated I/O controllers to be as far as 3 kilometers apart.

Infinity is conceptually similar to a shared-memory MPP except that the actual memory is shared via its "dynamic reflection" capability; memory is accessed and modified at hardware speeds, on the order of nanoseconds. Shared-memory based software mechanisms provide inter-process coordination and synchronization. In this paper we describe the software mechanisms which provide fault-tolerant input/output processing.

From the fault-tolerant input/output perspective, Infinity is different from the low-level approaches such as RAID in that it provides high-level mirroring. High-level mirroring allows for an entire file system, including cache, to be replicated, resulting in more flexibility and better performance. Moreover, it supports any file system since the file system resides at a lower level. For replicated caching with dual-hosted disk subsystems, Infinity uses mirrored caching in Reflective Memory. For full replication, Infinity's Log-Ahead algorithms bear similarity to other algorithms such as HARP [9], though the actual implementation is simplified by the capabilities of Reflective Memory.

1.4 Design Objectives

The main objective of the Infinity is to provide fault-tolerant file system and disk storage service to processing nodes interconnected via Reflective Memory. The fault-tolerant configuration offers the following features and functionality:

- support for mirrored disks and RAIDs with a unified file system
- automated on-line recovery
- no data loss from buffer cache on failures
- no overhead for mirrored buffer cache
- small overhead (5% or less) for replicated file system operations
- full utilization of system hardware, no standby modules

- fiber optic connection up to 3 km for disaster recovery
- supports all file systems and disks with no modifications to underlying file system or disk driver code

Key aspects of the dual controller system are the minimal performance overhead it imposes over conventional file systems and the ability to repair and recover the system on line, restoring it to full capacity without bringing the entire system down. On line repair and recovery is possible through the modularity of the Infinity controller, allowing subsystems and components to be added and removed without affecting the entire system.

In addition to fault-tolerance, utilization of redundant hardware during normal mode of operation effectively increases system capacity for transactions. In particular, transactions that update are broadcast to parallel controllers without very little or no degradation in performance; read transactions are routed among those controllers for better load balancing and higher overall I/O capacity.

In order to meet the above design objectives and simplify the implementation, the following constraints have been assumed:

- Recovery addresses single point of failure only. We assume the probability of the same component failure on multiple systems is low.
- Reflective Memory is available (minimum of 1 megabyte) for logging purposes

The goal of this paper is not to provide a panacea for all possible system failures of a disk storage or file system. The aim is to demonstrate an efficient model for building scaleable, highly available systems based on Reflective Memory.

2. Fault-Tolerant Architecture

The essential elements of the storage and file system are a pair of Input/Output cache controller nodes interconnected via Reflective Memory. We first present a brief overview of Reflective Memory and look at the various configuration options.

2.1 Reflective Memory

The Reflective Memory bus is the backbone of the Infinity computer, capable of interconnecting multiple processing nodes (or nodes) with at least two Input/Output controller nodes (or controllers) [14]. Each Reflective Memory bus provides a peak throughput of 53-100 megabytes per second. The high bandwidth of the bus, combined with a simple shared memory-based

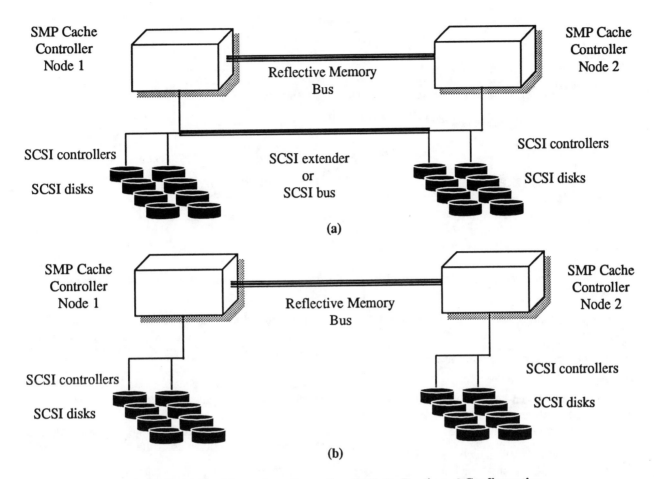

Figure 3: (a) Dual-hosted configuration (b) Fully Replicated Configuration

RPC, allows nodes to access the storage system residing on controllers at local speeds. A total of up to nine nodes and/or controllers can be configured to share Reflective Memory.

The actual Reflective Memory is a VME compatible board that contains 64 to 512 megabytes of memory to provide efficient coupling of processor nodes for time-critical applications. From an operating system point of view, it is an external memory board that is mapped in to an otherwise unused address range, with an access time of 75 nanoseconds. It behaves very similarly to a conventional memory board but allows memory updates to be selectively reflected across the Reflective Memory bus to other interconnected subsystems.

Although the Reflective Memory bus is a very high-bandwidth bus, it provides a reliable memory abstraction protected via parity checking. Network protocols with checksums are not necessary to ensure data integrity between communicating subsystems. Similarly, flow

control is provided by hardware, maintaining the shared memory abstraction without affecting the way software is written. Utilizing shared memory principles offers "zero protocol" communication between physical memories on separate machines [10].

To provide replication spanning separate buildings, Reflective Memory supports a fiber-optic link (FORMS) allowing the bus to span distances up to 3 kilometers. The capability to physically separate the subsystems of the MPP provides a basis for supporting disaster recovery [8].

2.2 Configuration Alternatives

One of the main design objectives is to provide a flexible, user definable fault-tolerant configuration. This section describes two configurations, both providing transparent support for failure recovery and controller reconfiguration without directly interrupting service on processing nodes. Each has a different level of avail-

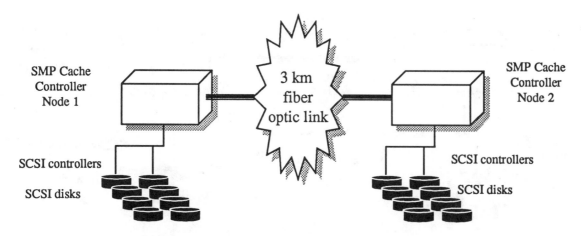

Figure 4: Fully replicated configuration using fiber-optic link

ability designed to meet the needs of various end applications:

- **dual-hosted configuration:** dual controller, single disk subsystem

- **fully replicated configuration:** dual controller, replicated disk subsystems

Figure 3 illustrates a dual-hosted configuration and the fully replicated configuration. Figure 4 shows a fully replicated configuration using FORMS.

Even the basic non-fault-tolerant configuration provides functionality to satisfy applications that cannot tolerate failures but can maintain pending I/O requests during the period of time a controller is down. This configuration emulates uninterruptible service by restoring all node state once a controller subsystem comes back up. File system caching maintained in non-volatile memory can be recovered following a failure. Since no error is returned to end application on the processing node, it may resume as if the failure never occurred.

Typical applications that take advantage of this configuration are automated applications, that do not impose the non-stop requirements of on-line transaction processing. If a controller failure is detected, all activity to that controller pauses, requests are kept pending and subsequently reissued once the controller is restored. This stop/start capability of the controller allows a controller subsystem to be taken down for repair or reconfiguration and restored, without having to restart the applications running on the processing nodes.

To enhance the reliability of the disk subsystem, mirrored disks or RAIDs may be used in conjunction with this configuration. Typically, on detection of a single disk failure, the controller subsystem can continue to

function with the mirrored disk and recovered on line with a new disk.

The dual controller, dual hosted disk mirroring subsystem steps up reliability offering true uninterruptible service in the case of a single controller subsystem failure. Upon failure, all activity to that controller is rerouted to a backup controller and resumes seconds later in a manner transparent to the end applications. With a dual-hosted disk subsystem, both controllers share the same disks, requiring no file system resynchronization once a failed controller has been restored.

Unlike most dual-hosted systems, Reflective Memory does not limit the maximum number of processing nodes in the system to the amount of hosts that can be configured to use the disk subsystem. Multiple processing nodes can share the same dual-hosted controller system over Reflective Memory.

The fully replicated dual controller, separate disk subsystem offers the highest level of availability, providing uninterruptible file system service and data replication on physically separate media. As in the previous dual controller case, a controller subsystem failure causes requests to that controller to be rerouted to a backup. However, after restoring a failed controller, its file system is resynchronized by executing redo logs maintained on the other controller while it was down. Resynchronization does not require either controller to be taken off-line, and, hence, occurs on-line, while updates are in progress from processing nodes.

In addition to on-line controller recovery, this system also offers on-line disk recovery. Similarly to a controller failure, requests for a failed disk are rerouted to the corresponding disk on the second controller transparently to the end application.

Table 1: Comparison of different levels of high availability controller

NODE	STORAGE	CONTROLLER HOT SWAP	DISK HOT SWAP	DISASTER RECOVERY
dual	single	yes	yes w/RAID	no
dual	replicated	yes	yes	yes

Meanwhile the system administrator may insert a new disk to replace the old one and initiate an on line recovery of the failed disk from the new disk.

"Hot swaps" of both disks and controller components are possible in this configuration with zero down time. For instance, a disk showing initial signs of failure such as multiple retries by the device driver can be replaced by a new disk and resynchronized on line.

The fully replicated configuration naturally provides a higher level of disaster recovery than do mirrored disk systems or disk arrays. Reflective memory may use a fiber optic link spanning up to 3 km. The dual controllers and disk subsystems could be located in separated rooms or even separate buildings using the fiber-optic link between the controllers.

2.3 DASD Configuration

In a DASD configuration, one or more Infinity controllers may be used to service mainframe requests. When two or more controllers are used, they comprise a fault-tolerant system that supports the following DASD functionality:

- dual-copy : disks may be mirrored between controllers over a fiber optic link

- concurrent copy : database snapshots can be backed up on line

- stable storage cached writes : I/O completes when it resides in Reflective Memory of two controllers

The DASD architecture, illustrated in Figure 5, allows a mainframe front end to communicate through its channel controllers and special MUX Channel boards. CKD simulation software allows emulation of 3380 type devices. This software is able to access the mirrored Infinity cache to issue I/O requests.

3. Implementation

To achieve mirroring, fault-tolerance and on-line recovery, the Infinity controllers make use of logging,

sequencing and global data structures to provide on-line resynchronization. This section describes, in detail, the algorithms used for fault detection and recovery.

3.1 Health Monitor

A key aspect of fault detection is a non-intrusive health monitoring that determines the status of the entire MPP from each node. Changes in this status can trigger recovery events in the health monitor to provide uninterruptible service.

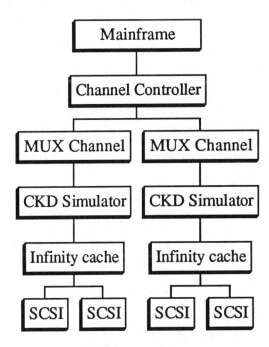

Figure 5: DASD Architecture

In brief, a global data structure is shared in Reflective Memory by all the nodes comprising the MPP. Each node is allocated a portion of this data structure in which it must increment a counter or "heart-beat". The status of other nodes can be monitored in their corresponding sections. The end result is the ability to detect node failures quickly so that requests can be rerouted to a back up node in a manner transparent to end application.

3.2 No-overhead Cache Replication

Using Reflective Memory, a replicated buffer cache can be maintained with no overhead over a conventional buffer cache. With the cache residing in Reflective Memory, all writes can be reflected to the cache memory on two controllers. On a dual-controller setup, the cache memory is able to survive any single point of failure on each controller.

Since each controller manages its own portion of cache memory, the mirrored controller need not do anything unless the other controller crashes, at which point it initiates recovery. Given that Reflective Memory imposes no overhead for broadcasting, there is no added latency associated with a replicated cache. No processing or bus cycles are lost in replication.

On a fully replicated disk setup, data needs to be flushed from the cache to a separate set of disks residing on separate controllers. In order to maintain consistent copies of both disks, a Primary Copy Log-Ahead mechanism is used on each controller. Before a buffer is flushed locally, the buffer descriptor and associated information are logged in memory and issued to the other controller. The buffer is then flushed locally. Once the remote controller returns completion, the buffer can then be replaced on the cache LRU for future use. If a controller fails, logs are kept on the active controller and replayed when the failed controller is restored. We describe this log-ahead algorithm in more detail in the following section.

Because of the asynchronous nature of writes to the cache, this logging does not introduce any added latency other than the logging of data in memory. To the end application, writes still complete asynchronously by virtue of residing in two controller memories.

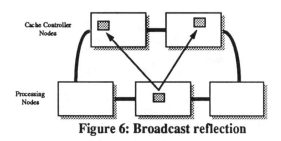

Figure 6: Broadcast reflection

3.3 File System Mirroring

The file system uses a Primary Copy Log-Ahead replication scheme where disks are replicated or shared on two controller subsystems. The disks are distributed in such a way so that one controller serves as a primary for half of the disks while the other controller is a secondary. All accesses that do not modify data occur only on the primary controller; updates of data occur on both the primary and secondary to maintain file system consistency. As shown in Figure 6 and mentioned previously, updates are broadcast to replicated controller nodes, introducing no added transmission latency.

The primary controller for a particular file system uses the Log-Ahead protocol to continuously log control data for each file system update using a circular buffer in Reflective Memory. Each log entry contains control data corresponding to a single disk update. The log-ahead protocol forces every update to enter the log before it is processed on either controller; this ensures that a record is kept of each change until both controllers acknowledge its completion.

A typical request to modify data is first logged on the primary controller's Reflective Memory, making it visible to the secondary controller; the request is then processed on the primary. Once the request completes on the primary, a completion is posted to the processing node (the end application), regardless of whether the secondary has also completed the request. When the request completes on the secondary, the secondary marks a status in the log and finally removes the log entry. Figure 7 demonstrates this log-ahead scheme.

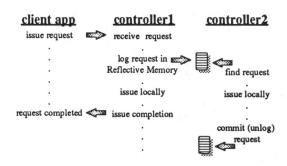

Figure 7: Log Ahead protocol

The log kept in Reflective Memory has four points used to ensure consistency. There is a log pointer (LP) indicating the next available log entry. A local commit point (LCP) indicates the last log entry which has been applied locally on this controller. A global commit point (GCP) indicates the last log entry that has been applied both locally and on the mirrored storage node. Finally the log base is the point below which log entries can be removed. Figure 8 indicates the points of the log.

Because of the asynchronous nature of updates between the replicated storage nodes, at any particular instant, the two controllers may be not be consistent between updates. To provide switchover upon failure that guarantees consistency between storage nodes, all requests for updates by the processing nodes are sequenced. Sequencing ensures that logs have been drained on the primary controller before the secondary replaces it. This scheme guarantees that the last update on the primary will always be accessible on the secondary.

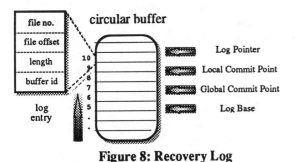

Figure 8: Recovery Log

Processing of all updates is guaranteed by the log-ahead protocol. If a secondary controller should go down and not receive an update, the log entry for that update will remain until it is reissued once the secondary is restored. Figure 9 illustrates the sequence of events following a controller failure.

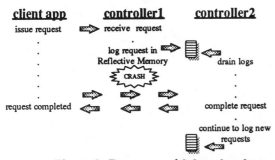

Figure 9: Recovery with log ahead

3.4 Recovery from Controller Failures

While a controller is down, its mirrored controller continues to log modifications in its circular log buffer. The size of the circular buffer is configurable; typically it may be configured to store up to 30 minutes of I/O updates for a moderately loaded system. Should the log buffer overflow, all affected disk subsystems must be copied and restored. As a rule of thumb, the log should be large enough to accommodate updates not exceeding the time it takes to copy each of the disks in parallel.

Assuming that the failed controller can be restored within a reasonable amount of time (less than the length of the log buffer), recovery occurs automatically with the active controller executing its recovery log; the log is drained while activity is still in progress to the active controller. If the time for recovery exceeds the length of the log buffer, a full disk subsystem on-line recovery is required. Ensuring a quick recovery period may involve slowing down incoming updates to a point that will not exceed the worst case recovery speed. This slowdown only occurs when recovery is in progress and adjusts dynamically depending on system load and log utilization.

Updates to a mirrored controller are asynchronous and may be issued very quickly. However, the logged updates only contain control data, and recovery involves local reads of data followed by remote writes. Since the remote cached writes complete asynchronously, local reads are sped up to keep pace. Batching reads, using a look-ahead technique on the log, achieves a speedup in recovery, minimizing resynchronization time.

Once recovery of a mirrored controller is complete, mirrored updates resume in the same fashion as before the failure. In addition, the recovered controller broadcasts a message to all of the other nodes in the cluster requesting that it be reinstated.

3.5 Recovery from Disk Failures and On-line Reconfiguration

When a disk failure is detected on one of the controllers under a fully replicated disk configuration, all I/O to that disk is rerouted to a backup controller, and a system message indicates the failure. The failed disk can then be "hot swapped" and recovered on-line. Once the disk is replaced, on line recovery may be initiated.

Unlike a recovery of an entire controller, where only logged modifications are required to be redone, the case of a disk failure generally requires cloning a new disk in its entirety. Since modifications to that disk could be in progress during the recovery period, the mirroring mechanism provides an "atomic update mode" for that mirrored disk pair (see Figure 10). This mode effectively ensures atomicity of updates to a particular disk across two controller subsystems while recovery is in progress. Using global device locking, a recovery process can resynchronize a new disk while updates are in progress.

When the new disk is fully cloned, the mirroring mechanism takes the disk out of "atomic update mode" and continues mirroring updates.

Highlights of the on-line recovery/reconfiguration include:

- Zero down time for single disk failures

- Can upgrade existing storage system on-line

- Can upgrade an Encore Infinity to a replicated Infinity on-line

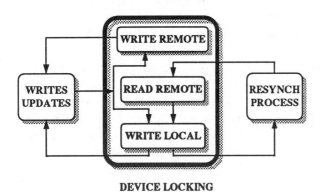

DEVICE LOCKING

Figure 10: Coordination to recover or migrate data on-line

4. Experience and Summary

The goal of the Infinity design has been to support an open, fault-tolerant architecture for massively parallel input/output services. The Infinity architecture accommodates standard hardware and software components. Although the interconnect is the proprietary Reflective Memory bus, the shared memory interface runs applications that range from standard OLTP applications to DASD emulation software.

Preliminary experience with the fault-tolerant DASD configuration has indicated that the Infinity is able to provide fault tolerance to high performance I/O-based applications. In a dual controller setup, controllers can be added or removed from the configuration without affecting the behavior of end applications. Each node has a separate power supply, Reflective Memory and cabling. These components can be repaired while the rest of the system remains on-line. Disks or RAIDs can be shared by the controllers or replicated. Replication may span a fiber-optic link so that critical information may be replicated in separate locations to provide disaster recovery.

This system comprises the first step in achieving a fault-tolerant hardware and software environment. It is a fault-tolerant system that survives single component failures. Beyond fault-tolerance, the modularity of the system supports on-line repairs, software upgrades and data reorganization.

The DASD configuration uses a replicated cache in Reflective Memory with the option to have critical disk storage fully replicated. To conserve memory, a portion of the cache is used for write updates that is visible to both controllers while the remainder is used as read cache. Since the read cache portion is not required for recovery, it is not replicated. With a fully replicated disk residing on dual controllers, it is important that each controller make modifications that go to stable storage. For this case, the log-ahead algorithm is used.

Performance testing on a prototype replicated cache only system showed that cache updates performed at the speed of the Reflective Memory bus, and, as expected, showed no added latency since only one controller manages its portion of the cache.

Table 2: Overhead of Replicated Updates

Update Type	End User Completion	Added Latency
Normal	complete I/O	-
Replicated Cache Only	complete I/O	none
Replicated Cache and Disks	log & complete I/O	less than 5%

For replicated cache and disk systems or replicated UNIX file systems, the log-ahead protocol adds a small amount of latency to each disk or file system update. There is no added synchronization between the controllers, but each replicated update involves logging recovery data in Reflective Memory. The recovery information varies depending on the type of update that is being processed. Typical disk updates may require as little as 16 bytes of log data. More complex file system calls may require slightly more.

Based on preliminary tests issuing replicated I/Os, this log-ahead protocol has shown a maximum of 5% added latency (Table 2). This is a conservative figure based on null I/Os. Actual I/Os make the added latency relatively smaller.

Infinity has also achieved the on-line recovery and reconfiguration goals by allowing an individual node to be taken off-line without affecting the rest of the configuration. This capability to reboot an individual node has been used not only to recover from CPU or memory failures but also to recover from software errors which often are followed by software upgrades. All of this has been done at run-time, without affecting the rest of the nodes. Furthermore, failures of the Infinity controller have been virtually unnoticed by Infinity users who have only experienced a slightly degraded response time due to the heavier load on the remaining controllers.

Failures of individual disks are also handled on-line. Having detected a failure of a disk, the operator replaces it with a new one and starts a disk-to-disk copy utility. This utility runs the disk in "atomic update" mode ensuring consistency of the primary disk and the secondary disk. Because recovery is synchronized with incoming updates, the elapsed time for getting the secondary disk back on line is not significantly delayed.

Overall, our experiences have indicated that flexibility is a main feature of the Infinity architecture, allowing configuration choices that best meet the needs of end applications. The goal has been to provide a massively parallel computer built out of standard components with clearly defined redundancy choices.

As a side effect of our development, we have learned that Reflective Memory when utilized as a shared-memory abstraction is a very powerful programming tool, able to significantly speed up the development cycle. Multiple Infinity nodes and controllers have been emulated on symmetric multiprocessors as UNIX processes having access to shared memory. Because Reflective Memory follows standard shared memory semantics, these emulations were subsequently moved into actual systems with little programming effort.

5. Conclusions

Reflective memory interconnected computers are well suited to building large scale fault-tolerant disk storage and file systems for I/O intensive applications. The modularity of both computational nodes and input/output controller nodes allows nodes to be removed or added to a Reflective Memory configuration without any down time in the remaining nodes. This modularity in a massively parallel architecture yields a very robust disk storage and file system. Preliminary experience with the system indicates that the broadcast capabilities of the Reflective Memory allow redundant operations, critical to achieving fault tolerance, to occur at speeds approaching conventional systems.

REFERENCES

[1] *AIM Performance Report*, AIM Technology, Santa Clara, CA 95054.

[2] *AIX High Availability Cluster Multi-Processing/6000*. International Business Machines Corporation, 1992.

[3] Bell. Ultracomputers, a Teraflop before its time, *Comm. of the ACM*, August, 1992.

[4] Erik DeBenedictis. *nCUBE Parallel I/O Software*, nCUBE Corporation, 1992.

[5] Gray and A. Reuter. *Transaction Processing Concepts and Techniques*, Morgan Kaufman Publishers, Inc., 1993.

[6] J. Gray and D. Sieworek. High-Availability Computer Systems, *IEEE Computer*, September, 1991.

[7] J. Hennesy and D. Patterson. *Computer Architecture A Quantative Approach*. Morgan Kaufman Publishers, Inc., 1990.

[8] *Intel Paragon XP/S Supercomputer Spec Sheet*. Intel Corporation.

[9] Liskov et. al. *Harp File System*, MIT Technical Report, 1992.

[10] *Memory Channel II*. Encore Computer Corporation, Publication no. 307-2468, 1994.

[11] D. Patterson, G. Gibson. *A Case for redundant arrays of inexpensive disks (RAID)*, University of California, Berkeley, 1988.

[12] Pieper. *Parallel I/O Systems for Multicomputers*, CMU-CS-89-143, June, 1989.

[13] Reese and K. Stukenborg. Implementing Highly Available Oracle Solutions, *Proc. International Oracle User Week*, October, 1993.

[14] Reflective Memory Patents, United States Patent, No.4,991,079, February 5, 1991. Continuation of No. 710,229, March 11, 1985.

[15] Slingwine, M. Sweiger. Node Recovery in the Sequent Distributed Lock Manager, *Journal of Open Systems*, Spring, 1993.

[16] Transaction Processing Performance Council, *TPC Quarterly*, San Jose, CA 1112-6311,

[17] Zajcew, O. Roy, D. Black and et. al. An OSF/1 UNIX for Massively Parallel Multicomputer, *1993 Winter USENIX*, January 25-29, 1993, San Diego, CA.

Application-Transparent Checkpointing in Mach 3.0/UX

Mark Russinovich and Zary Segall

Department of Computer and Information Science

University of Oregon

Eugene, Oregon 97403

Abstract

Checkpointing is perhaps the most explored of software based recovery techniques yet it has typically been developed only for special purpose or research oriented operating systems. This paper presents virtual memory checkpointing algorithms that have been designed for concurrent Unix applications using a hard disk as the stable storage medium. These algorithms can serve as the checkpointing support required on each node of a distributed computation made up of concurrent processes running on each node. Snapshot algorithm execution, during which the application is suspended, typically is less than 10 seconds. Checkpoint commit execution, during which system performance is degraded as a checkpoint is written to disk, is less than 45 seconds. The checkpoint dedicated disk storage requirement for the implemented system is less than 10MB. The implementation is based on the Mach 3.0/UX version of Unix 4.3BSD and uses Mach 3.0's external pager facility to back memory. .

1: Introduction

The ability to tolerate faults is an important characteristic of any system used in areas where data loss is costly in time or effort. If a fault occurs it is desirable to minimize the amount of computation that must be repeated as well as the amount of lost data. Perhaps the most popular of fault tolerance techniques is that of *checkpointing*. Periodically the entire state of an application or system is saved to stable storage. In the case of a fault, the system can be restored to a previously valid checkpointed state. With checkpointing in place, loss of computation and data can be reduced to that which is performed between checkpoints. If it is combined with the complementary technique of *journaling*, data and computation loss can be minimized further. In journaling, information about events between checkpoints is saved to stable storage so that the application's behavior up to the time of the fault can be precisely repeated, resulting in an identical state.

Another feature of checkpointing that has made it attractive as a fault tolerant technique is that it can be made *application-transparent*. This means that an application does not have to aware that it is being checkpointed or modified in any way to take advantage of checkpointing. It is by placing the checkpointing algorithms inside the operating system that this can be accomplished.

While there has been a great deal of research into checkpointing algorithms [2], [4], [5], [6], [7], [8], [10], [14], [16], [17], [18], it has primarily focused on methods to obtain consistent checkpoints in distributed systems. There is very little published on checkpointing implementation and performance. In [15], aspects of checkpointing in a modern operating system environment are described. Specifically, methods of optimizing virtual memory and disk checkpointing are presented. However, they were not implemented so there are no performance measurements.

In [2] there are performance measurements, but they are in the context of comparing two types of distributed recovery algorithms and are based on the misleading use of static object code sizes of Unix programs. While the programs had between 4 and 48 KB of static memory allocated. their dynamic memory usage is not analyzed. One i486 version of the X-window system server, for example, only has about 70 KB of static memory, but uses almost an order of magnitude more memory dynamically.

This paper presents the design of checkpointing algorithms for concurrent Unix programs. In addition, the algorithms have been implemented on a i486 processor using a hard disk as stable storage and performance measurements of the algorithm have been obtained for the popular X-window system [16] and some popular X-windows client programs. The measurements show that at the time of a checkpoint a user will typically encounter a 5-10 second pause in interactivity, followed by a 15-45 second period of degraded system responsiveness. Less than 10MB of dedicated disk storage is sufficient space to checkpoint even large sessions. These numbers are exciting in that they show that checkpointing with no special

This research has been supported by the Office of Naval Research under contract N00014-91-J-4139. The views and conclusions contained in this paper are those of the authors and should not be interpreted as representing the official policies, either expressed or implied, of ONR, the University of Oregon or the U. S. Government.

purpose hardware is a truly practical fault tolerant technique in the modern workstation environment.

2: System model

The computation model supported by the checkpointing algorithms is that of a concurrent Unix application. Application processes are descended from a common ancestor known as the *root*. In the current implementation application processes are allowed to communicate with each other via messages, or in Unix flavors, that support it, via shared memory. Application processes are not allowed to communicate with processes outside the process tree. If such interaction is desired then applications can be treated as *recovery units* [4] and a distributed checkpoint algorithm can be layered on top of the algorithms presented here.

In this model the application's state is divided among its virtual memory, disk and device usage. Disk state is the entire state of the disk at the time that a checkpoint is taken. This is an integral part of any modern workstation application, however, this paper presents virtual memory and device checkpointing results; disk checkpointing implementation and performance is the subject of a future paper.

Checkpoint interval, or time between successive checkpoints, is an issue that is also outside the scope of this paper. In most cases, the checkpoint interval will be dependent on factors such as the rate of user interaction, the occurrence of certain events, or, if journaling is used, the amount of stable storage space remaining as the journal grows. We assume that some appropriate interval control has been implemented.

The Mach 3.0 microkernel was used as the basis for this research, although the applications are restricted to using Unix services only, which are provided by the UX operating system server. UX is the Mach implementation of Unix 4.3BSD and details of the architecture of Mach 3.0 can be found in [1] and [13].

3: Checkpointing

The checkpointing process involves several problem areas which had to be addressed. First covered is the naming convention used to identify checkpoint files. Next, the process whereby virtual memory is checkpointed and the memory data organized is presented. Details of operating system checkpointing are then discussed followed by the snapshot and commit algorithms. Finally, issues related to device checkpointing and application recovery are reviewed.

3.1: Naming strategy

Naming refers to the naming convention that is used to identify files which pertain to different checkpoints. The approach taken is to organize all process related checkpoint files into one directory that is tagged with the application's root process identifier. For example: */ftback/mem.432/*. Device related files are also placed in a separate directory like */ftback/dev.432/*.

The strategy taken for individual checkpoint files is to add the process identifier the file is associated with to the name of the file, and add as a suffix the checkpoint interval. For example, the second checkpoint of the process control block of process 768 would have the name *proc.768.2*.

3.2: Memory checkpointing

Modern applications have become very memory intensive in comparison with the applications of just a few years ago. Applications such as X, which are made up of many processes, can have on the order of several megabytes of virtual memory in use at a given point in time. Saving the entire address space of each process at every checkpoint would be extremely inefficient. Fortunately, incremental checkpointing [35], a technique where only those parts of the system which have *changed* since the previous checkpoint are saved, can be used instead, substantially reducing disk space and performance impacts.

Mach 3.0 allows a process to use a pager that is external to the kernel to manage its memory. The checkpointing implementation relies on this feature by adding memory management to UX. Processes run with the checkpoint policy in effect using the UX pager to keep track of page modifications.

An implied checkpoint exists at the start of the application that consists of the disk checkpoint and command, parameters, and environment variables that started the application. After a process has started, the pager keeps track of any modifications on a page by page basis. At a checkpoint these modified pages are saved to stable storage. The checkpoint is complete, or *committed*, when all modifications have been saved and at that point the previous checkpoint can be deleted.

At the time of recovery, a process is loaded as it would be if it were started for the first time. Its address space is then allocated and copied from the checkpointed memory information. After this has been done for each process in the application, the entire memory space of the application has been restored.

The stable storage medium plays a role in determining how to organize the data that is checkpointed. In a disk based system like the one implemented, practicalities have to be faced. Ideally, a separate file would be dedicated to each page. Unfortunately, this is infeasible in the Unix file system. Consider an application that uses 6 megabytes of memory. In a typical system the virtual memory page size is 4 kilobytes. This would mean that during a checkpoint there would be 3072 files in the checkpoint directory (1536 files for the old checkpoint and 1536 files for the new checkpoint). Each file requires an *inode*, or special disk block, that provides a map of the file's data. Inodes are a limited resource in the Unix file system where only a fixed number exist. This fact, coupled with the fact that directory searches are linear, make 3072 files, or even 1536, impractical. Performance of operations on a directory with so many files becomes severely degraded and inodes become a scarce commodity.

To make disk based checkpointing practical, pages are divided up among a fixed number of files. In the system implemented, a process' pages are managed as a hash table. When a page is needed, the hashing function is applied to locate the appropriate bucket, and a linked list is traversed to find the requested page. This hash table maps perfectly to the file limit solution. For example, if the hash table has 25 entries, a process will create, at most, 25 files in a memory checkpoint. All the pages in a bucket are written to the bucket's page file. The number of files is then a function of the number of processes in the application, rather than the amount of memory used. If there are 10 processes, at most 250 files will be created.

When a page is modified, the entire list of pages in the modified page's hash bucket must be saved at the next checkpoint. This indicates that it is potentially advantageous to put spatially close pages in the same bucket. Then, if an application touches only a localized set of pages between checkpoints, the number of buckets that will have to be checkpointed will be minimized. The hashing function that achieves this is:

$$hashbucket = (pagenumber/\text{LOCALPAGES}) \bmod \text{NUMBUCKETS}$$

where the LOCALPAGES is the number of pages grouped together and NUMBUCKETS are the number of buckets in the hash table. If LOCALPAGES were 10, for instance, page 1 would map to bucket 0, as would pages 2-9. Page 10 would then map to bucket 1. Figure 1 shows an example hash table and the layout.

In addition to placing the pages on disk in easily identified files, it is also necessary to know which files belong with which checkpoint. Since incremental checkpointing is used, a page file from the first checkpoint may be the current file even after 6 checkpoints. If a failure occurred during a checkpoint, the recovery procedure would have to perform a search of the directory to find the most recent checkpoint for each hash table entry. This is avoided through the use of a *process page catalog*. When a checkpoint is taken this file is written out for each process (e.g.

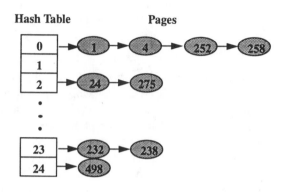

Hash Function:
(pageno/10) mod 25

Figure 1. Example hash table

pagecat.432.4). The catalog has an entry for each bucket in the hash table that identifies the most recent checkpoint of that particular bucket. For example, if a process touches a page in hash table entry 0 before the first checkpoint and then doesn't touch it again, the 0th entry in its page catalog would be 1.

3.3: Operating system checkpointing

When a process is checkpointed, operating system data structures such as the process control block, communications structures and file descriptors opened by the process, are saved to a file. This file contains the "brains" of the process. The only issue that needs to be addressed is resource identifiers during a recovery. Many operating system data structures contain pointers to other structures. When a process is allocating data structures during the recovery it is extremely unlikely that it will get the same data structures it had in the original run. For this reason a fixup data structure is used to record the location of pointer references that cannot be resolved until after all processes have been recovered.

A visible example is the application's family tree. Each process control block contains pointers to the process control blocks of the process' parent, child, older sibling and younger sibling. As the recovery proceeds the mapping of old process identifier to new process control block is recorded in the fixup data structure. Instead of storing process control block pointers in the family tree entries, the old process identifiers are recorded. As one of the final phases of the recovery, a fixup routine goes through each process recovered and changes the family tree pointers by looking up the old process identifiers in the fixup mapping table and replacing them with the new process control block pointers. This same process occurs for other less visible structures such as the terminal and communications control data structures.

3.4: Taking a snapshot

Taking a snapshot of the application involves obtaining a view of each process that is consistent with an overall view of the application. Basically, this means that if one process was checkpointed with a state indicating it received a message from another process, the other process' checkpointed state must reflect the fact that it has sent the message. A second factor that must be addressed is that all of the processes must be in *checkpointable* states. A checkpointable state means that it is in a state that is self contained and can be readily reproduced during a recovery.

When the checkpoint routine looks at a process to see if it can be checkpointed the process can be in a variety of different states:

1. executing in its own address space
2. in the entry or exit of a system call
3. temporarily blocked in a system call
4. semi-permanently blocked in a system call

The first case is a trivial one to handle. The process must be frozen and a snapshot of its registers, operating system data structures and address space must be made. To recover the application a new process must be created and loaded with the saved data.

The second case is not so easy to deal with. When the process is executing a system call, its registers and address space reflect the fact that it is waiting for a system call to return. The process' operating system data structures might be in the process of changing or about to change depending on the operations of the system call. To recover a process in this state it would be necessary to recover the state of the operating system thread that is servicing the system call as well. While this might seem easy, it introduces a great deal of additional complexity that can be easily avoided. It is therefore desirable to have the process move out of this state and into another one that can be checkpointed, such as the first case.

The third case introduces additional levels of complexity. A process that made a system call to read data from a file might be waiting for the call to return. The operating system thread servicing the call could be temporarily blocked while it is waiting for the disk to provide the requested data. The state of the process could therefore be spread across its user space, the operating system, and the device involved in the system call (in this case the disk drive). It is impractical, or in this case impossible, to checkpoint the dynamic characteristics of the device. If the disk drive were to be checkpointed, all the device driver routines would need to be checkpointed and the recovery routine would have to be able to reset the disk to be reading the exact byte it was reading at the time of the checkpoint.

The last case is similar to the previous one. A process will be in a semi-permanent sleep if it has made a blocking request for data from a communications port and the port is empty. The process will wait indefinitely for data. This case can be detected by looking for the process on the operating systems semi-permanent sleep queues. Again, checkpointing the process would mean that the operating system would need to be checkpointed.

So, how are the dilemmas of cases 2-4 to be solved? The first key to the solution is to realize that if a process is in a semi-permanent sleep (4), and the system call that lead to the sleep was restarted given the same conditions, that the process would again enter the sleep. Next, processes in cases 2 and 4 will, within a bounded period of time (provided there is a fair scheduling algorithm) move into either state 1 or state 4. Of course there is no guarantee that if the process is polled that it will not always be in states 2 or 3, just executing different system calls. To prevent this from occurring a flag is set in the checkpointing entry sentry to force processes to halt before entering a system call if a snapshot is being taken. A process blocked in an entry is a variant of state 4.

If a process is in a state where the system call it is in needs to be restarted in the recovery, the registers are fixed so that this will occur. This means that the process program counter and stack pointer are copied and adjusted before they are saved.

Once the snapshot has been taken, individual checkpointing threads are spawned that write out the memory checkpoint of each process and the application processes are resumed. The hash table queues are written to files and asynchronously flushed to speed their movement to disk. After all processes have been written to disk, the checkpoint is committed by having the last checkpointing thread write the new checkpoint number to a *committed checkpoint log* and performing a synchronous flush of all disk buffers. This insures that the new checkpoint is on the disk and that the disk checkpoint associated with the new checkpoint is also stable. The checkpoint is now said to be *committed*. The last thread then deletes the old checkpoint. Performance of the application during this commit period can be affected because of the additional CPU load caused by the threads performing the commit and the load on the disk caused by writing the checkpoint.

A high level pseudocode listing of the snapshot algorithm is shown in Figure 2. The first step of the algorithm is to suspend all processes involved with the application. Then a loop is entered where each process is checked to see if it is in a safe state to checkpoint. If a process is not able to be checkpointed, it is resumed so that it can move into a safe state. After a each process has been checked, the snapshot algorithm sleeps for a small time interval if there were any processes that were not checkpointed. The sleep interval is large enough so that on average, any pro-

```
routine snapshot()
   begin /* snapshot */
   suspend all processes in the application;
   set flag indicating processes should stop in system call
         entries;
   while(processes left not checkpointed)
         begin /* while */
         for(each process not checkpointed)
               begin /* for */
               curproc := next process not checkpointed;
               /* state 1 */
               if(curproc is executing in its own address space)
                     begin /* if */
                     checkpoint_process(curproc);
                     mark curproc as checkpointed;
                     end /* if */
               else
                     begin /* else */
                     /* state 4 or call entry */
                     if(curproc is in system call entry or in a
                           semi-permanent sleep)
                           begin /* if */
                           copy curproc's regs and
                                 adjust so system
                                 call will be restarted
                                 in recovery;
                           checkpoint_process(curproc);
                           mark curproc as checkpointed;
                           end /* if */
                     else
                           begin /* else */
                           /* process not currently
                                 checkpointable
                                 (state 2 or 3) */
                           resume process;
                           end /* else */
                     end /* else */
               end /* for */
         if(all processes not checkpointed)
               delay();
         suspend processes that were resumed above;
         end /* while */
         resume all processes;
   end /* snapshot */
```

Figure 2. Snapshot algorithm

cesses not in a checkpointable state will enter one within the time interval.

3.5: Device initialization

During application execution the state of external devices may be changed. An example is a video display card which is set to a certain mode of operation. If no provision is made for these operations, then recovery to a checkpoint may result in the device being in a sate that is inconsistent with the application's expectations. There are two ways to checkpoint a device's state and the method of choice is determined by the characteristics of the device. If the application's state modifications of the device are transparent to the operating system (as in the case of a memory mapped video card), there must exist some way to read the entire state of the device from the operating system. To recover the device state the entire state is read from the checkpoint and the device is initialized to this state.

```
routine checkpoint_recover()
    begin /* checkpoint recover */
    read the commit log to obtain the committed checkpoint
        numer;
    if(an uncommitted checkpoint exists)
        begin /* if */
        delete the uncommitted checkpoint;
        append the uncommitted journal to the commited journal;
        integrate the uncommited disk checkpoint with
            the commited disk checkpoint;
        end /* if */
    for(each process of the application)
        begin /* for */
        create a new process;
        restore the process control block from the checkpoint;
        restore the address space of the process;
        end /* for */
    restore devices;
    do any pointer and resource id fixups;
    start all processes;
    end /* checkpoint recover */
```

Figure 3. Checkpoint recovery algorithm

If all state modifications are visible to the operating system through system calls, then it may be advantageous or necessary to log the state modifying commands to a special device checkpoint log. When the device is being recovered, the state modifying commands are replayed in succession, moving the device to the correct state. This device checkpoint log is not deleted when a new checkpoint is taken as the other checkpoint files are, but is copied to the new checkpoint and appended with any state modifying commands that have occurred since the previous checkpoint. If the number of modifying commands is expected to be high for a particular device resulting in a checkpoint log that is the same order of magnitude in size as the device's state, then the option of checkpointing the device's state in its entirety should be pursued if possible.

In the system implemented there are examples of both types of device. The video display card contains part of the X application's state - namely, the display image. X sets the device into a graphics mode, initializes a palette of colors for display, and then draws the display image in the display card's memory. These state changes are all made through special assembly language device instructions and through memory mapped I/O, and therefore are transparent to the operating system. Even if they were not transparent, the number of state modifications made when a window is drawn on the screen, for example, makes logging impractical for this type of device.

The second type of device is exemplified by the mouse and the keyboard. In the Mach/UX architecture, the low level device driver's are in the kernel and since the checkpointing policy has been placed in the UX server, it does not have access to the state of the device drivers. During the course of X initialization, `ioctl` (I/O control) system calls are made to set the state of the mouse and keyboard device drivers. The checkpointing policy journals these calls into a *device log file* so that at the beginning of a recovery, the device drivers can be initialized by replaying them.

3.6: Checkpoint recovery

Recovery of a checkpoint is a fairly straight-forward process. First, the commit log is read to ascertain the most recently committed checkpoint. A check is then made to see if an uncommitted checkpoint exists, and, if so, it is deleted. Processes are created for each process in the checkpoint with their process control blocks, registers, and memory map restored from information in their individual checkpoint files. It is in this part of the recovery that the fixup structure referred to earlier is created. Next, the memory maps are filled with the checkpointed pages. The external pager hash tables are recreated as this occurs. Device checkpoint recovery is then performed followed by the fixup routine that adjusts pointers. Finally, the processes are all started. These steps are outlined in Figure 3.

4: Checkpointing examples and performance

This section presents measurements of overheads for taking a snapshot, and committing a checkpoint. It is necessary to measure instantaneous overheads as well as profile real applications in order to obtain an overall view of the performance impact of checkpointing. The first part of the section presents measurements based on a well defined synthetic program. Following this are examples of real checkpoint sessions taken on the same applications that were used in the journaling measurements.

The machine that the experiments were run on is an i486 processor, 50MHz with a 25Mhz bus, with 16 MB of physical memory and a disk drive with an average access time of about 40 ms.

4.1: Snapshot performance

The most visible part of a checkpoint to a user is the snapshot. During the snapshot the application is essentially suspended so the duration is an important factor if a checkpoint interval is determined based on user concerns. A smaller snapshot would in most cases allow for more frequent checkpointing. To measure the performance of snapshots in a controlled environment, a synthetic program is used. The program allocates a specified amount of global memory and then proceeds to sequentially touch each page (4 KB) by writing one byte to it. In this experiment the size of global data is varied and the page touches performed. Then a checkpoint is taken and the snapshot interval is measured. The measurements are graphed in Figure 4. The duration of the snapshot increases at roughly a constant factor as the amount of memory used increases. Recall that all that is done during this phase is that the snapshot algorithm is writing the process control block of the program and its registers to a file and requesting that the kernel flush all of the application's modified pages. When the kernel notifies the snapshot algorithm that a page has been flushed it does not need to immediately provide the page. It simply marks the page as flushed so that if the application modifies the page again it will have to request it from the external pager. The page is provided to the checkpoint algorithm when it touches the page to save it to the checkpoint file. When there is only one process being checkpointed, this occurs during the commit phase of the checkpoint. If the kernel provided the page when the flush request was made, in many cases it would have to pagein the page from the disk paging file substantially increasing the snapshot duration.

4.2: Commit performance

The time period between the time that snapshot has been taken and the checkpoint is committed is the *commit delay*. The application is resumed from its suspended state, but it may experience performance degradation due to the load of the checkpoint commit routines on the processor and the disk. During this period, the kernel is flushing pages to the external pager, and the checkpointing threads are writing the pages out to disk. To measure the commit delay for various sizes of checkpoint, the synthetic pro-

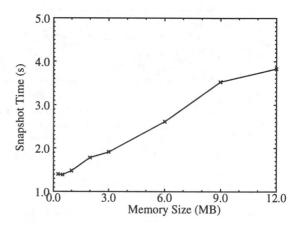

Figure 4. Snapshot duration for synthetic program

gram is again used. Two curves are graphed in Figure 5, one for compressed checkpoint, and one for an uncompressed checkpoint. Run-length compression usually is able to significantly reduce the space taken by memory pages. It is therefore used in the implementation to compress both checkpointed pages as well as the video data. Besides saving disk space, compression can improve performance because fewer disk blocks need to be written and flushed to disk. The compressed curve is a lower limit on the commit duration because only one byte of each page is nonzero (the byte that is modified). This is the optimal situation for the compression algorithm and results in the smallest checkpoint size and therefore the lower bound on commit delay. The uncompressed plot represents a checkpoint where every byte on the checkpointed pages differs from its neighbor so that no run-length compression is possible. It therefore represents the upper bound on checkpoint size and performance. Paging activity starts to create disk accesses causing the kinks at about 6 MB in both curves.

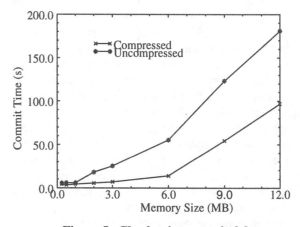

Figure 5. Checkpoint commit delay

For 12 megabytes of modified data, one can expect a commit time of 2 to 2 and 1/2 minutes. Recall that the application is allowed to run during this time. The effect of performance degradation during this time can decrease responsiveness of the system which must be considered in determining the checkpoint interval.

4.3: Recovery time

Although most people would consider recovery time of secondary importance if the alternative was the loss of critical data, it is desirable to minimize it. Figure 6 shows the time taken to recover the synthetic program. *Recovery* here refers to the time that it takes to recreate a process from a checkpoint. Times to recover for a given data size are about one third the commit time for the same amount of memory. A great deal of this is due to the fact that the checkpoint is read instead of written and disk read operations are faster than write operations. Also, since there is no memory copying or flushing in the recovery, there are fewer page faults. Once again, the sharp rise coincides with disk paging activity.

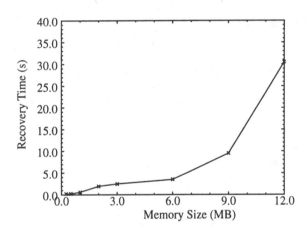

Figure 6. Recovery time

4.4: Examples of checkpointing

The dilemma facing checkpoint measurement is that there are no standard benchmarks. Synthetic programs like the memory toucher have very little relevance when the question is asked, *"how long will a checkpoint of this application take?"* Results in the synthetic case can only be used to make crude approximations of the performance of real applications. Even when a real application is used in measurements, the correlation between the circumstances that existed at the time of the checkpoint (state of the paging file, buffer cache, etc.) can be much different than for the same application just a few seconds later. Still, measurements must be taken and presented if only to provide an order-of-magnitude reference.

A few programs were selected as representative of the most popular generally available programs used in the X system. Bitmap is a simple bitmap editor included with the X release. With it, a bitmap can be drawn or edited, and saved or read from a file. A variety of drawing functions are presented as buttons along the left side of the window. The gnu-emacs editor is perhaps the most popular X/Unix text editor and is commonly used in program development (like the development of Mach and the checkpointing implementation). It has powerful facilities that allow one to view and edit multiple files simultaneously. Xterm gives terminal programs like shell and cshell (csh) an interface to the X-window system. With its use the user can have several shell programs running concurrently and moving between them is as easy as moving the mouse cursor from one xterm to another. X-standard is the name given to X and its batch of standard start-up clients. In these experiments, like in the journaling runs, an xterm, window manager (twm), and a clock (xclock) are all part of the environment. Finally, X-large is a more typical working environment. It includes all that X-standard does plus 3 additional xterms and a gnu-emacs editor with a file loaded.

The first set of measurements seen in Table 1 show performance of taking a checkpoint immediately after the programs have finished their start-up sequences. For bitmap this means that a bitmap editor window has been drawn on the screen and is ready for input. The same applies to gnu-emacs and xterm/csh. X-standard initialization is complete when the xclock and xterm windows are drawn and the shell (csh) in the xterm is ready to accept input. X-large is checkpointed after all 4 xterms have been created and the gnu-emacs editor has finished its initialization after loading a file.

A variety of different metrics are shown for each program with all sizes in bytes and all times in seconds. The program size indicates the size of the object file, or files, and can be an indicator of the complexity of the program. Checkpoint size is the size of the memory checkpoint, which is compressed, and the final column shows the amount of compression that was possible by comparing it to the projected uncompressed size. The video card is checkpointed when X is checkpointed. If no data compression were applied to the video data, its checkpoint would be 1 MB in size. Fortunately, video, especially an X desktop image, tends to compress highly when a run-length algorithm is applied. In this case the video checkpoint is 3-6% of the original size. The table shows that even for very large applications (X-large) the snapshot is less than 10 seconds in duration. A delay such as this is usually tolerable in an interactive environment about once every 30 minutes. The total checkpoint sizes are less than 2 MB in size. If this is combined with an additional checkpoint (before a new checkpoint is committed both the old and

Application	program size	pages ckpted	snapshot delay(s)	commit delay(s)	ckpt size(b)	% of no cmprsn
bitmap	559K	73	0.7	2.9	137K	47
xterm+csh	813K	103	0.7	3.2	155K	38
gnu-emacs	1466K	58	0.7	2.6	149K	64
X-standard (video card)	1095K	441	2.3	10.7	591K 29K	33 3
X-large (video card)	9881K	826	5.2	25.7	1236K 60K	37 6

Table 1. First checkpoint performance

Application	snapshot delay (s)		commit delay (s)		checkpoint duration (s)	
	cmprss	none	cmprss	none	cmprss	none
X-standard	2.1	2.1	10.7	18.0	12.7	20.1
X-large	4.0	4.0	25.7	32.2	29.7	36.2

Table 2. Checkpoint duration with and without compression

Application	pages ckpted	snapshot delay(s)	commit delay(s)	ckpt written (b)	% of no cmprsn
bitmap	53	0.7	2.2	91K	42
xterm+csh	102	0.7	3.0	149K	36
gnu-emacs	63	0.7	2.7	164K	65
X-standard (video card)	266	1.9	9.4	436K 35K	41 3
X-large (video card)	356	3.9	17.2	595K 65K	42 6

Table 3. Second checkpoint performance

the new checkpoint exist on disk) the disk space requirements of a such a system is less than 10 MB.

In order to see the effects of data compression on checkpoint duration, measurements were taken for checkpoints of the X-standard and X-large applications with no data compression. The measurements obtained are shown in Table 2. Times are shown for the snapshot delay, the commit delay and the sum of those delays in the checkpoint duration column. The total duration is reduced by 20-30% in both cases when data compression is used. This savings is due to the fact that fewer disk blocks must be written when the data is compressed to take less space.

Checkpointing an application after it has finished its start-up indicates how much data is modified during initialization. Measurements for a second checkpoint are shown in Table 3. The checkpoints are taken after the programs are exercised in their respective ways. Xterm commands are entered, a drawing is entered with Bitmap and text is edited with gnu-emacs. The table shows that the amount of data saved in a second checkpoint can be significantly smaller than in a first checkpoint. Snapshot durations are expectedly smaller as well.

The final measurement of recovery time is shown in Table 4. Only X-standard and X-large are shown because the other programs are not true applications. If considered individually, a program like `xterm` violates the system model because it communicates with processes that are not descendents of its root process. X must therefore be the root process for any X based program.

Application	Recovery Time
X-standard	4.1
X-large	16.9

Table 4. Checkpoint recovery

Recovery times are comparable to the snapshot durations and are relatively low considering the complexity of a full recovery of the scale of `X-large`, for example. `X-large` takes significantly longer to recover than `X-standard` due to the fact that there are 9 more processes involved in the recovery. Low recovery times such as these indicate that user's should expect checkpoint recovery to be under one minute in duration.

5: Conclusion

This paper has presented the design and implementation of checkpointing algorithms for concurrent Unix applications. The contributions of significance are the application of checkpointing to a widely used operating system running well known applications such as the X-window system.

In the checkpoint algorithm, the checkpointing process is divided into the two phases of snapshot and commit. In the snapshot phase, the application is suspended while a consistent view of it is obtained. In the commit phase the application is resumed and the obtained snapshot is written asynchronously to disk. Performance measurements reveal that for typical workstation environments snapshots are less than 10 seconds and commit duration is less than 45 seconds. In addition, dedicated checkpoint disk storage requirements are less than 10 MB.

Disk checkpointing as well as journaling algorithms have been designed and implemented and their results are left to a future paper. The combination of these algorithms provide Unix programs that use disk storage with minimal data loss. Details can be found in [14] and [15].

Other future work includes integration of the concurrent application checkpointing algorithms with distributed algorithms functioning as a higher layer. This will provide fault tolerance for distributed Unix applications.

6: References

[1] M. Accetta, R. Baron, W. Bolosky D. Golub and R. Rashid, "A new kernel foundation for Unix development," USENIX 86, July 1986.

[2] A. Borg, W. Blau, W. Graetcsh, F. Hermann, and W. Oberle, "Fault-tolerance under Unix," *ACM Trans. Comput. Syst.*, vol. 7, no. 1, Feb. 1989, pp 1-24.

[3] B. Bhargava, S. Lian, and P. Leu, "Experimental Evaluation of Concurrent Checkpointing and Rollback-Recovery Algorithims," in *6th Int. Conf. of Data Engineering*, 1990, pp. 182-189.

[4] K. M. Chandy and L. Lamport, "Distributed snapshots: Determining global states of distributed systems," *ACM Trans. Comput. Syst.*, vol. 3, no. 1, Feb. 1985, pp. 63-75.

[5] E. N. Elnozahy and W. Zwaenepoel, "Manetho: transparent rollback-recovery with low overhead, limited rollback, and fast output commit," *IEEE Trans. Comput.*, vol. 41, no. 5, May 1992, pp. 526-530.

[6] D. B. Johnson and W. Zwaenepoel, "Sender-based message logging," in *Proc. 17th Int. Symp. Fault-Tolerant Comput.*, June 1987, pp. 14-19.

[7] D. B. Johnson and W. Zwaenepoel, "Recovery in distributed systems using optimistic message logging and checkpointing," *J. Algorithms*, vol. 11, no. 3., pp. 462-491.

[8] T. Juang and S. Venkatesan, "Crash recovery with little overhead," in *Proc. 11th Int. Conf. Distributed Comput. Syst.*, May 1991, pp. 454-461.

[9] R. Koo and S. Toueg, "Checkpointing and rollback-recovery for distributed systems," *IEEE Trans. Software Eng.*, vol. SE-13, Jan. 1987, pp. 23-31.

[10] L. Lamport, "Time, clocks, and the ordering of events in a distributed system," *Commun. ACM*, vol. 21, no. 7, July 1978, pp. 558-565.

[11] K. Li, J. F. Naughton, and J. S. Plank, "Checkpointing multicomputer applications," in *Proc. 10th Symp. Reliable Distributed Syst.*, Oct. 1991, pp. 2-11.

[12] L. L. Peterson, N. C. Bucholz, and R. D. Schlichting, "Preserving and using context information in interprocess communications," *ACM Trans. Comput. Syst.*, vol. 7, no. 3, Aug. 1989, pp. 217-246.

[13] R. Rashid, *et. al.*, "Mach: a foundation for open systems," in *Proceedings of the Second Workshop on Workstation Operating Systems*, Sept. 27-29, 1989.

[14] M. Russinovich, Z. Segall and D. P. Sieworiek, "Application-transparent fault management in fault tolerant Mach," in *Proc. 23rd Int Symp. Fault-Tolerant Comput.*, June 1993, pp. 10-19.

[15] M. Russinovich, "Application-transparent fault management," Ph.D. dissertation, Carnegie Mellon University, August 1994.

[16] R. W. Scheifler and J. Gettys, "The X-window system," *ACM Trans. on Graphics*, vol. 5, no. 2, Apr. 1986, pp. 79-109.

[17] R. E. Strom and S. A. Yemini, "Optimistic recovery in distributed systems," *ACM Trans. Comput. Syst.*, vol. 3, no. 3, Aug. 1985, pp. 204-226.

[18] R. E. Strom, S. A. Yemini and D. F. Bacon, "Toward self-recovering operating systems," in *Int. Conf. Parallel Processing*, 1987.

[19] R. E. Strom, D. F. Bacon and S. A. Yemini, "Volatile logging in n-fault-tolerant distributed systems," in *Proc. 18th Int. Symp. Fault-Tolerant Comput.*, June 1988, pp. 44-49.

[20] Y. Tamir and T. Frazier, "Application-transparent process-level error recovery for multicomputers," in *22nd Hawaii Int. Conf. Syst. Sciences*, Jan. 1987.

[21] Z. Tong, R. Y. Kain, and W. T.Tsai, "A Low Overhead Checkpointing and Rollback Recovery Scheme for Distributed Systems," in *8th Symp. Reliable Distributed Syst.*, Oct. 1989, pp. 12-20.

MPP UNIX Enhancements for OLTP Applications

Greg Schaffer

Encore Computer Corporation

300 Nickerson Rd, Marlborough MA 01752

Abstract

This paper describes an MPP UNIX in terms of goals, implementation and initial experience in using it to port OLTP applications. Most MPP Unix systems strive towards the goal of a conventional but massively scaled up shared memory multiprocessor. In reality this goal has never been achieved without compromising scalability or fault-tolerance. The Infinity architecture achieves scalability with no single point of failure by running a separate copy of UNIX on each node. UNIX extensions make it appear as a single machine to applications. Results indicate that complex OLTP applications can be ported with ease; other applications may need to be rewritten to take advantage of the MPP Unix.

1 Introduction

The Infinity 90 is the result of integrating two products: shared memory multi-processor UNIX systems with a reflective memory interconnect. Both products individually are mature technologies — the combined system is unique. The Infinity 90 architecture is positioned for large database applications.

Reflective memory (RMS[12]) was originally designed to connect Concept 32 real-time systems together. Applications which outgrew one machine could be decomposed across multiple machines, while having access to the shared state as "global common". These machines typically ran a single application which used a static layout of reflective memory. The initial setup changed, but the application itself needed little modification.

Reflective memory on the Infinity 90 is used to implement remote procedure calls for the remote file system, transfer the read/write data buffers themselves,

and regions of memory are also available for user applications. Reflective memory is a resource which is dynamically allocated by the kernel to these various uses. One important use of this memory is for inter-processes communication.

1.1 Reflective memory

Reflective memory can be thought of as network shared memory implemented in hardware with a local copy on each node. Note that there is no atomic read-modify-write cycle across the reflective memory bus, thus syncronization is performed in software. Each node's reflective memory card is populated with tri-ported memory – a local bus port for processor references, VME bus port for direct I/O to SCSI disks, and the "write only" reflective memory bus port. Reads are satisfied locally and do not result in reflective memory bus traffic. Writes to this memory from the processor local bus or VME device are also placed on the reflective memory bus by the hardware. The reflective memory card on other nodes updates the local memory copy from the bus writes. If only one node is using the bus it has the entire bus bandwidth available; round-robin arbitration is used when there are multiple simultaneous writes. Thus reflective memory is replicated with physically distributed copies.

Each 8-Kbyte "window" of reflective memory can be programmed to be either "open" or "closed" for "transmit" and/or "receive" on a particular "network address". The remote procedure call is implemented in uni-directional regions of memory set aside for each processor pair. The network address range is much larger than the the physical address range; thus nodes 1 and 2 can communicate using one network address, and nodes 3 and 4 communicate using a second network address but use only one window of RMS on each node. "RMS Shared memory" is implemented by opening a region of network addresses as both transmit and receive on all of the nodes.

Reflective memory provides the system and application developer a very simple programming model

---

*Infinity 90, Reflective Memory, Infinity File System, UMAX, and Concept 32 are trademarks of Encore Computer Corporation. UNIX is a trademark of AT&T Bell Laboratories. UniKix is a trademark of Integris. CICS and MVS are trademarks of International Business Machines.

based on shared memory concepts, but there are subtle differences. First RMS does not provide test and set atomic locking on memory location (as is provided with local shared memory). Second, access to RMS memory is slightly slower than local memory as it bypasses the cache. Third, RMS memory tends to be more precious than local memory as there is no virtual memory paging. [1]

The Infinity 90 is a "hybrid" multiprocessor system, using symmetric shared memory within a node and programmable distributed shared memory between nodes. A single node can fail without affecting the remaining nodes. Multiple RMS cards can be used to provide redundant connections between nodes. Reflective memory is well suited for building large scale fault-tolerant transaction processing systems.

1.2 Infinity 90

The Infinity 90 system [5] depicted in Figure 1 incorporates up to 48 Motorola 88k RISC processors for general purpose computing (GPC) and 16 88k processors for intelligent I/O (IC/SC), resulting in a performance of 2 billion instructions per second. The system supports 840 SCSI disks with a total of 1000 Gbytes of storage and an I/O bandwidth of 230 Mbytes/sec[1].

Reflective memory provides efficient coupling of multiple processor nodes to shared data in a distributed computing environment. The physical use of the RMS system is essentially as a memory I/O channel. I/O operations between different nodes are actually memory-to-memory transfers, as VME-SCSI disks go directly to the memory card without processor memory copy. New "Memory Channel" hardware provides double the bandwidth for block writes and 256-Mbytes.

1.3 Infinity file system

The Infinity File System (IFS) provides fast and efficient file system services that scale nearly linearly with the disk and CPU resources provided. Reflective memory is used both for remote procedure call (RPC), and for the I/O data buffers, and I/O transfers are done direct to RMS to minimize data copying. The IFS client intercepts all UNIX file system calls — when a remote operation, it packages a RPC request and sends it to the server. Thus the majority of file system handling is done by the IFS server; while the client can service other jobs.

---

[1] RMS-II boards are populated with 16 Mbytes, RMS-III boards have 64 Mbytes.

IFS can support "mirrored servers" for redundant I/O transactions and increased fault tolerance. Write requests are "broadcast" to multiple servers using a single RMS data buffer. Read requests select one of the servers for better load balancing.

2 Interprocess communication

The Encore Infinity 90 Series offers great potential for application software to take advantage of a closely coupled distributed architecture. The first application able to leverage the resources of this machine is Oracle Parallel Server (OPS[10]), due mostly to the fact that OPS has an inherently distributed design. Central to the OPS design is the distributed lock manager (DLM[11]), which Encore has implemented in reflective memory.

Encore has developed extensions to System-V interprocess communication (IPC[4]) for the Infinity architecture using reflective memory. The Development Application Library for the Infinity (DALI[6]) allows for straightforward porting of programs which already use System-V IPC. It provides a well understood framework for porting other programs to be distributed across multiple processes and computing nodes. In order to to fully leverage all the capabilities of the Infinity 90, a certain amount of adaptation and re-architecting may be necessary.

In addition to the System-V compatible shared memory, messages queues, and semaphores, DALI also provides RMS spinlocks and counting semaphores. Daemons handle cleanup on abnormal process termination. Other synchronization or communication mechanisms can be constructed using these facilities.

2.1 RMS shared memory

Reflective Memory is available to the application through the System-V shared memory primitives. To request RMS shared memory instead of local memory, add IPC_RMS to the flags specified to shmget. Once the RMS shared memory identifier is created, it may be attached to with shmat, detached from with shmdt, and its attributes examined or changed using shmctl.

```
shmid = shmget(key, size, shmflg|IPC_RMS)
st = shmctl(shmid, cmd, buf)
shmaddr = shmat(shmid, shmaddr, flags)
st = shmdt(shmaddr)
```

These extensions to shared memory are implemented in the kernel instead of the DALI library as it must manipulate the process' virtual memory page

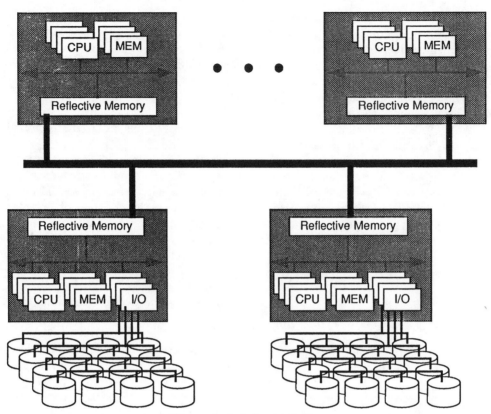

Figure 1: Infinity 90 System

tables. The kernel uses internal RMS spinlocks to guard the allocation and changes to the data structures; these internal spinlocks are not accessible from user-level.

A portion of RMS broadcast memory specified in a configuration file holds the RMS shared memory descriptors. For each shared memory descriptor slot, this consists of the "shmid_ds" structure to hold the key and permissions, the "creator_id", the "node_regions" array, and one 8-Kbyte page to list it's RMS network addresses, which allows for a total of 16-Mbytes of memory for one RMS shmid.

The creator_id is important as the network address ranges are divided between the nodes so that each node can independently allocate network addresses without taking a global lock. When the RMS shmid is removed, it must be removed on this node last, so that the network addresses can be made available again.

The node_regions array holds the local "region" pointer for each node which has that RMS shmid mapped. Thus it is valid to follow this pointer this only on that node; on other nodes a non zero pointer indicates that the RMS shmid has been mapped.

Network addresses are dynamically allocated when the RMS shmid is first created. The first time a node

attaches to the RMS shmid, RMS windows are allocated from the available pool and the windows are opened for transmit and receive on those network addresses, the local "region" descriptor is created and its address placed into it's node_regions slot. If this RMS shmid has already been mapped on other nodes, which may have written to the memory, then one of those nodes must "refresh" this memory so that the new node's copy is valid. Similarly, when a node is rebooted, it must get a refreshed copy of the RMS shmid descriptor area and immediately zero out it's node_regions since the region pointer is no longer valid. RMS memory refresh is one of the functions coordinated by the "health monitor" which runs on each of the nodes[7].

Removing the RMS shmid is complicated since each node has a local region pointer. The RMS memory windows can be released only if no process on that node is still accessing that memory. Further the RMS network addresses cannot be released until all other nodes no longer have the RMS shmid mapped. The "IPC_RMID" command of shmctl attempts to remove the local region and clear it's node_regions slot, but does not attempt to remove the RMS shmid on other nodes. The DALI command "ripcrm -m id" will issue the remove on each of the nodes, with the **creator** node last – but this will still fail if any process still has the shmid mapped.

2.2 RMS spinlocks

In the local shared memory model, any location in memory can be used as a lock for atomic test and set locking operations. On reflective memory, the test and set interlock instruction does not provide for an atomic operation across the reflective memory bus. DALI provides locking functions loosely based on Dekker's algorithm [2, 3, 9]. They are implemented in the library, instead of as a kernel call to avoid the extra scheduling overhead.

Each node has its own slot in the "bid" array. If it sees no other bid; it marks its own bid, and waits for the round-trip RMS delay. Using the "loopback" feature by mapping one page as transmit and another as receive on the same network address, a write is known to have gone on the bus when it has been updated in the receive window. If no other bids are found that node is granted the lock, otherwise it will back-off. A separate "guard" lock in local memory is used so that only one process on each node can get to the bid array in reflective memory. The (simplified) mechanism is shown in Figure 5.

```
#include <rms_dali.h>
id = rms_spinlock_get (key, numlocks, mode)
st = rms_spinlock (id, lockd)
st = rms_spinunlock (id, lockd)
st = rms_spin_try_lock(id, lockd, n)
st = rms_spin_rmid(id)
```

Rms_spinlock_get takes a "key" and returns a spinlock id for the spinlock set. The "mode" consists of the UNIX permissions, plus the flags IPC_CREAT to create set if it doesn't exist, IPC_EXCL to give an error if it already exists, and IPC_DALI_EXITOK to disable code to cleanup the lock if the process exits while holding it. The set of spinlocks are referenced in the lock and unlock calls by the spinlock id, and the lock number (0 to numlocks-1).

When either the RMS lock or the guard lock has been awarded to a process, its process-id is recorded to facilitate error recovery when a process terminates abnormally. A DALI daemon running on each node periodically watches the health of processes which are using DALI spinlocks and semaphores. When it detects that a DALI process has exited and owns the spinlock, it puts the lock into the "dubious" state. A dubious lock is next awarded with errno ERESTART.

If other nodes are bidding for the lock they get errno EINPROGRESS, until the rms_spinunlock call. Thus it is very important to check the return status of rms_spinlock.

2.3 RMS semaphores

DALI provides two flavors of blocking semaphores: the classic signal/wait style counting semaphore, and also a System-V semaphore with the restriction of supporting only a single semop. Supporting multiple semops as an atomic operation would require maintenance of undo lists, and additional locks which would degrade performance; and this functionality is rarely used in practice. These should be used instead of spinlocks when the lock could be held for a longer period of time.

Internally there is one RMS spinlock for the allocation of semaphores, one RMS spinlock for each semaphore set descriptor, and also for each individual semaphore. The semaphore set descriptor contains the "ipc_perm" permissions structure, and describes the range of semaphore indices. The semaphore data structure consists of the value, head and tail index, and a circular buffer of blocked process ids to avoid maintaining a linked list in RMS. Just before the process blocks, it places its process-id in a circular buffer, when another process signals the semaphore, it unblocks the next blocked process. The semaphore also contains semval and sempid fields for System-V semaphore semantics, and it is not permissible to mix the flavor of semaphore operations.

```
semid = rms_sem_get (key, numsems, mode)
st = rms_sem_setval(semid, semp, val)
st = rms_sem_wait(semid, semp)
st = rms_sem_cwait(semid, semp)
st = rms_sem_signal(semid, semp)
st = rms_sem_rmid(semid)

semid = semget(key, numsems, mode|IPC_RMS)
st = semop(semid, sops, nsops)
st = semctl(semid, cmd, args)
```

Rms_sem_get takes a key and creates a counting semaphore set, with the mode as previously described for RMS spinlocks. When first created, each semaphore's value is "undefined", and rms_sem_setval need be called to initialze it; typically to 0 or 1. Once the value is set, the wait and signal operations can be issued. Rms_sem_wait decrements the count and blocks the process if the count is negative. Rms_sem_cwait is similar, but decrements the count only if it was positive, otherwise it returns −1 and sets the errno to EWOULDBLOCK. Rms_sem_signal increments the semaphore count and unblocks the first process waiting on the semaphore if the count was negative.

As with RMS spinlocks, the DALI daemon detects when a process exited while owning a semaphore. If so the semaphore becomes "dubious", any blocked processes are revived: one gets errno ERESTART and is responsible for cleanup and then uses rms_sem_setval to clear the error state, any other blocked processes get EINPROGRESS. The failure semantics are disabled if the semaphore id is created with IPC_DALI_EXITOK.

For the System-V compatible semaphores, the mode IPC_RMS is used to specify RMS semaphores instead of local per-node semaphore. A single semaphore operation can be specified in the "sops" structure: a positive sem_op adds to semval, a negative sem_op will decrease semval or block (unless IPC_NOWAIT is specified), and zero sem_op is used to check or wait for semval=0. Semctl is used to get or set the semval, to remove the identifier or change the permissions, or to retrieve other information.

2.4 RMS message queues

Processes can communicate with other processes using RMS message queues. Again the interface and semantics are the same as System-V message queues, with the addition of the IPC_RMS flag. For performance reasons each queue is allotted a set of message buffers to avoid contention on a global message allocation lock. Internally the RMS messages use RMS spinlocks to guard data structures, and RMS semaphores to wait for message headers or message text space to become available.

```
msqid = msgget(key, msgflg|IPC_RMS)
st = msgctl(msqid, cmd, buf)
st = msgsnd(msqid, msgp, msgsz, msgflg)
st = msgsnd(msqid, msgp, msgsz, msgflg)
```

UNIX signals are "held" during critical sections so the process is not interrupted while it is manipulating the RMS message data structures. If a process is abnormally terminated during a RMS message queue operation while it holding an internal RMS spinlock then the next message operation performed on that queue will return with the errno ERESTART and the DALI daemon will initiate recovery by checking for data structure consistancy and resetting the lock. Meanwhile, other message operations on the queue will wait for the cleanup to finish. The ERESTART return allows the application program to be aware that a queue

recovery was required; but the application itself need not necessarily take any further action on it.

2.5 DALI commands

DALI provides two commands to examine and remove RMS-IPC identifiers: "ripcs" and "ripcrm" which correspond to the System-V UNIX commands "ipcs" and "ipcrm", A "-s" switch is added for the RMS spinlocks, and "-v" switch to show which nodes have each RMS shared memory region mapped.

2.6 DALI configuration

The DALI configuration file "/etc/dalicf" describes parameters used in determining the data structure layout in RMS memory when the first DALI daemon is started. The data structures are then self-describing, so that changing the file does not corrupt a running system. A sample configuration file is given in Figure 2.

```
spinlocks        100     # total RMS spinlocks
spinlockid       50      # spinlock ids
semaphores       100     # total RMS semaphores
semid            50      # semaphore ids
semwaitq         10      # depth of sema waitq
message_queues   10      # total RMS msgqs
message_headers  150     # max active msgs/queue
msgssz           8       # sizeof text alloc unit
msgseg           4096    # text alloc units
msgmax           16384   # max size of a message
msgsleepers      10      # slots on recvr sleep Q
nspins           10000   # lock attempts then blk
```

Figure 2: DALI configuration parameters

2.7 DALI deamon

DALI spinlocks and counting semaphores have a reference count, which is incremented when the process gets the identifier using the key and also during fork(). In addition DALI keeps a list of the spinlock and semaphore ids that each process is referencing. The DALI daemon process running on each node periodically checks to see that these processes are still alive, and if not cleans up the reference and decriments this reference count — when it reaches 0 the spinlock or semaphore set is deleted, unless it was created with the IPC_DALI_EXITOK flag. System-V semaphores are not automatically deleted in this way, and must be explicitly deleted with the IPC_RMID semctl or ripcrm. This DALI daemon must be started on all the nodes before any processes which use DALI services can run.

As previously mentioned, the DALI daemon also checks if the spinlock or semaphore was owned by the process which exited, and must be put into the "dubious" state. Similarly when the daemon detects that node has gone down, a daemon on one of the remaining nodes will check all of the spinlocks and semaphores, to see if they were owned by a process on the crashed node, and need to be put in the dubious state. [2]

2.8 Global processes

DALI requires some minimal UNIX kernel support for global process ids. First **getpid()** will uniquely identify a process by storing the node id in the upper bits of the pid. Signals can be sent to any process via kill(pid,sig), and particularly useful is **kill(pid,0)** to check if a process is alive, with the added error return of ENOLINK if the node is not responding. A blocked process on any node may be resumed with **unblock(pid)**. Initially this functionality was part of the DALI library with remote signalling via the DALI daemon; later global process support was added to the kernel. The **ps** command is extended to retrieve process information from all the nodes. These extensions make it appear as a single machine even though each node is running a separate copy of UNIX.

Applications also require a mechanism to start a process on another machine. This was prototyped using ethernet based "remote shell", until support for later **rexece()** system call was finished.

    rexece(path, argp, envp, home, tty, subsys)

The program "path" is run on node "subsys", passing it arguments and environment, setting the working directory to "home", and controlling terminal "tty". If successful, this call does not return.

3 Distributed applications

Encore is concentrating on porting OLTP applications to best utilize the Infinity 90 system. The majority of that effort is directed towards Oracle7 Parallel Server, in particular the Oracle distributed lock manager. The DLM uses global process support, RMS shared memory, and a similar implementation of RMS spinlocks to guard its internal data structures.

---

[2] Since each node maintains its own reference lists, the actual reference count cannot be adjusted; "ripcrm" can be used to remove the identifier.

3.1 Porting with DALI

Specifing the IPC_RMS flag is a trivial source change. Spinlock usage must be identified and changed to use a spinlock id and spinlock number; and the spinlock set must be created and initialized before its first use. More subtle is checking spinlock and semaphore routines for error returns. For testing purposes, DALI can be even configured to run on a single node using a regular System-V shared memory region instead of reflective memory.

DALI will provide its best scalable results when synchronization points are somewhat more coarse than on a tightly coupled shared memory multiprocessor, as the RMS spinlocks in particular are more expensive than a local spinlock, and there is some latency in unblocking a process on another node. There may also be increased lock contention due simply to running more processes on the larger MPP. Tuning parallel programs is still somewhat of an art. Future work is to include statistics gathering of collisions and waiting time to help pinpoint synchronization bottlenecks.

3.2 Fault tolerance

Each node runs its own copy of UNIX and thus can tolerate another node going down. When a process dies (or node goes down) while holding a spinlock the next call to acquire the spinlock gets the errno ERESTART to indicate it is dubious, and then when released clears the dubious state. Thus the application doesn't hang, and indeed can choose to take some action. However there is no automatic notification that a process in the application has died.

A more sophisticated fault recovery mechanism must be added by the application writer, typically by having one or more "monitor" processes periodically issue **kill(pid,0)** for each process in the application. For example the Oracle DLM has a primary and secondary process monitor – the primary watches all processes using DLM services, and the secondary running on a different node watches the health of the primary monitor. The primary detects that a process has exited and will release any resources it still held. If the secondary detects the death of the primary, it becomes the primary itself, and creates a new secondary on another node if possible.

3.3 CICS

The Customer Information Control System (CICS) is a teleprocessing monitor software product from IBM which forms an inteface between on-line application programs and operating system resources. It provides services such as terminal communications and various database operations. CICS runs on IBM mainframes under MVS, and is also ported to AIX/6000.

UniKix [8] is a CICS-compatible on-line transaction processing software product which runs on UNIX systems and provides for migrating CICS Cobol applicications from MVS to UNIX systems (Figure 3).

The environment has a set of transaction servers, a recovery server and additional database servers. Each terminal session has a client process. These processes communicate using message queues for transaction reguests, recovery logging, and terminal updates. The transaction servers themselves use shared memory to store information about each user, terminal, database buffers, and dynamic VSAM. Spinlocks and semaphores are used to coordinate access to this shared memory.

To migrate CICS to the Infinity 90, we can immediately use RMS shared memory, message queues, and semaphores, just by specifing IPC_RMS | IPC_DALI_EXITOK flags when creating them to disable the automatic cleanup mechanism as the "recovery server" already monitors processes to handle recovery on abnormal process termination. Fortunately there are fixed number of spinlocks, so a single spinlock set is used, and individual spinlocks are given RMS spinlock numbers during initialization. Finally "rexece" is used to spawn server processes on other nodes.

3.4 Oracle parallel query

Oracle parallel server allows for multiple nodes to access the same database. Oracle also has a "parallel query" option where the query is decomposed into pieces which are separately processed by multiple query slaves, for improved response time to a complex query. Oracle provides an operating system independent interface, and each vendor can write specific code designed for their system. Adding Oracle parallel query requires four vender specific routines: to create and destroy a message queue descriptor, to send and receive (non-blocking) a message.

A non-trivial query would typically involve the "query coordinator" sending a set of messages to instruct the "query slaves", which then send a flurry of messages between themselves, and finally the slaves send some reply messages back to the coordinator (Figure 4). The messages themselves are short as tablespaces contain the actual data.

This could have been implemented using the DALI message queues. Rather it has been implemented in RMS shared memory; where each process has its own area to write in, and the receiver checks for any messages written for it. There are separate regions for coordinator to slave, slave to coordinator, and slave to slave messages. This has the advantage of requiring no spinlocks for either the send or receive. although RMS spinlocks are required when allocating the message queue descriptor for the process.

Early performance runs of OPQ on a large test database has shown very good performance improvement as nodes and slave processes are added. One interesting discovery was that Oracle uses its own internal messaging to communicate with processes on the same node, and uses the external interface only for remote processes.

4 Summary

Encore's reflective memory technology enables us to efficiently implement a shared file system and support System-V shared memory semantics across the Infinity 90. Spinlocks, semaphores and message queues are implemented using RMS shared memory. Each node runs its own UNIX kernel with local memory, but with access to reflective memory, shared file system, and global process support; which is much less complex and better tolerates failures than running a single UNIX kernel. Multiple process applications using these standard interfaces can be easily ported to run across multiple nodes.

Acknowledgements

Many people have worked on portions of this project. Jeff Holsapple wrote rexec. Udaya Hegde wrote the RMS shared memory interface and also the health monitor refresh. Peter Ogilvie designed and implemented message queues. Marcy Davis ported the CICS environment thereby stress testing DALI functions. Cindy Davidson integrated the RMS messaging into Oracle parallel query.

References

[1] Aim performance report. AIM Technology, Santa Clara, CA, May 1992.

[2] E. W. Dijkstra. Solution of a Problem in Concurrent Programming Control. *Communications of the ACM*, 3(9), September 1965.

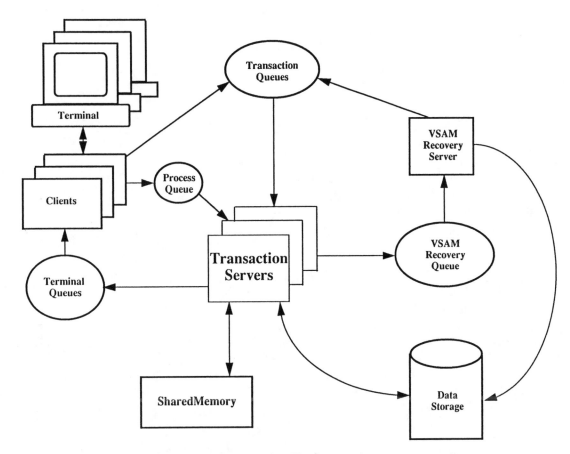

Figure 3: CICS Execution Environment

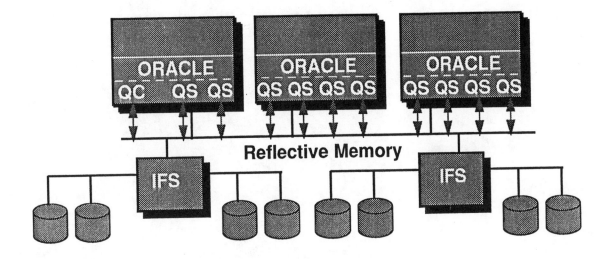

Figure 4: Oracle Parallel Query

[3] M. A. Eisenberg and M. R. McGuire. Further Comments on Dijkstra's Concurrent Programming Control Problem. *Communications of the ACM*, 15(11), November 1972.

[4] Encore Computer Corporation. *UMAX V Programmer's Guide Part 1*, March 1991. Chapter 8: Interprocess Communication.

[5] Encore Computer Corporation. *Infinity 90™Series Systems*, December 1992.

[6] Encore Computer Corporation. *Development Application Library for the Infinity 90™(DALI)*, July 1994.

[7] Udaya Hegde. Infinity health monitor and reflective memory refresh. Unpublished.

[8] Integris Integrated Information Solutions, 2626 W. Beryl Avenue, Phoenix, AZ 85021. *UniKix User's Guide, LZ15-00*.

[9] L. Lamport. A New Solution of Dijkstra's Concurrent Programming Problem. *Communications of the ACM*, 17(8), August 1974.

[10] Oracle Corporation, Redwood Shores, CA 94065. *Oracle 7™Parallel Server Administrators Guide*, 1992. Part No. 5990-70-1292.

[11] William E. Snaman and David W. Thiel. The VAX/VMS Distributed Lock Manager. *Digital Technical Journal*, September 1987.

[12] Reflective memory patents. United States Patent No. 4,991,079 dated February 5, 1991. Continuation of No. 710,229 dated March 11, 1985.

```
int _Dali_spin_n (lock, guard, ntries, nspins)
    rms_spinlock_t lock;
    guard_t guard;                    /* guard spinlock in "real" memory */
    int ntries;                       /* tries for RMS spinlock */
    int nspins;                       /* tries for guard spinlock */
{
    int i, bkoff;

    /* make sure only 1 process per node can get to rm spinlocks */
    while (_Dali_ntry_lock(&guard->lock,nspins) == 0) {            10
        if (--ntries <= 0)
            return 0;                 /* unable to acquire lock */
    }
    guard->owner_pid = Mpid;

    for(;;) {
        for(;;) {                     /* minimize bid collisions */
            if (CountBids(lock,&bkoff) == 0)
                break;                /* no bidders */
            if (--ntries > 0)                                      20
                back_off(bkoff);
            else {                    /* failure */
                guard->owner_pid = 0;
                spin_unlock(&guard->lock);
                return 0;
            }
        }
        lock->bid[Mnodeid] = 1; /* now make our bid */
        if (lock->owner == Mnodeid) {
            /* Optimization: last owned by this node and no collisions;   30
             * other nodes see our bid and wait. */
            lock->prev_own = Mnodeid;
            lock->owner_pid = Mpid;
            return 1;
        }
        rms_propogation_delay();
        if (CountBids(lock,&bkoff) == 1) {
            /* if no one else wants the lock, it's ours */
            lock->owner = Mnodeid;
            lock->prev_own = Mnodeid;                              40
            lock->owner_pid = Mpid;
            return 1;
        }
        lock->owner = 0;              /* collision happened */
        lock->bid[Mnodeid] = 0;       /* clear our bid */
        if (--ntries <= 0) {
            guard->owner_pid = 0;
            spin_unlock(&guard->lock);
            return 0;
        }                                                          50
        back_off(bkoff);
    }
}
```

Figure 5: DALI RMS spinlock

A Distributed Lock Manager on Fault Tolerant MPP

Mark Aldred, Ilya Gertner, Stephen McKellar

Encore Computer Corporation
300 Nickerson Road, Marlborough MA, 01752
(Extended Summary)

Abstract

The Distributed Lock Manager (DLM) is the cornerstone of running the Oracle Parallel Server on a MPP UNIX system. The DLM grants resource locks in NULL, READ, WRITE, and other levels. The DLM is typically implemented either with distributed message passing or in global shared memory, depending on the architecture. Reflective memory on the Encore Infinity 90 architecture permits a shared memory style DLM. Each node runs a separate copy of UNIX so failure of one node is isolated and DLM recovery can cleanup state. A node can later rejoin the Oracle session after node repair.

Introduction

The Oracle Parallel Server (OPS) is a unique parallel computing technology that supports both high-availability and multi-computer scalability. OPS maintains a per-node cache of buffers in shared memory, sharing the cache between all appropriate processes running on that node. Such a buffer cache minimizes I/O operations while maximizing performance. Multiple processes can access the information in the cache repeatedly with no internode processing required and no I/O, assuming the cache contains the buffers desired.

Since the buffer cache is directly visible to all processes which wish to reference the cache, arbitrating access to the information in the cache is relatively easy, with a local lock manager using local spinlocks and/or semaphores.

In a clustered environment, however, multiple nodes - each with its own local buffer cache - cannot arbitrate access to the information in the caches in such

---

Infinity 90, Reflective Memory, Infinity File System, and UMAX are trademarks of Encore Computer Corporation. UNIX is a trademark of AT&T Bell Laboratories.

a painless manner. Oracle's Parallel Cache Management ensures the consistency and integrity of the various buffer caches in such an environment, while still striving to minimize I/O and maximize performance. In order to provide this cache coherency, the Parallel Cache Management uses a Distributed Lock Manager (DLM) to track the location of blocks of data as they enter and exit the various buffer caches in the cluster. In effect, the DLM extends the semantics of local spinlocks/semaphores into a cluster-wide service available to all Oracle processes.

Features of a DLM

A DLM is a set of library routines that arbitrates locks on resources in a clustered (distributed) environment. When multiple processes on the same or different nodes wish to use the facilities of the DLM to coordinate access to a particular resource, they must each open a DLM lock, supplying the same resource name.

DLM locks that have been opened (initialized) exist in one of several levels (ie NULL, READ, WRITE) and are associated with exactly one resource. The actual resource being locked is not visible to the DLM; the DLM sees only a resource name provided by its caller, such as Oracle Parallel Cache Management.

The processes then attempt to convert the lock to the level desired. If the desired level is compatible with other locks on the resource (for example, any number of processes may simultaneously own locks on the same resource at the READ level), the DLM grants the lock (completes the convert operation).

However, if desired level is not compatible with other DLM locks on the resource, the DLM will notify the process(es) holding those locks on the resource in the blocking levels. Presumably, the blocking process will then lower the level of its lock (using a convert operation) such that the lock is no longer blocking the pended conversion request. When the pended conversion request is no longer blocked, the DLM will notify the issuing process that the its lock request has been granted.[2]

A DLM must also provide deadlock detection when appropriate. Since deadlock detection can be expensive, the caller can disable the function by specifying the proper flags when opening a lock and converting an open lock to another level.

Associated with each resource (actually part of the resource structure internal to the DLM) is a small buffer called the value block. The value block can be written to and read from by processes holding locks (in appropriate levels) on the resource. This facility allows processes to easily and efficiently coordinate access to protected resources other than blocks of information in a buffer cache.

A DLM must also guarantee consistency of its own data structures (and, by extension, the resources protected by those structures) in the event of a process failure or node failure.

DLM Implementations

A DLM implemented on an architecture which has no global shared memory must utilize a messaging paradigm in order to communicate information between the DLM processes on the various nodes in a cluster.

The overhead of an message passing implementation includes

- the processing required for the protocol used
- the latency inherent in the medium used
- the complexity of the deadlock detection algorithm required

In such an implementation, the DLM's internal database (containing, among other items, DLM lock and resource structures) is either located at a single node or distributed among multiple nodes in the cluster. In the former approach, the node quickly becomes the bottleneck in the system, and is a single point of failure. In the latter approach, the added complexity of a partitioned DLM database - and the processing required to recover and repartition this database after a node crash - make it undesirable as

well.

In a global shared memory implementation the DLM's database exists in global shared memory, immediately and directly accessible by all processes on all nodes in the cluster. The integrity of the data structures residing in global shared memory is ensured using a combination of local and distributed spinlocks.

In addition, the advantages of a global shared memory over an message passing include

- no protocol for inter-node communication; each node sees updates made to the global shared memory from all other nodes
- a transmission medium several orders of magnitude faster than a traditional message passing medium
- a simpler, faster deadlock detection algorithm
- immediate value block reading/writing
- more easily managed recovery from process and node failures
- faster prototyping on new hardware, using local shared memory for initial testing

With global visibility of the DLM's internal database, processes can directly manipulate DLM structures (including locks and resources), performing operations on locks with minimal inter-node interaction and therefore minimal overhead.

Reflective Memory

Encore Computer Corporation's global shared memory clusters (the Infinity 90) are built on Encore's Reflective Memory System (RMS) architecture, which provides replicated shared memory implemented in hardware.

Because the entire DLM database exists in RMS, all processes in the cluster can readily obtain the status of all objects in the DLM database, allowing the processes to quickly process lock operations using DLM library calls. This direct interaction among processes eliminates the need for a lock granting daemon (or set of daemons), thereby removing another potential bottleneck.

Maintaining the DLM database in RMS also allows efficient implementation of software to repair the effects of errant processes. Because of the persistent qualities of RMS, DLM daemons can also quickly repair the effects of failed nodes.

---

2. For more information, refer to 'The Oracle Lock Manager', a publication written by Chuck Simmons and Patty Greenwald of Oracle Corporation.

Fault Tolerance

All DLM data structures which need to be referenced by processes on two or more nodes in the cluster are maintained in RMS. Maintaining these structures in RMS allows for easy and efficient implementation of fault tolerance.

Prior to accessing RMS, Oracle processes must register with the DLM. This involves acquiring an entry in the DLM process table, a data structure which resides in RMS and contains the process id and the process log.

```
/* Process slot entry */
struct {
    uchar_t  proc_log[LOGSIZE];  /* process log */
    pid_t    pid;                /* global pid */
} proc_slot;
```

Upon obtaining a process table entry, a process will write its global process id into the process table. This global process id is unique across the cluster. The process log contains records of execution of critical regions of DLM code. These critical regions include operations such as modifying a globally shared linked list or getting a RMS spinlock. For example the LOG macro enters information into the process log.

```
LOG_AND_GET_SPINLOCK(list_slock);
LOG (MODIFYING_LIST);
add_to_linked_list (list_name, element);
LOG (DONE_MODIFYING_LIST);
LOG_AND_REL_SPINLOCK(list_slock);
```

The combination of spinlocks, logging, and fault recovery allow operations, such as the link list modification shown above, to appear atomic to all processes on the system.

The DLM daemons exists mainly to support fault tolerance. One daemon sends signals to every process registered in the process table. If the signal returns an error indicating that the process no longer exists, then the process log of the crashed processes is scanned. Information concerning the final activities of the process are easily accessible because the process log is maintained in RMS. Any DLM data structures that were being modified by the process at the time of the process crash will be checked for inconsistency and repaired if necessary. All RMS spinlocks held by the crashed process will then be released by the DLM daemons for use by other processes. Once recovery of spinlocks and damaged DLM data structures is complete the recovery of affected DLM lock and resource structures is undertaken.

If one or more nodes in the cluster crash, the DLM daemons will manage this as a series of single process crashes, using the algorithm described above. Due to the persistent qualities of RMS all surviving Oracle processes will maintain uninterrupted access to RMS even during a node crash.

At some point in the future, when the node has been repaired it will rejoin the cluster. The operating system will refresh the RMS on that node with the current copy in the cluster. Oracle processes which are then started on the repaired node will be able to participate in database access as before. If a new node is added to the cluster a similar refresh of RMS will occur. This "persistence of RMS" is one of the greatest assets to programming distributed fault tolerant applications.

An added benefit of storing data structures in RMS is that there is no need to replicate information in software across several nodes to support fault tolerance. The replication is transparently managed by the RMS hardware.

Summary

The library routines in our RMS based DLM contain about 7000 lines of commented C source code. Tools and daemons contain about 6000 lines of commented C source code.

We have used this DLM to run in configurations with >15 nodes (where each node is a 4CPU SMP machine), >200 GB of disk storage, and 64 total MB of RMS, 48 of which contained DLM data structures. Using just such a machine, we have set the world's record for the tpcB benchmark running Oracle Parallel Server 7.0.15. Given the inherent capability and extensibility of the global shared memory architecture - and Encore's RMS architecture in particular - we expect to achieve similar breakthroughs in other industry standard and customer benchmarks in the near future.

Tuning Oracle7 for nCUBE

Gilberto Arnaiz

Oracle Corporation

400 Oracle Parkway
Redwood Shores, CA 94065
(Extended Summary)

1 Introduction

This paper summarizes the experience in porting and tuning Oracle7 Parallel Server for nCUBE, a Massively Parallel Processing (MPP) computer that contains hundreds of processing elements. The idea of the parallel server where multiple instances of Oracle run against the same database was first developed for a loosely coupled VAX cluster. With the advent of Massively Parallel Systems, nCUBE was chosen to be first MPP platform to support Very Large Database systems.

The nCUBE parallel computer supports a hypercube array of up to 8192 individual nodes. Each node consists of and nCUBE processor and 1 to 64 Mbytes of memory. There are 28 unidirectional DMA channels on each nCUBE processor: 14 for input and 14 for output. Each channel has its own DMA registers. The processor uses cut-trough routing hardware, which accelerates message passing. A message is not stored in the memories of nodes along the routing path, and software is only executed at the initiating and receiving nodes. All messages are sent serially from node to node in packets of 32 data bits, at a rate of 2.2 Mbytes per second (external clock at 40 MHz).

Porting Oracle to the nCUBE computer was a very difficult task, because of the primitive OS support. The first port took five people one year and a half to complete. We implemented an RPC mechanism, a message based DLM, a logical volume manager and a distributed cache. Overall we wrote around 60000 lines of C code, and ported around 1000000 lines of C code.

There were a set of problems, which were inherent to the single image database implementation of Oracle, that needed to be solved to achieve the required performance and scalability.

In particular the performance problems were:

- instance load balancing (at the connection level)
- distributed access to disks
- handling hundreds of log files
- block pings between instances through disks

The performance tuning effort took as long as the port itself. The results were very positive: Oracle on nCUBE was the first computer to break the 1000 transactions/second barrier.

After the benchmark the efforts have been to productize Oracle 7.1. This has been a full time job for around 8 people, and we have focused in the following areas:

1. system administration
   - backup/restore tools
   - startup/shutdown of multiple instances
   - monitoring tools

2. performance and reliability
   - distributed lock manager
   - file system reliability
   - redo generation
   - data striping

- block pinging

Following is a more detailed description of the issues that have been solved to have a successful Oracle7 implementation in Massively Parallel Machines.

2 File system

Oracle Parallel Server requires that all the files have to be visible to all the instances of Oracle. To provide this functionality, we designed a distributed file system. Basically having a set of nodes as file system servers, presenting a single image file system to the clients.

The file system needs to be reliable. Oracle (and databases in general) have a very precise definition of a reliable file system, data integrity must be maintained in spite of computer, disk or network failures. In an event of a system crash, the integrity of the file system has to be warranted. This resilience is provided by a transaction based model (much like Oracle itself), that is, any file system operation that modifies meta-data is atomic (transaction), and journalling information is generated for it.

In order to support Oracle, the file system must provide high throughput for read and write operations to a fixed length file. This implies that the management of a single file must be distributed over multiple nodes to avoid bottlenecks on the I/O bandwidth or CPU cycles of a single processor. In the current implementation of the filesystem file striping is provided. The data is partitioned at the client level. We found out that the best stripe size is 32 Kbytes, which corresponds to the SCSI transfer size.

I/O load balancing is very important both for OLTP and DSS. In the case of OLTP data striping provides the best I/O performance. We also provided as part of the filesystem, a large distributed cache (the memory in an nCUBE node is very small 1 - 32 Mb). This large cache was going to be used as a write through cache to speed up the block pinging between instances of Oracle. As I will explain later, we used it as a write behind cache.

3 Block pings

The current implementation of Oracle Parallel Server uses a Distributed Lock Manager to keep its cache consistent. It statically allocates a set of locks to protect a fixed number of blocks in the database. This model generates a lot of false pings in an OLTP environment (picture an instance requiring a block protected by a lock that is being held exclusively by another instance because of a different block, the block will be flushed to disk even though it is not going to be read by the requesting instance).

We implemented a different locking model, where a lock protected a single block. With this we avoided the false pings, and we used the file system cache (gigacache) to speed up true pinging. We called this locking model DBA (Data Block Address) locking. To be able to use this new locking mechanism, the DLM has to handle "persistent resources". This term refers to the ability of a resource to maintain some state if all processes holding it have died abnormally.

4 Redo generation and archival

There are two separate problems. The first problem is a performance vs. cost. The optimum performance is obtained if there is a disk dedicated for each redo stream (log file). With few instances of Oracle this is not a big issue, but if we start looking at hundreds of instances, it clearly becomes a problem.

The second problem is administration of the hundreds or thousands of log files that need to be archived in order to be able to do media recovery in event of a major system crash.

We solve these two problems by having a redo server process running in a separate node. This process receives all the redo information generated by all of the instances of Oracle, merges it and writes it to disk as a single stream. Archiving also becomes easier (one large file instead of tens or hundreds of small ones). This clearly eases the administration of log files.

This approach presented several problems, specifically by the fact that a log switch forced all the instances of Oracle to checkpoint (flush dirty data blocks).

We decided to use this global checkpoint as a synchronization point for the gigagcache, thus effectively allowing for delayed writes to the file system. We used some spare time threads in the file system servers to flush dirty buffers from the cache, so that the Oracle checkpoints would not be to expensive.

5   System administration tools

Several new tools were developed to administer, and monitor multiple instances of Oracle. Specifically a tool that will allow for starting up and shutting down multiple instances of Oracle transparently. As well as a globalization of internal system tables.

6   Decission Support Systems

New challenges have been emerging as we start promoting MPP's for Decision Support Systems (DSS) that require support for parallel query execution as well as other parallel operations such as parallel load and merge. There are conflicting requirements that need to be worked out between OLTP (which is a mix of random reads and small writes) and DSS environments (which are dominated by long long sequential reads).

7   Summary

Currently we have successfully installed around 10 systems worldwide. The systems range between 64 and 512 processing nodes, running from 32 to 128 instances of Oracle and between 16 and 128 instances of the distributed file system (GFS). Most of this systems are being used for OLTP, and a couple of them in DSS environments. The size of the databases ranges from 5 Gbytes to 80 Gbytes.

A Simulation-Based Comparison of Two Reflective Memory Approaches

Milan Jovanović   Milo Tomašević*   Veljko Milutinović

Department of Computer Engineering
School of Electrical Engineering
University of Belgrade
POB 816
11000 Belgrade
Yugoslavia

(*)Department of Computer Engineering
Institute Mihajlo Pupin
University of Belgrade
POB 15
11000 Belgrade
Yugoslavia

Abstract

The Reflective Memory/Memory Channel (RM/MC) system represents a modular bus-based system architecture that belongs to the class of distributed shared memory systems. The RM/MC system is characterized by an update consistency mechanism for shared data and efficient block transfers over the bus. This work has two main goals. First, an extensive simulation analysis using the functional RM/MC simulator based on a very convenient and flexible synthetic workload model was carried out in order to evaluate the different design and implementation decisions and variants of the RM/MC concepts for a wide variety of the values of the relevant application-, architecture-, and technology-related parameters. In this way, an optimal set of values of relevant parameters was found. Second, this paper presents one improvement to the basic concept introduced to enhance the real-time response of the system. The proposed idea combines the compile- and run-time actions intended to reduce the latency of short messages. A set of experiments is performed to evaluate the efficiency of the proposed enhancement. The most important results are presented and discussed here.

1. Introduction

Distributed shared memory systems (DSM) are one of the most promising types of parallel systems, since they represent a successful hybrid of two important classes of computer systems: shared memory multiprocessors and distributed computer systems [Pro95]. They provide the shared memory abstraction on physically distributed memories of independent processor nodes. Consequently, they combine the advantages of both worlds: the simple and general shared memory programming paradigm and good portability of shared memory multiprocessors, as well as the scalability and cost-effectiveness of distributed systems. DSM systems vary greatly in regard to their architectures, algorithms, and approaches for implementation of DSM mechanism. Among others, hardware implementation of DSM mechanism is the most attractive, because of its transparency to the software layers and the best inherent performance [Gru94].

This research was partially supported by the FNRS (email: emilutiv@ubbg.etf.bg.ac.yu).
Proceedings of the Twenty-eighth IEEE/ACM Hawaii International Conference on System Sciences, Maui, Hawaii, U.S.A., January 3-6, 1995.

Hardware implementations are also more frequently found in the commercial systems.

These techniques are founded on the well-studied principles of coherence maintenance of private caches in shared-memory multiprocessor systems [Tom94a,Tom94b]. A prominent example of the hardware-implemented DSM mechanisms is the reflective memory concept [Ger93, Map90]. It is an anticipatory approach for preserving the coherence of shared regions of distributed memory, where the write to one copy of shared data is forwarded to all other sites with the copies of the same data, in order to keep them updated. In this way, low-latency local access to coherent shared data is provided. This mechanism is quite similar to the principles of snoopy write-update cache coherence protocols [Tom93].

This method is applied in the Encore line of high-performance computers, known as the RM systems. A typical RM system consists of a number of processing nodes with local memories connected by means of the non-multiplexed RM bus, which is used to propagate the updates of shared regions. The RM bus traffic consists of distributed write transfers on the word basis (address + value of data word item). Further evolution of this approach has augmented the RM concept with the MC (Memory Channel) capability, in order to improve the efficiency for transfers of blocks of data, frequently demanded by transaction-oriented processing applications. Besides single word transfers on the shared bus, block transfers are also allowed in an RM/MC system. This type of transfer exploits the fact that the initial address of the entire block and word count can be sent in the first cycle, and, after that, both address and data lines of the RM/MC bus are used for sending data. This is a way to nearly double the nominal bus bandwidth.

2. Problem statement

The major problems solved by this research are as follows. First, the goal was to develop a solution (referred to here as the RM/MC++) which represents an improvement in comparison with the existing solution (referred to here as the RM/MC*). Both the existing solution RM/MC* and the proposed improvement RM/MC++ will be elaborated in detail later. Second, the goal was to demonstrate that the proposed solution exhibits a better performance, for a slightly increased complexity. This was to be achieved using an appropriate simulation methodology.

Both problems defined above are important, for the following reasons. First, the RM/MC* approach is in its basic concept similar to the RM/MC approach of Encore Computer Systems [Ger93], and the developers of the Encore's future RM/MC systems may benefit from the proposed improvement. Second, the existing RM/MC approach is in wide use, and the users of the existing RM/MC approach will get a better (both qualitative and quantitative) indication of the potentials of the RM/MC concept.

3. Existing solution and its criticism

The concept which is here described as the RM/MC* will now be elaborated in details of interest for the discussion to follow. We will first give a general overview, and will cover the details only in the area in which the RM/MC* and the RM/MC++ differ from each other.

Basic architecture of RM/MC* systems is given in Figure 1, and the internal organization of one RM/MC* node is given in Figure 2, together with the related explanations. For more details, the interested reader is referred to the original Encore Computer Systems literature.

We will now elaborate the transmit FIFO and the receive FIFO parts of the RM/MC*, because that is where the major

differences are between the proposed RM/MC++ approach and the existing RM/MC* approach. The transmit FIFO buffer and the receive FIFO buffer are essential parts of the interface to the RM/MC bus. For synchronization purposes, parts of the transmit FIFO buffer and the receive FIFO buffer are located on two different boards: the TMI board which is placed at the interface to the RM/MC bus, and the HPI board which is placed at the interface to the local bus and the host bus (also shown in Figure 2).

The essence of the above described structure is as follows. The short (single transfer) RM messages and the long (block transfer) MC messages share the same FIFO, and do not interact with each other. Therefore, the RM/MC* approach can be treated as a straightforward additive combination of the well-known RM and MC approaches. Still, this approach is highly beneficial, because the sequences of data from consecutive memory addresses can share the address generation overhead and can be sent over both address and data lines. However, if the RM and MC messages were able to interact in the appropriate way, the performance of the overall system will improve, and that is the direction of our research to be presented in this paper.

It is clear, our criticism of the existing RM/MC* is oriented to the fact that the potentials of the interaction of short and long

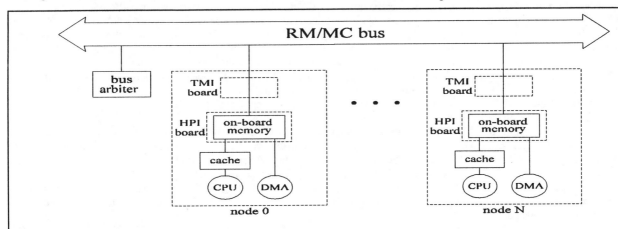

Figure 1: The RM/MC* system
CPU - Central Processor Unit   **HPI board** - Host Port Interface board
DMA - Direct Memory Access unit   **TMI board** - Transition Module Interface board
Description: The system consists of a variable (up to 9) number of identical nodes connected via the RM/MC bus. Each node consists of a processor-memory pair. Processor (responsible for single transfers) is connected to the RM/MC* node via the local processor/memory bus or the host system bus. The DMA unit (responsible for block transfers) is attached to the node via the host system bus. Memory can be configured as private memory and reflective memory. Private memory is exclusively accessed by each particular node. Reflective memory is accessible to all nodes connected to the RM/MC bus and consists of transmit regions and receive regions. The on-board memory fully supports the protocol for the coherence maintenance of private caches in the host system. A separate module - bus arbiter - is responsible for granting the access to the RM/MC bus for the requesting nodes. The arbitration module incorporates a modified round robin synchronous arbitration algorithm. The incorporated modification provides that a programmable number of requests from one node can be granted one after another in some specific situations.
Explanation: All writes to shared memory (both single and block) are written into the local RM memory, and into the transmit FIFO buffer (and later onto the RM/MC bus) if the transmit window for that particular write is open (i.e., mapped as a shared region). Other nodes accept the transfer and, if the receive window of some particular node is open, a write into the local RM memory of that node will take place.
Implication: The RM/MC bus is used for hardware maintenance of coherence between local copies of the shared memory. In other words, the system does not wait for a node to request a shared data item for read before sending the most up-to-date copy to that particular node; instead, remote copies of data are updated on each write. Consequently, reads of shared data are always satisfied from the local RM memory, which drastically decreases the latency of shared reads.

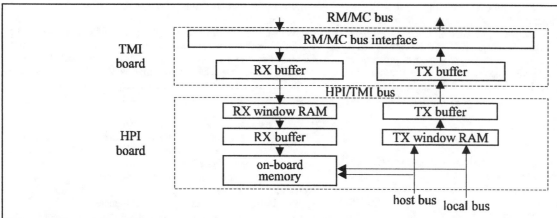

Figure 2: The RM/MC* node
HPI board - Host Port Interface board
TX window RAM - transmit window translation RAM
TX buffer - transmit FIFO buffer

TMI board - Transition Module Interface board
RX window RAM - receive window translation RAM
RX buffer - receive FIFO buffer

Description: The requirement for system modularity was fulfilled in the way that two boards are needed to implement a single RM/MC* node: the HPI board and the TMI board. The HPI board provides the interface to the host system bus (and to the local bus, if present), while the TMI board implements the interface to the RM/MC bus. The central element on the HPI board is the on-board memory (256 or 512 MB memory). The HPI board also includes the TX window translation RAM and the RX window translation RAM. Their role is to perform the address mapping and to select the transfers being sent to or received from the RM/MC bus. The HPI board is connected to the TMI board through the HPI/TMI bus. The HPI/TMI bus consists of two 32-bit unidirectional data links (plus the related control links). To make the communication protocol between two boards easier, two FIFO buffers (transmit and receive) are provided on the HPI board. The TMI provides the standard interface to the RM/MC bus through the bus transceiver circuitry. Just like the HPI, the transmit FIFO buffer and the receive FIFO buffer are also available on the TMI board. An attempt was made to improve the node expansion capability and to reduce the bulk of cabling in the hardware interface to the RM/MC bus. For that purpose, one TMI board could interface multiple HPI boards to the RM/MC bus. A connection scheme for the case with 2-way and 4-way multiporting between the HPI/TMI bus and the RM/MC bus has been proposed.

Explanation: If the most significant N bits of the address of a memory write from the host bus or the local bus fall within the open transmit address window (TX window) during address translation, the transfer will be reflected onto the RM/MC bus. The write message (data and address) is first placed into the TX buffer on the HPI board. From there, via the HPI/TMI bus, it moves into the TX buffer on the TMI board, where a grant for access onto the RM/MC bus is waited for. After the bus access is granted, the node broadcasts the write message on the RM/MC bus. All other RM/MC* nodes receive the transfer from the RM/MC bus. If the address of the received message hits into an open RX window of some node, address translation takes place, and a write into the local RM memory of that node will happen.

Implication: When some new host system has to be connected to the RM/MC bus, the design reuses the standard RM/MC interface (TMI), and only the host interface (HPI) has to be redesigned. In this way, design process is faster, more efficient, and more reliable. By virtue of multiporting the TMI board, the limitation to 9 physical nodes can be exceeded. The number of physical nodes can be effectively expanded to either 16 or 32, by virtue of the multiported HPI/TMI bus interface.

messages were not taken into account. In other words, the system will perform better if the probability is minimized that a short message follows with a delay after a long one, in conditions when the two are of the same priority (from the application point of view) and data-independent (from the algorithm semantics point of view). Our proposed solution is based on this criticism, and is aimed towards the elimination of the basic ground for this criticism.

4. The proposed solution and its essence

The question is now what is the most efficient method of putting the RM and MC messages to interact with each other, in order to achieve the above described goal. One solution, which is the subject of this paper, is to introduce two separate FIFO buffers on the transmit side (and consequently on the receive side, as well, for compatibility purposes), which is just a part of

the improvement, and also to enable the two FIFOs to talk together, which is the deep essence of the proposed improvements. In other words, the separation of the FIFO buffers enables the RM and MC streams to be controlled independently, while the incorporation of the interaction of the two FIFO buffers enables the two streams to interact in a more efficient synergistic way.

With the above organizational philosophy in mind, the proposed solution for the RM/MC++ is as follows. The RM FIFO buffer contains only the RM messages. The MC FIFO buffer contains the MC and quasiRM messages. The quasiRM sequence of messages carries the relevant information about the data dependence in relation to the MC stream. This information is prepared at compile time, and is relatively easy to generate. This information is incorporated without any increase in the storage capacity of the transmit FIFOs - by careful ordering of quasiRM and MC messages in the MC FIFO. Mutual data dependency is not an issue, since the two streams (RM and MC) are mutually independent.

However, the above described structure is not all. Some data dependencies can not be accurately estimated at compile time. In such cases, the compiler is forced to follow the worst case scenario, and some of the short (quasiRM) messages will end up in the MC FIFO unnecessarily, which may (and typically will) slow down the application. This is where an appropriate level of interaction of the two FIFOs can help.

In other words, at run time, some of the quasiRM messages, once the run time decision is generated that they are better off in the RM FIFO (from the performance point of view), in conditions when such a transfer is allowed (from the data dependency point of view), should be moved back into the RM FIFO. The question is how to generate (at run time) the knowledge of the fact that some potential data dependency (which was seen as possible at compile time, and resulted in the compile time insertion of some quasiRM message) did not materialize at run time (because of the way in which the data and instruction streams ended up flowing, which means that the inserted quasiRM message has to be moved back into the RM FIFO). There is a simple solution, as indicated in Frame 1.

When it is known in run time that the data and/or instruction stream have flowed in the direction which implies no data dependency (which was the cause of the insertion of the given short message into the MC FIFO), the information of this "critical address" has to be kept somewhere until the corresponding quasiRM comes. At that time, the quasiRM message can be moved back into the RM FIFO. The question is

now, where to keep the critical address information, and at which point in the system to check that critical address, for possible sending of the quasiRM message back into the RM FIFO.

A small buffer (quasiRM buffer) can be added at the beginnings of the two FIFOs, to contain the critical address information supplied dynamically to trigger the move of a quasiRM message from the MC FIFO into the RM FIFO. This position of the quasi RM buffer is determined by the fact that RM messages are more critical, and that it is important to avoid the unnecessary delay of the "wrongly accused" quasiRM message in the slower MC FIFO. Therefore, the point in the system where the critical address checking and the quasiRM message redirection are to be done should be as early in the FIFO streams as possible (at their beginnings). A solution which does the redirection of the quasiRM message at the exits from the transmit FIFO should bring virtually no performance benefits, since the quasiRM message would be redirected after all the unnecessary waiting. Consequently, a link between the two FIFO buffers is needed only between the two outmost (beginning) entries.

Regarding the obtaining of the RM/MC bus, the RM messages, being the shorter ones, are given higher priority with respect to the longer MC messages, however only up to the point which will not violate the possible hard deadlines of the application which is typically in the domain of the real-time distributed databases (this information is also extractable at compile time). This is controlled by the parameter which refers to the relative importance of the RM and MC streams. In other

---

- **The compile-time actions:**

1. Compiler analyses the data declared as shared, which is to be placed into reflective memory regions.

2. Compiler prepares the mapping information for the loading of TX and RX window translation RAM (that can be subsequently processed by the linker/loader).

3. During the compile analysis, long write messages are tagged as MC, and data-independent short messages are tagged as RM. All other short messages (possibly and surely data-dependent) are tagged as quasiRM.

4. If the compiler realizes that some quasiRM message can become data-independent of the MC stream during a certain outcome of program flow, a special *embed* instruction with the corresponding address is inserted in the code at this place.

5. When the compiler eventually later realizes that the quasiRM write can become again data-dependent, it issues an alternate *draw-out* instruction which will nullify the effect of the previous *embed* instruction.

- **The run-time actions**

1. At the very beginning, TX and RX window translation RAMs are loaded with the address mapping and open/close window information.

2. Execution of an *embed* instruction results in sending the appropriate address to the quasiRM buffer.

3. On each write to an address within an open window, RM messages are directed to the RM TX buffer and MC messages are inserted into the MC TX buffer. If the message is of the quasiRM type, its address is compared to the contents of the quasi RM buffer. If match is successful, the message is forwarded to the RM TX buffer; otherwise, it is sent to the MC TX buffer.

4. Execution of a *draw-out* instruction results in deleting the entry with specified address from the quasiRM buffer.

Frame 1: Outline of the algorithm for migration of messages between two transmit FIFO buffers

Description: The algorithm is presented as a list of the actions that have to be taken, both in compile time and in run time. This makes it possible to convert the short quasiRM messages into short RM messages.

Explanation: Compiler analysis is conservative; i.e., only those short messages that are data-independent are tagged as RM messages, while all other short messages are declared as quasiRM. The RM messages, on the one side, and the MC and the quasiRM messages pass two separate ways (excluding the RM/MC bus) through the system (the RM messages through the RM FIFOs, and the MC and the quasiRM through the MC FIFOs). If the flow of program through specific paths can make some quasiRM message data-independent, a special instruction is used to send its address to the quasiRM buffer. If it happens, this is supposed to precede the execution of the quasiRM messages in question. Therefore, the address matching with the quasiRM buffer can be performed before the message enters one of the HPI FIFOs. After a quasiRM write to an open window, if corresponding address hits into the quasiRM buffer, this message becomes RM and it is redirected into the RM FIFO.

Implication: Since the address matching in the quasiRM buffer is performed simultaneously with the address translation in the TX window RAM, no additional time penalty for handling quasiRM messages is incurred with this algorithm.

---

words, if this parameter has a value of n (n=1, 2, 3, ...), then one MC message will follow after every n RM messages. As will be seen later, this parameter is an important element of the analysis. Its value can be determined (or statistically estimated) at compile time, and dialed into the RM/MC++ hardware. It is worth to mention at this point, that the present description refers to one node, and that the nodes are connected using the round robin methodology, as described earlier in this paper.

Of course, if no MC message is ready at the moment when the n-th RM message is out, there are at least three possibilities: (a) one is that a new stream of n RM messages starts and so on, (b) the second is that the first MC message will preempt the ongoing RM stream, while (c) the third is that the counting of RM messages will start after the first MC message appears. In our analysis to follow, only the third option was analyzed, because it favors the RM messages, which is consistent with most applications of interest for RM/MC users.

The amount of quasiRM messages to be moved back (relocated) depends on the ability of the compiler to create efficient critical addresses. The impact of the compiler quality with respect to this issue, can be judged through the incorporation (into the simulator to be described later) of a parameter which tells about the percentage of relocated quasiRM messages. The value of this parameter can be varied in the range of 0% to 100%.

In addition to the above mentioned parameters related to issues that make the major difference between the RM/MC* and the RM/MC++, there is a relatively long set of parameters which refer to the basic concept. These are relevant for both the RM/MC* and the RM/MC++, and will be defined later, in the section on the simulation.

5. Conditions and assumptions of the research

In our research methodology, the term condition refers to the specification of the real environment. The term assumption refers to the simplifications which make the analysis either possible or easier, without any negative impact on the generality and representativeness of the results.

Both the conditions and the assumptions will be presented here, classified in the following categories: (a) application, (b) system software, (c) architecture, (d) organization, (e) design, and (f) technology. The two lists are given in the form of two tables, with explanations and justifications, where so required (Table 1 and Table 2).

6. Simulator structure and the simulator dial-in parameters

Our simulator is based on the DARPA standard N.2 package, and its basic structure is determined by the underlying essence of the ISP' (an efficient HDL) and the general N.2 simulation environment. However, our research was required to be based on the synthetic workload model of Archibald and Baer [Arc86], modified for the RM/MC environment. Therefore, this choice of simulation methodology eliminates all but the major three N.2 system programs from our simulation environment. For more details about the N.2 package, ISP', and their applications, the interested reader is referred to the following reference [TDT92].

P	The applications can support either only the RM type of transfers, or only the MC type of transfers, or both types of transfer together.
S	The compiler is supposed to provide the information about the sharing status of the potentially shared data within a given task. Before a task starts running on a processor, this information is written into the TX window RAM and the RX window RAM.
A	A system is considered that consists of a variable number of RM/MC nodes and one bus arbitration unit.
A	The global on-board memory can be accessed from four ports: a) the local bus port, b) the host bus port, c) the receive RM FIFO buffer port (RM/MC++ only), and d) the receive MC FIFO buffer port.
O	Every single node is composed of one TMI (Transition Module Interface) board and up to four HPI (Host Port Interface) boards, connected by the HPI/TMI bus.
O	Contention in accessing the global memory is resolved using a prioritized arbitration scheme: a) the highest priority is assigned to the local bus (except when the *shared write (sub)block transfer* is going on the host bus, or the HPI transmit buffer is full), b) the next priority is assigned to the RM receive buffer port (the RM/MC++ only), c) higher priority is given to the host port, compared to the MC receive buffer port, when the MC receive buffer is less than half full; otherwise, the MC receive buffer will be given upper hand.
O	With the RM/MC* system, the DMA blocks move around the system as indivisible units. It is possible that a block transfer is preempted by a higher priority access (read or write) to the local RM memory; however, at the entry into the transmit FIFO, the DMA block must exist in one piece.
O	With the RM/MC++ system, the DMA blocks are divided into sub-blocks of fixed size. It is possible that a sub-block transfer is preempted by a higher priority access (read or write) to the local RM memory; however, at the entry into the transmit FIFO, the sub-block must exist in one piece.
O	When multiported to the TMI, all HPI boards have equal priority; and the round robin arbitration policy is applied.
D	The design is based on off-the-shelf memory, FIFO, and buffer chips, with the random logic incorporated into the appropriate PLD chips.
T	The applied cabling technology implies the limitation of up to 9 nodes on the RM/MC system.

Table 1: Conditions of the analysis

Description: The conditions of the analysis are presented here, classified into the following categories: (a) P-application, (b) S-system software, (c) A-architecture, (d) O-organization, (e) D-design, and (f) T-technology.

Explanation: With the RM/MC* system, the global on-board memory is of the 3-port type. In the contention resolution for the global memory access, the receive buffer on the HPI board (the only one on the HPI board) is treated as the MC receive buffer.

Implication: The RM/MC++ system includes a more complex memory access control logic.

P	A synthetic workload model is used for the trace generation.
P	The transfer time is measured from the beginning of memory write (from the host bus or the local bus, at the local node) until the beginning of the memory write (at the remote node).
P	Cache memory instruction misses are neglected.
S	The compiler is responsible for the characterization of short messages into RM and quasiRM. The RM messages are data independent from the MC messages. The quasiRM messages are data dependent from the MC messages.
S	The compiler is responsible for the insertion of the *embed* instruction which will submit addresses into the quasiRM buffer, so that the quasiRM messages can be recognized on-line.
S	The compiler is responsible for the elimination of the address (from the quasiRM buffer) of the quasiRM message, which was moved back into the RM transmit queue.
A	The experiment related to the HPI/TMI multiport effects (for the case of one HPI and one TMI) was conducted for the cases of up to 16 nodes, although the current RM/MC systems are limited to 9 nodes. The rationale behind this is to enable a fair comparison with other experiments.
O	The cache read misses fetch the entire cache blocks from memory.
O	The ability of asserting multiple grant requests is enabled when the TMI transmit buffer count reaches the pre-programmed threshold.
O	The bus cycle (on the local or the host bus) related to the instructions which manipulate the quasiRM buffer is neglected.
D	If arbitration is necessary for the HPI/TMI bus, the arbitration logic is placed on the TMI board.
D	The local bus (and the host bus) to memory access synchronization time is neglected.
D	The local bus write buffer is assumed to include two words (data + address).
D	The quasiRM buffer can be implemented as an associative or a set-associative memory.
T	On-chip cache hit is completed within one CPU cycle.
T	The FIFO memory read and write times are neglected.

Table 2: Assumptions of the analysis

Description: The assumptions of the analysis are presented here, classified into the following categories: (a) P-application, (b) S-system software, (c) A-architecture, (d) O-organization, (e) D-design, and (f) T-technology.
Explanation: An exhaustive simulator (to the smallest details) was impossible to realize because of the lack of information about the system details. Fortunately, it occurred that this was not needed, since the level of details of a functional simulator of the system was good enough to serve the intended purpose. Moreover, low level unnecessary details may decrease the efficiency of the simulation, without improving the quality of the results.
Implication: A simulator with very convenient and flexible stochastic workload model was built, to achieve the functional modeling of the RM/MC* and the RM/MC++ system behavior in the time domain.

Before we continue, a note is needed to explain our choice of the synthetic workload simulation methodology. The choice of the workload model is recognized as one of the most critical issues in any simulation methodology, because of the fact that the performance of the RM/MC system is greatly influenced by the type and frequency of memory references. Although artificial in nature, a reliable and flexible synthetic workload model can be very useful. It represents the workload in a compact and efficient manner. Moreover, careful varying of appropriate parameters that characterize applications in a flexible synthetic model is a convenient way to evaluate the performance of simulated solutions over the broad range of various workloads and system configurations, which is exactly what was the major requirement of our research.

We now list all major simulation parameters. The parameters are given in the form of the tables, with minimal, typical, and maximal values [Jov93]. The list of workload parameters is presented in Table 3.1. The list of system-oriented and technology-oriented parameters is provided in Table 3.2.

The simulator is realized with the possibility to collect the large amount of statistics. Counters for all relevant events which serve as direct or derived performance indicators are provided. Our basic performance measure is the processor utilization, since this figure directly expresses the amount of work that can be done in specific period of time. Another important performance indicator, especially for real-time response, is the average latency of short write messages from write to an open window of on-board memory until the shared copies in memories of other nodes are updated. This indicator is calculated as a weighed sum of average the latencies of the RM and quasiRM messages (according to their relative percentage). Other relevant statistic includes: utilization of various buses (RM/MC, local, host), average waiting for memory access on different ports, average waiting for the RM/MC bus grant, etc.

7. Analysis

All experiments (to be shown later) have been conducted under the above specified conditions and assumptions, and the results are presented next. Each experiment is dedicated a special figure with: (a) description of the relevant issues, (b) explanation for each issue, and (c) implications of each issue.

The first group of experiments is related to the general RM/MC environment (Figures 4 to 8). For the case of the RM/MC* solution, they show the impact of various system parameters. The rational behind these experiments was the selection of the right environment for the analysis of the RM/MC++ solution. From Figure 4 it follows that the version with both the local bus and the host bus offers a better performance, because of shorter average latency of memory accesses from the processor via the higher priority local bus. From Figure 5 it follows that shared data should be cached, from the reason of more efficient access in spite of the fact that this requires the coherence of private caches should be maintained for shared data. From Figure 6 it follows that the higher level of sharing degrades the processor utilization because of increased contention for on-board memory. Figure 7 and Figure 8 demonstrate the impact of technology-oriented parameters. It was shown that the speed of the RM/MC bus is not the only factor that limits the system power and scalability (especially when this bus is not much utilized), and that the beneficial effects on the processor utilization can be achieved by simultaneous improvement of the RM/MC clock, the HPI/TMI bus clock, and the memory access time.

Parameter	Min	Typ.	Max
Number of processor cycles between two memory references	0		8
Probability of referencing the RM memory		0.5	
Probability of referencing an open transmit window	0.2*	0.8	1.0*
Write probability	0.2*	0.4	
Probability that a write from the RM/MC bus will hit in an open receive window	0.1	0.5	0.9
+ Data-independence factor of short messages	0.0	0.25	1.0
+ Recovery factor - probability that a quasiRM message can be moved back into the RM transmit FIFO	0.0	0.25	1.0
Number of shared blocks		256	
Cache miss ratio for private data		0.05	
Block size [words]	64		512
+ Sub-block size [words]	16	16	64
Max. time between two DMA transfers [ms]	0.5	0.5	1*

Table 3.1: The list of workload parameters

Parameter	Min	Typ.	Max
CPU cycle [ns]	15*	30	
HPI/TMI bus cycle [ns]	18	37	
RM/MC bus cycle [ns]	37	75	
Single mode memory access time [ns]	60	110	
Fast page mode memory access time [ns]	25	45	
Size of the transmit FIFO buffer on the HPI board [Kwords]		4	8*
Size of the receive FIFO buffer on the HPI board [Kwords]		4	8*
Size of the transmit FIFO buffer on the TMI board [Kwords]		4	8*
Size of the receive FIFO buffer on the TMI board [Kwords]		4	8*
Number of processors	4		16
Cache block size [B]		16	
Word length [B]		4	
+ The RM favorization factor - maximal number of RM messages followed by one MC or quasiRM message (for each particular node)	1	1	∞
Maximal number of sequentially granted multiple grant requests	0*	10	100*

Table 3.2: The list of system-oriented and technology-oriented parameters

+ refers to parameters used only in the RM/MC++ model.
* refers to values considered only in the RM/MC* model, not presented here.

Description: All major simulation parameters are listed here. The parameters are given in the form of a table, with minimal, typical, and maximal values.

Explanation: Where the minimal and maximal values are missing, the typical value was used. Where the typical value is missing, a randomly generated value which is in the minimum to maximum range is used (except for the number of processors).

Implication: The selection of parameters, as well as their ranges, is of a crucial importance for the representativeness of the generated simulation results.

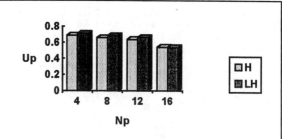

Figure 4: CPU utilization for different implementation strategies
Up - processor utilization
Np - number of processors
H - dual-ported on-board memory (from the host bus and the receive buffer)
LH - three-ported on-board memory (from the host bus, the receive buffer, and the local bus)
Description: The LH variant (with the local processor-memory bus) has a better processor utilization than the H variant.
Explanation: The main drawback of the H variant is an increased contention on the host system bus, which induces higher average waiting of the processor in accessing the on-board memory.
Implication: Since the variant with the local bus port appears to have the best performance, only that variant will be considered in the subsequent simulation experiments.

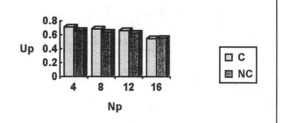

Figure 5: CPU utilization for two different caching strategies
Up - processor utilization
Np - number of processors
C - caching for shared regions of on-board memory is allowed,
NC - caching for shared regions of on-board memory is forbidden.
Description: The figure shows processor utilization in the cache and no-cache variants, for different numbers of processors.
Explanation: The advantages of caching the shared data are reflected in a better processor utilization for the cache variant, as a consequence of the lower latency cache access. In addition to that, the problem of contention of accesses to memory is mitigated, which gives positive effects on the utilizations of other two ports.
Implication: The overall effect in the cache variant is that more memory references are generated in the same period of time, and more work is done.

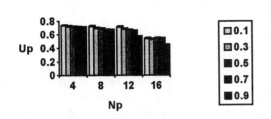

Figure 6: CPU utilization for various levels of sharing
Up - processor utilization   **Np** - number of processors
Prx - probability that a write from the RM/MC bus will hit into an open receive window of the particular processor.
Description: General conclusion is that processor utilization decreases with the increase of the receive probability. This decline is more evident as the number of processors grows.
Explanation: One of the vital elements in the RM/MC system is the efficient access to the on-board reflective memory. Being three-ported, the RM memory is a potential source of serious contention. The degree of contention is highly dependent on the traffic from the receive buffer port, i.e. from the RM/MC bus. The amount of data being written to memory from this side is directly proportional to the level of sharing in the system. Looser sharing assumes a lower number of open windows - shared reflective memory regions, and tighter coupling of individual nodes results in a larger shared address space mapped into the open windows.
Implication: Level of sharing in the system is one of the main characteristics of the application being executed in the system.

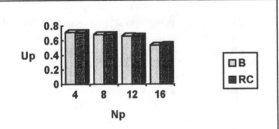

Figure 7: The influence of a faster RM/MC bus on system performance.
Up - processor utilization   **Np** - number of processors
B - the RM/MC bus cycles has the default value equal to 75ns
RC - RM/MC bus cycles is halved
Description: The processor utilization is not affected for a lower number of processors when the bus bandwidth is not fully utilized.
Explanation: Even in the system with 16 processors, the processor utilization is not significantly improved, which means that other system elements are also responsible for system saturation.
Implication: This leads to the conclusion that the improving the bus bandwidth itself is not enough for a significantly better performance.

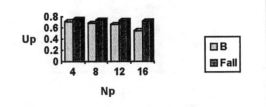

Figure 8: Combined influence of a faster RM/MC bus, the HPI/TMI bus, and the memory, on the overall system performance.
Up - processor utilization   **Np** - number of processors
B - system with default parameter values
Fall - system with the halved RM/MC bus and HPI/TMI bus clock cycles, and a faster memory (single memory cycle is 60ns, and the fast page mode cycle is 25ns).
Description: Figure clearly demonstrates improved processor utilization due to lower latency of memory accesses in the faster variant. It also expresses much better scalability of the faster variant - a very desirable characteristic that denotes the ability of the system to deliver the performance directly proportional to the system cost (processor utilization is almost constant for different system sizes).
Explanation: The above described effect is a result of the much lower waiting of processor to access the on-board memory
Implication: It can be concluded that the system is expandable to larger node counts without significant processor degradation, and a higher overall system power can be attained even with the same processor cycle time.

The second group of experiments is related to the newly proposed RM/MC++ system (Figures 9 to 13). Again, the figure captions explain all major results and their implications. Figure 9 shows a slight positive impact of the finer sub-block sizes (all later experiments are based on the sub-block size equal to 16 words) on processor utilization. Figures 10 and 11 shed more light on the overall average propagation time of short messages and clearly demonstrate the expected effectiveness of the proposed solution. Introduction of separate RM and MC FIFOs evidently decreases the turnaround time of short messages compared to the case with a single FIFO (which is equivalent to zero data-independence factor), and that was the primary intention of the proposed enhancement. The effects are directly proportional for an increased data-independence factor found in an application. The ability to remove the conservative detection of data dependence during compile time and to dynamically redirect some quasiRM messages into the RM FIFO further cuts the latency of short messages in quite alike manner. Figure 12 gives the impact of the RM favorization factor (this figure is especially important, because it gives the information about the optimal system design for a given application characterized with an apriori known value of th RM favorization factor). Finally, Figure 13 gives a quantitative indication of the impact of the chosen arbitration scheme for the access to on-board memory.

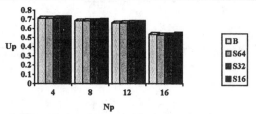

Figure 9: Influence of various sub-block transfer sizes on the processor utilization

Up - processor utilization   **Np** - number of processors

B - there is no sub-blocks

S64 - size of each sub-block transfer is 64 words + address

S32 - size of each sub-block transfer is 32 words + address

S16 - size of each sub-block transfer is 16 words + address

Description: The processor utilization increases insignificantly (only about 1%) with the decreasing of the sub-block transfer size. Exception to this rule is the system with 16 processors, in which the non-increasing trend can not be noticed.

Explanation: The local bus has a lower priority only when the shared write block transfer goes on the host bus, and processor is in the wait state. At the end of the sub-block transfer, the processor is allowed to preempt memory. If the sub-blocks are shorter, the processor will preempt the memory earlier. The performance improvements are not great, because the shared write block transfer on the host bus is sparse. However, the trend is regular, except for the system with 16 processors, because of the RM/MC bus saturation effects.

Implication: Only the systems with the sub-block transfer size of 16 words will be considered in the rest of this analysis, and will be presented in the subsequent simulation experiments (unless specified differently).

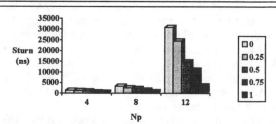

Figure 10: Influence of the data-independence factor of short messages on the overall average propagation time of short messages

Sturn - overall average propagation time of short messages

Np - number of processors

Description: The overall average propagation of short messages decreases with increase of data-independence factor of short messages. The influence is higher with increasing the number of processor in the system.

Explanation: With increasing of data-independence factor of short messages, there is more short messages which run through system with higher priority, bypassing the longer block transfers, and the probability is minimized that a short message follows with a delay after a long one. Because of saturation effect, the graph does not follow the pattern of Np = 4 to 16. Still the advances of our approach are clearly visible, but not presented because the effects are evident for a longer execution time.

Implication: If there are more data-independent short messages the overall average propagation of short messages will decrease.

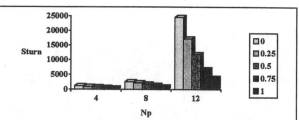

Figure 11: Influence of the recovery factor (R) - probability that a quasiRM message can be moved back into the RM transmit FIFO - on the overall average propagation of short messages

Sturn - overall average propagation time of short messages

Np - number of processors

Description: The graph is presented for the system with the data-independence factor of short messages equal to 0.25. The overall average propagation time of short messages decreases with the increase of the probability that a quasiRM message can be moved back into the RM transmit FIFO. The influence is higher with increasing number of processors in the system.

Explanation: When increasing the probability that a quasiRM message can be moved back into the RM transmit FIFO due to run time detection of data independence, the number of short independent messages (which run through system with higher priority) increases, so the average turnaround time is decreased. Because of the saturation effects, the graph does not follow the pattern of Np = 4 all the way to Np=16. Still, the advances of our approach are clearly visible, but not presented because the effects show up for a longer execution time.

Implication: The possibility of run-time detection of data-independent quasiRM messages enables their return back into the RM transmit FIFO buffer, which means that the average message propagation time is (considerably) decreased.

The above results demonstrate the superior performance of the proposed solution, in the applications characterized with a high value of the recovery factor (typical transactions processing applications). Fortunately, preliminary implementation analysis has pointed out that the complexity increase is minimal. In short, the complexity increase of the RM/MC++ over the RM/MC* is negligible.

8. Conclusion

This paper presents the extensive analysis of the RM/MC concept - a reflective memory approach which combines the non-demanded write-broadcast coherence mechanism for distributed shared memory on a snoopy bus with the ability to provide the efficient block transfer between different nodes. The work has two major purposes: a) to analyze the behavior of the existing RM/MC in respect to the conditions of typical end-user applications and to various design issues, and b) to introduce and elaborate an improvement which is intended to reduce the turnaround time of short, time-critical messages. The first set of simulation experiments was used to derive the optimal set of system parameters of the interest for the application and to propose the specific design decisions, having in mind cost/performance point of view.

The second set of experiments starts from this set of optimal parameters and examines the performance of proposed enhancement, proving its effectiveness in specified conditions. Therefore, the results of this analysis are found to be relevant

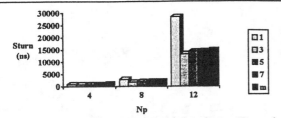

Figure 12: Influence of the RM favorization factor (F) - the maximal number of RM messages followed by one MC or quasiRM message (in each particular node) - on the overall average propagation time of short messages
Sturn - overall average propagation of short messages
Np - number of processors
m - the case when a MC message is sent from the node which was granted to use the bus only if the RM transmit FIFO on the TMI board of that node is empty (logically F tends to infinity)
Description: The graph is presented for the system with the data-independence factor of short messages equal to 0.5. The functions from the bar-chart have a minimum (no matter what is the value of Np). This minimum is more obvious as the number of processors in system increases.
Explanation: It is important to give a higher priority to as many short messages as possible, because that makes the system faster. However, it is not recommended to choose the maximal number of RM messages followed by one MC or quasiRM message to be too high, because the saturation of the quasiRM short messages (from the lower-priority FIFO buffer) makes the overall system slower. Because of the saturation effect, the graph does not follow the pattern of Np = 4 all the way to Np = 16. Still, the advantages of our approach are clearly visible in the simulator, but not presented in the bar-chart, because the effects can distort the picture.
Implication: For the given value of Np, the best engineering solution is to choose the value for the F factor corresponding to the minimum of the Sturn function. For the case of this figure, the optimal value of the F factor is equal to three.

both for application writers and system designers in their strive to obtain the better performance of the RM/MC system.

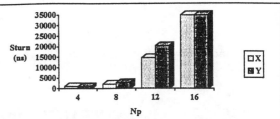

Figure 13: Impact of the arbitration scheme for memory access onto the overall average propagation time of short messages
Sturn - overall average propagation time of short messages
Np - number of processors
X - the case when the RM receive FIFO buffer has a higher priority compared with the host bus
Y - the case when the RM receive FIFO buffer has a higher priority compared with the host bus, only when the RM receive FIFO buffer is over half full.
Description: The overall average propagation time of short messages depends a lot on the utilized arbitration scheme for memory access. The used four-port memory enables a large variety of arbitration schemes to be used. This figure is essentially a comparison of two different arbitration schemes (X and Y).
Explanation: Since the priority of the RM receive FIFO buffer is increased (containing the short data-independent messages), the long messages from the host bus will not slow down the short messages from the RM receive FIFO buffer. The arbitration scheme which provides a shorter overall propagation time does include some drawbacks, too. Its average waiting time for the host bus is (somewhat) increased.
Implication: One has to be careful with the choice of the arbitration scheme, since this choice has an evident impact on the performance of the system.

10. References

[Arc86] Archibald J., Baer J.-L., "Cache Coherence Protocols: Evaluation Using a Multiprocessor Simulation Model," ACM Transactions on Computer Systems, Vol.4, No.4, November 1986, pp. 273-298.

[Ger93] Gertner, I., "The Reflective Memory / Memory Channel System Overview," Encore Computer Systems, Fort Lauderdale, Florida, U.S.A., 1993.

[Gru94] Grujić, A., Tomašević, M., Milutinović, V., "A Simulation Analysis of Hardware-Oriented DSM Approaches," Proceedings of the TENCON-94, Singapore, August, 1994.

[Jov93] Jovanović, M., Tomašević, M., Milutinović, V., "A Simulation Study of the RM/MC Proposals," Final report for the phase #3, IFACT, Budapest, Hungary, 1993.

[Map90] Maples, C., Wittie, L., "Merlin: A Superglue for Multicomputer Systems," COMPCON '90, March 1990, pp. 73-81.

[Pro95] Protić, J., Tomašević, M., Milutinović, V., "Tutorial on Distributed Shared Memory: Concepts and Systems," IEEE Computer Society Press, Los Alamitos, California U.S.A., 1995.

[TDT92] "N.2 User's Manual", TD Technologies, Cleveland Heights, Ohio, U.S.A., 1992.

[Tom93] Tomašević, M., Milutinović, V., "Tutorial on Cache Coherence Problem in Shared-Memory Multiprocessors: Hardware solutions," IEEE Computer Society Press, Los Alamitos, California U.S.A., 1993.

[Tom94a] Tomašević, M., Milutinović, V., "A Survey of Hardware Solutions for Maintenance of Cache Coherence in Shared Memory Multiprocessors: Part 1," IEEE Micro, October 1994.

[Tom94b] Tomašević, M., Milutinović, V., "A Survey of Hardware Solutions for Maintenance of Cache Coherence in Shared Memory Multiprocessors: Part 2," IEEE Micro, December 1994.

INSTRUCTION LEVEL PARALLELISM

Minitrack Coordinator:

Robert Yung

Instruction Level Parallelism

Robert Yung

Sun Microsystems Inc.

yung@sun.com

(415) 336-5954

In the quest for higher performance, state-of-the-art processor designs currently employ various techniques to exploit and increase instruction level parallelism. Some of these optimizations are attempted at compile time while others are handled in hardware during program execution. In general, these hardware or software techniques exploit instruction level parallelism by increasing instruction dispatch rate, by reducing control transfer overhead, and by reducing average operand access latency.

The rate at which instructions can be dispatched is largely affected by the nature of the program and the efficiency of instruction scheduling. Scientific programs generally contain much instruction parallelism and few control transfers. For these programs, the instruction dispatch rate is usually limited by hardware resources such as the number of execution units and available memory bandwidth. In contrast, an integer or commercial program contains many data dependent control transfers. Unless correctly predicted and properly handled, data dependent control transfers reduce the efficiency of instruction scheduling and in turn reduce instruction dispatch rate.

Control transfer overhead can be minimized by speculative execution and branch reduction techniques. Speculative execution is a technique that allows execution of instructions following a branch prior to its resolution while maintaining the sequential execution model. Branches can be reduced by conditional execution of instructions following them. For example,

- trace scheduling is a compile time technique that reschedules a program based on branch statistics collected from a sample run. The drawback of such a scheme is the potential larger code size and its reliance on a representative sample.

- conditional, guarded, or predicated execution may be used to eliminate an if-then-else decision branch by conditionally executing one or more instructions after the branch. This technique requires support via a new instruction set architecture (ISA) or changes in an existing one. Besides the compatibility issue, the merit of these techniques is not conclusive in running real world programs. Generally, conditional branches are difficult to eliminate in integer and commercial programs.

- loop unrolling is a compile time technique that eliminates loop-terminating branches by concatenating multiple iterations of the loop in the code. This is a common technique used in vectorizable numeric programs.

- dynamic branch prediction is a general hardware technique that predicts the outcome of branches based on the history of previous branches. In general, dynamic prediction techniques achieve very good hit rates. Their disadvantages are increased hardware complexity and increased die area.

These techniques can be applied at compile time by software or handled during program execution by hardware.

As integrated circuit process technology advances, there is a growing gap between the processor and the memory sub-system. Memory access latency can be reduced with a larger set of programmer visible registers, higher cache hit rate, faster memory access, and by software techniques such as loop unrolling and software pipelining. Memory access overheads can be reduced by increasing the

151

distance between a memory access and its dependent instruction.

- One or more levels of caches have been employed to reduce the average memory access latency. Caches work well when there is a high locality of references. Most integer and commercial programs exhibit both temporal and spatial locality of references. A fully- or set-associative cache has a better hit rate than a direct-mapped cache, but the associative cache has a larger access time and takes up more area.

- Loop unrolling and software pipelining are compile time techniques that increase the load-use distance between a load and its dependent instructions. The limitation is that they require a large set of programmer visible registers. Windowed register files have been used to increase the number of addressable registers in a register file. Hardware register renaming can also be used in conjunction with these techniques to reduce the register bottleneck. This is done by remapping the programmer-visible register set to a larger set of physical registers implemented in a design.

Today processor designs employ these and other techniques to obtain higher performance. The main differences in these different designs lies in the hardware and software interface.

- Superscalar and dataflow designs place heavy emphasis on hardware for efficient instruction scheduling. A compiler first compiles a program into a sequence of instructions. After the instructions are fetched into the processor, the dataflow information is rediscovered by elaborate hardware. This information is used to schedule hardware resources and resolve data dependencies in the program during execution. Because the complexity for instruction scheduling is $O(n^2)$, a high instruction issue rate becomes increasingly difficult to realize with a fast cycle time.

- A Very Long Instruction Word (VLIW) design exposes the underlying hardware resources and constraints to the compiler. Instruction scheduling is handled entirely in software. The advantage of this design approach is potentially simple hardware which may lead to faster cycle time. Its disadvantages are increased software complexity, binary incompatibility, and reduced ability to handle dynamic situations such as cache misses during program execution.

In this architecture track, we will examine these techniques and designs that exploit instruction level parallelism in a program.

Acknowledgment

This minitrack will not be possible without the help of John Fu, Scott Mahlke, Trevor Mudge, Nancy Warter and the referees. Thanks also go to Renee Beauvais, Dennis Duprie, Dave Roberts and Neil Wilhelm for the administrative supports.

An Architecture for High Instruction Level Parallelism

Siamak Arya, Howard Sachs, Sreeram Duvvuru

Sun Microsystems Inc.[†], Mountain view, CA

Abstract

High instruction level parallelism (ILP) can only be achieved when data flow and control flow constraints have been removed or reduced. Data flow constraints, not inherent in the original code, arise from lack of sufficient resources for initiation and execution of multiple instructions concurrently. Control flow problems are caused by branches which force unpredictable changes in the sequential order of code execution. Removing these obstacles allows for the formation of larger basic blocks, resulting in higher ILP. The data flow problems are reduced by increasing the number of functional units, registers, condition bits, by pipelining the functional units, and using nonblocking caches. The control flow problem is reduced by using techniques such as conditional execution, speculative execution, and software pipelining, leveraging hardware support. Thus, for high ILP, the processor architecture should include a very closely tied hardware and compiler architectures. An architecture that supports the above features, Software Scheduled SuperScalar, is presented in this paper.

1. Introduction

The evolution of computer design has been dominated by hardware engineers designing the state of the art hardware, and requiring the compiler to do its best to use all of the neat hardware features for higher performance. Almost all micro processors fall in this category; except for a very few like SPARC, [28], with register window support for subroutine calls. Even-though, recently, a lot of effort has been put into the development of optimizing compilers for these processors, the hardware is still in charge. A different approach developed in early 1980's starting from horizontal microcode compaction, Fisher [5], and resulting in a new processor architecture called Very Long Instruction Word (VLIW) architecture, Fisher [6] and [7]. Two versions of the VLIW architecture have, so far, been commercially produced, Multiflow, Schuette [22], and Cydra5, Beck [1] and Rau [19]. This approach

put the software in charge, dictating to the hardware what to execute and when to do it. The compiler took charge of instruction scheduling, resource allocation and assignment, and conflict resolution. We believe that the best is achieved when functionality is assigned to software or hardware with respect to increased performance and reduced complexity.

The compiler and the hardware are inseparable elements of the design of a highly instruction level parallel processor. Instruction level parallelism may be defined as the ability to identify many independent instructions and to issue multiple instructions per cycle, fully utilizing available resources. The compiler views a very large window of code and analyzes the relationship between instructions. It, then, determines the instructions to be issued concurrently. The hardware is responsible to provide support for the compiler to issue as many instructions as possible concurrently and as often as possible. The compiler and the hardware, together, can achieve high ILP. However, high ILP can only be achieved when data flow and control flow constraints have been removed or reduced.

In this paper, we will describe the control flow and data flow problems, and discuss some solutions to these problems, and present an architecture designed for high ILP.

2. Control flow

Control flow is the order of instruction execution. Instruction execution creates a dynamic order of execution generating a very large trace of instructions. This code cannot be used for general case execution due to its specific order of instruction for a specific data set and the size of the trace. To condense the code to a manageable size and general case, a static order of execution is forced by the compiler. The static code, then, must have directives (branches) to specify the blocks of code and the conditions under which these code blocks are executed. This creates the control flow problem. Lam [13] and Rau [20] provide extensive discussion on this topic.

2.1 Restrictive control flow

Control flow problem is the result of mapping a two dimensional code space into a one dimensional instruction sequence. The code space is a tree with branches

---

†. Part of this work was performed at the Advanced Processor Division of Intergraph Corporation.

containing pieces of the code, and a condition attached to each branch determining whether or not to take that branch. When this sequence is mapped into a one dimensional space of instructions, blocks of instructions must be placed in a sequence, separated with a decision and skip mechanism. This mapping forces the blocks of code to be separated by branch instructions; see Figure 1. These blocks of code may be ordered in many different permutations.

The mastery of the compiler is measured by how efficiently it orders the instructions in the blocks of code separated by branches (basic blocks), and how it orders these blocks with respect to each other. Obviously, the larger the basic block, it is more likely to discover higher number of independent instructions. Independent instructions are used for concurrent issue and utilization of the available issue bandwidth. They can float within their dependence boundary and fill in issue gaps, thus contributing to the reduction in the execution time.

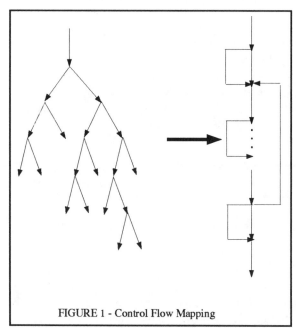

FIGURE 1 - Control Flow Mapping

The control flow problem (small basic block problem) has been recognized and understood for some time. The effort was concentrated to solve the problem by implementing faster branches or speculating on the direction of the branch. With the control flow problem in effect, the ILP was predicted to improve performance by a factor of 2, Tjaden [26]. And, even with hardware solutions, the parallelism is expected to increase about seven fold, Wall [29].

2.2 Expanded control flow

The solution is in the cooperation of the compiler and the hardware to reduce or eliminate the block boundaries.

Three techniques to increase the basic block size and the ILP are addressed here that are conditional execution, speculative execution, and software pipelining. These techniques eliminate many block boundaries and allow for larger basic blocks, resulting in more efficient instruction schedules. Such techniques have been studied by researchers or implemented by designers for some time. However, no single implementation has fully taken advantage of the combination of these techniques.

Some recent studies indicate a very high level of parallelism to be available when using these techniques, Lam [13] and Uht [27]. Though they differ in software and hardware approaches, they agree on availability of high levels of parallelism in existing code. It appears from Lam's paper that given the above features, we could be looking at an upper bound of 39 times speed up over sequential code for non-numeric applications. We believe that the architecture we propose allows for the extraction of high levels of parallelism with a generalized speculative, conditional (predicated), and software pipelining approaches. In the following we briefly describe these techniques.

2.2.1 Conditional execution

Conditional or predicated execution is a general scheme where an instruction is executed based on the state of a condition. SPARC-V9, Weaver [31], and Alpha, Sites [23], provide support for restricted conditional execution (guarded execution) by allowing some Move and Arithmetic and Logical operations to be performed conditionally as part of the delayed branch. iHarp, Steven [25], addresses the topic with a much broader scope. iHarp allows many of the instructions, but not all, to be executed based on true or false conditions. ARM, Someren [24], has defined a fully conditional instruction set. Each instruction is executed if the condition specified by the instruction is satisfied based on the condition bits in the Processor Status Register. We extend this to provide a fully conditional instruction set where the execution of each instruction is conditioned on one of many condition bits (single bit conditions). Cydra5, Dehnert [3], is the first processor to implement 128 1-bit guard registers that were used to suppress the execution of operations and for iteration control in software pipelining. Karl, [18], studies a generalized fully conditional instruction set.

A fully conditional instruction set implies that each instruction that is dependent on a branch instruction can be treated individually and not as a block of Then/Else. This allows the instructions to be moved up or down and be mixed with other basic blocks; though never preceding the condition generating instruction. In many cases, the branch condition can be determined far in advance of the branch. But, since a sequential order has to be maintained for basic blocks, the branch code cannot be executed without waiting its turn in the sequential order of basic blocks. When instructions following the branch are freed from their obligation to the basic block order, they can be moved individually forwards or backwards in the code to achieve the best schedule.

Conditional execution, in many cases, can eliminate conditional branches by executing both sides of a branch conditionally. Branch elimination will increase the size of its preceding basic block, allowing for more efficient instruction scheduling and resource utilization. Of course, this approach causes some code that need not be executed, code from the not taken side of a branch, to use issue bandwidth and then get annulled. The advantage is gained when the number of effective instructions that are issued in parallel is increased. An effective instruction is defined as an instruction that is not annulled and produces useful result. The topic of conditional execution and scheduling with predicates is explored in Gray [10], Beck [1], Park [18], and Mahlke [15].

2.2.2 Speculative execution

Speculative execution means executing an instruction prior to the instruction that determines whether this instruction must be executed or not. This allows for moving instructions before a branch that precedes them. Speculative code motion increases the parallelism of the code by allowing the creation of larger instruction groups. The compiler orchestrates speculative execution. The results of speculations are ignored if it is determined that these instructions should not have been executed due to the condition of the branch. However, some measures must be taken to ensure the correctness of the code; the code should behave the same with and without speculation. A speculatively executed code should not cause any traps or exceptions beyond what would have been generated by the original program (page fault is okay). If any such conditions occur due to execution of speculative instructions, the resulting traps will not be invoked. The trap conditions will be marked and will be invoked when it is determined that the speculated instructions are necessary. Some relevant discussions can be found in Mahlke [16]. Again, advantage is gained when the number of effective instructions that are issued in parallel is increased.

The speculative and conditional executions are different and complementary. The speculative execution enables the instructions to be executed prior to the branch that precedes them in the original code, while the conditional execution permits the instructions to move up or down in

the code, but never to precede the compare instruction that determines their status. Both of these approaches fill issue holes to reduce execution time. We have not discussed any designs that use a limited form of speculative execution; speculating on instructions following the branch or at the branch target during the time required to determine the direction of the branch. Most of today's processors fall under this category to some extent. We are only interested in full speculation so that the compiler can relocate the instructions for a better code schedule.

2.2.3 Software pipelining

Software pipelining is the overlapping of the execution stages of one loop iteration with different stages of other iterations. This allows for issuing instructions of many iterations in one cycle, resulting in earlier execution of iterations and increased parallelism. Many loops have small basic blocks. And, due to data dependencies, a limited intra-loop parallelism is available. Overlapping multiple iterations dramatically increases parallelism since the instructions of different loop iterations are likely to be independent from each other; except for recursive loops that can not be pipelined without some hardware or algorithmic support. Software pipelining has been studied in a lot of depth in Rau [21], Dehnert [3], Mahlke [6], Moon [17], Lam [14], and Warter [30].

The general software pipelining technique does not require any special hardware support, aside from providing multiple issue and multiple functional unit capabilities. The advantages of software pipelining is slightly reduced due to the increase in code size. The code generated has a prologue to set up the pipeline, a body that consists of multiple versions of an iteration, and an epilogue. The impact of the code size increase is expected to be very little. Instruction cache miss rates, say for SPEC92 benchmarks, are generally small, Gee [9], and inner loops are not a large portion of the code. Even if the code size doubles due to an n fold increase in the size of the software pipelined loops, for some n, the instruction cache miss rate impact may not be very significant. And, also, we believe that most software pipelined loops will fit in modest size instruction caches, and only the initial instruction fetch misses impact the execution time. This penalty can be reduced with a prefetch mechanism because of the sequential nature of the software pipelined code.

The size of the software pipelined code can be reduced using conditional execution. The prologue and the epilogue can be merged with the loop body and the instructions that should not be executed in the prologue or the epilogue can be annulled using conditional execution. For example, consider a loop to load elements of two arrays, multiply them, and store them into a third array. One can start the loads while multiply and store instructions are issued at the same cycle, but are conditionally annulled. When the result of the load is available, the condition for the multiply instruction is modified and the multiply is now executed. The same can be done for the store. The process is reversed for the epilogue. This can all be set up statically, of course. Some special condition bits such as staging predicates can be used to self modify from iteration to iteration, and eliminate the need for issuing explicit instructions to stage the prologue and the epilogue. For example, Cydra5, Beck [1], used rotating register files and staging registers to support software pipelining.

3. Data flow

Data flow refers to the availability of data when it is needed by an instruction that is, otherwise, ready to be issued. The flow of data is blocked when the input data for an instruction is not available and the instruction issue is held. One reason for this is the availability of a limited number of resources.

3.1 Limited resources

The data flow problem is caused by resource constraints. When an instruction cannot be issued because its operands are not available, the instruction is data dependent on some preceding instruction and that instruction has not completed execution. This is either due to data dependence or resource unavailability for early execution of that instruction. The data dependence inherent in the code can not be changed; or the compiler will. However, the impact of resource constraints may be reduced using additional resources.

Multiple independent instructions compete for a limited number of resources. The ones that lose are delayed issue which potentially will delay the issue of their dependent instructions, eventually increasing the total execution time. Ideally, one would want to find the critical path through a code and map the rest of the instructions onto that path without increasing the length of the critical path. When resource restrictions exist, new critical paths develop that are not due to data dependence and are due to resource conflicts. The resource constraint problem relates to both the number and the access delay (bandwidth) of the resources. Consideration must be given to registers, functional units, issue unit, condition codes, and caches.

3.2 Impact of increased resources

Theoretically, the solution is trivial, more and/or higher bandwidth resources. Given infinite resources the problem is completely solved. That not being an option, one has to determine the number of resources based on a trade off between cost, complexity, feasibility, and performance. The increase in one type of resource may affect other resources, and must be carefully examined. For example, increasing the number of registers, expands the register-number bit-fields in the instruction format, causing a potential redesign.

The functional units, such as adder, multiplier, or load unit can be duplicated or pipelined for increased performance. Duplication allows multiple independent-instructions to be issued concurrently. Pipelining increases the bandwidth of the functional unit by allowing a faster reuse of the unit. The increase in the bandwidth of the issue unit (issue more instructions per cycle) also allows earlier issuing of independent instructions. However, it may dramatically increase the complexity of the dynamic instruction scheduling; e.g. for superscalar processors.

The number of registers can be increased, reducing the data dependencies due to register reuse, and not the nature of the code. As we increase the size of the basic block with techniques like conditional execution, speculative execution, and software pipelining, the need for larger number of registers increases. Registers are needed to keep data for many cycles and perhaps iterations. Register file complexity increases because of increase in the number of registers and higher number of ports needed to serve the increased number of functional units. Multiported register files and caches are perhaps the most complex part of a highly parallel processor.

Caches, while providing short access times, must provide high bandwidth when multiple loads and stores per cycle are necessary for high ILP processing. A load miss can hold a pipeline for many cycles resulting in the delay of many multiple-instruction issue opportunities, even when the succeeding instructions have no resource conflicts. Nonblocking caches are required to prevent such delays. This requires multiporting and pipelining of caches. In general, the load operations can be made independent from each other when no address conflicts occur. A missed load may be followed by many hits before another miss occurs. This is necessary to increase the ILP. However, it makes for a complex cache design, especially when combined with store conflicts. Load-store conflict resolution may be much more complex when multiple loads and stores are issued per cycle with potential address conflicts with each other and/or previously issued and missed loads/stores.

Multiple independent single-bit condition bits will facilitate computation of condition codes far in advance of their use by branches and conditional instructions. Firstly, multiple condition bits are necessary to allow the instructions from multiple Then/Else blocks to be combined creating a large scheduling block. In other words, the condition may be generated multiple basic blocks before the first or last use of condition bit. Therefore, conditional instructions can be promoted multiple blocks up or down without violating their data dependency. Secondly, generating single bit condition bits, in contrast to a traditional 4 bit condition code, is a matter of performance. Multi-bit approach requires a condition evaluation after decoding the branch or the conditional instruction. In contrast, for the single-bit approach, a true or false test of the condition bit is all that is needed. When fetching and testing the condition bit is on the critical path, a single-bit condition is preferred; this may be true for instruction annulling in the decode stage and branch target decision in the fetch stage, Duvvuru [4].

4. An ILP architecture

We introduce a new architecture for instruction level parallelism based on control flow and data flow solutions. Most of what is discussed above is not new. We just presented it with our view of the ILP. Now, we introduce an architecture that is a mix of Superscalar and VLIW, and includes features that are expected to increase ILP. We propose Software Scheduled SuperScalar (4S) architecture to achieve high levels of instruction parallelism.

The existing approaches to ILP architectures are superscalar and VLIW ones. These architectures have more in common than meets the eye. It is their differences that is important here. Defining such differences is essential before describing the 4S architecture.

4.1 Superscalar and VLIW: the difference

Superscalar and VLIW architectures are fundamentally different only in the instruction selection logic and scoreboarding. Both architectures can use optimizing compilers to set the instructions in the best possible order. VLIW architecture, Fisher [8], issue the compiler specified long instructions without further dynamic checking. The compiler will package instruction groups into fixed length instructions, padding with noops when necessary. Some encoding mechanism has been used by some VLIW implementations to avoid this problem. Superscalar architecture, Johnson [11], on the other hand, rediscover the independent instructions in hardware. The instruction selection logic scans the instructions in a small window and selects the appropriate instructions for issue. Given a wide enough window of instructions to select from and sufficient hardware, the

Superscalar architectures can have the same instructions to issue as the VLIW ones. Both architectures decode instructions. And, both use similar functional units to execute the instructions. If both architectures were allowed the same types of operations per cycle, their execution units would fundamentally look the same.

Conflict resolution process or score boarding or detection of dependence between two issue groups, is another fundamental difference between VLIW and Superscalar architectures. VLIW saves hardware by delegating the responsibility of issuing instructions when their registers and functional units are available to the compiler. The VLIW compiler, having been given the details of the pipeline design, orders wide word instructions at proper distances, resolving inter wide-word-instruction dependencies; sometimes resorting to noops. This approach has major drawbacks such as debugging difficulties and implementation limitations. For example, if the length of the pipeline is increased, the instructions have to be rescheduled to achieve correct results or some protection hardware must be included, which defeats the purpose of saving hardware. Compatibility across the VLIW family of processors is also an issue.

To overcome the major Superscalar problem, i.e. complex instruction selection logic, and VLIW problems such as introduction of noops in the code for static scheduling, inflexibility of the wide instruction word format, and associated implementation limitations, we propose the 4S architecture.

4.2 Software scheduled superscalar architecture

Software Scheduled SuperScalar (4S) combines the best of Superscalar and VLIW architectures to achieve a high level of instruction level parallelism. It avoids the hardware complexity of dynamic instruction scheduling inherent in Superscalar designs, by delegating the task of instruction scheduling to the compiler; a small amount of logic is used to route instructions. 4S also avoids the memory overhead and inflexibility of VLIW by permitting variable length instruction groups. In 4S, regular fixed-length instructions are scheduled by the compiler into groups of instructions to be issued at the same time. The hardware identifies the group by a special tagging scheme and issues them to their appropriate pipes. 4S, like Superscalar, delegates the conflict resolution to hardware.

In the following subsections, we will briefly discuss the main architectural features of the 4S.

4.2.1 4S Architectural features

The following presents a summary of the architectural

features of 4S.

Compiler:

Optimized code through speculative and conditional execution
Software pipelining
Compiler scheduled instruction groups
Compiler specified functional unit pipes

Instruction set:

Independent, individual, and fixed length instructions
Explicit grouping and function information
All instructions are conditional
Every instruction has a speculative and non-speculative version, except for store operations

Hardware:

Multiple instructions issued per cycle
multiple replicated functional units
multiple load/store units
multiple integer units
multiple floating point units

tion coding or tagging mechanism that allows the identification of independent instruction groups. As Figure 2 illustrates, instructions are packed into instruction groups that in turn are packed into instruction frames. A frame is the maximum number of instructions that can be fetched at the same time. An instruction frame contains N instructions. A frame contains one or more groups of instructions. A group is the unit of parallel issue; i.e., instructions of a group are issued at the same time. A group can contain 1 to M instructions where M is the smaller of the frame size (N) or the number of pipes available for issuing instructions. The instructions of a group are identified by a group number or a group identification bit. When a frame of instructions is fetched by checking the tag bit(s), the instructions of the group (group to be issued) are transferred to the decode unit(s). Figure 2 shows a possible single bit coding scheme to identify the starting address of a group and its members. The current coding scheme identifies the first instruction in the group with a zero tag bit. The instructions following the first instruction with tag bit of one are members of that group. The next instruction with tag bit of zero indicates the beginning of the next group.

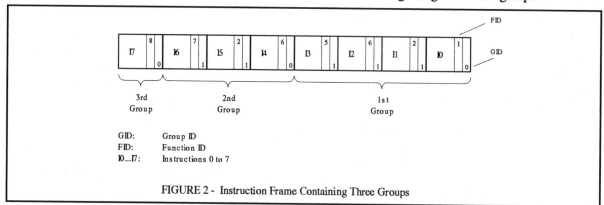

FIGURE 2 - Instruction Frame Containing Three Groups

Multiple condition bits
Large multiported integer and floating point register files
Speculative bits (one per register; logically, but not physically, attached)
Nonblocking primary cache
Partially blocking secondary cache (very large)
Fast branch mechanism
Software pipelining support under study

Now, we will describe some of the new concepts and features. The number and the size of the units are design and implementation dependent. More details about the architecture and some specific implementation data will be soon available in a Sun publication.

4.2.2 Groups and parallel instruction issue

4S proposes the addition of a single or multi bit instruc-

This technique allows regular, fixed length, individual, and independent instructions, like RISC or superscalar instructions, to be grouped together for issue. It allows the instructions to be self contained and be scheduled in any group without any change to the instruction or the group. Hence the name Software Scheduled SuperScalar.

4S simplifies the decoding mechanism further by allowing the compiler to add a second tag to each instruction that identifies the type of the instruction. This tag is called a pipe or function id. A special crossbar mechanism, shown in Figure 3, reorders the instructions from their arbitrary order in their group to the specific order of assignment to their corresponding decode units. The cross bar can be simplified to a shift or scatter unit if an order of appearance for instructions based on function id is imposed. This mechanism allows instructions to

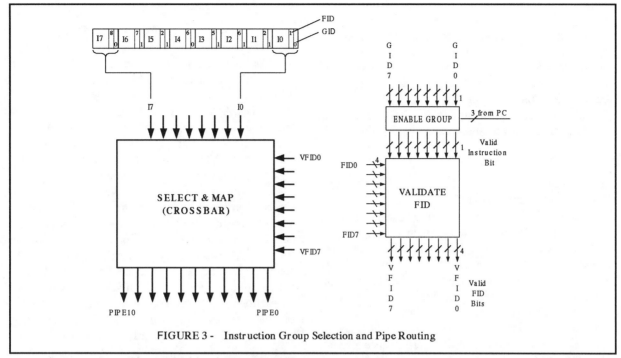

FIGURE 3 -   Instruction Group Selection and Pipe Routing

appear in any order and in any position in the group. The VLIW architectures have suffered from wasting instruction space by the use of noops in a wide word to enforce the proper functional order of the instructions. The function id tags make it possible to create variable size instruction groups and eliminate the need for noops for proper ordering of instructions.

Creating and executing a group of instructions should comply with the following rules:

Instructions in a group are guaranteed by the compiler to be independent. They will appear contiguous in the frame. The single-bit tagging scheme or some equivalent encoding scheme is necessary to mark the beginning and end of a group.

A group must be contained in a frame

A group will be issued when the resources for all of its instructions are available, i.e., all of the instructions of a group will issue at the same time. However, they may finish at different times. 4S instruction execution may be best described as an in-order-issue and possibly out-of-order completion. Register scoreboarding is used to determine the readiness of a group to be issued.

The order of instructions in a group is insignificant except for the branch, which should be the first instruction in the group. A group can contain at most one branch instruction.

Each instruction in a group must have a distinct pipe

or function ID; only one instruction can be issued to a pipe per cycle.

Loads have precedence over stores. If they use the same address, the compiler and the hardware assume that the load occurs before the store, though the issue is in the same cycle.

If a register is shared between two instructions, register read precedes register write. As a side effect, it allows for a single-cycle register swap.

When a branch is taken, the execution continues with the group at the target address.

4.2.3 4S Instruction Set

The 4S instruction set is based on three operand RISC style instructions, with some major extensions for exposing instruction level parallelism. All instructions are conditional on any of the condition bits. An instruction whose condition of execution is set to false, will be annulled. Annulling can be done at decode/issue stage, first cycle of execution, or at the time of write back. The best approach is code dependent; see the next section.

To accommodate all of the requirements of these instructions, including GID, FID, and conditional execution bits, after careful study of various options, we chose 64-bit instruction formats. Figure 4 shows a sample of instruction formats. All instructions have a 1-bit GID and a 4-bit FID. Every instruction has an 8-bit (6 bits used initially) condition code that determines whether the instruction is to be executed or annulled. Some instructions such as condition setting ones have two conditional bit references. One determines whether the instruction should be executed, and the other is the destination bit for the result of the compare. Branch instructions only have one condition bit since a branch by definition is a conditional instructions; an unconditional branch is a conditional branch with its condition bit set to true.

4.2.4 Conditional Execution

In 4S, all of the instructions are conditional. It allows for many condition bits so that the conditions for branches (now conditional instruction directives) can be computed in advance. It also allows for calculating through multiple branches. In reality, it brings back the two dimensionality of the code space. This, of course, can not be done without the support of the hardware. The hardware support required is to provide multiple condition bits, with instructions that include a condition bit number for execution or annulment. The condition bits can be set through compare instructions. For performance reasons, the condition bits are single bits per compare and represent the outcome of one condition only. The main reason is that the condition bit can be used quickly to determine the state of the instruction without having to decode the instruction to determine one of many choices allowed in a multi-bit condition code.

The stage at which a conditional instruction is annulled has some performance and hardware implications. Let's only consider the cases where due to the condition of the instruction, it is annulled at the decode or first cycle of execute stage. Annulling in write back stage has no advantages. Annulling in the decode stage has the benefit that the instruction will not block the group from being issued if its register or functional unit dependencies are not resolved. This will require that the condition is calculated in advance. Otherwise, the condition bit may not be available and the instruction must be held for one cycle. On the other hand, annulling at the first cycle of execute has the benefit that condition bits need not be scoreboarded when compare operations can be done in one cycle. And, no issue delay will result due to unavailable condition bits. So, it is very code dependent. In a code where conditions can be evaluated in advance, and instructions to be annulled are on the critical path, the decode stage annulling is preferred. Otherwise, execution stage annulling is less hardware intensive.

4.2.5 Speculative execution

When a speculative instruction is trapped, the speculative bit of its destination register is marked. If that register is used by a speculative instruction, the destina-

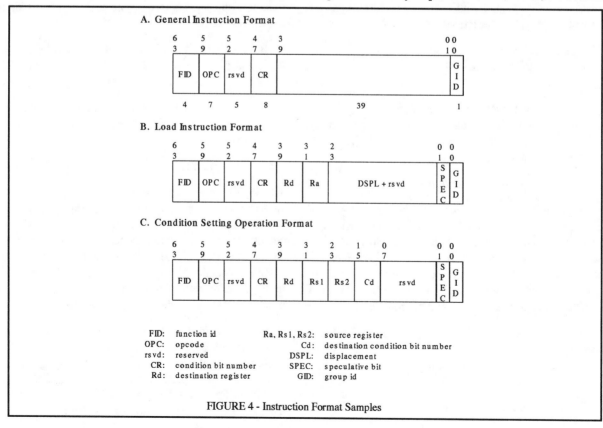

FIGURE 4 - Instruction Format Samples

tion register of that instruction is also marked. If a marked register is used by a non-speculative instruction, a trap will occur.

When a register is marked due to a speculative instruction causing a trap, trap information can be stored in that register, and passed down when that register is used. When the marked register is non-speculatively used, the trap information can be used for trap handling or debugging. While this information can be very helpful, saving trap information in the register will be slow and will increase design complexity.

Every instructions can be executed speculatively, except for stores. Speculatively executing stores adds a tremendous amount of complexity to the architecture since all of the speculated stores have to be held in buffers till their execution is confirmed. Otherwise, a store can not be undone.

2.7 Non-blocking caches

A large percentage of the execution time is spent awaiting completion of memory access, especially in floating point code and programs that access large amounts of data. Also, the speed of memory systems increases at a lower rate than that of the processors. Caches alleviate this problem to some extent, especially, in cases with spatial and temporal locality of access. However, a cache miss forces the CPU to hold issue till the data is fetched from memory; this is called a blocking cache. One solution for hiding the latency of memory access is to overlap the latency with other CPU and memory activities through using nonblocking caches. Nonblocking caches allow the CPU to precede issuing other instructions even after a cache miss has occurred until the datum from the pending miss is actually needed in a computation. It allows subsequent cache hits to be serviced even when one or more pending cache misses await service. Every cache access must be compared with all pending cache accesses to detect conflicts and ensure correct execution. This is the most complex part of the 4S architecture. This fits the 4S design philosophy of only allowing complexity when the potential performance gain is high. Conte [2] presents a study of the impact of nonblocking caches with varying degrees of blocking, confirming the need for nonblocking caches.

5. Conclusions

High levels of instruction level parallelism can be achieved with the cooperation of the compiler and the hardware. The compiler is responsible to generate independent instructions by reducing the control flow constraints. This is achieved through techniques such as speculative and conditional execution and software pipelining. The hardware is responsible to execute as many independent instructions as it can and as fast as possible. This is accomplished with increasing the number, size, and the bandwidth of hardware resources such as functional units, condition bits, and registers.

We discussed the control flow and the data flow problems and solutions. The control flow problem arises from mapping a two dimensional code (decision tree) into a one dimensional instruction sequence. The data flow problem is the result of not having enough resources to issue the ready to execute instructions. Reducing the control flow constraints is the challenge of the compiler, where the data flow constraints are what the hardware struggles with. Both of these problems can be reduced with the use of the above techniques.

We presented an architecture called 4S for high ILP computing. 4S is a synthesis of Superscalar and VLIW architectures. The task of discovering instruction level parallelism is delegated to the compiler. The compiler can examine large sections of the program to perform static instruction scheduling and optimally utilize the machine resources. The 4S architecture provides support for conditional and speculative instruction execution, enabling the compiler to perform sophisticated optimizations across basic blocks while preserving the semantics of sequential program execution. The hardware is simplified because most of the instruction scheduling responsibility is assigned to the compiler. This will enable very high speed implementations of 4S, taking advantage of advances in process technology. The hardware saved may be invested in other performance enhancing features such as nonblocking caches.

We presented a novel technique for packaging instructions into variable length groups that can be issued in parallel. We discussed how the instructions are tagged with a group ID for quick identification for issue. This mechanism, while consuming little hardware, avoids padding groups with noops to create fixed length long words. And thus, it allows for efficient use of the memory and caches. We also discussed a functional tagging of the instructions to allow for routing instructions to appropriate functional units quickly.

Acknowledgments
We would like to thank everyone who has contributed to this paper directly or indirectly. Especially, we thank Intergraph's C5 design team for their contributions to the architecture and the people who have contributed to our understanding of speculative and conditional execution and software pipelining. Thanks to Gerry Atterbury for his support through out the course of writing this paper.

References:

[1] Beck, G. R., Yen, D. W. L., Anderson, T. L., "The Cydra-5 Minisupercomputer Architecture Implementation," The Journal of Supercomputing, Vol. 7, No. 1/2, May 1993, pp. 143-180.

[2] Conte, T. M., "Trade-offs in Processor/Memory Interfaces for Superscalar Processors," MICRO-25, The 25th Annual International Symposium on Microarchitecture, December, 1992.

[3] Dehnert, J. C. and Towle, R. A., "Compiling for the Cydra 5," The Journal of Supercomputing, Vol. 7, No. 1/2, May 1993, pp., 181-227.

[4] Duvvuru, S. and Arya, S., "Evaluation of a Branch Target Address Cache," The 28th Hawaii International Conference on System Sciences, January, 1995.

[5] Fisher, J. A., "Trace Scheduling: A technique for Global Microcode compaction,", IEEE Transactions on Computers, Vol. C-30, No. 7, July 1981, pp. 478-490.

[6] Fisher, J. A.,"Very Long Instruction Word Architecture", Yale University, New Haven, Conn., April 1983.

[7] Fisher, J.A., Ellis, J. R., Ruttenberg, J. C., and Nicolau, A., "Parallel Processing: A Smart Compiler and a Dumb Machine," ACMSigplan 84 Compiler construction conference, June 1984.

[8] Fisher, J. A., "Very Long Instruction Word Architecture and ELI-512," Proceedings of the 10th Annual Symposium on Computer Architecture, 1983, pp. 140-150.

[9] Gee, J. D., Hill, M. D., and Smith, A. J., "Cache Performance of the SPEC92 Benchmark Suite," MICRO 26, Proceedings of the 26th annual International Symposium on Microarchitecture, 1993, pp. 17-27.

[10] Gray, S.M., Adams, R. G. and Steven, G. B., "Static Instruction Scheduling for the HARP Multiple-Instruction-Issue Architecture," Technical Report No. 142, Division of Computer Science, The University of Hertfordshire, Hatfield, Herts UK, October 1992.

[11] Johnson, M., "Superscalar Microprocessor Design," Prentice-Hall, Englewood Cliffs, New Jersey, 1991

[12] Karl, W., "Some Design Aspects for VLIW Architectures Exploiting Fine-Grained Parallelism," Proceedings of the 5th International PARLE Conference, 1993, pp. 582-99.

[13] Lam, M. S., Wilson, R. P., "Limits of Control Flow on Parallelism," Computer Architecture News, Vol. 20, No. 2, 1992, pp. 46-57.

[14] Lam, M. S., "Software Pipelining: An Effective Scheduling technique for VLIW Machines," Proceedings of ACM SIGPLAN '88 Conference on Programming Language Design and Implementation, 1988, pp. 318-327.

[15] Mahlke, S. A., Lin, D.C., Chen, W. Y., Hank, R. E., and Bringmann, R. A., "Effective Compiler Support for Predicated Execution Using the Hyperblock," MICRO 25, Proceedings of the 25th Annual International Symposium on Microarchitectures, December 1992.

[16] Mahlke, S. A., Chen, W. Y., Hwu, W., Rau, B., and Shlansker, M. S., "Sentinel Scheduling for VLIW and Superscalar Processors," In. Proceedings of ASPLOS V, October 1992, pp. 238-247.

[17] Moon, S. M., Ebcioglu, K., "An Efficient Resource-Constrained Gloabal Scheduling Technique for Superscalar and VLIW Processors," MICRO 25, Proceedings of the 25th Annual International Symposium on Microarchitectures, December, 1992, pp. 55-71.

[18] Park, J. C. H., and Schlansker, M. S., "On Predicated Execution," Technical Report 91-58, Hewlett-Packard Laboratories, 1991.

[19] Rau, B. R., "Cydra-5 Directed Dataflow Architecture," Proceedings of COMPCON, 1988.

[20] Rau, B. R. and Fisher, J. A., "Instruction-Level Parallel Processing: History, Overview, and Perspective," The Journal of Supercomputing, Vol. 7, No. 1/2, May 1993, pp. 9-50.

[21] Rau, B. R., Glaeser, C. D., and Picard, R. L., "Efficient Code Generation for Horizontal Architectures: Compiler Techniques and Architectural Support," Proceedings of the Ninth annual International Symposium on Computer architecture, 1982, pp. 131-9.

[22] Schuette, M. A. and Shen, J. P., "Instruction-Level Experimental Evaluation of the Multiflow TRACE 14/1300 VLIW Computer," The Journal of Supercomputing, Vol. 7, No. 1/2, May 1993, pp. 249-71.

[23] Sites, R. (Editor), "Alpha Architecture Reference Manual," Digital Press, 1992.

[24] Someren, A. V., Atack, C., "The ARM RISC Chip, A Programmer's Guide," Addison-Wesley, 1994.

[25] Steven, G. B., Adams, R. G., Findley, P.A., and Trainis, S. A., "iHARP: A Multiple Instruction Issue Processor," Technical Report No. 125, Division of Computer Science, Hatfield Polytechnic, Hatfield, Herts UK, November 1991.

[26] Tjaden, G. S., and Flynn, M. J., "Detection and Parallel Execution of Parallel Instructions," IEEE Transactions on Computers, Vol. C-19, No. 10, October, 1970, pp. 889-95.

[27] Uht, A. K., "Extraction of Massive Instruction Level Parallelism," Computer Architecture News, Vol. 21, No. 3, June, 1993, pp. 5-12.

[28] The SPARC Architecture Manual, Version 8, Prentice Hall, New Jersey 1992

[29] Wall, D. W., "Limits of Instruction Level Parallelism," Proceedings of the Fourth International Conference on Architectural Support for Programming Languages and Operating Systems, April 1991, pp. 176-188.

[30] Warter, N. J., Bockhaus, J. W., Haab, G. E., and Subramanian, K., "Enhanced Modulo Scheduling for Loops With Conditional Branches," MICRO 25, Proceedings of the 25th annual International Symposium on Microarchitecture, 1992, pp. 170-9.

[31] SPARC International Inc., Weaver, D., Germond, T., Editors, "The SPARC Architecture Manual - Version 9," PTR Prentice Hall, Englewood Cliffs, New Jersey

The Architecture of an Optimistic CPU: The WarpEngine.

John G. Cleary[†], Murray Pearson[†], Husam Kinawi[§]

[†]Dept. of Computer Science, University of Waikato, Private Bag 3105, Hamilton, New Zealand.
{jcleary, mpearson}@waikato.ac.nz

[§]Dept. of Computer Science, University of Calgary, Calgary, Alberta T2N 1N4, Canada.
kinawi@cpsc.ucalgary.ca

Abstract

The architecture for a shared memory CPU is described. The CPU allows for parallelism down to the level of single instructions and is tolerant of memory latency. All executable instructions and memory accesses are time stamped. The TimeWarp algorithm is used for managing synchronisation. This algorithm is optimistic and requires that all computations can be rolled back. The basic functions required for implementing the control and memory system used by TimeWarp are described. The memory model presented to the programmer is a single linear address space modified by a single thread of comtrol. Thus, at the software level there is no need for explicit synchronising actions when accessing memory. The physical implementation, however, is multiple CPUs with their own caches and local memory with each CPU simultaneously executing multiple threads of control.

1. Introduction

Computer designers currently face a very interesting set of challenges. The steady increase in the number of transistors on a chip and the speed at which a chip can be clocked has continued its inexorable progress. In 1994, chips with 3×10^6 transistors and clock speeds of hundreds of MHz are in routine production and there are no short-term barriers to these numbers continuing to double every three years into the foreseeable future [5]. However, off-chip and memory speeds have not increased to nearly the same extent [12]. This has lead to a situation where system performance is constrained by the latency of memory fetches and off-chip interactions. One response to this has been to achieve additional performance through the use of parallelism extracted at two levels.

Within a single chip, pipelining and superscalar execution techniques are used. These techniques have lead to increasingly complex and baroque CPU architectures where increases in performance require changes to the architecture. The second approach is to use many CPUs in a single system. Initially, such systems were configured with disjoint memory where communication between CPUs required explicit calls in software to send messages. More recently, shared memory systems, where the communication is effectively handled by the memory system, have become commercially available [3, 17, 22]. In these systems the user is presented with a single shared linear address space which can be seen by all CPUs. The underlying hardware implementation of such systems can vary markedly, from systems with single shared buses [3] to asynchronous systems where shared memory pages are communicated by hardware messages [1, 11, 22]. Shared memory systems are significantly harder to build than distributed memory systems because of the need to deal in hardware with remote memory accesses and cache coherence. However, they have the great advantage that they remove from the programmer the burden of partitioning data-structures to spread them across multiple disjoint address spaces.

Programming (and achieving good performance) on shared memory systems remains a significantly harder task than programming on sequential processors. This is because two significant tasks are still left to the programmer. These are ensuring that access to shared memory locations is synchronised (by locks, semaphores etc.) and decomposing the code into minimally communicating units that are to execute in parallel.

This paper presents an architecture that addresses these problems. The virtual view seen by the programmer is a single address space operated on by a single thread of control. The intended physical implementation is multiple CPUs with their own local memory operating on many parallel threads of control. Parallelism is provided at three levels. At the first level, within a single CPU, individual instructions can be executed by functional units that execute in parallel, synchronised by a data-flow protocol. The number of functional units per CPU can be scaled to fit hardware performance parameters rather than redesigning the architecture. A second level of parallelism organises instructions into blocks (of up to 16 instructions). A single CPU may simultaneously execute many blocks. The third level of parallelism has multiple CPUs executing different blocks of instructions.

Synchronisation is achieved (at the hardware level) by assigning a unique "time stamp" to each execution instance of a block. Reads and writes to memory refer to a time stamp as well as to an address. The overall co-ordination of these time stamps uses the TimeWarp algorithm which is introduced in section 2. Section 3 then describes how TimeWarp can be integrated into a memory system and how time stamps are generated for the execution blocks. The rest of the paper concentrates on the internal architecture of the CPU including its instruction set. The paper concludes with order of magnitude estimates of performance and a discussion of future work.

2. TimeWarp

TimeWarp is an algorithm for distributing and parallelising discrete event simulations. The algorithm was originally proposed by Jefferson in 1982 [7, 14, 15, 24].

Parallelising discrete event simulations is a difficult problem because of the need to synchronise the simulation times of different simulation objects without violating the principle of causality [8]. The TimeWarp algorithm solves this by executing events optimistically and later, if necessary, rolling-back (undoing) events that should not in fact have been executed. A simulation executed using TimeWarp is usually decomposed as a series of objects which communicate by passing messages. In simulation terms, these messages can be thought of as scheduling events which are specified to occur at a particular receiving object at a particular time.

To rollback the execution of an event two things must be accomplished: restore the state of the system; and undo the effect of any messages sent by the event. This latter is accomplished by sending anti-messages following the earlier messages. When an anti-message is received, it can cause two effects. If the original message had not as yet been executed (it is queued somewhere waiting to be scheduled) then it is annihilated and no further action is taken. If the original message had been executed then it will be rolledback (with possible transmission of further anti-messages), the antimessage and message will "annihilate" and execution will resume as if the original message (and anti-message) had never been received.

A common technique for restoring the state of objects on a rollback is to take a copy of the object's state each time it receives a message (much more efficient techniques are possible but do not concern us here). Then when a rollback occurs, the appropriate previous state can be copied back into the object. One side effect of this is that

each object builds up a queue of old state copies. It is hence necessary to eventually garbage collect these old state copies (this is referred to as "fossil" collection). This can only be done when it is known that a state copy will never be required for a rollback. This is done by periodically computing a value called the GVT (Global Virtual Time) which is equal to the minimum time of any currently active object or message between objects. It is guaranteed by the TimeWarp mechanism that no object will rollback to a virtual time prior to GVT, and hence it is possible to fossil collect all state copies with time stamps less than GVT. GVT is also used to "commit" other interactions with the outside world. For example, a request to print cannot be honoured until GVT passes the time that the request was made.

Results about the performance of TimeWarp are surveyed in [8]. Good performance by TimeWarp relies on a number of factors. First, the cascades of anti-messages induced by rollbacks must damp out quickly and not continue building. The overheads required to restore state on a rollback also cannot be too expensive. In practice, this means that the cost of recording state changes during forward execution must be low. Given all of this, TimeWarp is capable of parallelising and speeding up problems that are otherwise intractable. Fujimoto [8] concludes that TimeWarp is the only algorithm known which is capable of robustly speeding up a wide range of discrete event simulation problems but that this is contingent on good implementations with low overheads.

It has been recognised ever since the algorithm was originally proposed that TimeWarp is not just an algorithm for parallelising discrete event simulations but is also a general purpose technique for synchronising parallel computation. For example, it can be used as an undo mechanism in editors [23], consistent checkpointing for fault tolerance, incremental recovery in data bases, selective undo in groupware tools [21], or debugging for parallel and distributed programs [4]. In this context it can be seen as a generalisation of optimistic commit protocols. It has also been described as an algorithm for synchronising AND-parallel Prolog [20]. Fujimoto has proposed a Virtual Time Machine [6, 9] for use with discrete event simulation systems. Fujimoto's work is seminal for the current WarpEngine design.

3. Time-stamped Memory

The first component of the WarpEngine that we will describe is the time stamped memory subsystem for a single CPU. The memory subsystem receives from the CPU read and write request messages and sends back reply messages in response to the reads.

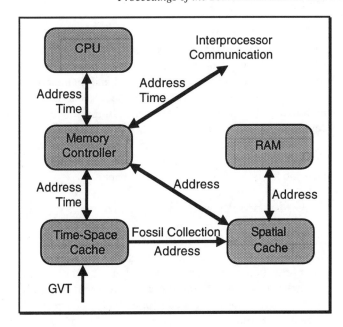

Figure 3.1. Components of the Memory Subsystem.

Each read is accompanied by an address, a time stamp and a tag (which is used by the CPU for identifying which read request is being satisfied when the memory subsystem finally replies). We will see in the next section how the time stamps are generated, but for now it is sufficient that the time stamps impose a single linear temporal order relating all the reads and writes ie., a memory access issued before another in program order would be time stamped with an earlier time. Similarly, a write is accompanied by an address, a time stamp and a value. The value returned for a read is the value from the last write prior to the read (in time stamp order) for that address. Note that we are assuming an optimistic system here, so that writes may be physically generated in a different order from their time stamps.

As a consequence of using TimeWarp, the CPU may issue an "anti-write", this specifies a time stamp and address. Its effect is to delete the original write. As we will see below it may require some read requests to be re-satisfied.

3.1. Implementation of the Time-stamped Memory

A naive implementation of such a scheme would clearly not be sufficiently efficient. The scheme we propose has a three level memory system. At the level closest to the CPU there is a fully associative memory cache, the "time-space" cache. This contains triples of the form: address, time stamp and value for all recent writes. As well it contains a record of all reads in the form of

address, time stamp and tag triples (we will see why this is necessary shortly). Only read traces with time stamps greater than GVT need to be stored; traces prior to GVT are fossil collected during GVT computation.

The next two levels of the memory hierarchy are the standard ones of a cache, which we call a spatial cache, and local dynamic RAM. At these levels, memory is referenced only by address; time stamps are not involved. Values stored in this "timeless" part of the system are committed and are guaranteed never to be rolledback.

Four operations are possible on the memory subsystem: read, write, anti-write, and fossil collection as a result of an advance in GVT. Figure 3.1 shows a diagram of the memory subsystem's major components and the interactions between them.

A read will generate two parallel accesses one to the time-space cache and another to the spatial cache. In the time-space cache the read's trace will be recorded. As well, all recorded writes with the same address will be matched and the one which is most recent but prior to the time on the read will be fetched. There are two possible results to this operation. There may be a memory tuple which matches the read in which case this is returned to the CPU. But if there is no match then a check is made to see if the spatial cache returned a result. If it did then that is used as the result. If there is still no value available then the read request is passed up the (standard) memory hierarchy. If there is no local record of the address then action is needed to obtain a copy of the appropriate memory page from whatever remote CPU it is located (or to generate a memory reference error).

A write is sent only to the time-space cache where its trace is recorded. As well, all recorded read requests (for the same address) with time stamps greater than the time stamp of the write but less than the time stamp of the next recorded write to the same address are retrieved. Each of these is sent back as a reply to the CPU using the value just written. When these replies arrive at the CPU they will cause a rollback and re-execution of code in the CPU.

An anti-write functions similarly to a write. It first locates the original write entry at the specified time and address and deletes it. It then finds all recorded reads later than the deleted write and before the next recorded write to the same address. For each such read request, a reply is generated to the CPU giving the value of the earlier write (or an invalid value if there is none).

The fossil collection process deletes both read requests and write entries. All traces of read request traces earlier than the current value of GVT can be deleted immediately. Each write entry earlier than GVT is retrieved and its address noted. If it is later than all other writes to this address (which are earlier than GVT) then the value can be written directly to the spatial cache. All the entries less than GVT at that address can then be deleted. We anticipate that this process of fossil collection will run "in the background" concurrently with the requests from the CPU.

3.2. Inter-processor Communication

Being a shared memory system, all inter-processor communication is via the memory subsystem. The use of time stamps eliminates the need for standard memory consistency protocols since it ensures sequentially consistent memory accesses [16, 19]. Assuming some directory technique is in place for recording which addresses are to be shared between processors, then sharing memory is very simple. Whenever a write (or anti-write) is done to a shared address then the address, time stamp, value triple is sent to all machines sharing this address. There is no need to wait until the write arrives at all its destinations or to explicitly invalidate remote entries. When a (anti-)write arrives at a remote machine it is treated the same way as a (anti-)write from the local CPU which may cause the generation of multiple read replies to the CPU and consequent rollback. Furthermore, values fossil collected to the spatial caches will be automatically coherent without the need for any cache coherency protocols.

Because synchronisation is implicitly handled by the time stamping there is no need to implement any explicit locking or atomic operations between processors.

3.3. Size of the Time-space Cache

Clearly the time-space cache will be critical to the performance of the system and will present an implementation challenge; it will be significantly more complex than a standard fully associative cache. It does have one redeeming feature which is that its effectiveness does not depend on its size. The size will be determined by the number of read and write entries that have to be stored in it rather than in the spatial cache. There can only be a limited number of read/write requests from the local CPU or remotely from other CPUs on each clock cycle (in the performance estimates below we assume at most one cache operation per clock cycle). So the number of entries required will be some constant multiplied by the time gap between the highest time stamped entry and the current value of GVT. This spread will be determined by the spread in different time stamps which are actively being executed by different CPUs and the lag in computing the current value of GVT. Getting a good estimate for this spread and the size of the cache will require more detailed simulations than have been possible to this point. Initial

estimates indicate that it will be dominated by the GVT lag which is determined by the diameter of the communications graph for the multiple-CPUs. Given at most one read or write per clock period and diameters of tens or hundreds of clocks the time-space cache may be effective with a thousand or so entries. In the single CPU case a few tens of entries are probably sufficient.

The size of the spatial cache and its structure is determined in the same way as conventional processors [13] and hence is not discussed in this paper.

4. Code Blocks and Time stamps

Within the WarpEngine CPU instructions are organised into blocks. Conditional execution selects (or rejects) a complete block for execution, that is, individual instructions cannot be conditionally executed. Also, all instructions within a block can (potentially) be executed in parallel. Figure 4.1a gives an example of a code block. A block roughly corresponds to a basic block in classical CPUs. A block has a fixed maximum number of fixed-width instructions (in the current incarnation of the instruction set it is 16 instructions).

During execution each code block is dynamically allocated a time stamp when it is scheduled for execution. This time stamp is used for all read and write requests issued from within the block. Time stamps are assigned so that they mimic sequential execution. The way that this is done is to associate with each block an interval of time and to allow it to schedule only a small, fixed number of "child" blocks (the current incarnation of the instruction set allows at most four children). The actual time stamp associated with a block is the earliest time point in the interval. The intervals of the children are disjoint and contained within the parents interval. In this manner, all the time intervals form a nested hierarchy or tree. A sequential execution of a program would then consist of a pre-order traversal of this tree of blocks, where the parent is always executed before its children.

Figure 4.1 shows a simple example of this process. The code to be executed is a simple loop that counts the number of zeroes in an array. This code splits into two blocks, one that does the loop execution and test for zero, and the other which increments the counter. The figure shows part of the tree generated for a particular set of values in the array.

Ultimately the time stamps have to be represented concretely as numbers. Space precludes us from going into details here but a number of different schemes are currently being investigated. One of the simplest is to allow the root of the block tree to use the range from 0 to $2^{32}-1$. Each node then would have a range from i to j and would allocate the time stamp i to itself and four (approximately) equal ranges $i+1..i_1$, $i_1+1..i_2$, $i_2+1..i_3$, $i_3+1..j$ to each of the four possible children. This scheme is somewhat naive as with deeply nested and unbalanced trees precision will be rapidly lost. The use of a floating point representation together with occasional collection and re-scaling of the intervals gives a good compromise solution.

```
for I:= 1 to N do
        if V[I]=0 then C:=C+1;
```

(a) High Level Code

```
Block A:
        I := I+1;
        if V[I]=0 then schedule child 1 as block B;
        if I<N then schedule child 2 as block A;

Block B:
        C:=C+1;
```

(b) Blocks generated for Code shown in (a)

Example execution:

	1	2	3	4	5	
V	42	0	1	2	0	...

Tree of blocks in time stamp order:

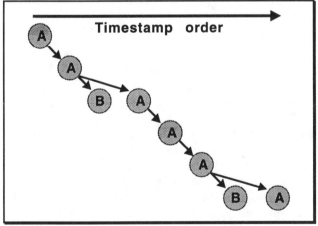

c) Trace of execution of blocks using the example data

Figure 4.1. Example of Execution of Blocks

The loop example above also illustrates the parallelism between blocks that is possible. In conventional parallel architectures it is not possible to parallelize the loop as written as there is a causal dependency between the successive iterations of the loop because of the counter C. However, in an array with few zeroes, C will seldom be incremented and the dependency will be very "weak". In the WarpEngine all the blocks can potentially be run in parallel. This parallelism will be limited only by rollbacks caused by increments to C rolling back later iterations which use C. The other limitation is the sequential order in which the successive blocks are dispatched. A more aggressive approach is to generate the successive iterations in a tree.

Whenever a block is scheduled for execution it can be executed either on the local (generating) processor or sent to another processor for execution. The time stamps on the blocks give some clues about how to do this. For example one strategy is to try and execute blocks with low time stamps as soon as possible. This would imply that as soon as a processor starts running ahead it should obtain low time stamped blocks from the rest of the system. This approach is probably too naive as rapid migration of blocks will cause poor cache coherence and consequent poor overall performance. In the end it may be that the software needs to provide hints or directives about when to dispatch blocks to other processors.

5. GVT Calculation

GVT is defined as the minimum time stamp of any object in the system, so calculation of GVT requires access to all time stamped objects in the system. This includes both blocks which are currently executing and memory requests currently being sent by CPUs or being transmitted between memories. Various GVT algorithms have been discussed in the literature [2, 18]. The important point here is that the calculation can be done in a time proportional to the diameter of the communication network between CPUs and that it requires both the CPUs and memory controllers to transmit their current minimum times.

GVT will be continually updated, probably by a separate communications channel running through the various CPUs. Once computed it then needs to be transmitted back to all the memory controllers (so that they can fossil collect the time-space cache) and to the CPUs so that they can delete blocks which cannot possibly be rolledback and re-executed.

6. Instructions

In this section a particular instruction set is described as an example of the WarpEngine architecture. A number of decisions about sizes (32-bit words, 16 instructions per block and so on) have been made for the sake of a concrete example. Clearly many variants of these basic ideas are possible. We have chosen for our example an architecture that closely follows that of a simple load store RISC

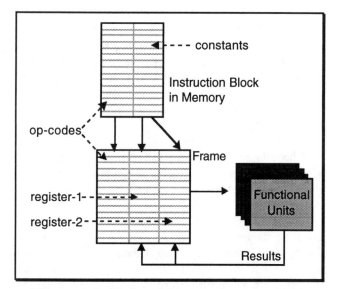

Figure 6.1. Flow of Instructions in CPU.

architecture using 32-bit words. This makes it easier to compare with modern designs.

6.1. Instruction Execution

We start with a description of the structure of a block and the path followed by an instruction during its execution. In an attempt to wring out as much parallelism as possible the individual instructions within a block execute in parallel. Rather than using time stamps to control this parallelism (which would require issuing a separate time stamp for every instruction) a dataflow mechanism is used. Instructions specify where their results will go (rather than where their arguments will come from). Figure 6.1 illustrates how this mechanism works.

In memory each instruction is represented by two 32 bit words. The first, the I-word contains the op-code and related information. The second, the C-word, contains a single literal or constant value, its use is explained below.

An instruction goes through a number of stages in its execution. After a block is initially dispatched it may be queued or migrated to another processor. Eventually it is "initiated". At this point the block is allocated a "frame". A frame resides in the CPU and consists of 16 slots (recall that there are 16 instructions in a block) with one instruction loaded into each slot. A slot contains three 32 bit fields: an op-code field and two "registers". The op-code is loaded directly from the instructions I-word. It specifies the instruction to be executed as well as other information. Potentially all the instructions in one block are loaded into the frame in parallel. (It is assumed that

one such load can complete every clock cycle in the performance estimates below. So if a cache line were 16 words long the whole cache line would be loaded in parallel).

The registers in a slot can be loaded either from the C-word of an instruction or as a result of another instruction. Two bits in the I-word specify how the C-word is to be used. It can be either stored in register-1 or register-2 of the corresponding slot or ignored. Because some instructions require both their register slots to be filled with constants a C-word can also be directed to register-2 of the adjacent slot. There are thus only 16 constants for 32 register slots in a block. However, this seems in practice to be a very weak constraint.

Once both registers in a slot have been filled with valid values then the instruction can be "fired". That is, transferred to a functional unit for execution. The 5-bit op-code acts as an address and specifies which functional unit the instruction and its accompanying registers are to be routed to. The functional unit then receives the contents of both the registers as well the residual 25 bits (32 bits less two for C-word routing and 5 for the functional unit address - we refer to this as the F-field). Using these three pieces of information the functional unit computes anywhere between 0 and 5 results. The F-field specifies a register in the frame for each result. The functional unit then sends each result back and fills in the corresponding slot which will enable that instruction in turn to be fired completing the cycle.

6.2. Individual Instructions

Figure 6.2 shows an example instruction layout at each stage for an ADD instruction which adds 5 to a value 7 received from another instruction .

Within the I-word the value CC=01 specifies that the constant is to be stored in the register-1 of the current slot. Following that two fields dest1 and dest2 specify where the results of the instruction are to be stored. There are 32 possible registers in the current frame so 5-bits suffices. The first destination specifies where the actual sum truncated to 32 bits is to be stored, the second destination specifies where the overflow from the addition is to be stored. (The second value can be used to test for exception and overflow conditions). The 25 bits in the F-field allow up to 5 destinations to be specified. Three of these are used for the sum and the other two for the overflows. The convention is used that a destination of 0 means do not store that result. So three potential destinations are unused in this instruction.

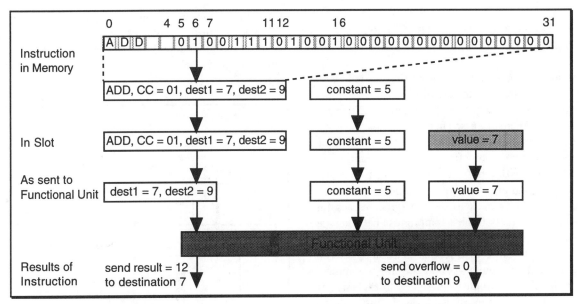

Figure 6.2. Instruction Format During Execution Stages.

All instructions (except the no-operation) take two parameters. All arithmetic and logical instructions (add, subtract, divide, shift, and, or, xor) use the F-field to specify (up to) 5 destinations.

There are three memory instructions which communicate with the memory subsystem. The load instruction adds the two values in its registers and uses the sum as the address to read from memory at the time of the current block. As with the arithmetic instructions the F-field is used to specify up to 5 destinations for the value returned from the read. The store instruction takes a value and an address and stores the value at that address at the time of the current block. As there is no need for any destination fields the F-field is used as a signed offset to the address.

There is one rather more exotic memory instruction. This allows a parent to store values directly into the register slots of its children. It was included because hand compilation of code showed that this process was very awkward with just a load and store and that it was frequently required. The instruction takes one value (it ignores its other register, the only instruction which does so) and stores it into a specified destination (5 bits) for one of the 4 possible children of this block (2 bits). (Thus 18 bits of the F-field are ignored).

There is a single instruction for comparing values. It takes its two input values and compares them. Three results can be generated from the one instruction. Each result is specified in the F-field by a 5 bit destination and 3 bits for the comparison operator ($<, \leq, >, \geq, \neq, =, 0, 1$). The results are 0 if the comparison fails and 1 if it succeeds.

There are three control instructions which use the results of such comparisons. The jump instruction specifies a block to be executed. It takes as values the address of the block and the result of a comparison operation (or a constant). If the comparison failed (the value is 0) then the block is not executed otherwise the block is dispatched for later execution. The F-field uses 2 bits to specify which child the block is to be and uses 23 bits as an offset to the block address.

There are two other control instructions, a halt and a trap, which are used to raise error conditions. They take as values a literal to indicate the cause of the error and a comparison flag which says whether to raise the error. For example, the trap could be used to raise an error if an arithmetic instruction overflowed.

6.3. Execution Rollback

Rollback of instructions is initiated when the memory subsystem returns a revised value from a read. It will have already returned some value and as a result of a (anti-) write the read may be resatisfied. What will appear to happen from the point of view of a slot is that a register that already has a valid value stored in it will receive a new value. If the slot has fired previously then it can deal with this by firing again.

One significant optimisation is to detect when the new value is the same as the old one, then the instruction does not need to be fired again. In some cases this optimisation may prevent a cascade of unnecessary recomputation. For correctness of the TimeWarp algorithm it is essential that the memory subsystem detect when the same value is stored into memory and does not do any memory replies as a consequence. However, from the point of view of instruction execution this is an optional optimisation.

7. The Hardware Structure of the WarpEngine CPU

An initial investigation is currently being carried out to evaluate the proposed architecture of the CPU. A number of issues that could influence the success of the CPU have been identified and are discussed in this section.

Success in implementing the Warp Engine will be heavily dependent on an efficient implementation of communication paths between the frames and the functional units and also the return communication paths from functional units back to the registers. Successful implementation is likely to be a compromise between the number of functional units and the complexity of the logic necessary to steer instructions and data between frames and functional units. At one extreme a complete set of functional units would be assigned to each slot of every frame. This would mean that a simple bus could be used to implement the communications paths between the slot and its set of functional units. This approach is very inefficient as only one of the functional units connected to a slot would be active at a time. This approach introduces redundancy as only one of the functional units connected to a slot would be active at a time.

At the other extreme, functional units would be shared between all slots of all frames of the CPU. While this would minimise the number of functional units necessary, the steering logic would be extremely complex if satisfactory performance is to be obtained. In addition a frame address would be required to be sent with an instruction so that its results can be routed back to the correct frame and the results pathway would also be more complex.

In the case that more than one slot can access a particular functional unit it is necessary to have a mechanism in place to ensure that instructions and data are not lost because a functional unit is not ready to receive them. One solution to this problem is to prevent the transfer from taking place until an appropriate functional unit becomes available. This solution is possibly unfair in that it cannot be guaranteed that all slots that can potentially communicate with a particular functional unit have equal priority. Alternatively, a buffer could be placed on the input stages of each of the functional units. This approach may however cause higher instruction execution latencies in the case where the buffers are empty.

There is a special case during execution that requires some additional hardware. This occurs when an instruction has been dispatched from its slot and is currently executing in a functional unit. If at this point, one of the registers (in the slot for the active instruction) receives a new value a difficulty arises. If the instruction is

dispatched again then it may be executing simultaneously in two functional units (which may have different latencies). If these complete out of dispatch order then the wrong (rolled back) value will be stored in the result register.

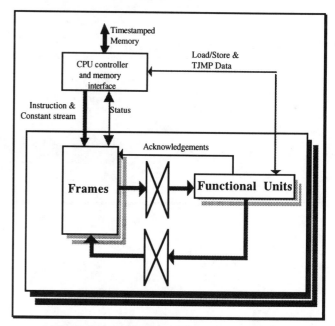

Figure 7.1 Block Diagram of CPU.

To deal with this an acknowledgment mechanism is required to allow the functional units to notify the slot that dispatched the instruction that it has finished and the results have been returned (see Figure 7.1). Only when the current execution has been acknowledged can any new re-execution be started.

As can be seen the final organisation of the CPU is far from being finalised. While the next section on *estimated performance* may give some insight into the number of frames required in each CPU, no estimates have yet been obtained for the numbers and types of functional units and the overall organisation. It is hoped that an initial functional simulation will give insight into these details.

8. Estimated Performance

As yet, it is not possible to give any detailed performance estimates. However, order of magnitude estimates give a good taste for requirements of each of the components of the architecture. The basic assumption we make in this analysis is that the different parts of the architecture are balanced, that is, there is no single bottle-neck to system performance.

The start of the analysis assumes that one memory operation can be completed per clock-cycle. This seems a reasonable assumption on the grounds that while it might be possible to multi-port the time-space cache this would be very complex and it might well be better to split the CPU into two before doing this.

Using a 95% on-chip cache hit rate this gives one external memory operation every 20 clock cycles. It seems likely that this difference will be consumed by the ratio between the differences in speed between the internal cache and external memory [13].

Using the estimates from [13] approximately 20% of instructions will be references to memory. So for instruction execution to keep up, 5 instructions must complete and be dispatched per clock. This requires the switch to transmit 5 instructions per clock. Each of these instructions requires between 0 and 2 data values. Examination of hand generated code gives an average of about 1.5 values per instruction, so the result switch must return on average 7.5 results per clock.

Examination of the contents of hand coded blocks shows that they average about 10 instructions each. At 5 instructions per clock this implies that one block must be started every 2 clock cycles. This is possible if all the instructions in a block are loaded in one clock and then all the constants are loaded in the next.

Operation	Number completing per cycle	Cycles to complete
Memory read/write	1.0	
External memory	0.05	
Instructions	5.0	
Results	7.5	
Code block	0.5	
Minimum Latency		3.0
Average latency		5.0
Number slots for blocks		> 8.0

Table 8.1. Summary of Performance Estimates.

Causal links between instructions limit the average number of instructions that can be executed in parallel to roughly 3 (that is the critical path through a block is 3 to 4 instructions long). This implies that the number of blocks active at any one time will be $5/3$ times the average latency of instructions. Some idea of this latency can be gained by looking at a few representative instructions. Every instruction has to be dispatched, will take at least one clock to execute and then will take one clock for the results to be returned. That is, the minimum latency will be 3 clocks. A memory read that comes directly out of cache will likely require one extra clock to compute the address. Assuming 5% of references will require 20 clocks (for an off-chip fetch) an average

memory reference will have a 4.9 clock latency. Using an average of 5 clocks for an overall instruction latency gives 8 to 9 ($= 5/3 \times 5$) blocks currently active. More space needs to be allocated for blocks than this as the lag in computing GVT means that some blocks, although they are inactive and will not be rolledback, still cannot be released until GVT advances. Table 8.1 summarises these performance estimates.

9. Summary and Future Work

So what can be said about an architecture like this where a great many details are still to be refined and where it is far from clear what the final performance or size of the system will be? The first claim that we would like to make is that to a first approximation the WarpEngine is feasible. Clearly some parts of the design are complex but it is more a question of by what date we could build such a system rather than whether it could be built at all. The second claim we would like to make is that it presents a scalable and conceptually simple approach to extracting parallelism from programs. The parallelism in the WarpEngine is limited only by the dynamic causal links between instructions. It is possible to envisage more efficient mechanisms but not ones that extract more parallelism. The other major advantage of the WarpEngine approach is that the burden of synchronising shared memory is completely removed. So at least from the point of view of achieving correct code the programmer is faced with the same problem as on a sequential computer. One implication of this is that it may be feasible to parallelise (and more daringly speed up) dusty deck code.

Given this there are still ways in which the approach could fail. First, the conceptual simplicity could vanish in the details of implementation. For example, it is unclear how best to implement key elements including the switch and the time-space cache. Second, the burden of control parallelism still remains to some extent. It is unclear how smart compilers will need to be to get good performance and the extent to which this burden will be forced back onto the programmer. The programmer must shoulder at least some of the burden as there are cases where the best algorithms are different on sequential and on parallel computers.

The final proof of this approach will be in demonstrating that the complete system from user code through compilers to execution can deliver good performance. The author's have had sufficient experience with the frustrations of extracting parallelism from real problems to realise that this is no small project. We look forward to the challenges of constructing the simulators and compilers (and eventually hardware) to prove these ideas.

Acknowledgments

Husam Kinawi would like to acknowledge support by the Natural Sciences and Engineering Research Council of Canada.

References

[1] Agarwal, A., Chaiken, D., D'Souza, G. , Johnson, K., Kranz, D., Kubiatowicz, J., Kiyoshi Kurihara, K., Lim, B-H. , Maa, G., Nussbaum, D., Parkin, M. and Yeung, D., (1991) "The MIT Alewife Machine: A Large-Scale Distributed-Memory Multiprocessor," Proceedings of The Workshop on Scalable Shared Memory Multiprocessors, Kluwer Academic Publishers.

[2] Bellenot, S., (1990) "Global Virtual Time Algorithms," Proceedings of the 1990 SCS Multi-conference on Distributed Simulation, Vol. 22(2), pp. 122 - 130, January.

[3] Catanzaro, B., (1994) "Multiprocessor System Architecture," Sun Microsystems Inc., Mt. View, CA, SunSoft Press, Prentice Hall Title.

[4] Choi, J. D., Miller, B. P. and Netzer, R. H. B., (1988) "Techniques for Debugging Parallel Programs with Flowback Analysis," Dept. of Computer Science, Univ. of Wisconsin Tech. Report No. 786, later in ACM Transactions on Programming Languages and Systems.

[5] Courtois, B., (1993) "CAD and Testing of ICs and Systems - Where are we going?" Techniques of Informatics and Microelectronics for Computer Architecture, Grenoble, France, November.

[6] Fujimoto, R. M., (1989) "The Virtual Time Machine," Dept. of Computer Science, Univ. of Utah Tech. Report UUCS-88-019.

[7] Fujimoto, R. M., (1990a) "Time Warp on a Shared Memory Multiprocessor," Trans. of the SCS 6(3), pp. 211-239, July.

[8] Fujimoto, R. M., (1990b) "Parallel Discrete Event Simulation," Comm. of the ACM, Vol. 33, No. 10, pp. 30 - 53, October.

[9] Fujimoto, R. M., Tsai, J., Gopalakrishnan, G., (1992) "Design and Evaluation of the Rollback Chip: Special Purpose Hardware for Time Warp," IEEE Transactions on Computers, Vol. 41, No. 1, pp. 68 - 82, January.

[10] Ghosh, K. and Fujimoto, R. M., (1991) "Parallel Discrete Event Simulation Using Space-Time Memory," International Conference on Parallel Processing, pp. III-201 - III-208.

[11] Hagersten, E., Haridi, S. and Warren, D., (1990) "The Cache-Coherent Protocol of the Data Diffusion Machine," Cache and Interconnect Architectures in Multiprocessors.

[12] Hennessy, J. L. and Jouppi, N. P., (1991) "Computer Technology and Architecture: An Evolving Interaction", IEEE Computer 24(9), pp. 18 - 29, September.

[13] Hennessy, J. L. and Patterson, D. A., (1990) "Computer Architecture: A Quantitative Approach," Morgan Kaufmann Publishers.

[14] Jefferson, D. R., (1985) "Virtual Time," ACM Transactions on Programming Languages and Systems, 7(3), pp. 404 - 425, July.

[15] Jefferson, D. R., (1989) "Virtual Time II: Storage Management in Distributed Simulation," Proceedings of the Annual Symposium on Principles of Distributed Computing, pp. 75 - 89, August.

[16] Lamport, L., (1979) "How to make a multi-processor computer that correctly executes multiprocess programs," IEEE Transactions on Computers, Vol. C-28, No. 9, September.

[17] Lenoski, D., Laudon, J., Stevens, L., Joe, T., Nakahira, D., Gupta, A. and Hennessy J. L., (1992) "The DASH Prototype: Implementation and Performance," Proc. of 19th Annual International Symposium on Computer Architecture, pp. 92 - 103, May.

[18] Lin, Y. and Lazowska, D., (1990) "Determining the Global Virtual Time in a Distributed Simulation," Proceedings of the International Conference on Parallel Processing III, pp. 201 - 209.

[19] Mosberger, D., (1993) "Memory Consistency Models," Operating Systems Review, Vol. 17, No. 1, January. Also in, Dept. of Comp. Sci., Univ. of Arizona Tech. Report 93/11.

[20] Olthof, I. and Cleary, J. G., (accepted 1994) "The Design of an Optimistic AND-parallel Prolog," Journal of Logic Programming.

[21] Prakash, A. and Knister, M. J., (1992) "Undoing Actions in Collaborative Work," ACM Conf. on Computer Supported Cooperative Work: Sharing Perspectives, Toronto, pp. 273 - 280, November.

[22] Rothnie, J., (1992) "Overview of the KSR1 Computer System," Kendall Square Research Report TR9202001, March.

[23] Thimbleby, H., (1990) "User Interface Design," ACM Press, pp. 261 - 286.

[24] Unger, B. W., Cleary, J., Dewar, A. and Xiao, Z., (1990) "A Multi-Lingual Optimistic Distributed Simulator," Transactions of the Society for Computer Simulation, Vol. 7, No. 2, pp. 121 - 152, June.

Evaluation of a Branch Target Address Cache

Sreeram Duvvuru, Siamak Arya

Sun Microsystems, Inc. Mountain View, CA

{sduv,siamaka}eng.sun.com

Abstract

Branches interrupt the sequential flow of instructions and introduce pipeline bubbles. Branch penalty can be a significant component of effective *cpi* (cycles per instruction) in multiple instruction issue processors. Two key issues need to be resolved to alleviate this problem: a branch resolution scheme to decide the direction and target of a branch early in the pipeline, thus allowing target instruction fetch to start, and mechanisms to minimize the impact of unpredictable branches. We propose a technique of cacheing branch target addresses for our fully predicated processor architecture, that would allow the branch decision to be made in the fetch stage of the pipeline. We discuss the impact of different branch target cacheing policies and cache sizes on the efficiency of branch target address cache. Impact of register-relative branches which may have variable target addresses is considered and a solution is suggested.

1 Introduction

Branches in the instruction stream represent control flow in the source code. Taken branches introduce bubbles in the pipeline because instructions from the target of a taken branch could not be fetched in time to execute in the cycle immediately following the branch, reducing pipeline efficiency. It is well understood that branches pose a more serious performance problem for multiple issue, multiple functional unit processors because a missed instruction issue slot causes several functional units to be idle. Branch handling has performance implications for the two reasons. Firstly, if the branch outcome, taken or not-taken, is not resolved until the execute stage. Unless some sophisticated prediction scheme is used merging two instruc-

tion streams involves significant penalty. Secondly, if branch target address is not available to start a prefetch, until later in the pipeline, it increases branch penalty.

Predicting the outcome of a branch ahead of time permits the correct target instruction stream to be fetched for execution early, improving pipeline efficiency and resource utilization. Branching behavior is workload dependent and ranges from completely predictable unconditional branches, to almost predictable branches for loops, and dynamic data dependent branches that may be impossible to predict statically.

1.1 Review of Branch Handling Schemes

Static branch prediction strategies rely on the branch direction or static prediction bit(s) in the opcode to guide instruction fetch. With the collaboration of an intelligent compiler this method can be quite effective. Execution profiling enables the branch probabilities to be accurately determined increasing the effectiveness of static prediction[8]. The effectiveness of profile based static branch prediction is studied by Fisher and Freudenberger in [8]. Various forms of static branch prediction have been implemented in AT&T CRISP[7], Intel 80960[10]. More recently, SPARC-V9 [21] instruction set introduced branch instructions that utilize static prediction information embedded within the instructions.

Dynamic branch prediction stores limited branch history information to predict branch outcome. Purely dynamic branch prediction is implemented in Intel Pentium[2] and Motorola 68060[6]. The Pentium uses a two bit saturating history mechanism and a target address cache. The first Alpha implementation[1] used a combination of static prediction, based on branch direction and dynamic prediction. The technique of *correlation* based dynamic branch prediction relies on the premise that the outcome of a branch is influenced by the outcome of its neighboring branches. This improves dynamic prediction accuracy by a small amount over the simple two bit scheme[16].

The Delayed Branch scheme allows up to *n* instructions placed immediately after the *delayed* branch (*branch delay slots*) to be executed before the target instructions. Support for instruction *annulment* when the branch is not taken permits the delay slots to be filled even with instructions from the target, if possible. This technique is used in many RISC pipelined processors to hide branch latency. Compilation techniques to fill branch delay slots are well understood[9].

The RS/6000[15] and PowerPC/601[14] employ separate branch units that scan ahead in the instruction stream looking for branch instructions, and merge instruction streams when possible, with zero cost. No prediction or caching is involved in this scheme, though it is possible to incorporate such methods. Schemes for executing multiple instruction streams from both sides of a conditional branch, and discarding the results when the branch is resolved were implemented in some IBM mainframes but appear infeasible for microprocessor designs. IBM System/360 Model 91 fetched instruction from both the target and fall-through path[3].

Ball and Larus study the effectiveness of static heuristic schemes to predict branch direction statically at compile time[5]. General Branch Target Buffer design and some dynamic branch prediction algorithms are presented by Lee and Smith in [13], and Perleberg and Smith in [17].

Current processor designs aim to exploit fine grained instruction level parallelism for high performance, such as in wide instruction word and superscalar processors. The impact of branch penalty is worse for these multiple instruction issue processors because branches inhibit exploitation of instruction level parallelism by causing bubbles. [18, 12, 11]. Techniques like delayed branches do not extend easily to multiple issue processors, and complicate interrupt and trap handling even for single issue processors. The motivation for our proposal of a Branch Target Address Cache (BTAC) arose from an effort at building a new processor architecture, codenamed 4S, that combined superscalar and wide instruction word paradigms, to exploit instruction level parallelism[4].

2 The Branch Target Address Cache

Condition codes in 4S are single bits in a 64-bit Condition Code Register (CCR). The instruction set architecture is completely predicated *i.e* each instruction specifies a condition code(*cc*) bit, upon which it's execution is predicated. If the specified bit is clear in the CCR, at the time of issue, the instruction is annulled. Full predication allows conditional branches, such as those arising from *if-then-else* conditional statements in the source code, to be eliminated to a large extent. These eliminated branches are the ones that are difficult to predict and likely to be in the critical path. The remaining branches need to be handled efficiently to minimize performance impact. Our scheme relies on the fact that the condition code upon which a branch is based, can be determined slightly ahead of the branch. The BTAC stores branch target addresses, used to start an instruction cache prefetch for expected target instruction flow. The BTAC also stores the associated condition code bit number, together with the branch target address.

4S architecture required that the compiler demarcate instruction issue groups by using a running single *continue* bit in the instruction format. Also, if a branch belongs to an issue group, it is expected to be the first instruction in the group. The BTAC is accessed with the current *pc*. If we hit in the BTAC the target address and associated *cc* bit number are read out. If the specified *cc* bit is set in CCR, the next-*pc* is set to the cached target address, otherwise it is set to the start of next sequential issue group. If the *cc* bit that determines the direction of this branch is ready (early compare), the appropriate instruction sequence is correctly forwarded to the decode stage in the very next cycle, achieving a zero penalty branch. Thus unconditional branches and conditional branches with condition code determined sufficiently in advance, can be executed in one cycle without any penalty; assuming that the branch target address is found in the BTAC. If the BTAC did not contain the target address of a branch, the target address was computed later in the pipe, and the BTAC is updated depending on the cacheing policy and the actual result of branch execution. Figure 1 shows the proposed BTAC operation.

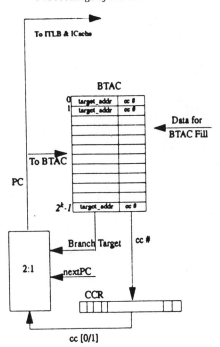

Figure 1: Operation of Branch Target Address Cache

Work with BTAC was done while the authors were working on a new VLIW-Superscalar hybrid processor at Intergraph Corporation, Palo Alto, CA. Our motivation for studying the BTAC design parameters was to determine the ideal size and cacheing policy for BTAC, keeping in mind that we were designing a brand new processor and instruction set architecture[4]. Since the architecture supported full predicated execution, we expected to see fewer and more predictable branches e.g unconditional and loop-closing branches, in the instruction stream. For these "predictable" branches, the required condition code can be expected to be set well in advance and hence a very simple BTAC was thought sufficient to guarantee high performance. This report is a study of simple target address cacheing schemes without any consideration to branch prediction. Since we did not then, yet have an optimizing compiler to schedule using full predication, we used the results of the following study as "reasonable" upper bounds on the effectiveness of a BTAC. To our knowledge no previous study presented the results for all of the SPEC92 benchmark suite.

In this paper, we present results of a study on BTAC design parameter tradeoffs, in particular target address caching policies and the size of the cache.

The problem of register-relative branches, where the target of a branch is likely to change dynamically, is considered. We propose that each branch instruction be tagged to indicate whether its target address is cacheable or not. If a branch is tagged as cacheable, the compiler guarantees that the target address will not change dynamically.

2.1 Simulation Methodology and Benchmarks

This simulation study was performed using c4sim, which interprets the Intergraph Clipper C400[19] instructions. C400 is a pipelined and dual issue superscalar architecture. C400 instruction set is divided into two classes, and independent instructions from two classes can issue in the same cycle. We used Intergraph/Apogee advanced optimizing compilers to compile the benchmarks. We simulated all of the SPEC92 suite of programs. Table 1 presents the branch behavior of all simulated benchmarks. %Bra column gives the percentage of all executed instructions that were branch instructions. %Taken gives the percentage of all executed branches that were taken. % Uncond gives the percentage of all executed branches that were unconditional branches. The remaining branches are conditional. %RegRel gives the percentage of all executed branches that were register-relative. The remaining branches are program counter relative or *pc-relative*.

Intergraph/Apogee compilers perform a profile directed optimization called *branch profiling*, which aims to reduce the penalty of taken branches. Information on branch results gathered in a prior run of the program is used to rearrange code and reduce the percentage of taken branches. We chose to use branch profiled executables because we wanted to simulate only the most difficult to predict branches which could not be rearranged optimally even after full profile information. The remaining branches are not skewed in any one particular direction.

From Table 1 observe that:

All integer benchmarks gcc, espresso, eqntott, li, compress and sc have a high percentage of branch instructions.

The control flow did not change as often for the floating point benchmarks. Most floating point benchmarks, with the exception of spice, hydro2d,

Program	% Bra	% Taken	% Uncond	% RegRel
eqntott	22.76	79.6	4.70	3.23
li	17.74	37.7	22.52	9.68
sc	17.58	57.7	18.34	8.77
gcc	16.77	69.5	19.91	8.90
compress	16.00	66.1	17.31	3.04
espresso	14.73	51.5	9.77	2.78
spice	14.29	29.0	11.09	2.14
hydro2d	12.16	77.4	1.41	0.10
mdljsp2	11.62	84.6	5.85	0.28
mdljdp2	10.93	28.0	4.48	0.30
ora	9.53	57.7	28.73	13.68
doduc	9.37	43.7	14.61	5.68
ear	7.51	50.2	6.97	0.09
wave5	7.02	72.0	12.07	5.56
su2cor	5.37	65.0	12.21	5.37
nasa7	4.46	71.4	10.00	4.19
alvinn	4.44	92.5	2.20	0.75
tomcatv	3.88	99.1	0.06	0.02
swm256	2.32	98.6	0.26	0.11
fpppp	1.72	36.1	19.81	7.59

Table 1: Benchmark Charactarastics

mdljdp2 and mdljsp2 had a relatively low percentage of branches, and branch penalty may not have a significant impact on their performance.

The percentage of taken branches is very high for loop intensive programs such as tomcatv, swm256, and alvinn. However, for these programs, only a small percentage of the executed instructions are branches. Loop closing branches are very predictable and the loop terminating condition can often be determined sufficiently ahead.

Unconditional branches account for less than a fifth of all executed branches with the sole exception of ora.

We also observed that, almost all register-relative branches are unconditional. Only a negligible number of conditional register-relative branches were executed, which implies that predicting the direction of conditional register-relative branches is not critical. However, we did not study how often the target address of a register relative branch changed and all register-relative branch targets were assumed *unsafe* for caching. Unconditional register-relative branches are executed to effect indirect procedure calls and procedure return statements. Their outcome is trivially

predicted to be taken but the target cannot be statically determined. The issues regarding register-relative branches are discussed below.

2.2 Impact of Register Relative Branches

Register Relative branch instruction is emitted to implement a branch where the target is dynamically set. The branch target address is either computed on the fly or loaded from memory. For example, to effect a return from a called procedure or subroutine, the return address saved on the stack is restored into a register and a register-relative branch is executed. The computed *goto* statement in FORTRAN, longish switch statements in C where the branch target address array is predictably small, are other examples of control flow which may be efficiently translated into register relative branches. Also, indirect function calls; such as when function pointers are passed as arguments, calls to routines in Dynamically Linked Libraries (DLLs) are register-relative. Direct calls to external functions will also be translated to register relative branches by most compilers.

Register-relative branches may be cacheable, provided the compiler or linker can guarantee that the target address does not change. In our simulation study, we did not cache any register-relative branches. We do expect to see compilers and linkers that can predict statically whether the target address changes for register-relative branches. We propose that the instruction set be enhanced to provide two versions of register-relative branch instruction, one whose target is guaranteed by the compiler to not change and hence cacheable; and the other non-cacheable because such a guarantee could not be made statically. See [4].

DLLs have become the primary mechanism for abstracting the interfaces to a lot of system services. Kernel's system calls, interfaces to nearly every publicly accessible device or service are made available via DLLs. Unix SVR4 and Windows NT applications are expected to use these DLLs extensively and it can be expected that the percentage of register relative branches in real application may be much higher than what we have noticed in our benchmarks. If it can be guaranteed that once linked to an application the DLL cannot be relocated, the loader can patch all calls to DLL routines before the program begins execution, and it would be safe to use cacheable register relative branches even while calling external DLL routines. This solution should address the problem of most register-relative branches satisfactorily.

There is one class of register-relative branches which is executed with sufficient frequency to deserve special treatment even with our scheme of tagging branches as cacheable or non-cacheable with respect to the branch target address, and that is procedure return. The return address from a procedure is different if it is called from many places. A solution for this is already provided in the form of a small *procedure return stack* in DEC Alpha[20].

3 BTAC Simulation Results

We used trace driven simulation technique and performed complete simulations using reference inputs required for SPEC performance reporting. In all of our experiments, only absolute and program-counter relative (*pc*-relative) branches are selectively cached in the BTAC, depending on the cacheing policy. Henceforth, when we say, all cached branches, we mean all *pc*-relative and absolute address branches that were cached. When we refer to other types of branches

they will be explicitly qualified, for example register-relative branches. Two different cacheing policies are simulated. In the first policy, target addresses all executed branches are cached regardless of whether they are taken or not. In the second scheme, only taken branch target addresses are cached. The single statistic of merit is the percentage of taken branches that missed in the BTAC. BTAC size is varied between 64, 128 and 256 entries. Four way set associative BTACs are simulated for efficiency considerations. LRU replacement policy is used. Table 2 shows the number of taken *pc*-relative branches which miss in the BTAC as a percentage of executed branch instructions. For instance, while executing gcc with a 64 entry BTAC and cacheing all branches, nearly 23 out of every 100 executed branches are taken but miss in the BTAC, causing pipeline bubble(s).

Note that the integer programs gcc, sc, li, espresso, and compress have a significant percentage of taken branches that miss in the BTACs of smaller sizes. gcc proves to be a particularly difficult program in this aspect, because many taken branches miss even in the 256 entry BTAC. The remaining programs have a much smaller number of branches creating branch penalty cycles.

It appears from the tables that the policy of cacheing the target addresses of taken branches only, gives consistently better performance than cacheing target addresses of all executed branches. Cacheing only taken branch target addresses provides utilization of the BTAC by reducing contention. This strategy succeeds on the assumption that every branch instruction shows some temporal locality in its outcome, i.e., taken branches tend to be taken, at least in the next few executions of the same branch.

3.1 Impact of Branches on Cycles per Instruction

Branch penalty arises only for taken branches that miss in the BTAC and non-cacheable register-relative branches. We assumed that the penalty is 2 extra cycles for register-relative branches and 1 cycle for absolute and *pc*-relative branches that missed in the BTAC. The percentage of taken branches that missed in the BTAC for different BTAC cacheing policies, shown in Table 2 indicates that the policy of cacheing only taken branch targets in the BTAC is a better policy. We add the penalty from non-cacheable register-

Program	64 Entry		128 Entry		256 Entry	
	All	Taken	All	Taken	All	Taken
SPECint92						
gcc	22.64	20.47	16.65	13.51	9.38	6.98
li	7.37	1.66	3.22	0.53	1.00	0.07
sc	6.43	5.10	4.10	2.94	2.10	1.33
espresso	5.23	3.90	2.49	1.67	0.87	0.48
compress	1.53	0.64	0.00	0.00	0.00	0.00
eqntott	0.71	0.64	0.00	0.00	0.00	0.00
SPECfp92						
spice	2.45	0.45	0.94	0.04	0.15	0.01
hydro2d	1.81	0.26	0.10	0.09	0.06	0.06
mdljsp2	0.01	0.00	0.00	0.00	0.00	0.00
mdljdp2	0.00	0.00	0.00	0.00	0.00	0.00
ora	0.00	0.00	0.00	0.00	0.00	0.00
doduc	5.26	2.03	2.52	1.69	1.29	0.79
ear	3.72	0.54	2.54	0.42	0.09	0.00
wave5	2.00	0.53	0.71	0.07	0.15	0.02
su2cor	0.08	0.06	0.04	0.02	0.01	0.01
nasa7	0.79	0.01	0.01	0.00	0.00	0.00
alvinn	3.80	2.26	1.62	1.28	0.36	0.18
tomcatv	0.11	0.08	0.05	0.04	0.02	0.01
swm256	0.02	0.00	0.00	0.00	0.00	0.00
fpppp	6.56	1.92	2.71	0.21	0.30	0.01

Table 2: %Branches Taken and Missed in BTAC

relative branches to the penalty of BTAC misses for taken branches, to obtain the worst case branch execution time. We say worst case because we are assuming that all register-relative branches are non-cacheable. The column **No BTAC** shows the number of penalty when the BTAC or an equivalent scheme is not present. In reality a large percentage may of register-relative branches may be cacheable and the effective penalty is lowered. The results are presented in Table 3 as penalty cycles due to branches, per 100 instructions. The advantage of cacheing only taken branch targets seems to diminish as the BTAC size is increased.

The numbers indicate that our method is effective in reducing the contribution of branches to the overall cpi, to well under .07 *cpi* for branch intensive programs like *gcc*. The mean penalty for integer programs is reduced to 0.03 *cpi* and for floating-point code the penalty is .0024 *cpi*, even after including the cost of register-relative branches, with a modestly sized branch target address cache.

4 Conclusions and Future Work

We presented the operation of a simple Branch Target Address Cache. The effectiveness of different branch target cacheing policies and cache sizes are studied using trace driven simulation. The policy of cacheing taken branch targets appears to be consistently better than cacheing all executed branch targets. The problem of register-relative branches is addressed and a a suitable solution is suggested.

We have assumed that the condition code that determines the outcome of a branch can be determined in at least one cycle in advance. While this is true for conditional and loop closing branches, we have not found any recently published compiler studies measuring the distance between condition code setting and dependent conditional transfer, in non-numerical code. Our study of effectiveness of BTAC cacheing policies and BTAC size is relevant even in absence of such information.

Future work involves investigating how often the

Program	No BTAC	64 Entry		128 Entry		256 Entry	
		All	Taken	All	Taken	All	Taken
SPECint92							
gcc	14.55	6.74	6.38	5.74	5.22	4.53	4.13
li	10.12	4.74	3.73	4.01	3.53	3.61	3.45
sc	13.23	4.21	3.98	3.80	3.60	3.45	3.32
espresso	8.40	1.59	1.39	1.19	1.06	0.95	0.89
compress	11.55	1.22	1.08	0.97	0.97	0.97	0.97
eqntott	19.59	1.63	1.62	1.47	1.47	1.47	1.47
G.Mean	12.43	2.74	2.47	2.30	2.15	2.06	1.97
SPECfp92							
spice	4.76	0.96	0.68	0.75	0.62	0.63	0.61
hydro2d	9.44	0.24	0.06	0.04	0.04	0.03	0.03
mdljsp2	9.90	0.07	0.07	0.07	0.07	0.07	0.07
mdljdp2	3.13	0.07	0.07	0.07	0.07	0.07	0.07
ora	8.11	2.61	2.61	2.61	2.61	2.61	2.61
doduc	5.16	1.56	1.25	1.30	1.22	1.19	1.14
ear	3.78	0.29	0.05	0.20	0.05	0.02	0.01
wave5	5.84	0.92	0.82	0.83	0.79	0.79	0.78
su2cor	4.07	0.58	0.58	0.58	0.58	0.58	0.58
nasa7	3.56	0.41	0.37	0.37	0.37	0.37	0.37
alvinn	4.17	0.24	0.17	0.14	0.12	0.08	0.07
tomcatv	3.85	0.01	0.00	0.00	0.00	0.00	0.00
swm256	2.29	0.01	0.01	0.01	0.01	0.01	0.01
fpppp	0.88	0.37	0.29	0.31	0.26	0.27	0.26
G. Mean	4.23	0.24	0.08	0.08	0.07	0.06	0.06

Table 3: Branch Penalty Cycles for 100 Instructions

condition code determining the outcome is determined in advance and effectiveness of using static branch prediction bit for situations where the condition bit cannot could not be readied in time. We also plan to study how often the target of a register-relative branch changes in our benchmarks. If the target can be predicted not change a cacheable version of register-relative branch instruction can be used.

References

[1] DECChip 21064-AA RISC Microprocessor Preliminary Data Sheet. Technical report, Digital Equipment Corporation, Maynard, MA, 1992.

[2] *Intel Pentium Processor Databook.* Intel Corporation, Santa Clara, CA, 1993.

[3] D. W. Anderson, F. J. Sparacio, and R. M. Tomasulo. The IBM System/360 Model 91: Machine Philosophy and Instruction Handling. *IBM Journal of Research and Development*, 11:8–24, January 1967.

[4] Siamak Arya, Howard Sachs, and Sreeram Duvvuru. An Architecture for High Instruction Level Parallelism. In *The 28th Hawaii International Conference on System Sciences*. The University of Hawaii, January 1995.

[5] Thomas Ball and James Larus. Branch Prediction for Free. In *SIGPLAN Conference on Programming Language Design and Implementation*. ACM SIGPLAN, June 1993.

[6] Joe Circello and Floyd Goodrich. The Motorola 68060 Microprocessor. In *Spring COMPCON*. IEEE Computer Sciety, 1993.

[7] David R. Ditzel and Hubert R. McLellan. Branch Folding in the CRISP Microprocessor. In *14th Annual Symposium on Computer Architecture*. IEEE Computer Society, 1987.

[8] Joseph A. Fisher and Stefan M. Freudenberger. Predicting Conditional Branch Directions from Previous Runs of a Program. In *ASPLOS V*. ACM and IEEE Compuer Society, October 1992.

[9] T.R. Gross and John L. Hennessy. Optimizing Delayed Branches. In *15th International Workshop on Microprogramming*, October 1982.

[10] G. Hinton. 80960 - Next Generation. In *Spring COMPCON*. IEEE Computer Sciety, 1989.

[11] Norman P. Jouppi and David W. Wall. Available Instruction-Level Parallelism for Superscalar and Superpipelined Machines. In *International Conference on Architectural Support for Programming Languages and Operating Systems (ASPLOS)*, pages 272–282. IEEE Computer Society, April 1989.

[12] Norman P. Jouppi and David W. Wall. Limits of Instruction Level Parallelism. In *International Conference on Architectural Support for Programming Languages and Operating Systems (ASPLOS)*, pages 176–186. IEEE Computer Society, 1991.

[13] J.K.F. Lee and Alan Jay Smith. Branch Prediction Strategies and Branch Target Buffer Design. *IEEE Computer*, 17, January 1984.

[14] Charles R. Moore. The PowerPC 601 Microprocessor. In *Spring COMPCON*. IEEE Computer Sciety, February 1993.

[15] R.R. Oehler and R.D. Groves. IBM RS/6000 Processor Architecture. *IBM Journal of Research and Development*, 34(1):23–36, January 1990.

[16] Shen-Tai Pan, Kimming So, and Joseph T. Rahmeh. Improving Accuracy of Dynamic Branch Prediction Using Branch Correlation. In *ASPLOS V*. ACM and IEEE Compuer Society, October 1992.

[17] Chris H. Perleberg and Alan Jay Smith. Branch Target Buffer Design and Optimization. *IEEE Transactions on Computers*, 42, April 1993.

[18] E.M. Riseman and C.C. Foster. The Inhibition of Potential Parallelism by Conditional Jumps. *IEEE Transactions on Computers*, December 1972.

[19] Howard Sachs, Lee Hanson, Harlan McGhan, and Nathan Brookwood. Design and Implementation Tradeoffs in the Clipper C400 Architecture. *IEEE Micro*, June 1991.

[20] Richard Sites, editor. *Alpha Architecture Reference Manual*. Digital Press Inc, 1992.

[21] David Weaver and Tom Germond, editors. *The SPARC Architecture Manual - Version 9*. PTR Prentice Hall Inc., 1993.

An Improved Dynamic Register Array Concept
for High-Performance RISC Processors

Thomas Scholz and Michael Schäfers
Dept. of Design of Integrated Circuits
Technical University of Braunschweig, Germany
E-mail: scholz@eis.cs.tu-bs.de

Abstract

To avoid RISC processors accessing the external memory, an increased number of processor registers is desirable. However, sophisticated concepts are needed for the handling of large amounts of registers.

Multi Windows are an improved version of Threaded Windows, the first dynamic register array concept. Both utilize dynamic register allocation for handling a very large number of general purpose registers. This concept enables fast context switches and a short interrupt latency, which makes it suitable for real time systems.

In Multi Windows, the data structures were simplified and improved. Exception routines are less complex and faster. Both concepts will be discussed in this article.

1   Introduction

In the beginning of the 80s, the increase in processor complexity did not lead to adequate performance gains. A new branch in processor architecture called RISC began with a drastic reduction and regularization of the instruction set, for the remaining operations to be executed with simplified control effort, allowing higher clock frequencies and improving throughput. An upper limit of the clock rate is the bus. This "bottleneck" is the interface between the processor and its periphery, primarily the memory. Nearly every instruction and data fetch has to pass the bus.

One possibility to widen this bottleneck is the usage of on chip caches, which mirror parts of the external memory inside the processor. Caches are very popular because their interface with the heart of the processor is very simple, thus they can be developed independently from other parts.

Working on registers reduces bus load. Most RISC processors are equipped with about 32 registers. The efficiency of register usage depends not only on the number but also on the organization of the register array. Usage of more than 32 registers requires a management concept, that allows a dynamic sharing of the resources. This article deals with some traditional concepts, before presenting the first dynamic concept, the "Threaded Windows", and its improved version, the "Multi Windows".

2   Register Array Concepts

The organization of the register files is one of the main differences among RISC processors. Most existing register concepts can be divided into classes of static and stack-like organizations.

2.1   Static Register Arrays

A static register array is a fixed set of general-purpose-registers. The processor can always access any register. This represents a state independent register organization. Since all registers have to be addressed, it is important to keep their number small, because there is only a certain amount of bits for the coding of their number respectively address in the instruction code available. E.g. a three address RISC with 32 registers requires 15 bits for the register addresses. That is nearly half of the instruction code. Therefore the amount of static registers does generally not exceed 32.

Static registers are not suited to carry local data of recursive procedures, because they have to be saved to external memory before doing recursion. Nevertheless, most actual RISC processors use a static management. Typical examples are ARM [3], MIPS [5] or TOOBSIE [2].

2.2   Register Stacks

Since the beginning of RISC development in Berkeley, the static organization was questioned. Run-time examinations discovered the use of static registers mainly for short-living temporary data (scratch register) storage. An example is the temporary memory in the evaluation of arithmetic expressions. Procedure local data and parameters had to be saved to an external memory stack before other procedures can be called.

To deal with this kind of data, a management concept similar to an external stack is needed. The AM29000 [4] uses a part of its register array as procedure stack. Furthermore, there are some experimental variants of stack architectures, e.g. Fast [1].

2.3 Window Stacks

In contrast to the register stack, where stack elements are single registers, elements are complete register blocks on the window stack. Again, procedural hierarchy determines the top of stack. On call, a procedure receives a new block of registers (register window). Successive windows overlap in some registers and thus enable argument passing through the intersection.

Berkeley RISC [6, 13] and the SPARC series processors [12, 13] are successfully using a *Circular Window Stack*. By having just a window of registers available at a time, this concept is able to manage a higher total number of registers. The window position is bound to the procedure hierarchy of the running program. Window intersections allow arguments to be passed between procedures.

More windows reduce the memory traffic but increase the cost of context switches.

2.4 Motivation for Dynamic Management

Parameters of these architectures, e.g. number and size of windows, intersection size, etc. derive from runtime analysis of common programs. Unfortunately, the parameters are not necessarily well suited for programs that have no "average behavior". Hence, more flexibility is desired. Furthermore, stack concepts are unsuited for processing interrupts, exceptions or task switches.

More flexibility and a dynamic adjustment of the register array to the processor state could make it more suitable to a variety of tasks. *Threaded Windows* [7, 8, 9] are the first realization of such a behavior.

3 Threaded Windows

Threaded Windows were presented in 1988, with the MULTRIS (Multitasking RISC) project [8, 13]. They contain 1024 registers of 32 bits each and are divided into 64 disjunct windows with 16 registers. Direct access is limited to 4 windows at a time (one for global

data, two for procedure data, and one for user defined purposes). Furthermore, the processor manages up to 3 additional windows.

3.1 Program Status Words

The program status words contain information about the actual state of the processor, e.g., status flags and a mask for interrupt sources.

XW		Extra Window
INT_MASK		Interrupt Mask
I		Interrupt Flag
C, V, N, Z		Carry -, Overflow -, Negative -, Zero Flag
MW		Map Window
MWI		Map Window Index

Figure 1: Program Status Word 1 (PSW1)

Furthermore, they contain pointers to register windows and indices of special places inside windows. The figures 1 and 2 illustrate the detailed partitioning of the processor status words.

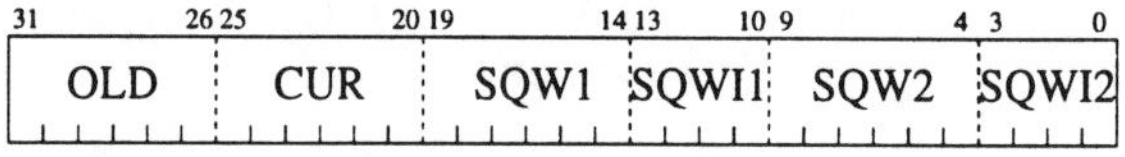

OLD	Old Activation Record
CUR	Current Activation Record
SQW1	S/Q (Stack/Queue) Window 1
SQWI1	S/Q Window Index 1
SQW2	S/Q Window 2
SQWI2	S/Q Window Index 2

Figure 2: Program Status Word 2 (PSW2)

3.2 Global Window

Only the *Global Window* is static and bound to number 0. Hence, window pointers to 0 indicate special conditions, e.g. a non existing or spilled window.

The global window contains 16 registers. Thus, it is generally too small for all global data. Therefore, choosing the most important data will be necessary.

3.3 Extra Window

The *Extra Window* (XW) is designed for universal purposes. Possibilities to use the Extra Window beneficially are:

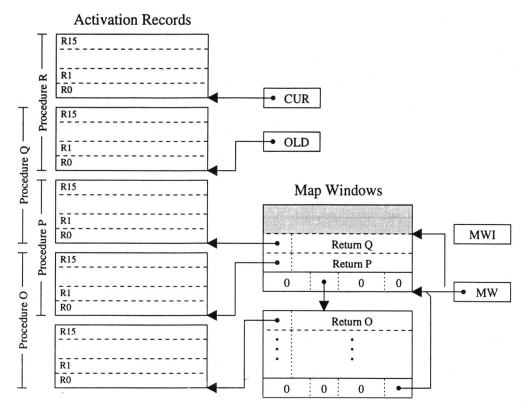

Figure 3: Structure of the procedure stack

- Expansion of global data area: Setting the Extra Window field in PSW1 to a constant number for the processors whole run-time doubles the global data area.

- Pointer adaption: Extra Windows solve some problems resulting from data accessed with pointers.

- Task-specific global data: The Extra Window is intended to be used in a multitasking environment. It is well suited for storing global data of an individual process, while the global window contains system wide global data.

3.4 Activation Records

The Current (CUR) and the Old Window (OLD) contain the local data of a procedure. A called procedure gets a pointer to an unused window in CUR. OLD is updated to the callers Current Window. This shared window enables parameter passing.

The main difference to the Berkeley Window Stack is, that parameter passing is handled through shared windows, instead of intersecting adjacent windows.

The window pointers enable the connection of any windows in multiple threads.

3.5 Map Windows

OLD and CUR are the top elements of the procedure stack. To track the activation records of procedures lower in the hierarchy, their numbers along with the return addresses are saved in Map Windows. At procedure call time the return address is bound with the content of the current OLD pointer. The result is moved to the actual position (indicated by MWI) in the Map Window, forming the top of the return stack. Then, the OLD pointer is changed to CUR and CUR receives the number of a free window.

```
if MWI = 15 then Map Window Overflow Exception
MWI ← MWI+1
MW[MWI] ← {OLD,Return Address}
OLD ← CUR
CUR ← free window
```

This task needs a single write access to the Map Window and can therefore be executed in a single instruction cycle, as long as one Map Window is sufficient. The first line of the pseudocode shows that an exception is triggered if the Map Window overflows. The exception routine has to allocate a new Map Window and update the links. Register 0 of each Map Window is used as a Link Register for maintaining the thread. The Link Register fields Link-Up and Link-Down point to the next and previous window. Fig. 3 illustrates the implementation as double linked list. The Link Register fields Memory-Down and Memory-Up (Fig. 4) are needed for spilling Map Windows to external memory [8, 9].

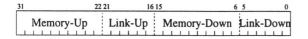

Figure 4: Structure of a Link Register

3.6 Single Element Stack and Queue

The Threaded Windows implement the important structures stack and queue, without bothering the user with pointer management.

The fields SQW and SQWI of PSW2 (Fig. 2) point to the top of a stack respectively to the head or tail of a queue. SQW contains the number of the actual window. SQWI is the index of the active register in this window. There are two of these pairs (SQW1/SQWI1 and SQW2/SQWI2), to allow control of a queue's head and tail. Nevertheless, they can be used independently.

The command PUSH puts an element onto the stack. It is removed by POP. To access a queue, the Threaded Windows provide the commands EN-QUEUE and DEQUEUE.

Stack and queue can occupy more than one window as well as the return stack. Similar to the Map Window, the first register of stack or queue windows links them in double linked lists.

3.7 Array Overflow

Even though there is the large number of 1024 registers, it is possible that a window request cannot be granted immediately, because every window is occupied. In this case, an exception program has to choose one window to be spilled, move its contents to external memory, and assign it to the requester.

The link register structure has two fields named Memory-Up and Memory-Down to save addresses of spilled windows. The methods of window spilling are to complex to be discussed (see [8] and [9] for further details).

3.8 Interrupts

Threaded Windows use interrupt control registers to manage 8 different interrupt sources. Each control register contains the start address of the corresponding interrupt program. In Threaded Windows an interrupt is very similar to a procedure call. The exception program receives a window in the CUR pointer. If there is no unused window available, the array overflow exception spills another window to external memory.

This additional exception increases the interrupt reaction time. To avoid a significant performance loss, a window can be *preallocated*. The number of the preallocated window has been entered into the control register. Preallocated windows are essential for the array overflow exception.

4 Advantages of Threaded Windows

The concept presented enables the handling of a very large set of registers. This was achieved by allowing a highly flexibile register use. The kinds of register use can be divided into four classes:

- Procedure stack: A procedure stack collects data on the procedures, including arguments passed up and down and pure local data.

- Global data: The Extra Window provides storage for larger amounts of global data inside the register array.

- Single element stack: A single element stack is a frequently used dynamic data structure.

- Single element queue: In communication tasks, queues are the most important data structures, buffering incoming and outgoing messages of the participating processes. Modern operating systems are using this extensively.

There are further advantages of Threaded Windows beside large capacity and flexibility:

- Context switches: Every data structure especially the procedure stack may be simultaneously used several times, allowing multiple tasks to reside inside the register array at the same time. This enables efficient multitasking, because run-time data does not have to be spilled to memory at context switch. By using pointers, context switching reduces to simply updating two program status words.

- Interrupts: Immediate reaction is guaranteed by using preallocated windows for specified interrupts. This enables use of Threaded Windows in real time systems.

5 Disadvantages of Threaded Windows

On closer examination of the above structures, some weaknesses complicating use of the Threaded Window become evident.

5.1 Restricted Address Space

In general, powerful processors have large virtual address spaces ($\geq$ 256MB). Unfortunately, the Threaded Windows concatenate procedure return addresses with a pointer to the old activation record for storing them together in a Map Window. Therefore, a return address consist of 26 bits only. Interrupt control vectors encode the number of preallocated windows in the same way.

5.2 Map Window Overflow

As long as programs do not need more than 16 levels of procedure hierarchy, just one Map Window is sufficient. Additional levels need further Map Windows to store the return addresses. These windows have to be allocated and the double links have to be maintained.

This requires two read and two write accesses to the link registers of the related windows. The number of register accesses is too high to be done by hardware. Therefore, a Map Window Overflow initiates an exception. The exception program now has to build a correctly linked return stack with an empty Map Window on top.

Assuming a RISC-style instruction set, such an exception program needs about 35 instructions. A highly recursive program could produce a Map Window Overflow at about every 15th execution of a procedure call, leading to an average execution time of more than 3 instruction cycles per call.

5.3 Stack/Queue Empty Mark

Unfortunately, no mechanism is defined to prevent read accesses to empty structures in [8, 9, 13]. Recognizing an empty queue requires comparing their head and tail pointers. Because the Stack/Queue pointers work independently, this comparison is not meaningful each time and is not performed.

Before reading the queue, software has to check if the access will be valid. The comparison and evaluation of the queue pointers will require execution of

several instructions. This overhead is annoying since the queue access itself needs just one instruction cycle.

6 Multi Windows

Multi Windows are the result of enhancements to the concepts and structures of Threaded Windows [11]. The aim of the enhancements was to preserve all advantages of Threaded Windows, e.g. multitasking abilities. Some of the most important goals of changes are:

- Simplification of data structures

- Increase of regularity

- Enhancement of capabilities

- Increase of performance

The following changes have been applied:

- Removal of Map Windows

- Simplification of the Link Registers structure

- Standardization of the window spillage methods

- Two write accesses per instruction cycle

6.1 Program Status Words

The Map Window pointers, the Extra Window pointer, and the I-flag have been removed from Program Status Word 1, leaving more bits for the interrupt mask. Furthermore, the Current and Old Window pointers are now located in PSW1.

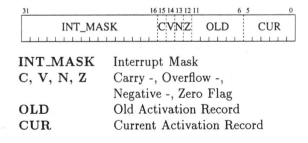

INT_MASK	Interrupt Mask
C, V, N, Z	Carry -, Overflow -,
	Negative -, Zero Flag
OLD	Old Activation Record
CUR	Current Activation Record

Figure 5: Program Status Word 1 (PSW1)

Program Status Word 2 contains all pointers to manage single element data structures and the pointer to the Extra Window.

XW	QI	QW	LW	SI	SW

XW	Extra Window
QI	Queue Window Index
QW	Queue Window
LW	Last Window
SI	Stack Window Index
SW	Stack Window

Figure 6: Program Status Word 2 (PSW2)

6.2 Link Register Structure

Exception programs use the memory pointer of a link register for restoration of spilled windows from external memory. The alignment of data structures was changed in a way that restorations have to be done on following a down link only. Therefore, the Memory-Up link is useless, leaving 10 bits to extend the Memory Down link (Fig. 7).

31	12 11	Down	6 5	Up	0
	Memory		Down		Up

Figure 7: Structure of a Link Register

With the Down pointer there are 26 bits to encode a spilled window memory pointer. If aligning spilled windows in 64 byte blocks (window frames), the lowest 6 bits of their address can be fixed to zero. Thus, the whole address space is covered. Fig. 7 shows the changed Link Register structure.

6.3 Removal of Map Windows

The Map Windows were used to store procedure return addresses and activation record numbers, serving as a return stack in the Threaded Windows. Because Map Windows have been removed, the return addresses have to be stored in the activation records. Register 1 of the Old Window is reserved for this purpose.

The activation records now form a double linked list like the Map Windows previously. Each register 0 serves as Link Register, pointing to the activation record of called procedures in its Up link and to the callers window in its Down link.

Fig. 8 illustrates the structure of a Multi Windows procedure stack.

6.4 Incomplete Linking

To maintain the linking of activation records, links have to be updated at every procedure call. This re-

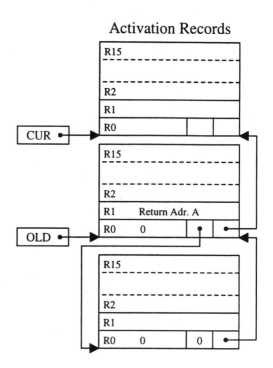

Figure 8: Procedure stack in Multi Windows

quires two read and write accesses in Threaded Windows. By using *incomplete linking*, Multi Windows require only a single write access.

The reduction was achieved by not writing the Down pointer immediately. In order to have a complete chain, the Current Windows Link Register should point to the Old Window. This information is redundant as long as the OLD pointer exists in the Program Status Word. Thus, the Down link will be written at the next procedure call, before changing the current OLD pointer.

The Current Window in Fig. 8 has an incomplete Link Register. After the next procedure call, the complete Link Register is entered. Figure 9 shows the activities at procedure call time. A new window is allocated from the Free Window List, e.g. organized as a bit array. The number of the new window, the OLD pointer and a zero memory pointer are concatenated and written to register 0 of the Current Window. The return address is written to register 1. Finally, the CUR field is moved to OLD, and CUR receives the number of the allocated window.

CUR[R0] ← {0,OLD,free window}
CUR[R1] ← return address
OLD ← CUR
CUR ← free window

Hence, Multi Windows need two write accesses to the

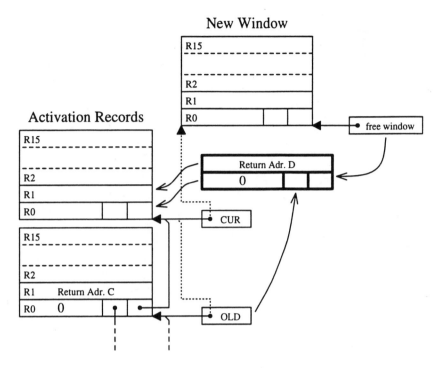

Figure 9: Procedure call at Multi Windows

register array, one for a link register and one for the return address, while Threaded Windows need only one. On the other hand, Threaded Windows trigger time consuming exceptions from time to time. In order to allow an easy implementation of the CALL instruction in a pipelined architecture, the two write accesses have to be performed in the same clock cycle. This is a special requirement for the register array, resulting in higher hardware costs in comparison to Threaded Windows.

6.5   Non-Allocating Procedure Calls

In order to prevent procedures that do not need that much register space from wasting windows, a version of the CALL instruction is provided which does not allocate a new window. The program itself has to take care of the return address and local data. The single element stack may be useful here.

A system using non-allocating procedure calls exclusively behaves like one with a static register management and a set of shadow registers to allow fast context switches. Sophisticated compiler techniques have been developed to handle static array management. Nevertheless, it is possible to mix allocating and non-allocating procedure call styles in a single program. Again, the compiler is burdened with the problem to choose the more efficient method.

6.6   Stack and Queue

The incomplete linking method can be used in the same way for stack and queue. Like activation records, the top window of the stack and the head window of the queue have incomplete Link Registers yet (Fig. 10 and 11).

An additional window pointer is required for the number of the previous top window of the stack or queue. The new pointer called LW (Last Window), is used like the OLD pointer for activation records. To utilize the same Link Register structure, the queue has to change orientation. It moves *downwards*.

To implement the empty test for stack or queue, structures use different pointers for their top or head elements. These are SW and SWI for Stack Window and Stack Window Index as well as QW and QWI for Queue Window and Queue Window Index. The pointers are also used as end pointers for each other. A comparison of both pointers is performed after each read access, producing an exception or setting a flag on equality.

6.7   Array Overflow Exception

A serious disadvantage of Threaded Windows is the lack of space in Map Windows to store memory addresses of spilled windows. Hence, an additional structure was needed to store the addresses after an array

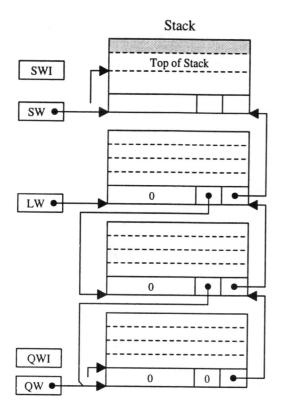

Figure 10: Stack structure

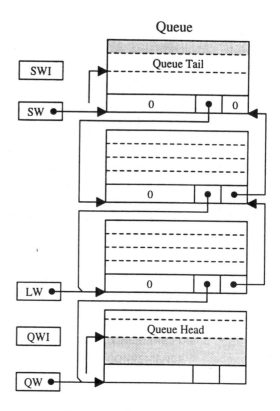

Figure 11: Queue structure

overflow, increasing the complexity of the technique.

Since Multi Windows use a simplified window linkage, no additional structure is needed. Thus, the Memory field in the Link Register (Fig. 7) is sufficient, enabling a more regular method of window spillage (Fig. 12).

The first task of the array overflow exception program is to choose a window for spillage. It is desirable to select a window that is likely to be not needed for a long time. There are many different approaches to reach this goal in an efficient way.

Spillage starts at the bottom window of the procedure or single element stack, or at the window following the head of the queue. It is even possible to spill windows of active tasks as long as the PSW fields point to available windows.

The spillage starts with copying the window contents to the external memory. Then the Memory pointer of the spilled window above is set and the spilled window is freed or prepared for its new purpose. Following the Up links, further windows can be stored into memory.

Restoration is initiated when following a Down link (e.g. at procedure return) with a non-zero Memory pointer. An exception program has to allocate a win-

dow and restore the data from the indicated memory location.

7 Multi Windows versus Threaded Windows

Multi Windows emerged through enhancements of Threaded Windows. Appreciable improvements could be reached by simplifying the initial data structures. The advantages of Multi Windows are:

- The instructions CALL and RETURN execute in just one clock cycle. There are no exceptions to maintain Map Window concatenation, because Map Windows are no longer needed.

- Linking stacks and queues does not involve exceptions, either. Any link work is done implicitly by the stack/queue manipulation instructions if necessary.

- By removing link exceptions, the corresponding interrupt vector registers are free for alternative use. Furthermore, the number of interrupt vectors has been doubled to 16. Exceptions occur only at register array overflows or underflows to spill windows out or to restore them.

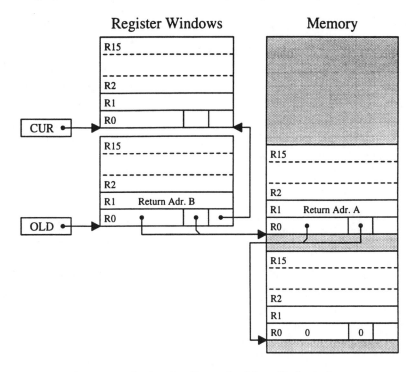

Figure 12: Activation Record with spilled windows

- The virtual address space has been expanded to 4GB.

- By removing redundant memory pointers and Map Windows, activation record spillage has become much easier. Now the whole address space can be used for spilling.

On the other hand, the improvements have to be bought with some disadvantages, too.

- At procedure call time, two write accesses to the register array are required. This increases hardware costs of the register field. In case of an alternative solution, one write access has to be performed per halfcycle.

- The removal of Map Windows is burdened with an increased management overhead inside the activation records. Only 14 registers of a window remain for general purpose use.

- Since a test of emptiness of the single element data structures is provided, the presented version of Multi Windows supports only one stack or queue directly. Additional status registers are needed for more of these structures.

8 Result

Both variants of a dynamic register array have been modelled with the hardware description language Verilog [14] and embedded into a RISC processor environment.

The processor has been implemented on behavioral level. It can execute common RISC instructions (ALU instructions, conditional branches, LOAD, STORE, ...) and the special instructions, previously defined with the dynamic register arrays.

The exception routines to deal with window and register array over- and underflows for the Threaded Windows have been written first. The cooperation of procedure stacks, as well as stacks and queues, with the exception routines, was tested using a few small benchmarks (quicksort, prime number sieve, ...). Although the exception routines were correct, they were called very often and are too complex to sustain the expected performance. Especially the unpleasant Map Window over- and underflows were the main reasons for the development of an alternative dynamic register array concept.

Multi Windows reached an average performance gain of about 4% in comparison to Threaded Windows, which is almost exclusively due to the absence of any exceptions to maintain window linking.

Unfortunately, this value is just an estimation, since

the above benchmarks were originally designed just for the testing of special components of the model.

Comparisons of this concept with others implemented in commercial RISC processors are very difficult and have not been performed for several reasons:

- The HDL models would have to be refined.

- Common processor benchmarks overtax HDL simulation environments [10]. Much more powerful simulations would be necessary to run benchmarks on a realistic processor model.

- There is no programming environment to implement more complex benchmarks, because the instruction set needs compilers designed to support the special register array capabilities.

The dynamic register arrays show their real performance gain in environments of concurrent communicating processes, fast context switches and interrupts under heavy load, e.g., in real time systems. A realistic simulation, based on an HDL model, is currently impossible.

9   Conclusion

The different data structures and multitasking abilities of register arrays are well suited for modern distributed systems. Good performance values are estimated for real time and embedded control systems because of the short reaction time to interrupts. Improved integration density lowers the relative cost of very high register numbers.

In Multi Windows, the concepts found in Threaded Windows were simplified and improved, e. g. the Map Windows were removed. There are no more important obstacles to the implementation of Multi Windows.

Unfortunately, the behavior of many features is too complex to prove the performance gain with simple simulations. The absence of a precise performance prediction might be a reason for the lack of implementations of this interesting concept so far.

References

[1] C. Aßmann: "A RISC Architecture with a Versatile Stack System". *Computer Architecture News*, 1993 (Vol.21), Dec. (No.5), pp.63-70

[2] E. Cochlovius, U. Golze, M. Schäfers, K.-P. Wachsmann: *Der RISC-Prozessor TOOBSIE2 als Beispiel eines großen VLSI-Entwurfs*, Band I. Report 930701, Abt. E.I.S., TU Braunschweig, 1993

[3] S. B. Furber: *VLSI RISC Architecture and Organization*. Marcel Dekker Inc, New York, 1989.

[4] M. Johnson: "System considerations in the design of the AM 29000". *IEEE MICRO*, 1987, pp. 28-41

[5] G. Kane: *MIPS-RISC Architecture*. Prentice Hall. Englewood Cliffs, 1987.

[6] M. G. H. Katevenis: *Reduced Instruction Set Computer Architecture for VLSI*. The MIT Press, Cambridge, Mass., 1985.

[7] D. J. Quammen, D. R. Miller: "Flexible Register Management for Sequential Programs". In *Proceedings of the 18th Symposium on Computer Architecture*, Toronto, 1991, pp. 320-329

[8] D. J. Quammen, D. R. Miller, D. Tabak: "Register Window Management for Multitasking Applications". In *Proceedings of the 21nd Hawaii International Conference on System Sciences*, 1988, pp. 135-142

[9] D. J. Quammen, D. R. Miller, D. Tabak: "Register Window Management for a Real-Time Multitasking RISC". In *Proceedings of the 22nd Hawaii International Conference on System Sciences*, 1989, pp. 230-237

[10] M. Schäfers, U. Golze, E. Cochlovius: "VERILOG HDL Models of a Large RISC Processor". In *Proceedings of the 4th EUROCHIP Workshop*, Toledo, 1993, pp. 242-246

[11] T. Scholz, M. Schäfers: "Eine nichtüberlappende Register-Window-Technik für RISC-Prozessoren". In *Proceedings of the 6th E.I.S.-Workshop*; Tübingen, 1993, pp. 57-66

[12] SUN MICROSYSTEMS Inc.: *The SPARC Architecture Manual – Version 7*. Mountain View, CA, 1987.

[13] D. Tabak: *RISC Systems*. Research Studies Press Ltd. 1990

[14] D. E. Thomas, P. Moorby: *The Verilog Hardware Description Language*. Kluwer Academic Publishers, Boston, 1991

A Three Dimensional Register File For Superscalar Processors

Marc Tremblay[*], Bill Joy[*] and Ken Shin[+]

*Sun Microsystems Inc., 2550 Garcia Ave., Mountain View, CA 94043.

+ Texas Instruments, 12201 S.W. Freeway, Houston, TX 77001.

Abstract

The register file is a key datapath component of a superscalar microprocessor. Its access time is critical since it can impact cycle time. Its size can easily become a problem: superscalar microprocessors have a large number of ports (typically 10 for a three-scalar machine) and the size is quadratic in the number of ports. The "3-D Register File[1]" uses the area inherently consumed by the metal wires used for the word and bit lines for each cell to hide N sets of registers. Each set is logically a plane in the third dimension. The ability to access multiple planes can be used for register windows or for extra register sets for real time tasks or microtask switching. The data array of a 3-D eight-window 10 ported register file is six times smaller than a flat register file. Access time is sped up by shortening bus lines and by sharing a large buffer between bit cells. The 3-D register file has been implemented on two high performance superscalar processors and early silicon confirms our simulations.

1. Introduction and Motivation

Register windows, first described in [1] and later enhanced by introducing the concept of overlapping windows in [2] and in [3], offer advantages over conventional flat register files. The ability to pass parameters on function calls/returns without having to store and retrieve data through the stack, can significantly increase performance since load/store operations are often a bottleneck in modern high performance machines. Detailed analysis

of the percentage of loads/stores eliminated due to register windows has been reported in [4]. The authors showed that for a program with a reasonable number of function calls, such as for the SPEC benchmark 022.li where calls represent 2% of the instructions, a processor with overlapping register windows can execute 19% less loads and 32% less stores when compared to a processor with a conventional register file.

Due to (a) their added functionality and (b) the large number of registers they contain (in order to provide nested function calls of reasonable depth, the register file must contain several windows), register windows are generally more difficult to implement than conventional register files. The number of windows supported in hardware is typically about 8 [5]. For a window of 24 registers with 8 overlapping registers between windows, the register file would contain a total of 128 registers (not including global registers) and would be several times larger than conventional register files commonly used in RISC processors [6], [7], [8], which typically include only 32 registers. The added functionality plus the larger number of registers make the implementation of a register file with windows challenging especially since RISC processors tend to base their cycle time, through heavy pipelining, on basic datapaths blocks such as the register file, ALUs, and caches.

---

1. A patent has been submitted on the ideas presented in this paper

Several papers [9], [10], have discussed efficient implementations of register files with windows in the context of simple RISC processors. Recent advances in microprocessors have render the implementation of the register file even more critical. Superscalar processors capable of executing 3 integer instructions simultaneously typically require 7 read ports and 3 write ports. For example the register file for SuperSPARC-II has 8 read ports and 2 write ports and the IBM 604 register file has over 10 ports. Preliminary announcements from computer companies indicate that the number of ports will only grow in the near future (DEC EV-5 [11], IBM-620 [12], SGI T5 [13], Sun UltraSPARC [14]). The data array portion of a flat register file grows approximately to the square of the number of ports, i.e. a register file with 6 ports is approximately 4 times larger than a register file with 3 ports. The access time, being highly dependent on the length of the RC delay of the word lines and bit lines, is also affected greatly due to the larger area.

In this paper, we introduce the concept of a 3-dimensional register file. By utilizing area typically wasted in conventional register file implementations we "hide" register windows in a way that reduces the area of the file significantly. Also, due to the novel implementation, larger buffers than the small driver usually attached to each individual cell can be used, which reduce the access time. Finally, the partitioning of the 3D register file allows independent decoding of the register index and the register window number, further reducing access time.

2. Active window

Pipelined microprocessors typically dedicate a stage to accessing the register for a read and another stage for the write. For the DLX

pipeline [15], (Table 1) these stages are the ID and WB stages respectively.

Pipe Stage	Function
IF	Instruction Fetch
ID	Instruction decode and register fetch
EX	Execution and address calculation
MEM	Memory access
WB	Write back

TABLE 1. The DLX pipeline, register accesses occur at fixed stages.

Existing superscalar processors also dedicate fixed stages for reads and writes to the register file. Instructions such as function calls/returns, window SAVE/RESTORE [16], do modify the current window pointer (CWP) so that subsequent instructions access a different window in the register file. Typically, the impact of a CWP modifying instruction is perceived only by the next group of instructions entering the pipeline. That is usually ensured by breaking the group after a CWP modifying instruction so that no instruction in the same group needs to access a different window. This means that all instructions in a group access the same window and that it happens always in the same fixed stage. This means that only one window needs to be "active" at any time.

In normal operation, registers are read from one window in the ID stage and results are written back in the WB stage to the same window. For deep pipelines it is desirable to keep issuing instructions after a CWP modifying instruction and not wait until all writes are done before modifying the CWP. This can be accomplish by having one window active for all reads, and a separate one active for all writes. This idea is illustrated by Figure 1.

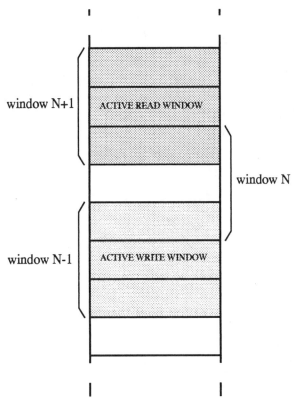

window N+1

ACTIVE READ WINDOW

window N

window N-1

ACTIVE WRITE WINDOW

Figure 1. Only one window is active for all reads (e.g. window n+1) and only one window is active for all writes (e.g. window n-1)

In Figure 1, the register file has windows implemented in a conventional way, with exactly one window active for all reads and one window active for all writes. In this figure we assume that the window pointer for reads and writes differs by two (reads and writes could be separated by two function calls for instance).

3. 3-D Register File

The fact that not all windows need to be accessed simultaneously suggests sharing circuitry among windows. We exploit this concept by constructing a three-dimensional register file as represented in Figure 2. Each plane in the figure represents a separate window. For the sake of simplicity we show a simple register file with four non-overlapping

windows. The concept of a 3-D register file can be extended to a register file with support for fast context switch. In this latter case, each plane in Figure 2 would represent a separate context. Context switch between microtasks is quickly accomplished by simply changing the context number (current window pointer in the figure).

As shown in the figure, the current window pointer is decoded through a separate decoder and the corresponding plane is selected. The register index for the selected window is decoded in the same manner as for a conventional register file. Once a register is selected, its content is put on the data bus shared by all windows. For the sake of simplicity, the figure only shows the read portion of the logic for the register file. The ability to write to a separate window, merely involves a separate decoder for a write window pointer which selects a different plane. Separate data lines are already provided for single phase pipelines, so no additional lines are required for the separate write window port except for the additional window decode if high performance is desired (described in more detail in a latter section).

4. Wasted area

Conventional implementations of register windows result in a large flat register file very similar to the one shown in the block diagram in Figure 1. For superscalar processors with multiple ports, a conventional implementation results in having a single bit of information stored underneath several metal wires. We show an example of this phenomena in Figure 3.

In Figure 3 we show a block diagram for a bit cell for a register file with 10 ports (7 reads and 3 writes - typical for a 3 scalar machine). We assume that 10 separate word

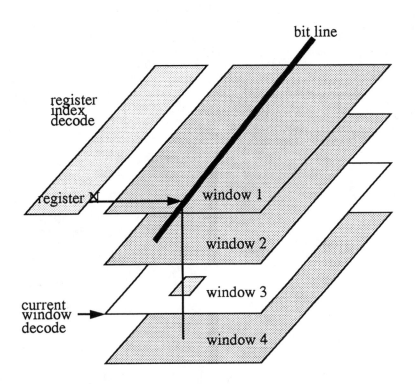

Figure 2. A Three Dimensional Register File

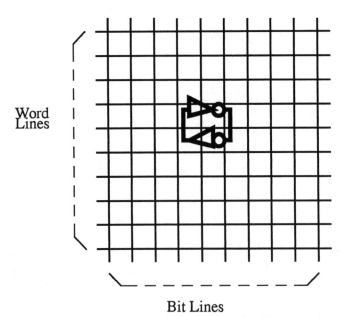

Bit Lines

**Figure 3. A conventional implementation of a 10 port register cell.
One bit of information is stored underneath multiple wires.**

lines, 7 single-ended sense-amplifiers lines for the reads and 3 single-ended write bit lines are provided, resulting in a 10 X 10 grid. For a 4-layer metal process, the word lines are typically on the second layer and the bit lines on the third layer. Power and ground are routed on the fourth layer and the first layer is used for local connections in the bit cells. For an aggressive 0.5 micron process with a metal pitch of 1.5 micron, a 10 X 10 grid results in an area of 225 square microns. Underneath the 10 X 10 grid, a single bit of information is stored, resulting in a poor utilization of the available area for logic devices. For double-ended sense amps and differential writes (very common [5], [7]), the wasted area is even worse. A grid of 10 X 20 is required, resulting in 450 microns for a single bit of information.

The data array of a register file with 128 64-bit registers implemented this way would roughly measure 128 * 64 * 225 = 1.84 square millimeters for the single ended scheme and 128 * 64 * 450 = 3.68 square millimeters for the double-ended implementation.

5. Using "wasted" area.

The 3D register file is possible because only one window is read and one window is written at a time. This allows us to use the wasted area to hide bits of information belonging to the other windows. In the case described above, bit i of register j for all windows {0, 1, ..., 7} can be hidden underneath the 10 X 10 grid (or 10 X 20 grid). One only needs to provide signals specifying which window (or which of the 8 bits) needs to be accessed. This can be accomplished by providing 3 additional wires for the window decode resulting in a 13 X 10 (or 13 X 20 grid). In this way, 8 bits of information are stored instead of 1 in an area only 30% larger than the original one (Figure 4). For the single-ended implementation each bit now requires around 36 square

micron (vs. 225), 6.15 times smaller. The double-ended implementation benefits even more by requiring only about 73 square micron (vs.450), also 6.15 times smaller but resulting in an even larger gain in total area saved.

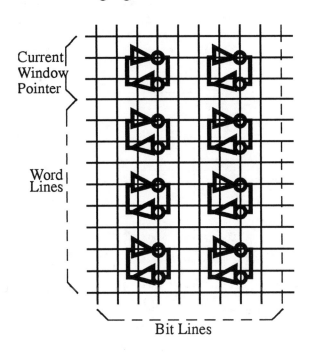

Figure 4.Hiding eight register windows underneath a 10 port register cell. Eight cells fit in the area under the 13 X 10 grid.

6. Circuit Implementation of Non-overlapping Windows

In Figure 5 we show an implementation of the circuitry for a one bit cell for a 3D register file composed of eight non-overlapping windows. This can be used for fast context switch or for implementing local registers [16] which are not shared across window.

In this implementation we have chosen to represent a cell with the following design criteria:

- seven read ports
- single-ended read bit lines

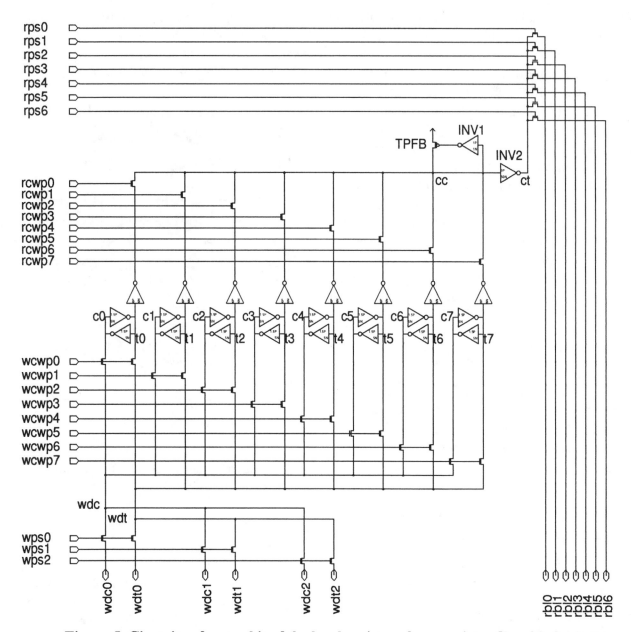

Figure 5. Circtuitry for one bit of the local registers for a register file with 8 windows.

- three write ports
- differential write bit lines
- separate read and write window
- multiple writes to same register are not allowed
- decoded (one-hot) current window pointer

Single-ended read bit lines require significantly less area than a differential sense amplifier implementation (seven lines vs. fourteen). Differential write bit lines allow fast write and robust noise margins. Providing a separate window pointer for reads and writes provide higher performance by allowing more than one window to co-exist in the pipe (as explained in "Active window" on page 2). Disallowing multiple writes to the same physical register in the same cycle simplifies the design and does not affect performance since this is a case that should not happen (especially for an in-order machine). Two consecutive writes (in the same cycle) without an intermediate read is not a common programming technique. Finally, a fully decoded current window pointer simplify the logic for each bit cell and offers a speed advantage since it can be decoded in parallel with the register index.

At the top of the figure, the seven signals [rps0, rps1,...,rps6] represent the select lines for this bit cell. These lines select register N and go across the full width of the register (64 bits). The decoded current window pointer is represented by eight signals [rcwp0, rcwp1,..., rcwp6]. Only one of these is active at the time. They select which window should provide register N (which plane in Figure 2). Cross-coupled inverters are used to store each bit cell. A local inverter amplifies the signal locally and also isolates each cell thus avoiding charge sharing. Data read from the individual bit cell is then buffered through INV2 which contains a large pulldown transistor (50 microns vs. 8 microns for the pullup). The seven bit lines are precharged therefore read access time is determined by read bit line pulldown speed. Inverter INV1 and pmos transistor TPFB are used to pull the node cc (intermediate local data bus) up to VDD.

The three write select lines are [wps0, wps1, wps2]. Differential writes is implemented so three pairs of bit lines are needed [wdc0, wdt0, wdc1, wdt1, wdc2, wdt2]. As mentioned earlier, a separate window pointer is provided for the writes, so only one of the eight signals [wcwp0, wcwp1, ..., wcwp7] is active at the time.

7. Sharing Registers Between Windows

Overlapping windows allow a function (caller) to send parameters to the callee without additional stores and loads. A function uses its "outs" registers (Figure 6) to pass parameters to the adjacent window, where the registers become the "ins" for the callee. Similarly, on a return from a function call, the callee can return results through its INs registers, which become the OUTs registers for the original callee.

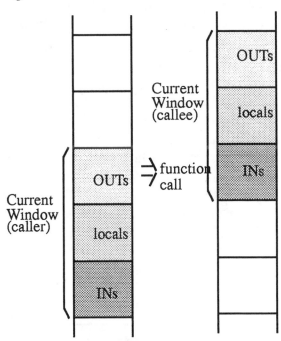

Figure 6. Sharing of registers amongst adjacent windows.

We described in Figure 5 how bit cells from adjacent windows can reside together "underneath" the metal wires used for accessing a single cell (plus the window decode signals). If we use the same concept for the INs (or the OUTs), bits for IN_n of $window_w$ all reside together (Figure 7). In that figure we show, for a four-window register file, how the set of four bits contains data for bit_i of register IN_n and for all four windows. The key point in this figure is that bit_i of register IN_n of window$_{w+1}$ is also bit$_i$ of register OUT$_n$ of window$_w$. For a given window pointer, for instance window$_0$ in the figure, two bit cells, representing the IN and OUT register need to be accessible.

We show an implementation of the 3-D register file for registers shared across windows in Figure 8. The core of the logic is similar to the implementation for the non-overlapping case (bit cells, read logic, local bus, etc.). Since the bit cells contain data for IN$_i$ and OUT$_i$ of window j, two bit cells may need to be accessed simultaneously. This is accomplished by always selecting two possibly addressed cells in the set of eight cells for each window select. For instance, in Figure 8, whenever rcwp1 is asserted, it selects two cells cc0 as a possible IN register and cc1 as a possible OUT. The content of the two cells is put on separate local buses ccin and ccout. The decision of which data to select for each read port (the IN or the OUT cell) is handled by the decoder. Separate lines are provided for INs and OUTs, so the correct register is selected.

The same large buffer with a wide pulldown device is provided for each bus in order to conditionally discharge the bit lines.

The write circuitry requires special circuitry to prevent erroneous overwrites between INs and OUTs. The part related to the current write window is similar to the current read window. One and only one of the signals [wcwp0, wcwp1, ..., wcwp7] is asserted and selects two cells, one IN bit cell and one OUT bit cell. The decision to write the IN or the OUT is made at the write decoder level. Separate signals for a write to an IN (e.g. wps0_in) and for a write to an OUT (e.g. wps1_out) are provided. Since a write is destructive, we have to make sure that a write to an IN does not corrupt the corresponding OUT register (and vice-versa). This could happen even though the write data is only forwarded to one of the two local write data buses. As can be seen on the figure, write data from one port will either go to the IN local bus or to the OUT local bus, but not to both. The relatively large capacitance of these local buses could eventually overwrite

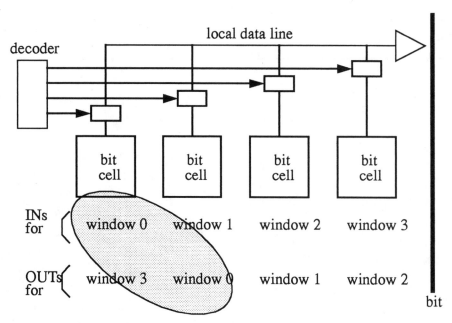

Figure 7. Adjacent cells can be accessed in the same window.

the content of one of the bit cells since the write window pointer provides direct access. To prevent the potential write disturb, pullup transistors [TPPU1, TPPU2, TPPU3, TPPU4] are used to precharge the local write data lines of inactive ports. This effectively acts as a read disturb of the bit cell with very little impact on the voltage levels. Finally, the situation where

two write ports try to write to the same IN or the same OUT does not occur since multiple writes to the same destination register are not allowed.

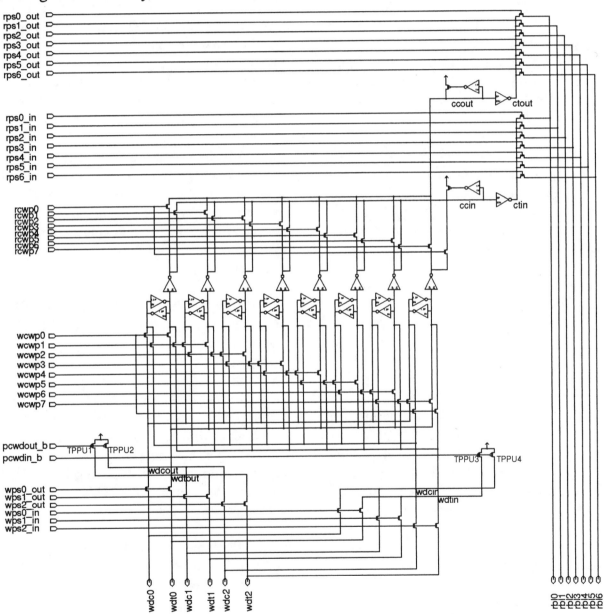

Figure 8. Implementation of INs and OUTs for an eight-window register file.

8. Peripheral Circuitry

For 64-bit superscalar processors with a relatively large register file (e.g. 32 registers), the data array represents around two thirds of the total area of the register file. In this paper we have chosen to focus on that part of the circuitry since it has the biggest impact and since the 3D concept mainly improves that part of the register file. For the sake of completeness we briefly describe the peripheral circuitry for the data array shown in Figure 5 and in Figure 8. The circuitry described corresponds to a register file that has been implemented on UltraSPARC-I.

Read address decoding is accomplished in two stages. Predecoders are simple static gates while the final stage decoders are three-input NAND domino-type gates. In order to speed up decoding, we use differential precharged read address signals. This allows evaluation to begin as soon as the address inputs become valid, resulting in significant address decode speedup.

As mentioned earlier, we use single-ended read bit line sensing. To maximize read sensing speed without compromising noise margin, the read bit line is precharged to 1.31V which is 0.61V above the sense amplifier trip point of 0.70V (for a typical 3.3V CMOS process, assuming TTLH). After the read bit line has been precharged, selection of one of the memory cells on the read bit line can result in either continuation of the precharged state which sense amplifier reads as a logic "1" or discharging of the bit line below the sense amplifier trip point which it reads as a "0".

Write address decoding is also accomplished in two stages. Predecoders are simple static gates. Second stage decoding is performed by four-input AND gates. One of the four inputs of the AND gate is a write enable signal. Write decoders are disabled when the corresponding write enable is disabled.

9. Summary

A "context-switchable" memory structure such as a register file with windows, which provide different "contexts" for function calls, or a register file with separate "planes" for fast context switching, can benefit greatly from the concept of a 3-D register file. We have shown that the data array portion of the register file, which typically represents 2/3 of the total area of the register file, can be reduced by a factor of 4 to 6 times, for a register file with 8 "planes". The amount of area saving is dependant on various design trade-off such as (1) differential vs. single-ended bit read sensing (2) decoded vs. encoded plane/window routing, (3) differential vs. single-ended writing, etc. In machines which do not have register windows, one get multiple contexts essentially "for free."

Besides providing area savings, 3-D register file provide faster access time, mainly by reducing the total capacitance on the bit lines. One bit line only connects to one window vs. all windows in a flat implementation. By reducing the total area, the bit lines are also shorter which reduces capacitance. By sharing logic among bit cells, the bit line driver can be made larger thus increasing bit line discharge. Finally, independent decoding between the window pointer and the register index also provides faster operation.

Implementation of the 3-D register file concept on two high-performance superscalar processors has proven very beneficial in terms of area and speed. We intend to expand the concept to VLIW memory structures, which typically require many ports, and to fast context-switching processors which support several contexts through a single structure.

10. REFERENCES

[1] R. L. Sites, "How to Use 1000 Registers", in Caltech Conference on VLSI, pp. 527-532., (January 1979).

[2] R. Sherburne, M. Katevenis, D. Patterson, and C. Sequin, "Datapath Design for RISC", Proceedings, Conf. on Adv. Research in VLSI, pp. 53-62, MIT (January 1982).

[3] D. A. Patterson and C. H. Sequin, "A VLSI RISC", Computer Vol. 15(9), pp.. 8-21 (September 1982).

[4] R. F. Cmelik, S. I. Kong, D. R. Ditzel and E. J. Kelly, "An Analysis of SPARC and MIPS Instruction Set Utilization on the SPEC Benchmarks", in Proceedings of the Fourth International Conference on Architecture Support for Programming Languages and Operating Systems, pp290-302, (April 1991).

[5] G. Blanck and S. Krueger, "SuperSPARC: A Fully Integrated Superscalar Processor", in Hot Chips III, Palo Alto, (August 1991).

[6] G. Kane, "MIPS R2000 RISC Architecture", Prentice Hall,Englewood Cliffs, NJ, (1987).

[7] Dobberpuhl and all. "A 200 MHz 64b Dual-Issue CMOS Microprocessor", in Digest of Technical Papers, 1992 IEEE International Solid-State Circuits Conference, pp. 106-107,(February 1992).

[8] G. Kurpanek, K. Chan, J.Sheng, E. Delano, and W. Bryg, "PA7200: A PA-RISC Processor with Integrated High Performance MP Bus Interface", in Proceedings of COMPCON 94, pp 375-382, (February 1994).

[9] M. Tremblay and T. Lang, "VLSI Implementation of a Shift-Register File", in Proceedings of the Hawiaii International Conference on System Sciences, January 1987.

[10] G. Russell and P. Shaw, "Shifting Register Windows", IEEE Micro, pp. 28-35, (August 1993).

[11] DEC 21164 Description, Slides from Hot Chips 1994, Stanford, CA.

[12] IBM 620 Description, Slides from Microprocessor Forum 1994, San Francisco.

[13] SGI T5 Description, Slides from Microprocessor Forum 1994, San Francisco.

[14] Sun UltraSPARC Description, Slides from Microprocessor Forum 1994, San Francisco

[15] J. L. Hennessy and D. A. Patterson. "Computer Architecture a Quantitative Approach", Morgan Kaufmann, San Mateo, (1990).

[16] D. L. Weaver and T. Germond, "The SPARC Architecture Manual", Version 9, Prentice Hall, Englewood Cliffs, New Jersey, (1994).

Reducing Memory Latency Using a Small Software Driven Array Cache

Chi-Hung Chi, Chi-Sum Ho, Siu-Chung Lau

Department of Computer Science
The Chinese University of Hong Kong
Shatin, New Territories
Hong Kong
Email: chchi@cs.cuhk.hk

Abstract

From the programming viewpoint, data references can be classified into two types: array reference and non-array references. Array references have relatively strong spatial locality while non-array references have relatively strong temporal locality. However, in current data cache designs, the hardware cannot distinguish between these two types of references. Both types of data are stored in the same cache space and all cache control mechanisms such as prefetching are applied to array references as well as to non-array references. As a result, data cache performance is often not satisfactory. The large working set of array references with weak temporal locality interferes with the small working set of non-array references with strong temporal locality and replaces them away from cache. Applying hardware driven data prefetching scheme to array references might improve cache performance. However, when the same scheme is applied to non-array references, cache performance might be lost due to serious cache pollution. To solve all these problems, this paper proposes a new software driven cache design, called the **Array Cache**. The main idea of this Array Cache is to use a separate cache space to store and handle array references with constant strides that are prefetched accurately with the help of the compiler and with extremely low runtime overhead. Our simulation result shows that this Array Cache is very useful in improving the performance of scientific computation applications, where most of the data references are array references with constant strides.

1. Introduction

With the maturity of VLSI technology, high performance computer system can now be integrated on a single chip. Microprocessors with more than 3 million transistors and with clock rate of 100 MHz to 275 MHz (such as MIPS R4600 and DEC Alpha 21064A) are now available [Lei93]. It is expected that in the coming two years, it is possible to build 300 MHz to 500 MHz microprocessors with about 10 million transistors. Furthermore, these high performance microprocessors are becoming the basic building blocks for most highly scalable parallel processing systems. Some examples are the IBM SP1 and SP2 using RS/6000 and CRAY T3D using DEC Alpha.

In these high performance computer systems (both uni- and parallel), the average throughput is always limited by the performance of their supporting memory systems [HeP90]. The slow memory system is simply not fast enough to supply data to the fast processor(s). To bridge this increasing speed gap between the fast processing unit and the slow memory system, cache is often used [Smi82] [HeP90]. Furthermore, caching issue is becoming more and more important in the microprocessor chip design. This is reflected in the increasing microprocessor chip space that is used for caching. For example, TI SuperSPARC chip has an instruction cache of 20 Kbytes and a data cache of 16 Kbytes.

In current cache design, it is generally agreed that while instruction cache is very useful in reducing the average instruction access time, data cache performance is not effective [HeP90] [Smi82]. It is because the access pattern of data references is random and less predictable, as compared to the access pattern of instruction references, which is sequential and highly predictable. Furthermore, for those problems that operate on very large amount of data (such as large matrices in scientific computation applications), data cache is also too small to hold the working set of data references and to allow cached data to be reused. This is the reason why traditional supercomputers simply do not include data cache in their design.

Careful study on the reference behavior of data shows that data references are actually not as random as they appear. One way of classifying data references is based on whether they are array references or non-array references. For array references, they have very strong spatial locality and their reference pattern is highly predictable. When array element $a[i]$ is referenced, the probability for the next element $a[i+1]$ to be referenced is very high. However, the temporal locality of array references is usually very weak (and sometimes zero). During the time an array element $a[i]$ is in cache, the reference frequency of $a[i]$ is quite low. On the other hand, non-array references have somewhat different characteristics. For references such as those due to stack variables and global scalar variables, they have very strong temporal locality. During the period when they are in cache, they are referenced quite often.

However, the spatial locality of non-array references is relatively not as strong as the spatial locality of array references. The reference pattern of non-array elements is also not as predictable as the reference pattern of array elements. When the reference patterns of array elements and non-array elements are mixed together, the predictability of the resulting reference pattern is even worse. This often contributes to the "random" nature of data references and explains why data cache performance is much lower than instruction cache performance.

One important observation on the reference behavior of data is on the interference of working sets of data references. For array references, the working set of data is usually very large. For example, to reference a double precision N X N matrix with N equal to 1000, 8 MBytes of data is involved. On the other hand, the working set of non-array references is usually much smaller than the working set of array references. When these two working sets of data references are mixed together, interference occurs. Non-array data with strong temporal locality are "bumped" away from the cache by array references with very weak temporal locality. Hence, when an array of data are being referenced, data references in the near future are most likely to be either *new* array elements that are not in cache or those non-array elements that might just be replaced from cache. In both cases, cache misses will occur and cache performance will be degraded. Even after the array data are referenced, cache misses that are similar to those due to cache cold start [Smi82] still occur. It is because the working set of non-array references has been destroyed and the working set of array references that is built up in cache has very weak (or even zero) temporal locality.

The other problem of this mixed data reference pattern is the effectiveness of some important cache control mechanisms such as data prefetching [HeP90]. Since the cache hardware cannot distinguish array references from non-array references, the same data prefetching scheme will be applied to both types of data. This certainly creates problems to data cache performance. Since array references have very strong spatial locality, it is beneficial to prefetch data based on the current references of array data. However, when the same data prefetching scheme is applied to non-array data, cache pollution might result. The spatial locality of non-array references is relatively not very strong and the prefetched data might not be used. As a result, the overall effectiveness of data cache prefetching using simple hardware controlled approaches is not satisfactory [Smi82].

In the past few years, with advances in compiler optimization and in program flow analysis, a number of software assisted (or compiler driven) cache prefetching schemes using *PREFETCH* instructions have been proposed [Por89] [GoG90] [CaK91] [ChM91] [KIL91] [MoL92]. All these schemes share similar advantages and limitations. With the help of the compiler, they can identify array references easily and can selectively prefetch array references with constant strides accurately. On the other hand, the runtime overhead associated with these schemes often limits their practical use.

In this paper, we propose a new cache structure, called the **Array Cache**, to improve cache performance for array data intensive applications. There are three main innovative features in this Array Cache. First, a very efficient software-assisted cache prefetching scheme, called the **Stride_CAM Data Prefetching (SCP)** scheme, is used to selectively prefetch array data with constant strides accurately into the cache with very low runtime overhead. The basic idea of the

SCP scheme is to use a small content addressable memory buffer, called the **Stride_CAM** buffer, to store the constant stride value and the instruction address of each array reference to be prefetched. This is done with the help of the compiler using some new *SCAM_SET* instruction. Then, when a *LOAD/STORE* instruction is executed at runtime, the program counter will be checked with the *Instr_Addr* field of all *Stride_CAM* cells. If a match is found, prefetching will take place and the address of the prefetching candidate is calculated by adding the current data reference address to the *Stride* field value of the matched *Stride_CAM* cell. Since no *PREFETCH* instruction is inserted into the program and the setting of the *Stride_CAM* cells can be done outside the loop containing the array references, the runtime overhead associated with the SCP scheme is much smaller than the runtime overhead of any current software assisted data prefetching schemes. On the other hand, the SCP scheme can still maintain the same prefetching accuracy as current software assisted data prefetching schemes. Second, an Array Cache is added to the existing caching system to store all array data that are prefetched by the SCP scheme and to handle all subsequent references to these prefetched array data. The original data caching system is left to handle demand-fetched data references (which are most likely to be non-array references). With this cache space partitioning, the interference between the working set of array references and the working set of non-array references can be reduced to its minimum. Cache design and control mechanisms of each of these two cache partitions can also be optimized according to the type of references it is supposed to handle. Third, the Array Cache is designed to avoid any unnecessary fetching of cache lines that are expected to be completely overwritten without being referenced for at least one time. Upon a cache miss, a cache line of data is fetched from the main memory into the cache. However, for stride one array references, every datum of the fetched line will subsequently be overwritten without being used. To avoid this "write after fetch" problem for array references using stride one, each entry of the Array Cache has a "valid" bit which indicates if the value of the entry is the most updated copy. When a prefetch request for a cache line is generated by the SCP scheme, the value of the *Stride* field used in the prefetch address calculation will be checked to see if it is equal to one. For all prefetch requests using stride one, "no fetch on miss" and "write allocate" scheme will be used. For all other memory requests, "fetch on miss" will be the default fetching scheme. Our simulation showed that this Array Cache is extremely effective in improving cache performance for array data intensive applications, yet the size of the Array Cache needed is very small (average size of 128 bytes).

The organization of this paper is as follows. Section 2 gives a brief survey of previous research related to the Array Cache design. The basic architecture of the Array Cache is proposed in Section 3. Section 4 details the control mechanisms for the Array Cache. Software support for the Array Cache is described in Section 5. Section 6 analyzes the runtime overhead of the SCP scheme in the Array Cache and proposes possible software enhancements. In Section 7, experimental results on the performance of the Array Cache are described. Finally, the paper concludes in Section 8. Note that in this paper, the discussion is only focused on data cache design.

2. Previous Related Research

The main idea of this Array Cache is to use a separate cache space to store and handle array references with constant strides that are selectively prefetched accurately with the help of the compiler and with extremely low runtime overhead. Thus, there are at least two issues that are related to this Array Cache design. They are cache prefetching schemes and prefetch buffer designs.

2.1. Cache Prefetching

In the past few years, cache designers start to look for new ways to improve the effectiveness of data cache prefetching. With advances in compiler optimization and in data flow analysis, software assisted cache prefetching using *PREFETCH* instructions is now possible. Recently, a number of software assisted (or compiler driven) cache prefetching schemes [Bre87] [Por89] [GoG90] [CaK91] [ChM91] [KlL91] [MoL92] have been proposed. All these schemes share some common properties:

[1]   Some non-blocking *PREFETCH* instruction is defined to preload a block of data into the cache.

[2]   *PREFETCH* instructions are inserted into some inner loops of a program by the compiler.

[3]   Prefetching candidates are array references with constant strides.

All these software assisted prefetching schemes are very successful in prefetching array references with constant strides. However, the use of these schemes is often limited by their runtime overhead. When *PREFETCH* instructions are inserted into some inner loops of a program, program execution time will be spent to execute these instructions, independent of whether these *PREFETCH* instructions can help eliminating cache misses. For any data caches with line size greater than one, the same *PREFETCH* instruction in some loop of a program might execute more than once, each time to prefetch the same cache line. In other words, to avoid one cache miss, the runtime overhead introduced by these schemes might range from 1 instruction to *Line_Size* instructions, where *Line_Size* is the size of the cache line. In fact, Porterfield reported in [Por89] that using the computing intensive programs in RiCEPS as the benchmark programs, he found that the percentage of *PREFETCH* instructions that is found to be *useful* only ranges from 1.7% to 58.2%, with the average[1] of 28.4%. However, the software prefetching overhead (in execution time) introduced is substantial, ranging from 6% to 34%, with the average of 28%.

To reduce this runtime overhead of software assisted prefetching schemes, Mowry and Lam [MoL92] proposed the concept of prefetch predicates, which determines if a particular iteration needs to be prefetched. Then, with the loop splitting technique, the runtime overhead of data prefetching is reduced by decomposing the loops into different sections so that the predicates for all instances for the same section evaluate to the same value. This implies that either the first iteration of the loop is peeled for temporal locality reason or the loop is unrolled by a factor of the cache line size for spatial locality reason. This prefetch predicate concept definitely improves

over previous software prefetching schemes. However, there are a number of important issues that still need to be solved by this predicate approach. As is also mentioned in their paper, for large cache line size, peeling and unrolling multiple levels of loops can potentially expand the code by a significant amount; also existing optimizing compiler is often ineffective for large procedure bodies. On the other hand, for small cache line size, the amount of runtime overhead that can be reduced by this technique is smaller because the improvement factor is a linear function of the cache line size. In fact, when the cache line size is one or when the distance between two successive array references[2] is greater than the cache line size, no reduction in runtime overhead can be achieved. Furthermore, the algorithm for this peeling and unrolling for prefetch predicates is quite complicated to be implemented in the compiler.

One other complication of using *PREFETCH* instructions is the amount of data that should be prefetched by one *PREFETCH* instruction. Since there is some runtime overhead associated with each *PREFETCH* instruction execution, one would prefer to prefetch a larger block of data per instruction. In this way, the overall runtime overhead of the scheme can be reduced. However, if a large block of data is prefetched into the cache, the current working set of references in the data cache might be destroyed by the prefetched data (especially for on-chip caches with a smaller cache size). This will introduce additional cache misses. Furthermore, execution of the *PREFETCH* instruction for a larger block of data might hold up the memory bus for too long and causes unnecessary delay to other bus requests such as demand-driven cache misses. One the other hand, if each *PREFETCH* instruction only prefetches a small block of data, the performance gain by the software prefetching scheme might not be large enough to cover its overhead.

People have been arguing that while the cost issue of software assisted data prefetching in scalar machines is important, the cost of software prefetching in superscalar and VLIW machines is negligible. It is because the *PREFETCH* instructions can be scheduled into unused slots for free. We do not agree with this argument because the required slots might not be available. Even if the slots are found, they are still not free. If the same slot is not occupied by the *PREFETCH* instruction, it can be used by some other function. Decoding one *PREFETCH* instruction in superscalar machines also implies that one less instruction is looked ahead and this can potentially reduce its parallelism width.

Unless the problem of runtime overhead associated with *PREFETCH* instructions is solved, software assisted cache prefetching schemes can only be used in some very limited and specific situations such as some hand optimized engineering library routines for vector processing.

2.2. Prefetch Buffer

The concept of using a separate cache space to store and handle prefetched data is also not new. The best example of this separate cache spacing approach is the use of a prefetch buffer [Smi82]. A prefetch buffer is a separate space in cache where data prefetched by some predefined scheme are stored. When there is a hit in the prefetch buffer, data will be sent directly to the processing unit. On the other hand, when a

---

1.   Even with overflow iteration technique [Por89], the average percentage of useful *PREFETCH* instructions is improved to about 60%.

2.   This is the case for stride Row_Size or Column_Size array references and is found to be very common.

cache miss occurs, the missing line will be fetched from the main memory and will be placed in the data cache *instead of in the prefetch buffer*. The purpose of the prefetch buffer is to handle data with weak temporal locality and to minimize cache pollution due to incorrect data prefetching. A good example of prefetch buffer design is found in AMD 29000 series [AMD88].

The pre-requisite of using a prefetch buffer is an accurate prefetch algorithm. The size of the prefetch buffer is usually quite small, ranging from 16 bytes to at most a few hundred bytes. This is to ensure that the cache space used to handle non-prefetched data is not reduced significantly. Furthermore, even if the size of the prefetch buffer is increased, it will not improve the performance of the prefetch buffer a lot. Prefetched data are supposed to be used soon after they are put into the prefetch buffer. Thus, if the prefetched data are not used after they are prefetched into the buffer for a while, it is likely that these data are prefetched inaccurately. Increasing the prefetch buffer size can only increase the time prefetched data stay in cache, but it does not increase the amount of data prefetched.

Currently, most prefetch buffer designs are mainly used for handling instruction references. It is because instructions have very strong sequential reference property and they can be prefetched very accurately even by simple scheme such as one block look ahead [Smi78a] [Smi78b] [Smi82]. For data references, current prefetch buffer designs are still not popular. It is because problems in data cache prefetching schemes (as are mentioned in the last section) have not yet been solved. In the past two years, data prefetch buffer designs have been proposed [ChM91] [FuP91] [AbS93]. However, they are only limited to read-only prefetched data. All writeable data and data fetched due to cache misses are handled by the main cache.

3. Architectural Model of Array Cache

In the last section, we discussed the advantages and disadvantages of both hardware controlled and software assisted cache prefetching schemes. We also looked at the effectiveness of prefetch buffers for data references. From our analysis, it is clear that most of all these data prefetching techniques and prefetch buffer designs need to be modified before they can be effective in handling data references. Hardware controlled cache prefetching schemes have the advantage of very low runtime overhead, but the accuracy of these schemes is usually not good enough to provide significant system performance improvement. Software assisted data prefetching schemes can prefetch data accurately into the cache, but the use of these schemes is often limited by their runtime overhead. Prefetch buffer is used to reduce the interference between prefetched data and demand-fetched data. However, most of them are only used to handle read-only data, just like instruction prefetch buffers. For writeable data, they still have to go through the original cache space, which implies that interference between the working set of array references and the working set of non-array references still exists.

To solve all these problems, we propose a new software assisted cache design, called the *Array Cache*, in this paper. The main idea of the Array Cache is to use a separate cache space to store and handle array references with constant strides that are prefetched accurately with the help of the compiler. The software data prefetching scheme supporting the Array Cache is different from current software cache prefetching

schemes. No *PREFETCH* instructions are needed by the new prefetching scheme and all prefetching actions are triggered by the content of some new preloaded hardware. The functionality of the Array Cache is also different from current prefetch buffers. The Array Cache is used to handle all data that are identified by the new prefetching scheme, independent of whether they are read-only or writeable, or they are prefetched or fetched-on-demand into the Array Cache.

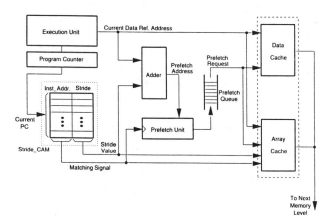

Figure 1: Architectural Structure for the Array Cache

The architectural structure of the Array Cache is shown in Figure 1. It is divided into two parts: a prefetch unit and a data storing unit. The hardware of the prefetch unit is mainly consisted of a small Stride_CAM array, a prefetch queue, a lockup-free cache and some hardware control logic. In additional to the hardware, the prefetch unit also supports a new software assisted cache prefetching scheme, called the **Stride_CAM Data Prefetching (SCP)** scheme. With the help of the compiler, candidates for prefetching — array references with constant strides in some inner loops of a program — are identified. Then for each array reference *a[i]* with constant stride *s* and instruction address *I*, the values of *s* and *I* are stored in the *Stride* field and the *Instr_Addr* field of some Stride_CAM cell respectively using some special *SCAM_SET* instruction that is defined for the SCP scheme. The semantic for the *SCAM_SET* instruction is defined as follows:

SCAM_SET   <Stride_CAM_Cell #>, <Instr_Addr>, <Stride>

where *Stride_CAM_Cell #* is the name of the Stride_CAM cell being used, *Instr_Addr* is the instruction address of the *LOAD/STORE* for the array reference *a[i]*, and *Stride* is the stride value used to calculate the address of the prefetched array reference. For example, "*SCAM_SET 6,1400,2*" sets the *Instr_Addr* field of the Stride_CAM cell #6 to 1400 and the *Stride* field of the Stride_CAM cell #6 to 2. With the help of the compiler, the *SCAM_SET* instruction for an array reference *a[i]* will be placed and be executed before the actual reference for *a[i]*.

When the *LOAD/STORE* instruction for *a[i]* is executed, the current program counter (which contains the instruction address of the array reference *a[i]*) will be checked with the *Instr_Addr* field of all *Stride_CAM* cells associatively. A matching in the *Stride_CAM* array means that the current array reference is a prefetched candidate chosen by the compiler. It also means that the constant stride used by the current array reference has already been placed in the matched *Stride_CAM* cell. Then, the hardware logic will calculate the address for the next array reference *a[i+s]* by adding the *Stride* field value *s* of the matched *Stride_CAM* cell to the current data reference address. This resulting address will then be placed in the prefetch queue for accurate data prefetching. "No fetch on write" and "write allocate" mechanisms are used to place the prefetched data into the Array Cache whenever the *Stride* value *s* used in the address calculation for the prefetched data is equal to one. For other stride values, the default "fetch on write" scheme will be used. Of course, just like any cache design that supports software prefetching, the cache needs to be lockup-free [Kro81] [ScD88]; that is, the cache must allow multiple outstanding misses. While the memory services the data miss, the program can continue to execute as long as it does not need the required data.

Note that the format of the *SCAM_SET* instruction proposed above is suitable for variable length instruction format. For fixed length instruction length format such as those in typical RISC architectures, all the fields defined in the *SCAM_SET* instruction probably cannot be fitted into a single 32-bit instruction. In this case, we can use two instructions instead of a single instruction to achieve the same function:

SCAM_INSTR_SET   <Stride_CAM_Cell #>, <Instr_Addr>
SCAM_STR_SET   <Stride_CAM_Cell #>, <Stride>

SCAM_INSTR_SET is used to set the *Instr_Addr* field of a *Stride_CAM* cell and *SCAM_STR_SET* is used to set the *Stride* field of a *Stride_CAM* cell. Both of these two formats work for our SCP scheme. To make our discussion easier, we will just use the first format in the rest of this paper.

In the SCP scheme, we choose to prefetch the array reference in the *i+1*th iteration when the array reference in the *i*th iteration is referenced. This one iteration ahead for prefetching is chosen because it often provides enough time for the prefetching to finish; yet the prefetched data do not arrive at the Array Cache too early to be replaced from the Array Cache before they are actually referenced. However, if the shortest path of the loop is really much shorter than the latency to prefetch data into the Array Cache, we can still use the scheduling technique proposed in [MoL92] and look *T/P* iterations ahead, where *T* is the prefetch latency and *P* is the shortest path of the loop. Of course, under this situation, memory pipelining techniques are also needed to be implemented in the Array Cache. It is because the data consumption rate is faster than the data transfer rate from the main memory to the cache and memory pipelining can improve the overall data transfer rate.

4. Control Mechanisms for the Array Cache

For each *LOAD/STORE* executed, the referenced data and some prefetched data might be transferred between the main memory and the caching system. The actions of data demand-fetching, data prefetching, and the location of data placement (i.e. in array cache or in data cache) are determined by the matching result in the *Stride_CAM* array and by the cache hit/miss in either the Array Cache or the data cache. There are six possible cases that can happen:

[1] *Stride_CAM* hit, Data Cache miss, and Array Cache miss,

[2] *Stride_CAM* hit, Data Cache hit, and Array Cache miss,

[3] *Stride_CAM* hit, Data Cache miss, and Array Cache hit,

[4] *Stride_CAM* miss, Data Cache miss, and Array Cache miss,

[5] *Stride_CAM* miss, Data Cache hit, and Array Cache miss, and

[6] *Stride_CAM* miss, Data Cache miss, and Array Cache hit.

Note that hit in the data cache and hit in the Array Cache are mutually exclusive (i.e. it is not possible for a reference to be found in both the data cache and the Array Cache simultaneously).

Case 1: *Stride_CAM Hit, Data Cache Miss, and Array Cache Miss*

A hit in the *Stride_CAM* array implies that the current data reference is a prefetching candidate for the SCP scheme. A data prefetching request with address equal to the sum of the current data reference address and the stride value found in the *Stride* field of the matched *Stride_CAM* entry is sent to the prefetch queue for data prefetching. The prefetched data will be placed in the Array Cache, replacing data from the Array Cache if necessary. If the value of the *Stride* field in the matched *Stride_CAM* cell is equal to one, "no fetch on miss" and "write allocate" mechanisms are used. Otherwise, "fetch on miss" mechanism is used. This is to avoid the situation where a cache line of data is fetched from the main memory into the cache and is then overwritten without even being referenced once.

A hit in the *Stride_CAM* array also implies that the current data reference is expected to be found in the Array Cache. However, in this case, the current data reference is not found in either the Array Cache or the Data Cache. This might be due to insufficient time for the data prefetching to be finished. The other possibility is that the current data reference that has been prefetched into the cache is replaced away from the cache before they can be used. In both cases, the current data reference will be fetched from the main memory and will be stored in the Array Cache. The reference is placed in the Array Cache instead of in the Data Cache because its temporal locality is expected to be very weak. This data placement action is quite different from the traditional prefetch buffer design where all references due to cache misses will be placed in the data cache instead of in the prefetch buffer.

Case 2: *Stride_CAM Hit, Data Cache Hit, and Array Cache Miss*

A hit in the *Stride_CAM* array implies that the current data reference is a prefetching candidate for the SCP scheme. All prefetching actions are exactly the same as in Case 1. It is because any prefetching action in the SCP scheme is triggered only by the matching result in the *Stride_CAM* Array.

A hit in the *Stride_CAM* array also implies that the current data reference is expected to be found in the Array Cache. However, in this case, the current data reference is found in the Data Cache instead of the Array Cache. This happens when a non-array reference which is accessed previously refers to the same memory location as the current array reference. Under this situation, the referenced datum will be sent from the Data Cache to the processing unit and there will be no change in the Data Cache and Array Cache contents. By keeping the referenced datum in the Data Cache, it is hoped that the datum can be kept in the caching system longer and can be reused by the previous non-array reference to this same memory location.

Case 3: *Stride_CAM Hit, Data Cache Miss, and Array Cache Hit*

Again, all the prefetching actions are exactly the same as in Case 1 and 2 because of the same explanation given in Case 2. A hit in the *Stride_CAM* array also implies that the current data reference is expected to be found in the Array Cache. Since this is exactly what happens, the referenced datum in the Array Cache will be sent to the processing unit and there will be no change in the Data Cache and Array Cache contents.

Case 4: *Stride_CAM Miss, Data Cache Miss, and Array Cache Miss*

A miss in the *Stride_CAM* array implies that the current data reference is not a prefetching candidate for the SCP scheme. Hence, no data prefetching request due to the SCP scheme will be issued to the prefetch queue.

A miss in the *Stride_CAM* array also implies that the current data reference should be handled by the Data Cache. Since the referenced datum is not found in both the Data Cache and the Array Cache, it will be fetched from the main memory and will be stored in the Data Cache.

Case 5: *Stride_CAM Miss, Data Cache Hit, and Array Cache Miss*

No data prefetching request due to the SCP scheme will be sent out to the prefetch queue because of the same explanation given in Case 4. A miss in the *Stride_CAM* array also implies that the current data reference should be handled by the Data Cache. If there is a cache hit, the referenced datum is expected to be found in the Data Cache. Since this is exactly what happens, the referenced datum in the Data Cache will be sent to the processing unit and there will be no change to the Data Cache and Array Cache contents.

Case 6: *Stride_CAM Miss, Data Cache Miss, and Array Cache Hit*

No data prefetching request due to the SCP scheme will be sent out to the prefetch queue because of the same explanation given in Case 4. A miss in the *Stride_CAM* array also implies that the current data reference is expected to be found in the Data Cache when there is a cache hit. However, the current data reference is found in the Array Cache instead of the Data Cache. This happens when an array element which is referenced previously refers to the same memory location as the current non-array reference. Under this situation, the referenced datum will be sent from the Array Cache to the processing unit.

Two possible situations might be happened to the contents of the Array Cache and the Data Cache. The first choice is to keep the contents of the Array Cache and the Data Cache unchanged. This is to simplify the hardware and the datapath inside the caching system. However, since the current referenced line is expected to be referenced again and cache lines in the Array Cache are only expected to be kept there for a short period of time, cache miss might occur when the current reference is accessed again in the near future. The second choice is to transfer the current referenced line from the Array Cache to the Data Cache after the reference. This kind of cache line transfer among various cache partitions might be beneficial because the current referenced cache line is expected to to be referenced again. It is better to keep the referenced data in Data Cache than in the Array Cache so that the data might be kept in the caching system longer. Of course, the cost of this choice is the additional data path and the hardware logic. In this paper, we suggest the first approach because the hardware is simpler and the frequency for this situation to happen is not frequent.

After we have described the architectural structure and the control mechanism for the Array Cache, we are going to discuss the compiler support for the Array Cache and describe how the *SCAM_SET* instructions for array references can be inserted into the program.

5. Compiler Support for the Array Cache

The compiler support for the SCP scheme for the Array Cache consists of three phases:

- Selection of array references with constant strides.
- Insertion of *SCAM_SET* instructions.
- Execution of the SCP scheme.

During the first phase of the SCP scheme, potential candidates for data prefetching are identified by the compiler. In this paper, we propose that only those array references with constant strides in some inner loops of a program are chosen for prefetching. It is because in typical scientific programs, most of the memory references come from array references in some inner loops of the program. Furthermore, these array references are most likely to generate cache misses because they usually refer to different elements of an array during each iteration of a loop.

To ensure the SCP scheme to be effective in hiding the time to transfer data between the cache and the main memory from the program execution, the prefetch request needs to precede the actual use of data by enough time to allow the prefetch request to complete. However, the prefetch request should not be so far that the prefetched data might be flushed out from the cache before they are referenced. As we mentioned in the last section, we propose that during the ith iteration of the loop, the prefetch candidates are those array references in the $i+1^{th}$ iteration of the loop. Also, when some array reference name A appears more than once in the inner loop, only one prefetch request corresponding to the first appearance of A is needed.

In the second phase of the SCP scheme, addresses of the SCP prefetch candidates are encoded into the program code by the compiler. This is the most important phase for any software assisted cache prefetching scheme because this determines the amount of runtime overhead associated with that scheme.

Recently proposed software assisted cache prefetching schemes suggest to use *PREFETCH* instructions as the means for data prefetching. As is discussed in Section 2.1.2, this results in some non-neglectable runtime overhead associated with the schemes. Since *PREFETCH* instructions are inserted in the inner loops of a program, the cost of avoiding one cache miss might be the execution of same *PREFETCH* instruction several times (even though the actual prefetch request is sent out once).

In order to reduce the runtime overhead for data prefetching, the SCP scheme uses an alternate way to store the prefetch information. Instead of inserting *PREFETCH* instructions into the program, the *Prefetch_Offset* of a prefetch candidate is stored in the *Stride* field of a *Stride_CAM* cell and its corresponding instruction address for the reference is stored in the *Instr_Addr* field of the same *Stride_CAM* cell. The **Prefetch_Offset** is defined as the distance of the prefetch candidate address from the current array reference address. It is calculated by the following formula:

$$Prefetch\_Offset = address(A[i\_v+Stride]) - address(A[i\_v])$$

where i_v is the loop induction variable. Then, at runtime, the hardware logic can use the information stored in the *Stride_CAM* array for accurate data prefetching. In the SCP scheme, a CAM array is used instead of a register array because with the associative search capability, there is no need to specific the name of the *Stride_CAM* cell in the *LOAD/STORE* instruction for the array reference. Since the number of active arrays operated simultaneously is usually very small, only a very small *Stride_CAM* array will be needed.

```
for each statement S in a program
    if S is a FOR loop with constant loop step
    then
            i_v = loop induction variable
            str = loop step

        for each array reference A with instruction address I_A in statement S
        if ((i_v appears in subscript of A) and (A appears in S for the first time))
        then
            Prefetch candidate = address(A[i_v + str])
            Prefetch_Offset = address(A[i_v + str]) - address(A[i_v])
            Insert "SCAM_SET <Stride_CAM_Name>, I_A, Prefetch_Offset" outside S
        endif
        endfor
    endif
endfor
```

Figure 2: Algorithm for Inserting *SCAM_SET* Instructions

The *SCAM_SET* instructions are inserted outside the inner loop body (instead of inside the inner loop body, as are the cases for most software assisted prefetching schemes). Hence, the runtime overhead for the SCP scheme is much lower than the runtime overhead for software assisted prefetching schemes. Figure 2 summarizes the above discussion and gives a typical algorithm for the insertion of *SCAM_SET* instructions.

From the above discussion, we see that the cost for prefetching an array of data is the execution of only one *SCAM_SET* instruction. However, the gain in cache performance (and thus the system performance) can be substantial.

In this last phase of the SCP scheme, data prefetch requests are generated at runtime using information stored in the *Stride_CAM* array and using the current program counter value and the current data reference address. The control flow for the SCP hardware and its associated timing diagram are shown in Figure 3.

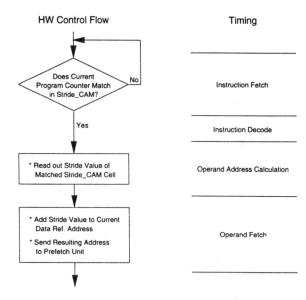

Figure 3: Control Flow and Timing for SCP Hardware

The left hand side of the figure shows the control flow for the prefetch hardware and the right hand side of the figure gives the timing relative to the instruction execution. From this control flow and timing diagram, it is clear that the execution of the SCP scheme can be overlapped completely with the execution of the program. The matching of the program counter value with the *Instr_Addr* field of the *Stride_CAM* array is done while the instruction is being fetched and decoded. Then, if a match is found in some *Stride_CAM* cell, the corresponding *Stride* value of the matched *Stride_CAM* cell is read out while the current operand address is being calculated. Finally, if data prefetching is needed, the address of the prefetched datum is calculated by adding the current data operand address with the fetched stride value and the result is then sent to the prefetch control unit for data prefetching. The address calculation for the prefetch candidate can also be overlapped with the operand fetching for the current *LOAD* or *STORE* instruction. Since all the runtime operations of the SCP scheme can be overlapped with the program execution completely, the SCP scheme does not introduce additional runtime overhead.

6. Runtime Overhead and Enhancement of the SCP Scheme

In the last section, we described the compiler support for the SCP scheme for the Array Cache design. The runtime overhead of the SCP scheme can come from two possible sources:

[1]   the setting of the *Stride_CAM* cell using the *SCAM_SET* instruction; and

[2]   the delay introduced during the address calculation for prefetch candidates and during the prefetch request issuing at runtime.

For the first source of overhead, since the *SCAM_SET* instruction is inserted outside the inner loop, this overhead is very small, especially when the loop is iterated many times. This is in contrast with current software assisted prefetching schemes, where *PREFETCH* instructions are inserted and executed inside the inner loop. An example of the SCP scheme is given in Figure 4. Figure 4(a) is the original program segment. By inserting *SCAM_SET* instructions outside the inner loop for prefetching array references, Figure 4(b) results.

For the second source of runtime overhead, since the address calculation for prefetch candidates and the prefetch request issuing of the SCP scheme can be overlapped with instruction decode, operand address calculation and operand fetch (as was discussed in the last section), neglectable runtime overhead is introduced by this source. Moreover, enhancement of the SCP scheme to reduce the runtime overhead of the SCP scheme further is possible. This is achieved by code motion for loop invariant assignment.

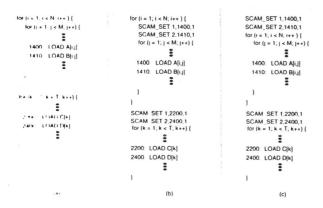

Figure 4: (a) Some Sample Program; (b) Program with *SCAM_SET* Added; (c) Program with Code Motion for *SCAM_SET* Instruction.

Very often, multiple-level nested loops are used to access N-dimensional data arrays. Thus the *SCAM_SET* instructions that are inserted outside the inner loops of a program might still be inside some outer loops of a program. For example, the first loop in Figure 4(a) is a two-level nested loop. The inserted *SCAM_SET 1,1400,1* and *SCAM_SET 2,1410,1* instructions are outside the *j*-loop, but they are still inside the *i*-loop. This is shown in Figure 4(b). However, since both *SCAM_SET* instructions are *always* loop invariant to the loop index, they can be moved outside the *i*-loop. This can reduce the runtime overhead introduced by the *SCAM_SET* instruction further because the *SCAM_SET* instruction is now executed only one time instead of *N* times. This is shown in Figure 4(c).

7. Experimental Result

To show the effectiveness of the Array Cache and its supporting SCP scheme on computing intensive scientific programs, two sets of experiments were performed. The first set of experiments was to find out how often the SCP scheme can be used for accurate array data prefetching. The second set of experiments was to determine how effective the Array Cache can be used to reduce processor stall due to cache misses. The benchmarks that were used in our study were the 24 Livermore Kernels (in C languages) and the 7 independent Kernels (MXM, CFFT2D, CHOLSKY, BTRIX, GMTRY, EMIT, and VPENTA) in the NASA.007 benchmark from the SPECmark 92. These benchmarks are chosen as our benchmark suite because they represent an important set of computational kernels typically found in large-scale scientific computing applications.

Applicability of the SCP Scheme

In this set of experiments, we want to find out how often array references can be prefetched by the SCP scheme in our benchmark suite. To do this, we compiled each of the 24 Livermore and the 7 NASA Kernels on a SPARC/20 workstation using its C compiler and with its optimizer turn-on (using -O4 flag). For the assembly listing of each of these kernels, every *LOAD* or *STORE* instruction was analyzed to determine: (1) if it was a prefetch candidate (i.e. array reference with constant stride) for the SCP scheme; and (2) the value of the *Prefetch_Offset* for the next array reference from the current data reference if it was a prefetch candidate. The result of the analysis was attached to the end of each *LOAD* or *STORE* instruction in the assembly listing. Then, the modified assembly listing of each program was simulated using our SPARC simulator. Statistics about the relative frequencies of various *Prefetch_Offset* values were collected and are shown in Figure 5. The percentages shown here are the averaging values across the 24 Livermore and the 7 NASA Kernels. From these figures, it is very clear that SCP scheme can improve cache performance significantly. Over 95 percent of the array references are in some inner loops and their *Prefetch_Offsets* are some constant. This also implies that this same amount of array references can be prefetched accurately by the SCP scheme. They will not generate any cache misses if there is no memory bandwidth limitation.

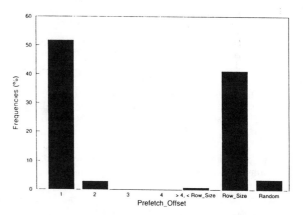

Figure 5: *LOAD/STORE*s with Various *Prefetch_Offsets*

Effectiveness of the Array Cache

In the second set of our experiments, we want to show the effectiveness of the Array Cache in reducing the processor stall. To do this, we use the following data cache design as our basic simulation framework and as our point of reference. The configuration of the data cache is as follows: cache size 16 KBytes, 4 way set associative, line size 32 bytes, bandwidth to the second level cache/memory system 64 bits r/w path, the time to obtain the first word after a cache miss is 12 cycles, and no data prefetching is performed. Furthermore, the effect of the second level cache/memory system is ignored, i.e. 100% cache hit in the second level cache/memory system is assumed. For our new Array Cache design, we used the following configuration in our simulation: Data Cache of size 8 KBytes, 4 way set associative, line size 32 bytes; Array Cache of size 4 Kbytes, 2 way set associative, line size 32 bytes; *Stride_CAM* of size 16 entries; and the bus bandwidth, second level cache effect, and same cache miss penalty are assumed as those in the original cache design. The modified 7 NASA programs developed in the first set of our experiments were simulated using our SPARC simulator. Assuming an one cycle execution time for each instruction and assuming no branch delay, the program execution time improvement by the Array Cache is shown in Table 1. From this table, it is very clear that the Array Cache is very effective in improving the performance of computing intensive scientific applications. The program execution time can be improved by a factor ranging from 1.16 to about 2.3, which is substantial.

Benchmark	Program Execution Time Improvement
MXM	1.16
CFFT2D	1.89
CHOLSKY	2.31
BTRIX	1.75
GMTRY	2.11
EMIT	1.17
VPENTA	2.34

Table 1: Program Execution Time Improvement

8. Conclusion

In this paper, we proposed a new cache design, called the Array Cache, and its supporting Stride_CAM Data Prefetching (SCP) scheme to improve data cache performance. We showed that the Array Cache design is effective in improving the overall system performance, especially in scientific computation applications. By comparing the Array Cache design with current data cache designs, we found that the Array Cache design is superior than current data cache designs at least in two aspects. First, the SCP scheme with its *Stride_CAM* Array provides selective and very accurate data prefetching for array references with constant strides. And, this can be achieved with neglectable runtime overhead. This is in contrast to current data prefetching schemes: software assisted cache prefetching schemes can achieve high prefetching accuracy but with high runtime overhead and hardware prefetching schemes achieves non-satisfied prefetching accuracy but with neglectable runtime overhead. Second, by partitioning the cache space into Array Cache and Data Cache, the interference between the working set of array references and non array references can be reduced to its minimum. Finally, the additional hardware such as the *Stride_CAM* array is not too high and the software support for this new cache design is also small.

References

[AbS93] Abraham, S.G., Sugumar, R.A., Rau, B.R., Gupta, R., "Predictability of Load/Store Instruction Latencies," *Proceedings of the 26th Annual International Symposium on Microarchitecture*, December 1993, pp. 139 - 152.

[AMD88] *AM29000 32-bit Streamlined Instruction Processor Manual*, 1988.

[Bre87] Brent, G.A., "Using Program Structure to Achieve Prefetching for Cache Memories," *Ph.D Thesis, University of Illinois at Urbana-Champaign*, January 1987.

[CaK91] Callahan, D., Kennedy, K., Porterfield, A., "Software Prefetching," *Proceedings of the Fourth International Conference on Architectural Support for Programming Languages and Operating Systems*, April 1991, pp. 40-52.

[ChM91] Chen, W.Y., Mahlke, S.A., Chang, P.P., Hwu, W.W., "Data Access Microarchitectures for Superscalar Processors with Compiler-Assisted Data Prefetching," *Proceedings of Microcomputing 24*, 1991.

[FuP91] Fu, W.C., Patel, J.H., "Data Prefetching in Multiprocessor Vector Cache Memories," *Proceedings of the 18th Annual Symposium on Computer Architecture*, May, 1991, pp. 54-63.

[GoG90] Gornish, E., Granston, E., Veidenbaum, A., "Compiler-Directed Data Prefetching in Multiprocessor with Memory Hierarchies, *Proceedings of the 1990 International Conference on Supercomputing*, 1990, pp. 354-368.

[HeP90] Hennessy, J., Patterson, D., *Computer Architecture: A Quantitative Approach*, Morgan Kauffmann, 1990.

[KlL91] Klaiber, A.C., Levy, H.M., "An Architecture for Software Controlled Data Prefetching," *Proceedings of the 18th Annual Symposium on Computer Architecture*, May 1991, pp. 43-53.

[Kro81] Kroft, D., "Lockup-Free Instruction Fetch/Prefetch Cache Organization," *Proceedings of the 8th Annual International Symposium on Computer Architecture*, 1981, pp. 81-87.

[Lei93] Leibson, S.H., "EDN's Twentieth Annual Microprocessor Directory," *EDN*, Nov. 25, 1993, pp. 59-184.

[MoL92] Mowry, T.C., Lam, M.S., Gupta, A., "Design and Evaluation of a Compiler Algorithm for Prefetching," *Proceedings of the Fifth International Conference on Architectural Support for Programming Languages and Operating Systems*, October 1992, pp. 62-73.

[Por89] Porterfield, A.K., "Software Methods for Improvement of Cache Performance on Supercomputer Application", *Technical Report COMP TR 89-93, Rice University*, May 1989.

[ScD88] Scheurich, C., Dubois, M., "Concurrent Miss Resolution in Multiprocessor Caches," *Proceeding of the 1988 International Conference on Parallel Processing*, 1988.

[Smi82] Smith, A.J., "Cache Memories," *ACM Computing Survey*, Volume 14, Number 3, September 1982, pp. 473-530.

A Study of the Effects of Compiler-Controlled Speculation on Instruction and Data Caches

Roger A. Bringmann *   Scott A. Mahlke †   Wen-mei W. Hwu

Center for Reliable and High-Performance Computing
University of Illinois
Urbana, IL 61801

Abstract

Compiler-controlled speculation has been shown to be effective in increasing instruction level parallelism (ILP) found in non-numeric programs. However, it is not clear the extent to which speculatively scheduled code may affect the instruction and data caches. In particular, the amount of time spent resolving cache misses may be significant enough to prevent the more aggressive speculation models from attaining their best potential performance results. The objective of this paper is to quantify these effects using aggressive speculation models.

Index terms - instruction cache effects, data cache effects, compiler-controlled speculation, safe speculation, VLIW, superscalar

1 Introduction

Instruction scheduling is the process used by the compiler to re-order instructions in an effort to minimize program execution time. Since instruction scheduling is NP-Hard, heuristics are used to approximate the best schedule. One common approach to scheduling is to perform list scheduling using greedy heuristics to approximate a *globally optimal* schedule [1]. Regardless of the scheduling heuristics, instructions are ordered based upon some priority mechanism. At each cycle, the instructions with the highest priority that have resolved all dependences and meet the issue requirements of the processor are scheduled.

The implementation of a scheduler is straightforward if list scheduling is applied only within basic blocks. Unfortunately, there is insufficient instruction level parallelism (ILP) available within basic blocks of non-numeric benchmarks to fully utilize the functional units of wide issue superscalar and VLIW architectures [2, 3, 4]. Therefore global scheduling techniques such as *trace scheduling* [5] and *superblock scheduling* [6] have been proposed to permit greater scheduling and optimization freedom beyond basic block boundaries. Using these techniques, the program is divided

into a set of traces or superblocks that represent frequently executed paths. These traces or superblocks contain multiple basic blocks and as a result can contain multiple conditional branches. When building a dependence graph for a trace or superblock, control dependence arcs are added from conditional branches to subsequent instructions. In order to gain additional scheduling freedom beyond the natural basic block boundaries found within these traces or superblocks, the compiler must remove some of these control dependence arcs. This permits speculation of instructions past conditional branches, thus the term compiler-controlled speculation.

When an instruction is speculated above a branch, it is executed regardless of the direction taken by the branch. As such, the speculated instruction could introduce instruction cache (Icache) and data cache (Dcache) effects that may not have been present in the original unscheduled program. If these effects are significant, much of the performance potential of aggressive speculation may be lost. This makes it critical that the processor and computer system designers understand the requirements of the speculation models being used by the compiler if they are to balance the potential performance of the compiled code with the cache implementation.

The next section briefly describes the static speculation models used in the experiments. Section 3 discusses the expected cache effects. Section 4 presents experimental results showing how these speculation models affect various configurations of instruction and data caches. Finally, concluding remarks are given in Section 5.

2 Scheduling Models

In order to gain greater scheduling freedom, instructions must be allowed to speculate above conditional branches found within a trace or superblock. In some cases, speculation of these instructions can introduce a *scheduling error* that can cause unexpected program termination. An example of such a scheduling error would be scheduling a divide before a branch that was implicitly preventing a divide-by-zero. The decision on what to do if the highest priority instruction could potentially introduce a scheduling error is

---

*Roger Bringmann is now with QMS, Inc.

†Scott Mahlke is now with HP Labs

1. **Avoid Errors** - do not permit an instruction to speculate if it could cause a scheduling error [2].

2. **Ignore Errors** - assumes that the likelihood of a scheduling error is small and will therefore speculate a non-excepting form of the instruction. As a result, any scheduling errors are hidden. This model requires non-excepting forms of each potentially excepting instruction that is speculated [2].

3. **Resolve Errors** - speculates instructions that could cause a scheduling error but assumes that the processor has some mechanism to resolve the error. Three examples of speculation models that fall into this category are boosting [7], sentinel scheduling [8] and write-back suppression [9].

Figure 1: Classifications of compiler-controlled speculation models.

based upon the speculation model and the processor support. As shown in Figure 1, the existing speculation models can be categorized into three classes based upon these decisions.

Each of the speculation models used for experimentation contain certain characteristics that permit different degrees of scheduling freedom. As such, they are expected to introduce varying Icache and Dcache effects. In order to evaluate the speculation models fairly, all benchmarks are aggressively optimized with superblock techniques [6]. Each of the speculation models are used to schedule the optimized code. This paper does not cover any of the *resolve error* speculation models since their recovery processes are not directly comparable to the other models.

2.1   No Speculation Model

This model provides a baseline for the typical Icache and Dcache effects that occur without code speculation. As a result, this model provides the best scheduling results that are attainable with no additional Icache and Dcache effects introduced from compile-time scheduling.

2.2   Restricted Speculation Model

Restricted speculation (formally called restricted code percolation [2]) assumes that correct program execution is always required as defined by the *avoid errors* class. Using this model, the compiler can only speculate instructions that will never cause an exception. The conservative definition of potentially excepting instructions used by this model assumes that if there is any way that an instruction could cause an exception, it will be classified as potentially excepting and may not be speculated. As such, this definition ignores the cases where the context in which the instruction is used can sometimes indicate if the instruction may or may not cause an exception. This conservative model prevents speculation of any memory instructions, integer

divide and remainder, and all floating point instructions. This model functions as a low-end for the speculation models. The advantage of this model is that it does not introduce any Dcache effects as a result of speculating memory instructions. The only Dcache effects introduced above those introduced by the no speculation model are a direct result of the increased register pressure created by the more aggressively speculated code.

2.3   Safe Speculation Model

Safe speculation expands the scheduling freedom of restricted speculation by using program analysis to identify potentially excepting instructions that can never cause scheduling errors or will introduce no new scheduling errors. An example of such a potentially excepting instruction would be a load from an array. If the potential values that the array may access can be proven to be within the declared array bounds, then the load is a safe load. This model also falls under the *avoid errors* classification. The advantage of this speculation model is that it requires no special hardware support in the processor as required for the *resolve errors* class and the *ignore errors* class and does not have the inherent risks associated with the *ignore errors* class. The safe speculation model results reported in this paper are based on inter-procedural and intra-procedural analysis algorithms reported in [10].

2.4   General Speculation Model

General speculation (formally called general code percolation) falls under the *ignore errors* classification. It requires a non-excepting form of every potentially excepting instruction that is desirable to speculate [2]. Thus, if a potentially excepting instruction is to be speculated, it will be replaced by its non-excepting form. Potentially excepting instructions are typically load instructions, integer divide and remainder, and all floating point instructions. The results on general speculation reported in this paper are based upon a full model where every potential exception causing instruction has a non-excepting counter part in the instruction set. The following architectures are examples that have implemented subsets of this model in an effort to increase instruction level parallelism.

1. Multiflow - non-excepting floating point instructions [11]

2. Cydra 5 - non-excepting floating point instructions, ability to disable exceptions for memory and arithmetic operations [12].

3. HP Precision Architecture - non-excepting floating point instructions, non-excepting dereferenced null pointer [13].

3   Expected Cache Effects

This section will provide a qualitative analysis of the expected instruction and data cache effects resulting from

Opcode	Description
add	32-bit integer add
beq	conditional branch on equal
bgt	conditional branch on greather than
bne	conditional branch on not equal
jump	unconditional branch
ld_c2	load signed 16-bit value
ld_i	load signed 32-bit value
ld_uc	load unsigned 8-bit value
ld_uc2	load unsigned 16-bit value
lsl	32-bit logical shift left
mov	move 32-bit value
st_c	store 8-bit value
sub	32-bit integer subtract
xor	32-bit exclusive or

Table 1: Instruction opcodes and descriptions.

Cycle	Instruction - (instruction id, opcode)				
1	45, ld_uc	48, mov	49, add	50, add	
2					
3	46, st_c	47, lsl	51, bgt	52, mov	
4	53, bgt	54, add	57, mov		
5	55, add	58, add			
6	56, ld_i				
7					
8	59, beq	60, mov			
9	61, add				
10	62, bne	66, ld_uc	63, lsl		
11	64, add				
12	68, lsl	67, st_c	65, mov	69, bgt	70, mov
13	71, bgt	72, add	75, mov		
14	73, add	76, add			
15	74, ld_i				
16					
17	77, beq	78, mov			
18	79, add				
19	80, bne	81, lsl	83, add	84, add	85, add
20	82, add	86, jump			

Figure 2: The most important loop in cccp scheduled using no speculation model.

compiler-controlled speculation. To accomplish this goal, scheduled code examples from two benchmarks are presented. These code examples were chosen because they show extreme cache effects due to speculation. The instruction opcodes and their descriptions for the examples are given in Table 1. The examples were scheduled with the no speculation and general speculation models using an eight-issue superscalar processor that has uniform functional units and instruction latencies of the HP-PA 7100 (see Table 5). The Icache and Dcache block sizes were 64 bytes each.

Icache Effects

Speculating instructions above branches moves them from less frequently executed paths to more frequently executed paths. As such, the instruction working set is increased which should result in more Icache requests and subsequently more Icache misses. The first example benchmark, cccp, is used to show the expected Icache effects. To accomplish this, the most frequently executed loop within cccp (found in the *rescan* function) was used. Based upon profile information, the IMPACT superscalar optimizer decided to unroll this loop three times. Tables 2 and 3 respectively show the scheduled code for the no speculation and general speculation models. As these tables show, none of the branches from Table 2 have been delayed in Table 3. In addition, the schedule was reduced from 20 cycles for the

no speculation model to 8 cycles for the general speculation model. It should also be noted that scheduling with the no speculation model provide insufficient freedom to schedule more than 5 instructions in any cycle for the 8-issue processor.

While none of the branches in the general speculation schedule were issued later than in the no speculation schedule, the location of the branches within the Icache blocks did change as shown by Tables 4 and 5. The most notable difference is that branch instruction 59 is located in block 2 of the no speculation Icache layout while it is located in block 3 of the general speculation Icache layout. As a result, there is one additional Icache block before the branch. If branch 59 is infrequently taken, this may not increase Icache misses since both no speculation and general speculation loops are contained within only 4 Icache blocks. However, as Table 2 shows this branch is taken 6192 times. This means that there is an additional Icache block in the working set of the taken path of branch 59 in the general speculation schedule than in the no speculation schedule. The increased working set of this taken branch increases the chance of mapping conflicts with other important Icache blocks. As such, the advantages of the more aggressive schedule have resulted in greater risk of Icache misses.

Dcache Effects

Speculating load instructions above branches moves them from less frequently executed paths to more frequently executed paths. This will not only have effects on the Icache, but will also increase the frequency that the load requests are made. As such, the data working set is increased which should result in more Dcache requests and subsequently more Dcache misses. The second benchmark, compress, is used to show the expected Dcache effects. To accomplish this, the most frequently executed loop within compress (found in the *compress* function) was used. Based upon profile information, the IMPACT superscalar optimizer decided to unroll this loop three times. Tables 6 and 7 respectively show the scheduled code for the no speculation and general speculation models. As the tables show, the no speculation model used 37 cycles while the general speculation model required only 18 cycles. It should also be noted that scheduling with the no speculation model provide insufficient freedom to schedule more than 6 instructions in any cycle for the 8-issue processor.

Table 3 shows the increased execution frequency of the six speculated loads from the general speculation schedule of this loop. By speculating a load above a particular branch, the memory reference patterns of the control flow paths reached from that branch have been altered. Depending upon the cache configuration, this could introduce more Dcache conflicts. For example, by speculating load instruction 163 above branch 159 in Table 7, the memory reference pattern of the paths reached by the taken path of this branch have been altered. Based upon the increased execution frequency of load number 163, and the resultant change in memory reference patterns, Dcache miss rates caused by this load could increase. Due to speculation of other loads and the change in their memory reference patterns, the to-

Cycle	Instruction - (instruction id, opcode[* = speculative])							
1	45, ld_uc	54, add*	57, mov*	60, mov*	52, mov*	72, add*	48, mov	49, add
2	55, add*	58, add*	61, add*	50, add	73, add*	63, lsl*	75, mov*	70, mov*
3	47, lsl	46, st_c	66, ld_uc*	51, bgt	53, bgt	64, add*	76, add*	78, mov*
4	56, ld_i	79, add*	81, lsl*					
5	68, lsl*							
6	59, beq	62, bne	67, st_c	74, ld_i*	65, mov	69, bgt	71, bgt	
7								
8	77, beq	80, bne	82, add	83, add	84, add	85, add	86, jump	

Figure 3: The most important loop in cccp scheduled using general speculation model.

cccp loop		compress loop	
Branch Instruction ID	Times Taken	Branch Instruction ID	Times Taken
51	0	159	46234
53	20	164	11
59	6192	166	0
62	1753	179	39594
69	0	184	8
71	5	186	0
77	2272	199	25981
80	130	204	1
86	9182	210	26824
		214	0
Total	19554	Total	138653

Table 2: Branch taken frequencies. (Total corresponds to the total entrance frequency of the loop.)

Icache Block	Instruction - (instruction id, opcode)							
1								
								45, ld_c
2	48, mov	49, add	50, add	46, st_c	47, lsl	51, bgt	52, mov	53, bgt
	54, add	57, mov	55, add	58, add	56, ld_i	59, beq	60, mov	61, add
3	62, bne	66, ld_c	63, lsl	64, add	68, lsl	67, st_c	65, mov	69, bgt
	70, mov	71, bgt	72, add	75, mov	73, add	76, add	74, ld_i	77, beq
4	78, mov	79, add	80, bne	81, lsl	83, add	84, add	85, add	82, add
	86, jump							

Figure 4: Icache layout for cccp loop after no speculation model (16 instruction block).

Icache Block	Instruction - (instruction id, opcode[* = speculative])							
1								45, ld_uc
	54, add*	57, mov*	60, mov*	52, mov*	72, add*	48, mov	49, add	55, add*
2	58, add*	61, add*	50, add	73, add*	63, lsl*	75, mov*	70, mov*	47, lsl
	46, st_c	66, ld_uc*	51, bgt	53, bgt	64, add*	76, add*	78, mov*	56, ld_i
3	79, add*	81, lsl*	68, lsl*	59, beq	62, bne	67, st_c	74, ld_i*	65, mov
	69, bgt	71, bgt	77, beq	80, bne	82, add	83, add	84, add	85, add
4	86, jump							

Figure 5: Icache layout for cccp loop after general speculation model (16 instruction block).

Cycle	Instruction - (instruction id, opcode)					
1	147, sub	151, sub	156, add			
2	148, mov	157, add				
3	149, lsl	152, mov				
4	153, lsl	150, add				
5	154, xor					
6	155, lsl					
7	158, ld_i					
8						
9	159, bne	161, add	160, lsl			
10	162, add					
11	163, ld_uc2	164, bgt	165, ld_c2			
12						
13	166, beq	167, sub	171, sub	176, add		
14	168, mov	177, add				
15	169, lsl	172, mov				
16	173, lsl	170, add				
17	174, xor					
18	175, lsl					
19	178, ld_i					
20						
21	179, bne	181, add	180, lsl			
22	182, add					
23	183, ld_c2	184, bgt	185, ld_c2			
24						
25	186, beq	187, sub	191, sub	196, add		
26	188, mov	197, add				
27	189, lsl	192, mov				
28	193, lsl	190, add				
29	194, xor					
30	195, lsl					
31	198, ld_i					
32						
33	199, bne	201, add	200, lsl			
34	202, add					
35	203, ld_c2	204, bgt	205, ld_uc	209, add	208, add	207, add
36						
37	206, mov	210, bne	211, mov	212, add	213, mov	214, jump

Figure 6: The most important loop in compress scheduled using no speculation model.

Load Instruction ID	Branches Speculated Above	Increase in Execution Frequency
163	159	46234
165	159, 164	46245
183	179	39594
185	159, 164, 166, 179, 184	85847
203	199	25981
205	159, 164, 166, 179, 184, 186, 199, 204	111829

Table 3: Increase in execution frequency of speculated loads in the compress loop after scheduling with the general speculation model.

Benchmark	Benchmark Description
008.espresso	truth table minimization
022.li	lisp interpreter
023.eqntott	boolean equation minimization
026.compress	compress files
072.sc	spreadsheet
cccp	GNU C preprocessor
cmp	compare files
eqn	format math formulas for troff
grep	string search
lex	lexical analyzer generator
qsort	quick sort
tbl	format tables for troff
wc	word count
yacc	parser generator

Table 4: Benchmarks.

tal increase in Dcache misses for instruction 163 could be greater than the increase in its execution frequency.

4   Experimental Evaluation

This section will quantify the effects that increasing levels of scheduling freedom can have on instruction and data caches. The speculation models used in the experiments from least aggressive to most aggressive are no speculation, restricted speculation, safe speculation and general speculation. Section 4.1 discusses the experimental approach used to generate the cache effects. Section 4.2 discusses the experimental results.

4.1   Methodology

Compiler support for each of the speculation models has been implemented in the IMPACT-I C compiler. The IMPACT-I compiler is a prototype optimizing compiler designed to generate efficient code for VLIW and superscalar processors [2]. The benchmarks used in this study are the 14 non-numeric programs shown in Table 4. The benchmarks consist of 5 non-numeric programs from the SPECint92 suite and 9 other commonly used non-numeric programs. Each of the benchmarks were aggressively optimized with superblock techniques [6] and scheduled using the four speculation models varying the processor issue width from 1 to 8 instructions per cycle.

The processor model used in this study is an in-order

Cycle	Instruction - (instruction id, opcode[* = speculative])							
1	147, sub	151, sub	161, add*	181, add*	165, ld_uc*	167, sub*	171, sub*	156, add
2	148, mov	162, add*	182, add*	157, add	196, add*	176, add*	185, ld_uc*	187, sub*
3	149, lsl	152, mov	197, add*	177, add*	201, add*	191, sub*	205, ld_uc*	
4	153, lsl	168, mov*	150, add	202, add*				
5	154, xor	169, lsl*	172, mov*					
6	160, lsl*	155, lsl	173, lsl*	188, mov*				
7	163, ld_uc2*	158, ld_i	189, lsl*	192, mov*				
8	193, lsl							
9	174, xor*	159, bne	170, add*	164, bgt	166, beq	206, mov*		
10	175, lsl	180, lsl*						
11	183, ld_uc2*	178, ld_i						
12								
13	194, xor*	179, bne	190, add*	184, bgt	186, beq			
14	195, lsl	200, lsl*						
15	198, ld_i	203, ld_uc2*						
16								
17	199, bne	204, bgt	207, add	209, add	208, add	210, bne		
18	211, mov	212, add	213, mov	214, jump				

Figure 7: The most important loop in compress scheduled using general speculation model.

Function	Latency	Function	Latency
Int ALU	1	FP ALU	2
memory load	2	FP multiply	2
memory store	1	FP divide(single-precision)	8
branch	1 / 1 slot	FP divide(double-precision)	15

Table 5: Instruction latencies.

Cache Sizes:	4K - 256K, perfect
Cache Associativity:	direct-mapped, two-set associative
Cache Block Size:	64 bytes with 12 cycle miss latency
Dcache Type:	blocking cache
Dcache Write Policy:	write-through, no write-allocate

Table 6: Cache configurations used in experiments.

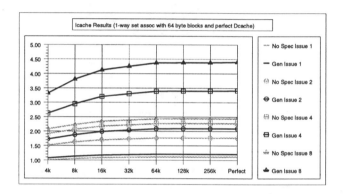

Figure 8: Icache effects for no speculation and general speculation models.

issue superscalar processor with register interlocking. The processor is assumed to have uniform functional units, 1 branch delay slot, and the instruction set of the HP PA-RISC processor. The instruction latencies assumed are those of the HP PA-RISC 7100 (see Table 5). For each machine configuration, the program execution times are derived from execution driven simulations of the benchmarks in Table 4. During the simulations, the issue widths were varied from 1 to 8 based upon the processor model that the code was scheduled for. Dynamic branch prediction was assumed using a 1024 entry direct mapped BTB with a 2 bit counter and a 2 cycle misprediction penalty. A perfect Dcache was used when measuring the Icache effects and a perfect Icache was used when measuring the Dcache effects. The cache configurations used for the experiments are given in Table 6.

4.2 Results

The shear volumes of data produced from the simulations made it impossible to present the individual benchmark results in this paper. In an effort to be more concise, the results presented in the subsequent figures are generated by computing the arithmetic mean of speedups for each speculation model, cache size and issue rate. Speedup was computed by dividing the execution time of the respective benchmark using the no speculation model at issue 1 with a 4K direct mapped Icache and Dcache by the execution time of the same benchmark using the specified speculation model at the specified cache size and issue rate.

Icache Performance Results

Figure 8 shows the performance results for direct mapped caches for the extreme speculation models - no speculation and general speculation. The first thing to observe from this figure is that the curves for the no speculation model show very little change regardless of the issue rate. In particular, there was an increase of only .35 IPC (16.9%) at issue 8 from a 4K to a 64K Icache. In contrast, the curves for the general speculation model showed a noticeable increase from the lower issue rates to the higher issue rates. In particular, their is an increase of .36 IPC (20.9%) at issue 2, .77 IPC (29.3%) at issue 4, and 1.05 IPC (31.5%) at issue 8. Thus, the benefits from larger cache sizes are more pronounced as the issue rate increases. Finally, the performance for all speculation models stabilized with a 64K Icache.

Figure 9 shows the performance results for 2-way set associative caches for no speculation and general speculation models. By comparing this figure to Figure 8, it is clear that there is little advantage in higher associativities with Icaches

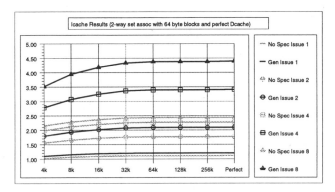

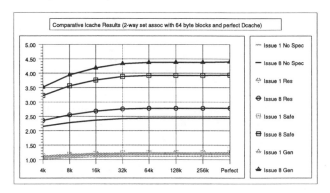

Figure 9: Icache effects for no speculation and general speculation models.

Figure 10: Icache effects for all speculation models at issue 1 and issue 8.

larger than 8K regardless of the issue rate or speculation model. Even at the lowest cache sizes, general speculation was only able to show a 6 percent speedup at 8-issue using 2-way set associative Icaches over direct mapped Icaches.

Figure 10 shows the comparative Icache results for all of the scheduling models at issue-1 and issue-8. As the figure shows, there is no significant performance advantage in using any of the aggressive speculation models for a single issue processor. Since only one instruction can be issued per cycle, the only potential slots that can be filled in the schedules of the integer benchmarks are branch and load delay slots. Therefore, there is very little opportunity to improve the performance of the benchmarks through more aggressive speculation. As a result of little speculation, only minor Icache effects are observed.

In contrast to the single issue performance, there is a clear advantage in using more aggressive speculation models at 8-issue. The no speculation model shows a 13.1 percent improvement between 4K and 64K Icaches. The restricted speculation model shows an 18.0 percent improvement, the safe speculation model shows 21.4 percent improvement and the general speculation model shows a 24.5 percent improvement over the same cache configurations. Thus, while the cache size was only a minor impediment to performance with lower issue rates, it is clearly a larger impediment to performance with higher issue rates for more aggressive speculation models. However, this set of benchmarks were not able to benefit from Icaches larger than 64K.

One additional point should be noted from the 8-issue results shown in Figures 10. The most aggressive speculation model's performance ranged from only 8.9 to 11.8 percent higher than safe speculation. Thus, safe speculation has great potential since it requires no special processor support that could potentially lead to slower clock rates. Also, it introduces none of the risks that result from ignoring scheduling errors like general speculation.

Analysis of Icache Results

To more fully understand the performance results, the Icache behavior is broken down in Tables 7 and 8. Table 7 contains the absolute number of read requests and read misses as well as the miss rate for each of the bench-

Benchmark	Read Requests	Read Misses	Miss Rate
008.espresso	412641852	1501759	0.36
022.li	35649513	943031	2.64
023.eqntott	1027576863	761471	0.07
026.compress	78221684	1716563	2.19
072.sc	72122569	1132815	1.57
cccp	3094004	37823	1.22
cmp	2198695	35	0.01
eqn	32813682	1508122	4.60
grep	1580207	2078	0.13
lex	46035584	208868	0.45
qsort	70546739	4041	0.01
tbl	2603306	45092	1.73
wc	1630199	35	0.01
yacc	43309632	350120	0.83
Average	130716038	586561	1.13

Table 7: Icache Access and Miss Rates at Issue 1 (direct mapped cache).

marks in the base case. The numbers from Table 8 represent the read requests and read misses as a percentage of the totals presented in the final row of Table 7. As Table 8 shows, the more aggressive speculation models tend to reduce the number of Icache read requests. This can be justified by understanding how the simulator's fetch model works. The fetch model fills buffers equivalent to twice the issue rate of the processor in an effort to provide the processor with the issue-width number of instructions at each cycle. Thus, each cycle, the fetch unit fetches a block of instructions to fill the fetch buffer. Any instructions that cannot be placed into the fetch buffer will be discarded and potentially fetched again the next cycle. Since the more aggressive speculation models have more independent instructions each cycle to choose from, the compiler is better able to group independent instructions together and reduce interlock. As such, more instructions can be issued each cycle, which reduces the need to re-fetch the same cache block repeatedly.

As Table 8 shows, even though the number of read requests decreased, the absolute miss rates increased for both 4K and 64K from the least aggressive speculation models to the most aggressive speculation models. In particular, there was a 1 percent increase in the miss rate from no speculation to general speculation. There was practically no change in the Icache miss rates with 64K Icaches since the Icache was sufficiently large to hold the working set for all speculation

Speculation Model	4K Caches			64K Caches		
	Read Req	Read Misses	Miss Rate	Read Req	Read Misses	Miss Rate
None	0.426	0.779	0.82	0.456	0.172	0.17
Restricted	0.379	0.848	1.00	0.401	0.176	0.20
Safe	0.286	0.841	1.32	0.300	0.173	0.26
General	0.255	1.068	1.88	0.265	0.176	0.30

Table 8: Average Icache Access and Miss Rates at Issue 8 (2-way set associative cache).

Icache Block	No Speculation Misses	General Percolation Misses	General Percolation - No Speculation	Percent Change
1	2003	1980	-23	-0.01
2	3408	2486	-922	-27.05
3	2323	6952	4629	199.27
4	3227	1334	-1893	-58.66
Total	10961	12752	1791	16.34

Table 9: Icache Misses for the no speculation and general speculation models of the cccp loop example at Issue 8 (2-way set associative, 4K Icache).

models. While the miss rates for general speculation at 8-issue with a 64K cache is only 1.5 percent lower then the miss rate with a 4K cache, the performance was 24.5 percent higher. Thus, even a small increase in the miss rate can significantly impact the performance for the more aggressive speculation models. The impact on performance would be even more pronounced if the cache miss latency was greater than the simulated 12 cycles.

The cccp loop example shown in Tables 4 and 5 can be used to illustrate the reasons for the increase in the miss rate with the 4K Icache. Table 9 shows the Icache misses caused by the first instructions in each Icache blocks. The misses caused by the instruction at the start of the loop are represented with Icache block 1. There was only a negligible difference in the miss rates for the two speculation models in this block. Icache blocks 2 and 4 decreased their cache misses from the no speculation model to the general speculation model. Icache block 3 showed a significant increase in Icaches misses. Most of these misses can be attributed to migration of the misses from Icache blocks 2 and 4 to Icache block 3 due to the small 4K Icache. However, even after considering the migration of misses, there was an overall increase in misses for the loop by 16.34 percent which is attributable to the additional Icache block before the frequently taken branch number 59 in the Icache layout for the general speculation model.

Dcache Performance Results

Figure 11 shows the performance results for direct mapped Dcaches for the extreme speculation models. The first thing to observe from this figure is that the curves for the no speculation model show a much smaller increase in performance than general speculation at the same issue rates. In particular, there was an increase of only .51 IPC (27.5%) at issue 8 from a 4K to a 64K Dcache while the general speculation model showed an increase of 1.32 IPC (45.4 %). In contrast to the Icache results, the performance for general speculation model still demonstrates a noticeable

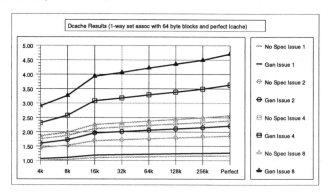

Figure 11: Dcache effects for no speculation and general speculation models.

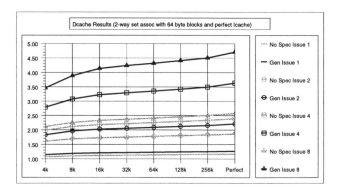

Figure 12: Dcache effects for no speculation and general speculation models.

improvement with Dcache sizes larger than 64K.

Figure 12 shows the performance results for 2-way set associative Dcaches for no speculation and general speculation models. By comparing this figure to Figure 11, it is clear that higher associativity significantly benefits the smaller Dcaches. In particular, general speculation showed a 19 percent improvement in performance at 8-issue for a 2-way set associative 4K Dcache over a direct mapped 4K Dcache. The no speculation model showed a 14 percent improvement in performance at the same cache configurations. Both speculation models showed some performance improvement with higher associativity when using Dcaches as large as 128K. Thus, higher associativity can be better used to offset the limitations of smaller Dcaches than the smaller Icaches.

Figure 13 shows the comparative Dcache results for all of the scheduling models at issue 1 and issue 8. As the figure shows, there is no significant performance advantage in using any of the aggressive speculation models for a single issue processor. However, at issue 8, there is a clear advantage in using the more aggressive speculation models. An increase in the Dcache size from 4K to 64K using the no speculation model resulted in a performance improvement of 13.8 percent while the restricted speculation model showed an increase of 16.3 percent. Safe speculation increased per-

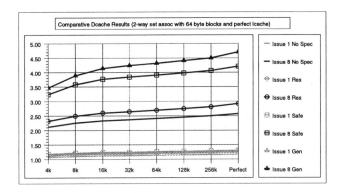

Figure 13: Dcache effects for all speculation models at issue 1 and issue 8.

Benchmark	Read Requests	Read Misses	Miss Rate
008.espresso	81609167	8517176	10.44
022.li	8059907	732281	9.09
023.eqntott	193278137	14396275	7.45
026.compress	9626725	3520353	36.57
072.sc	14788900	2094508	14.16
cccp	422760	21996	5.20
cmp	436248	163749	37.54
eqn	4343317	769148	17.48
grep	239327	2885	1.21
lex	7862729	314967	4.01
qsort	12206746	734301	6.02
tbl	548733	33554	6.11
wc	141527	2635	1.86
yacc	7488032	677821	9.05
Average	24382304	2284404	11.87

Table 10: Dcache Access and Miss Rates at Issue 1 (direct mapped cache).

formance by 20.6 percent and general speculation increased performance by 24.6 percent over the same region. While there was no performance advantage from increasing the Icache beyond 64K, this was not the case with the Dcache. The no speculation model improved its performance to 21.5 percent higher than 4K with perfect Dcaches. Restricted speculation improved to 26.2 percent higher than 4K. Safe speculation improved to 30.1 percent higher and general speculation improved to 35.9 percent higher. Thus, small Dcaches have been shown to be a significant impediment to the potential performance of more aggressive speculation models at higher issue rates.

Analysis of Dcache Results

To more fully understand the performance results, the Dcache behavior is broken down in Tables 10 and 11. Table 10 contains the absolute number of read requests and read misses as well as the miss rate for each of the benchmarks in the base case. The numbers from Table 11 represent the read requests and read misses as a percentage of the totals presented in the final row of Table 10. Table 11 shows that the Dcache accesses increase with the more aggressive speculation models. This is caused by an increase in the working set size resulting from speculation of additional load instructions.

The decrease in the miss rate from the less aggressive to the more aggressive speculation models is miss-leading since

Speculation Model	4K Caches			64K Caches		
	Read Req	Read Misses	Miss Rate	Read Req	Read Misses	Miss Rate
None	1.008	0.694	6.45	1.009	0.171	1.59
Restricted	1.017	0.712	6.56	1.019	0.181	1.66
Safe	1.143	0.725	5.94	1.145	0.173	1.41
General	1.313	0.776	5.54	1.315	0.193	1.38

Table 11: Average Dcache Accesses and Miss Rates at Issue 8 (2-way set associative cache).

Load Instr	No Spec. Misses	General Spec. Misses	General Spec. - No Spec.	Percent Change
158	124951	133596	8645	6.92
163	82058	132654	50596	61.65
165	1641	2444	803	48.93
178	84617	92107	7490	8.85
183	47746	91250	43504	91.11
185	890	1685	795	89.33
198	47566	50379	2813	5.91
203	23380	49579	26199	112.06
205	501	2346	1845	368.26

Table 12: Dcache Misses for the no speculation and general speculation models of the compress loop example at Issue 8 (2-way set associative, 4K Dcache).

the read requests have significantly increased. The Dcache misses actually increase from the less aggressive to the more aggressive speculation models. In particular, there was an 11.8 percent increase in the Dcache misses from the no speculation model to the general speculation model with a 4K Dcache and a 12.9 percent increase with a 64K Dcache. The 4.16 percent lower miss rate for general speculation with a 64K Dcache versus a 4K Dcache corresponds to a performance increase of 24.6 percent. Thus, the Dcache size can significantly affect the potential performance of aggressive speculation models.

The compress loop example shown in Tables 6 and 7 can be used to illustrate the reasons for the increases in Dcache misses. Table 12 shows the Dcache misses generated by the load instructions in the no speculation and general speculation codes based upon a 4K Dcache. It can be seen from this data that there were moderate to significant increases in Dcache misses from the no speculation case to the general speculation case. By comparing the increased Dcache miss rates for load instructions 163, 183 and 203 with their respective increases in execution frequency given in Table 3, it is apparent that the increase in miss rates for these loads was not constrained by the their increase in execution frequency. Other speculative loads actually caused further Dcache misses for these loads. In addition, the non-speculated load instructions 158, 178 and 198 also showed an increase in Dcache misses that is attributable to other speculated loads.

5 Conclusions

This paper has presented experimental results for four compiler-controlled speculation models over a variety of issue rates and cache configurations. The results indicate that the more aggressive speculation models create larger instruction and data working sets. As such, processor designers need to ensure that cache configurations can tolerate the increased working set if they expect to attain the *best* performance from aggressive speculation models. These experiments have shown that increasing the Icache and Dcache from 4K to 64K resulted in a performance increase of approximately 26 percent for the general speculation model at issue 8. Additionally, the results indicate that 2-way set associativity beneficially reduces misses for Dcaches up to 128K. In contrast, 2-way set associativity was only beneficial for Icaches up to 8K.

While small Icaches and Dcaches can significantly limit the potential performance of more aggressive speculation models, there is still an advantage in using the more aggressive speculation models at higher issue rates even if the cache configuration is held constant. Even though some of the potential advantages of the more aggressive speculation models are negated by the higher miss rates, it was not sufficient to offset the performance advantages. In particular, general speculation at issue 8 was 63.6 percent faster than no speculation with the same 4K cache configuration and issue rate. Safe speculation was 50.2 percent faster and restricted was 9.6 percent faster. When using a 64K cache, general speculation was 80 percent faster than no speculation. Safe speculation was 61.1 percent faster and restricted speculation was 14.3 percent faster. The improvements in performance were almost identical for the experiments that used a perfect Icache and varied the Dcache as those that used a perfect Dcache and varied the Icache. Thus, aggressive speculation effects the Icache and the Dcache in a similar fashion.

Acknowledgements

The authors would like to thank all members of the IMPACT research group for their comments and suggestions. This research has been supported by the National Science Foundation (NSF) under grant MIP-9308013, Joint Services Engineering Programs (JSEP) under Contract N00014-90-J-1270, Intel Corporation, the AMD 29K Advanced Processor Development Division, Hewlett-Packard, SUN Microsystems, NCR and the National Aeronautics and Space Administration (NASA) under Contract NASA NAG 1-613 in cooperation with the Illinois Computer laboratory for Aerospace Systems and Software (ICLASS).

References

[1] T. Cormen, C. Leiserson, and R. Rivest, *Introduction to Algorithms*. New York, NY: McGraw-Hill, 1991.

[2] P. P. Chang, S. A. Mahlke, W. Y. Chen, N. J. Warter, and W. W. Hwu, "IMPACT: An architectural framework for multiple-instruction-issue processors," in *Proceedings of the 18th International Symposium on Computer Architecture*, pp. 266–275, May 1991.

[3] E. M. Riseman and C. C. Foster, "The inhibition of potential parallelism by conditional jumps," *IEEE Transactions on Computers*, vol. c-21, pp. 1405–1411, December 1972.

[4] M. D. Smith, M. Johnson, and M. A. Horowitz, "Limits on multiple instruction issue," in *Proceedings of the 3rd International Conference on Architectural Support for Programming Languages and Operating Systems*, pp. 290–302, April 1989.

[5] J. A. Fisher, "Trace scheduling: A technique for global microcode compaction," *IEEE Transactions on Computers*, vol. c-30, pp. 478–490, July 1981.

[6] W. W. Hwu, S. A. Mahlke, W. Y. Chen, P. P. Chang, N. J. Warter, R. A. Bringmann, R. G. Ouellette, R. E. Hank, T. Kiyohara, G. E. Haab, J. G. Holm, and D. M. Lavery, "The Superblock: An effective technique for VLIW and superscalar compilation," *Journal of Supercomputing*, vol. 7, pp. 229–248, January 1993.

[7] M. D. Smith, M. A. Horowitz, and M. S. Lam, "Efficient superscalar performance through boosting," in *Proceedings of the Fifth International Conference on Architecture Support for Programming Languages and Operating Systems (ASPLOS-V)*, pp. 248–259, October 1992.

[8] S. A. Mahlke, W. Y. Chen, R. A. Bringmann, R. E. Hank, W. W. Hwu, B. R. Rau, and M. S. Schlansker, "Sentinel scheduling: A model for compiler-controlled speculative execution," *Transactions on Computer Systems*, vol. 11, November 1993.

[9] R. A. Bringmann, S. A. Mahlke, R. E. Hank, J. C. Gyllenhaal, and W. W. Hwu, "Speculative execution exception recovery using write-back suppression," in *Proceedings of 26th Annual International Symposium on Microarchitecture*, December 1993.

[10] R. A. Bringmann, "Determining instructions that are safe to speculate at compile-time," tech. rep., Center for Reliable and High-Performance Computing, University of Illinois, Urbana, IL, May 1994.

[11] R. P. Colwell, R. P. Nix, J. J. O'Donnell, D. B. Papworth, and P. K. Rodman, "A VLIW architecture for a trace scheduling compiler," in *Proceedings of the 2nd International Conference on Architectural Support for Programming Languages and Operating Systems*, pp. 180–192, April 1987.

[12] J. C. Dehnert and R. A. Towle, "Compiling for the cydra 5," *Journal of Supercomputing*, vol. 7, pp. 181–227, January 1993.

[13] H. Packard, *PA-RISC 1.1 Architecture and Instruction Set Reference Manual*. Cupertino, CA, 1990.

Commercializing Profile-Driven Optimization

J. Stan Cox*   David P. Howell*   Thomas M. Conte[†]

*Database and Compiler Technology   [†]Department of Electrical and Computer Engineering
AT&T Global Information Solutions   University of South Carolina
Columbia, South Carolina 29170   Columbia, South Carolina 29205

Abstract

There are a broad selection of code-improving optimizations and scheduling techniques based on profile information. Industry has been slow to productize these because traditional ways of profiling are cumbersome. Profiling slows down the execution of a program by factors of 2 to 30 times. Software vendors must compile, profile, and then re-compile their products. In addition, profiling requires a representative set of inputs and is hard to validate. Finally, profiling has had little success for system code such as kernel and I/O drivers.

This paper discusses experiences AT&T Global Information Solutions has had with commercializing profile-driven optimizations. Three approaches to profiling are discussed, along with results and comments concerning their advantages and drawbacks. The validity of profiling is discussed. One new innovation, hardware-based profiling, removes many of the problems vendors have with profiling. The paper also discusses methods to profile system code and support debugging. In general, the data and techniques presented in this paper can be used to productize profiling and advocate its use to the software business community.

1   Introduction

Advanced compilers perform optimizations across block boundaries to increase instruction level parallelism, enhance resource usage and improve cache performance. Many of these methods, such as trace scheduling [1],[2] superblock scheduling [3] and software pipelining [4] either rely on or can benefit from information about dynamic program behavior. For example, traditional optimizations enhance performance by an additional 15% when combined with profile-driven superblock formation [3]. Other examples include data preloading [5], improved function

in-lining [6], and improved instruction cache performance [8].

There are several drawbacks to profile-driven optimizations. Many of the techniques can result in code size explosion if they are performed too aggressively. Dynamic basic block execution frequencies can be used to reduce this phenomenon. More problematic is the task of profiling itself. Obtaining profile data through software methods can be complex and time consuming, requiring additional steps in the development process. The usual method employed is a compile-run-recompile sequence. First, the program is compiled with profiling probes placed within each basic block. The program is then run using several representative test inputs. The resulting profile data is used to drive a profile-based compilation of the original program.

Execution of the profiled version of the program is slow. With some methods, the profiled version runs 30 times slower than the optimized program. In addition it is difficult to choose and validate the test inputs used for profiling [9],[10]. Even given the obvious performance advantages, software vendors are hesitant to use profile-driven optimizations due to the added complexity of development, maintenance, support, and debugging.

Static estimation solves some of the problems related to gathering profile data [11]. However, these techniques are not as accurate as profiling [9],[10]. When used for superblock scheduling, static estimates achieve approximately 50% of the speedup that profiling can achieve [7]. In addition to this, static estimation cannot capture highly data-dependent branches, limiting the acceptance of this approach by software vendors.

AT&T Global Information Solutions is a server system company. Our key applications are third-party database products. Many of the published solutions to profiling's problems do not apply to our business. This paper discusses the how our profiling techniques evolved based on our experiences with third-party vendors. Several profiling techniques are presented and compared, along with our approach to commercializing profile-driven optimization.

2 Profiling Techniques

Techniques for implementing profiling often trade accuracy for profiled code speed. We started with highly accurate techniques, explored less-accurate methods, and gained experience in the advantages and disadvantages of each approach.

2.1 Probe-based profiling

Our first attempt at basic block profiling used the technique of gathering a trace of basic block id tokens, and then interpreting the trace and counting the transitions made between the basic blocks. In this technique, the transition data is written out to a data file organized by modules, functions in each module, and basic blocks in functions with transitions to other basic blocks and corresponding counts. The trace contains *handle* tokens and basic block tokens. To fully qualify a basic block requires a *handle* that holds string pointers to the module name and function name for the block, followed by a block number token. The handles and block tokens both use 32 bit containers. To differentiate them, the basic block numbers use the bottom 16 bits with the upper set to zero, and handles use the full 32 bits with the upper 16 always non-zero.

To shorten the trace, a handle is only generated if a transition out of the function is made, otherwise a stream of basic block number tokens are generated. For example, consider Figure 1. If the execution tran-

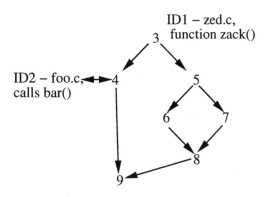

Figure 1: Probe-based profiling example.

sitions from blocks **3** to **4**, calls function `bar()`, returns to **4**, and then goes onto **9**, this results in the trace: **ID1, 3, 4, ID2, ..., ID1, 4, 9**. This is

then converted on-the-fly into a basic block transition count tree structure, shown in Figure 2. The profile

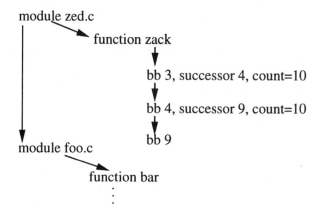

Figure 2: Transition count tree structure.

data file follows the same structure as the transition count tree, threaded with module pointers.

We designed the profile-driven optimizations around basic block transition count statistics since we felt that this was an accurate method for determining the behavior of an application for later optimization. A design goal of the profiling scheme was to provide flexibility of information collection and processing. To that end, either a trace or the summerized basic block transition count can be generated by switching the profile data handling library and relinking. Due to the size of the unprocessed trace, the transition count form of the profile data is used for the optimizer.

The optimizer reads in the profile data after building the flow graph for the program and correlates it with each node and node successor in the flow graph. Optimizations are then driven using the weighted basic blocks.

The primary weakness of this technique is the run time overhead incurred for profiling (about 26× on average, measured using SPECint92 benchmarks– see Section 2.5 below for the full data). Another major weakness is the inaccurate conversion from the trace to transition counts due to asynchronous events. These events include signal handlers, interrupts, and thread managers. This especially limits the optimizer's use of the profile data and forces the invalidation of the profile data for functions where it occurs. Many of our applications have high amounts of I/O, and this presented a major problem. This profiling scheme is also unacceptable for several key applications where asynchronous flow changes are common, like the Unix kernel and applications that use threads packages. We did manage to gather good profile data for these applications, but not without significant modifications to the profiling and application code.

Another problem is skewed program results due to the overhead of performing profiling. The few applications we tried to optimize with profile data didn't realize the full potential of profile-driven optimization due to timing impacts of profiling overhead.

We were able to successfully profile major commercial database products, with no change to the profiling implementation or application. The results of optimization using this data was very promising. This supplied the motivation to develop other profiling schemes with less shortcomings.

2.2 Node-based profiling

Node-based profiling is used in other commercial compilers that we have evaluated. In this technique, every basic block entrance is recorded by incrementing a counter, with one unique counter per block. A database that represents the program's control flow graph is generated by the compiler. Once the profiled program is run, the database with counts is read in by the optimizer to weigh each node in the flow graph and optimize accordingly.

While quick and effective, the node-based technique has some problems. The most-notable problem is the lack of block-to-block transition information. Counting the basic block transitions would give us a more accurate representation of the behavior of the program and weighting of the flow graph for optimization. Although transition counts can be approximated from the block counts, we found that more accuracy was required.

2.3 Arc-based profiling

The arc-based profiling approach counts the *dynamic transitions* between basic blocks during execution. This is similar to the node based approach except that the arc transitions are counted, instead of the block entrances themselves. To achieve this profiling technique, the compiler places probe instructions into the program that count each block transition. As in the node based approach the probe is simply a sequence of instructions which increment the corresponding element in the static table. For each basic block, if it has only one successor block, then the probe can be placed in the block. If the block has multiple successors, then the probe can be placed in a successor if the successor's only predecessor is the block. For each case where the block has multiple successors and a successor has multiple predecessors, a new block has to built and placed between the block and the given successor.

Table 1: Static control flow graph statistics for SPECint92 and arc-based profiling.

Benchmark	blocks	transitions	addional trans. blocks
compress	356	511 (144%)	118 (+33%)
eqntott	1032	1529 (148%)	482 (+47%)
espresso	6134	8791 (143%)	2803 (+46%)
gcc	22282	34633 (155%)	13199 (+59%)
li	2106	2819 (134%)	1026 (+49%)
sc	3029	4652 (154%)	1375 (+45%)
avg.	5823	8823 (152%)	3167 (+54%)

Table 1 shows the static number of basic blocks, block-to-block transitions, and additional transition blocks required for arc-based profiling for the SPECint92 benchmarks. Surprisingly, the average number of transitions is only approximately 1.5 times the number of blocks. Furthermore, the number of transition blocks that have to be added for this profiling approach is not excessive (an increase of 54% in the number of blocks). This makes the arc-based scheme an efficient and accurate method to perform basic block profiling. Unlike the node counting approach, the arc based approach is completely accurate. This accuracy is obtained by requiring a slightly larger static table. In addition, arc-based profiling has a slightly larger increase in run-time slowdown over node-based profiling. One minus is some post-processing is required to extract node weights from the arc-based profile information.

2.4 Hardware-based profiling

One significant revelation for us was that the entire information needed for the arc-based approach was already maintained inside the branch-target-buffer (BTB) of our processor. The BTB is indexed by the address of each branch and stores the most-recent target address of the branch. Thus, each entry in the BTB comprises a (source address, destination address)-pair, which is easily translated to identify specific arcs. In addition to this, the prediction information maintained is an approximate count of the number of times the arc was executed, although some post-processing is required.

Hardware-based profiling can be used with existing processors by exploiting BIST scan paths or performance monitoring features. The accuracy of the scheme is not as high as probe-based or arc-based profiling, since the BTB must be sampled. This is discussed in depth in [15]. One reason for the error is that short-lived arcs are not well represented in the sampled data. However, they comprise the less-frequently executed transitions in the program. The error is quantified in the following section.

2.5 Comparisons

The slowdown of each profiling technique for SPECint92 is shown in Table 2. Clearly, probe-based profiling is the worst, exceeding 37× for *espresso*. Node-based and arc-based profiling are relatively close, with arc-based profiling nearly as fast. Hardware-based profiling is by far the fastest, with two benchmarks showing no appreciable slowdown whatsoever.

Table 2: Slowdown of the profiling techniques.

Benchmark	probe	node	arc	hw
compress	14.2	1.36	1.71	1.03
espresso	37.2	1.51	1.56	1.05
eqntott	28.4	1.71	1.79	1.01
gcc	25.4	1.79	1.83	1.03
li	33.1	1.21	1.27	1.00
sc	19.6	1.31	1.32	1.00

The accuracy of the four techniques differ. In the absence of asynchronous events, probe-based profiling and arc-based profiling are perfectly accurate. In the presence of such events, arc-based profiling has superior accuracy. Node-based profiling is much less accurate than either probe- or arc-based because it does not fully model transitions between blocks. Hardware-based profiling is inaccurate, but for a different reason: it is forced to sample the execution instead of processing a full trace of all transitions. Nevertheless, the near-zero slowdown of the hardware technique allows it to be used in ways that the other techniques cannot. For example, it can be used without the users' knowledge– allowing an application to be installed for some period of time then later retrieved. Once retrieved, its accumulated profile data can be used to re-optimize the code based on actual usage.

Validation of hardware profiling is done by comparing traditionally-generated profiles (*actual profiles*) to hardware-generated profiles (*estimated profiles*). One method for this is to perform *trace selection* on both the actual and the estimated profiles and compare the results. An example of trace selection is illustrated in Figure 3. Graph (a) is annotated with the actual profile information, whereas graph (b) is the hardware-generated profile. Traces are formed using an arc

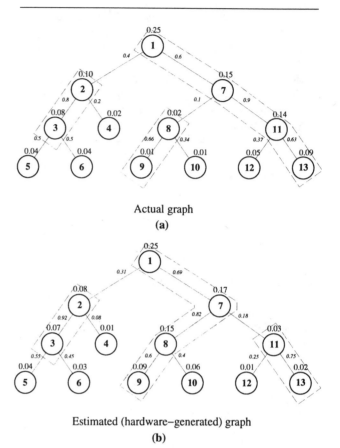

Actual graph
(a)

Estimated (hardware–generated) graph
(b)

Figure 3: Trace selection example.

trace selection threshold of 60% to group blocks [14]. Code explosion is avoided by not extending traces to blocks with low weights. This is also implemented as a threshold. Threshold values of 0.1%, 1%, 3% and 5% are considered below. The lower this threshold, the larger the code size of the generated executable, since additional patch-up code is required when instructions are moved inside a trace.

The metric for trace selection error is introduced using the example of Figure 3. In the actual graph (graph (a)), basic blocks **1**, **7**, **11** and **13** are grouped together to form a trace. Due to errors in the weights of outgoing arcs for block **7**, the blocks **1**, **7**, **8** and **9** are grouped to form a trace in the estimated graph. The error for block **7** is due to the difference in arc weights between the two graphs. The transition from block **7** to **8** will occur $0.15 \times 0.1 = 1.5\%$ of the total execution time. Similarly, the transition from **7** to **11** will occur $0.15 \times 0.9 = 13.5\%$ of the time. (Since the actual graph contains the real execution frequencies of the program, these frequencies are used.) Hence, the transition from **7** to **11** occupies a higher percentage of the total execution. The trace in graph (b) incorrectly assumes the transition of **7** to **8** is more likely. This assumption is wrong for $13.5\% - 1.5\% = 12\%$ of the execution. The figure of 12% is therefore the percentage of execution time that the incorrect trace membership will be exercised. In general, the trace selection error is the total percentage of execution time that incorrect trace membership is exercised due to errors in the estimated profile. Table 3 presents the trace selection error for the SPECint92 benchmarks.

The worst-case error is for *espresso* with a very relaxed cutoff threshold of 0.1%. The 18.49% in Table 3 is the amount of program execution where the trace selection would differ. Examination of the sources for this error revealed an interesting trend. For example, in *compress* a trace composed of blocks **33-36-37-38** in the actual profile was split into two traces between blocks **36** and **37** in the estimated profile. This occurred because of an error in the estimated arc frequency between blocks **36** and **37**. In this case the weight of this arc was less than the trace selection threshold, preventing the trace to grow beyond block **36**. Such errors in trace selection have the effect of reducing the scope of the profile-based optimizations, which has few detrimental effects.

Another method for comparison is the distribution of arc weight error versus block weights. This metric is useful since it shows where the trace selection error is occurring. The distribution is calculated by computing the maximum differences between the actual and the estimated arc weights for each category of block frequencies. The maximum difference is used in order to avoid over-counting a single error. For example, there is a 4% difference for two arcs with weights 40%/60% (actual) vs. 44%/56% (estimate), not an 8% difference. The distribution of arc weight error provides good insight into the performance of the hardware technique, as is shown in Figure 4.

Two features are evident in the figure. First, the majority of the error is for low-weight blocks. This appeals to intuition, since infrequently-executed branches will be sampled less frequently by the technique. A second feature is the lack of error between block weights of approximately 0.3 and 1.0. This indicates that very heavily-weighted blocks are captured correctly. Even the magnitude of the error for moderately small weights (e.g., 0.001) is small and therefore non-critical ($< 15\%$).

3 Commercialization Issues

The performance advantage obtained with profile driven optimizations are dramatic and have been pre-

sented in several papers [1],[2],[3],[4],[5],[6],[8]. Software vendors and developers of complex applications are, however, hesitant to use profile-driven optimizations. Their concerns vary, but usually involve the worry that the optimizations may not improve the performance of the application for all input sets, or could actually slow their application down for differing input sets. Developers are also uneasy about what input sets to choose for profiling. Current research suggests however that these concerns not critical. In particular, profile-driven optimizations improve program performance for all inputs.

Hwu, *et al.* [12] reported that with profiling they were able to obtain branch prediction accuracy comparable with much more expensive hardware mechanisms. They also report that 98% of the advantage of prediction was preserved across runs with varying input sets.

More research in this area was performed by Fisher and Freudenberger [9] and Wall [10]. Fisher and Freudenberger reported that "...*even code with a complex flow of control, including system utilities and language processors written in C, are dominated by branches which go in one way, and that this direction usually varies little when one changes the data used as the predictor and target.*"

Their experiments compared a run of an optimized application using an input from the profiling input set versus a run using an input not in the profiling set. Their data showed an application using an input not in the profiling set can expect to achieve 75% or more of the benefit obtained from the ideal case. Fisher and Freudenberger reported that branch prediction *"can be done almost as well as is possible by taking previous runs of a program, and using those runs to make decisions about which way branches will go in future runs."* Similarly, Wall concluded that profiles used to predict program behavior for different run characteristics might not do as well, but was *"often quit close, however and was usually at lease half as good."* Wall's data backs up Fisher's results of 75% of the benefit of use a "perfect" or identical data set run for runs with differing input.

The examples and conclusions above are further supported by work which is on-going at the University of Illinois. In [3], the different inputs were used to profile from the ones used to measure performance. Good performance benefits were sustained across these inputs. In [13], the same type of experiments were performed for superscalar processors. Again, profile-driven optimizations with different inputs from the profiling run sustained good results.

If the hardware-based profiling approach is used, the problem of input set selection is removed. This

Table 3: Hardware profiling - trace selection error (percent).

Benchmark	Trace selection error			
	Threshold: 0.1%	Threshold: 1%	Threshold: 3%	Threshold: 5%
espresso	18.49	5.51	0.02	0
xlisp	8.51	2.30	0	0
eqntott	3.66	3.64	3.64	0
compress	11.92	10.89	2.65	2.65
sc	3.46	1.14	0	0
gcc	5.99	0	0	0

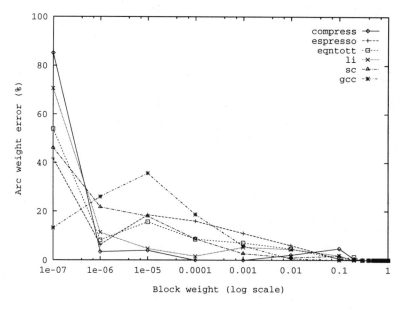

Figure 4: Distribution of arc weight error for hardware profiling.

is a direct consequence of the speed of this approach, which has a nearly imperceptible slowdown. Using hardware-based profiling, the application can be beta tested in a "real-world" environment and thus is exercised as it would be once released. The collected profile information would accurately capture the actual usage characteristics of the application. This approach is also more effective for real-time and other time-based applications.

3.1 Support

Another point of concern which prevents vendors from using profile-driven optimizations is the added effort for support. Gathering profile data to use for optimization is a time consuming process but is easily justifiable given the benefits obtained. Unlike the SPEC92 benchmarks, real applications' source code changes over time due to bug fixes and feature enhancements. These changes can in turn invalidate profile data that has been gathered for the application.

Software vendors are justifiably unwilling to reprofile an entire application for each bug fix and code change over the lifetime of an application release. On the other hand, software vendors cannot allow the performance of an application to decline over time because of code changes which invalidate profile data.

To alleviate this problem, it is important that the compiler invalidate profile data at the function or block level. If the profile data used is based on source lines and module names in the application, then a single bug fix can invalidate the profile data for an entire module. This is clearly unacceptable. The profile data should not be based on source line numbers and should invalidate only those functions that have changed due to a code change. Furthermore, it is easy for the compiler, based on the given profile data, to warn the developer when a frequently executed or "hot" function has been invalidated due to a source change. This profile set is then used by the compiler to optimize over the lifetime of the release. If code changes are made, only the functions involved will have their profile data invalidated. The compiler will warn when a "hot" functions profile data is no longer valid, and only in this case will the process of profiling be repeated.

3.2 Debugging

Debugging is also a major concern for software vendors. Relating assembly code back to source code seems to be a major concern. This is hard to do in the presence of the block-reordering optimizations performed by our compiler.

To address these issues and to enable additional tools to be written to utilize the basic block data, we have implemented a basic block table that describes each basic block in an application. Profiling is done using references to a basic block transition table, where each table slot is a (from, to) pair of indices to basic block entries that represent a transition between two basic blocks. A simple counter for each transition represents the profile data counts for the transition.

The basic block table entries carry the basic block handle which gives the module name and function name, the block number, the start text address, its size, and the start source line number. An entry is created each time that the compiler builds a basic block. Likewise, every time a block ends, a transition table entry is generated to its successors, and probes are inserted. Blocks and transition table entries from modules are appended together by the linker when an executable is built.

This structure enables a number of debugging and profiling tools. For example, an application that has been optimized will have very little correlation back to the source code due to block rearrangement. The basic block table can be used to look up the block number (each table entry has a start address and size) and display the source module, function, and line number where the block starts. This enables source level debugging for block-reorganized code.

Profiling tools can also make use of the basic block and transition to show program hot spots and hot paths. The transition counts can be correlated with the block counts to show hot basic blocks, or to show execution coverage of a set of blocks, which can then be related back to the source using the basic block table. The transition table, which is really a flattened flow graph, can be used to show the hot program traces or to show weighted arcs between blocks with a hypertext-type tool. These tools help developers realize the best performance from their applications and are an added benefit of profiling technology.

4 Concluding Remarks

Profile-driven optimizations have untapped potential for improving commercial application performance. Much of this is due to skepticism from software vendors based primarily on profiling input set selection, profiling performance, and problems with debugging and support.

We have implemented the major profiling approaches at AT&T Global Information Solutions and evaluated their tradeoffs. Several techniques have clear advantages over the others. Where before the overhead and intrusiveness of our original profiling made it impossible to profile the full Unix kernel, the new arc- and hardware-based implementations have made kernel profiling practical. Multithreading issues are also resolved by the new implementation as arc counts can represent any kernel process (or processor).

In terms of slowdown, arc-based profiling is nearly as fast as node-based profiling, yet more accurate. In addition, it handles asynchronous events such as interrupts and thread managers. Hardware-based is best for speed, allowing a new style of profiling where the program is installed and profiled unbeknownst to the users, then later collected and recompiled. This technique has been well-received by practicing database engineers.

5 Acknowledgements

Thanks to Marv Graham, Lorraine Lee and Linda Gray (of AT&T Global Information Solutions), and Burzin Patel (graduate student at South Carolina) for comments, suggestions and support.

References

[1] J. A. Fisher, "Trace scheduling: A technique for global microcode compaction," *IEEE Trans. Comput.*, vol. C-30, no. 7, pp. 478–490, July 1981.

[2] J. R. Ellis, *Bulldog: A compiler for VLIW architectures.* Cambridge, MA: The MIT Press, 1986.

[3] P. P. Chang, S. A. Mahlke, and W. W. Hwu, "Using profile information to assist classic code optimizations," *Software–Practice and Experience*, vol. 21, pp. 1301–1321, Dec. 1991.

[4] B. R. Rau and C. D. Glaeser, "Some scheduling techniques and an easily schedulable horizontal architecture for high performance scientific computing," in *Proc. 14th Annual Workshop on Microprogramming*, pp. 183–198, Nov. 1981.

[5] W. Y. Chen, *Data preload for superscalar and VLIW processors.* PhD thesis, Dept. of Electrical and Computer Engineering, University of Illinois, Urbana-Champaign, IL, 1993.

[6] W. W. Hwu and P. P. Chang, "Inline function expansion for compiling C programs," in *Proc. ACM SIGPLAN '89 Conference on Programming Language Design and Implementation*, (Portland, OR), June 1989.

[7] R. E. Hank, S. A. Mahlke, J. C. Gyllenhaal, R. Bringmann, and W. W. Hwu, "Superblock formation using static program analysis," in *Proc. 26th Ann. Int'l. Symp. on Microarchitecture*, (Austin, TX), pp. 247–255, Dec. 1993.

[8] W. W. Hwu and P. P. Chang, "Achieving high instruction cache performance with an optimizing compiler," in *Proc. 16th Ann. International Symposium Computer Architecture*, (Jerusalem, Israel), pp. 242–251, May 1989.

[9] J. A. Fisher and S. M. Freudenberger, "Predicting conditional branch directions from previous runs of a program," in *Proc. 5th Int'l. Conf. on Architectural Support for Prog. Lang. and Operating Systems*, (Boston, MA), pp. 85–95, Oct. 1992.

[10] D. Wall, "Predicting program behavior using real or estimated profiles," in *Proc. ACM SIGPLAN '91 Conference on Programming Language Design and Implementation*, (Toronto, Ontario, Canada), pp. 59–70, June 1991.

[11] T. Ball and J. R. Larus, "Branch prediction for free," in *Proceedings of the ACM SIGPLAN '93 Conference on Programming Language Design and Implementation*, pp. 300–313, June 1993.

[12] W. W. Hwu, T. M. Conte, and P. P. Chang, "Comparing software and hardware schemes for reducing the cost of branches," in *Proc. 16th Ann. International Symposium Computer Architecture*, (Jerusalem, Israel), pp. 224–233, May 1989.

[13] W. W. Hwu, *et al.* "The superblock: An effective structure for VLIW and superscalar compilation," *Journal of Supercomputing*, pp. 229–248, July 1993.

[14] W. W. Hwu and P. P. Chang, "Trace selection for compiling large C application programs to microcode," in *Proc. 21st Ann. Workshop on Microprogramming and Microarchitectures*, (San Diego, CA.), Nov. 1988.

[15] T. M. Conte, B. A. Patel, and J. S. Cox, "Using branch handling hardware to support profile-driven optimization," in *Proceedings of the 27th Annual International Symposium on Microarchitecture*, (San Jose, CA), Dec. 1994.

A Comparative Evaluation of Software Techniques to Hide Memory Latency

Lizy Kurian John and Vinod Reddy
Department of Computer Science and Engineering
University of South Florida
Tampa, FL 33620

Paul T. Hulina and Lee D. Coraor
Department of Computer Science and Engineering
The Pennsylvania State University
University Park, PA 16802

Abstract

Software oriented techniques to hide memory latency in superscalar and superpipelined machines include loop unrolling, software pipelining, and software cache prefetching. Issuing the data fetch request prior to actual need for data allows overlap of accessing with useful computations. Loop unrolling and software pipelining do not necessitate microarchitecture or instruction set architecture changes, whereas software controlled prefetching does. While studies on the benefits of the individual techniques have been done, no study evaluates all of these techniques within a consistent framework. This paper attempts to remedy this by providing a comparative evaluation of the features and benefits of the techniques. Loop unrolling and static scheduling of loads is seen to produce significant improvement in performance at lower latencies. Software pipelining is observed to be better than software controlled prefetching at lower latencies, but at higher latencies, software prefetching outperforms software pipelining. Aggressive prefetching beyond conditional branches can detrimentally affect performance by increasing the memory bandwidth requirements and bus traffic.

Keywords: Compiler Optimization, Data Prefetching, Loop Unrolling, Memory Latency, Software Cache Prefetching, Software Pipelining, Static Scheduling.

1 Introduction

Processor speeds have increased tremendously in the past few years, but memory systems have barely kept pace, widening the speed disparity between processors and memory systems. Several software and architectural techniques have been proposed in the past to hide and/or decrease memory access times by prefetching data and overlapping access delays with useful computations. Loop unrolling and static scheduling within the large loop, software pipelining [15] [5] [7], software controlled prefetching [20] [8] [12] [2] [4] [18] [23], lock-up free caches and non-blocking loads [13], hardware cache prefetching [10] [3], etc. are techniques aimed at overlapping accessing with computations and hiding memory access delays. In this paper, we consider three primarily software techniques to hide latency (i) loop unrolling and static scheduling within the unrolled loop (ii) software pipelining and (iii) software cache prefetching.

Loop unrolling is a basic block enlargement technique in which several copies of the original loop body are concatenated to form a large new loop body. Careful schedul-

ing of load instructions within the new large basic block often increases the time between the data request and data consumption and allows latency of accessing to be overlapped with computations. Melvin and Patt [17] showed that basic block enlargement and scheduling the memory access instructions within the enlarged block can reduce memory access delays in pipelined computers.

Software pipelining is a technique that can be used to overlap loads, computations and stores of different iterations in program loops. Software pipelining has been shown to be very effective for VLIW architectures [15] [5] and architectures such as the IBM RS/6000 [24] and the Cydra [21] which provide hardware support for software pipelining.

Software controlled prefetching is a technique in which programs are analyzed at compile-time and special prefetch instructions that load data into a cache (or prefetch buffer or local memory) are inserted ahead of the actual reference for data. The actual load instructions which follow the prefetch instructions find the data in the cache or prefetch buffer or local memory, which are faster than the main memory. Software cache prefetching requires instruction set architecture (ISA) and microarchitectural changes, but it may still be considered as a primarily software technique. In the past few years, there has been extensive research in software cache prefetching [2] [20] [12] [4]. Porterfield et al. [2] [20] presented the software cache prefetching strategy, and showed that it improves cache performance. They also observed that the overhead of executing the prefetches, the increased data traffic and unnecessary prefetches may nullify the benefits, but noted that further optimizations are possible. Gornish et. al. [8] presented a prefetch algorithm that prefetches data into a fast local memory. Klaiber and Levy [12] illustrated the software prefetching technique for a MIPS [11] style RISC processor. They showed how loop unrolling together with the multi-word cache block can be used to reduce the number of prefetch instructions. Mowry, Lam and Gupta [18] incorporate optimizations to avoid unnecessary prefetches and implement a selective prefetch algorithm and compare indiscriminate prefetching with selective prefetching. They show that a selective prefetch algorithm can reduce the overhead associated with software prefetching. For bus-based multiprocessors, software prefetching may result in increasing the bus traffic and reducing the benefits [23].

1.1 Objectives

Our primary objective in this paper is to characterize the features and benefits of loop unrolling, software pipelining and software prefetching techniques in a systematic and consistent manner. Although the different techniques have been individually evaluated in the past, a comparative evaluation portraying the relative merits and demerits of the different techniques in a consistent framework is lacking. These techniques are not in fact mutually exclusive; several of the techniques may be combined in the same system. A quantitative evaluation of the individual and combined techniques in a consistent framework, will enable the architect and the compiler designer to make intelligent decisions during the system design process. We study these techniques as they would apply to simple RISC processors such as the MIPS. The latency sensitivity of the different techniques is studied in detail.

Software controlled prefetching requires changes in the processor microarchitecture and instruction set architecture (ISA) while software pipelining can be implemented without any architectural changes. Klaiber and Levy [12] mention that software controlled prefetching compares favorably with nonblocking LOADs into a large register set, but quantitative results supporting the statement were not presented. We perform a quantitative comparison of software pipelining and software controlled prefetching for a broad range of latencies.

Loop unrolling requires no change in the processor architecture or instruction semantics. In terms of compiler complexity, it is simpler than software pipelining. It would be interesting to see whether loop unrolling and scheduling of loads in the bigger basic block can achieve a performance close to the other techniques. In this paper, we quantitatively analyze the performance of loop unrolling, software pipelining and software prefetching. Since the techniques are not mutually exclusive, software pipelining is combined with loop unrolling, and software prefetching is combined with principles of loop unrolling and software pipelining. A quantitative evaluation of the different techniques individually and in combinations, is presented.

1.2 Overview

The paper is organized into 4 sections. Section 2 describes the architectural assumptions, the benchmarks and the simulator used for the comparative study. In section 3, we present a comprehensive comparison of the three techniques. We compare the execution times with the different techniques and also analyze the hardware and compiler requirements, code size, run-time overhead etc. Section 4 offers concluding remarks.

2 Simulation Methodology

This study is in the context of pipelined RISC processors. We simulate a pipelined uniprocessor architecture with the MIPS instruction set and instruction latencies. The simulated processor supports nonblocking loads and a lockup-free cache [13]. For software controlled prefetching, a *prefetch* instruction as in [12] is added to the instruction set. One of the unused opcodes of the MIPS processor is used to represent this instruction. Trace-driven simulation with a cycle by cycle simulator is used to compare the techniques.

The system bus is 32 bits wide. Hence in the case of double precision data, two memory accesses are required for each data element. In our experiments with double precision data, we found that memory bandwidth was becoming a bottleneck at low latencies itself and the experiments were not yielding any valid results. Since the techniques being studied are latency hiding techniques, in order to see any differences, it is essential that bandwidth does not become a bottleneck. Hence the results presented are obtained from simulations with single precision floating point data, rather than double precision. Single precision simulation on a 32-bit architecture, would apply at least qualitatively to double precision computations on 64-bit architectures, regarding the number of memory access instructions, memory bandwidth requirements, and balance of memory references versus computations.

A four-way sequentially interleaved memory system is assumed for the simulations. Each memory bank is 32 bits wide. All memory bank conflicts during accesses are considered. A 1 Kbyte instruction cache and a 1 KByte data cache are assumed to be present. Our benchmarks are program loops and hence the instruction cache hit-ratio is very high for most cache configurations. The cache sizes are unrealistic for modern microprocessors, but they have been intentionally kept small because our benchmarks are small. The cache block size is 8 bytes because lower block size keeps spurious effects from memory traffic to a minimum. (One cache block can hold two data elements; so the 8 byte block with single precision data would be the equivalent of a 16 byte block in the case of double precision data.) The caches are 4-way set associative, and LRU replacement policy is employed. We did perform experiments with different block sizes, different associativity, etc, and the observations concur to results presented in previous cache studies, and hence we are presenting only the results from one typical cache configuration. The memory access time is varied between 10 processor cycles and 90 processor cycles, so that the impact of latency on the techniques could be studied. The data cache is nonblocking with four Miss Status Holding Registers (MSHRs).

We certainly appreciate the value of being able to incorporate the different techniques in a compiler and perform the experiments automatically as Mowry, Lam and Gupta [18] did and use large benchmarks such as the SPEC. But we faced the same problem as Rogers and Li [22] did, and without a compiler that would apply these optimizations, we were forced to intervene in the code compilation process. We perform simulations with a set of 8 programs that consist of two signal processing algorithms CONV and CORR, the SAXPY routine from Linpacks, the IFLOOP which has a data dependent IF-THEN-ELSE construct inside, three Lawrence Livermore Loops, an array copy program ACP, etc. All benchmarks involve sequential referencing of arrays and hence spatial locality. The signal processing algorithms, CONV and CORR, involve nested loops and exhibit significant temporal locality in the data reference pattern. The only loop which has an embedded data dependent control dependency is the IFLOOP. This loop has an IF-THEN-ELSE in every iteration, the IF testing a data dependent condition. The different characteristics of these different benchmarks should reveal the different features of the techniques being studied.

Total program execution time is the ultimate measure of performance and we use execution time and a speed up factor based on execution time as the performance metrics. Mowry, Lam and Gupta [18] also used execution time as the metric.

Traces are generated from the assembly output from the DEC station compilers. The benchmark sources are compiled with the highest level of optimization (-O4), and assembly code obtained. We incorporated the different techniques with manual intervention at this stage. Appendix II illustrates the code sequences for various techniques for the SAXPY routine with equal increments. Despite taking a lot of space, and despite the difference between some of the sequences being very minor, several code sequences are illustrated in Appendix II, so that readers could examine them and verify that the study used comparable quality implementations of the different techniques.

The baseline code is obtained from the MIPS compiler output by considering just one body of the loop within each iteration (in the optimized code). The baseline code (illustrated in part (a) of Appendix II) is thus state-of-the-art code, optimized in every respect except unrolling. In our experiments, we limit unrolling to degree one. Naive unrolled code as obtained from the MIPS compilers is illustrated in part (b) of Appendix II. It may be noted that the MIPS compiler allocates different sets of registers for different iterations. Then we rearrange the loads and stores in the code sequence to hide latency. Basically all the loads are moved to the beginning of the loop and all the stores to the end of the loop. The resulting code is illustrated in part (c) of Appendix II.

The code for the software pipelining (illustrated in part (d) of Appendix II) is obtained by rearranging the baseline code so that loads of iteration $i + 1$ and computations of iteration i are grouped together. A prologue and epilogue are also added. For this sequence, the basic block size is the same as the baseline code. Principles of loop unrolling and software pipelining are then combined to yield code sequences in part (e) of Appendix II. Two other methods for software pipelining are illustrated in [14]. It may also be noted that we pipeline only the loads. Stores could be buffered at the memory and the latency hidden/alleviated.

The code sequence for software cache prefetching is illustrated in part (f) of Appendix II. Then all optimizations as discussed in [12] and [18] are applied, and the code sequence illustrated in part (g) of Appendix II is obtained.

Loop unrolling is applied, and the overhead of prefetching is reduced by avoiding unnecessary prefetches (prefetches that would be cache hits). Principles of software pipelining are applied, and data for next iteration are prefetched during the current iteration.

The example in Appendix II does not have any conditional branches within the loop. When conditional branches are embedded as in IFLOOP, issues regarding anticipatory fetching beyond the conditional branch should be addressed. We generate 3 sets of code with no anticipatory fetches, anticipatory fetches along the IF-path, and anticipatory fetches along both paths, to study the effect of lifting loads above conditional branches.

3 Performance Comparison

In this section, we present a comprehensive comparison of the various techniques, based on our simulation studies. In section 3.1, the performance of the different techniques is compared to baseline performance using execution time and speedup metrics. The latency sensitivity of the execution time is discussed in section 3.2, and the sensitivity of the speedups is presented in section 3.3. Appendix I and Fig 3 in section 3.3 summarize the comparison. Section 3.4 discusses the effect of aggressive prefetching beyond conditional branches. In section 3.5, we compare the performance of software pipelining in an architecture with hardware register renaming to that in simple RISC architectures such as the MIPS. Miscellaneous hardware and software issues are discussed in section 3.6.

3.1 Comparison of Execution Time and Speedup

We performed experiments with loop unrolling, software pipelining (with and without unrolling), and software prefetching (with and without unrolling), at latencies of 10, 20, 30, 60, and 90 processor cycles. The execution time for each technique is presented in Fig 1, for memory latencies of 10, 30, and 90 processor cycles. Naive unrolling as in code sequence (b) of Appendix slightly reduces execution time due to reduction in number of branches and loop incrementing instructions. More significant reduction in performance is obtained by rearranging the loads and increasing the distance between data loads and data use as in sequence (c). At lower latencies, unrolling and rescheduling produce benefits comparable to software pipelining (sequence d) and software prefetching (sequence f). Loop unrolling and further optimizations as in code sequences (e) and (g) produce more significant benefits from software pipelining and software controlled prefetching. The IFLOOP is the only benchmark where the issue of aggressive prefetching beyond conditional branches arises. The results presented in Fig 1 are without aggressive speculative loading (lifting loads above data dependent conditional branches). Some results with speculative loading are presented later in Fig 4.

Appendix I illustrates a comparison of the speed up from the different techniques for latencies 10, 30 and 90 cycles. The speed up is calculated as the ratio of the execution time with the baseline code to the execution time with the corresponding technique. The mean speedup presented is the geometric mean of the speedup of the 8 programs.

At $t = 10$ cycles, naive unrolling results in a performance improvement of roughly 11%. Careful static scheduling within the unrolled loop increases the improvement to 23%. At this latency, the performance of naive software pipelining and software prefetching are not higher than that of static scheduling with loop unrolling. At lower latency, software pipelining combined with unrolling is the best technique, and software prefetching with unrolling is the next best technique. At a latency of 10 cycles, software pipelining (unrolled) exhibits better performance than software prefetching (unrolled), in 6 out of the 8 programs. In three of the benchmarks, ACP, L11 and L3, software prefetching is better than software pipelining even at lower latencies. At a latency of 30 cycles, naive software pipelining and software prefetching is better than unrolling and static scheduling in most of the benchmarks. Software prefetching (unrolled) is better than software pipelining (unrolled) in 5 of the 8 programs. Software prefetching (unrolled) is the best technique at a latency of 30 cycles and software pipelining (unrolled) is the next. At latency of 90 cycles, improvement by loop unrolling to degree one becomes less significant than pipelining or prefetching of degree one. Of course it is possible to increase the degree of unrolling and improve the performance. But higher degrees of unrolling increases the number of registers consumed and it may not be practical to incorporate several degrees of unrolling except in small loops. So we do not perform higher degrees of unrolling. At latency of 90 cycles, unrolling and scheduling yields 11% improvement, software pipelining yields 33% and software prefetching gives 48% improvement.

We applied all optimizations as discussed in [18] [12]. In spite of it, at lower latencies, software pipelining appears better than software prefetching. But as the latency reaches 90 cycles, 6 out of the 8 benchmarks show better performance for software prefetching. Thus the simulation results demonstrate that software pipelining is more fruitful at lower latencies and software prefetching is better suited for higher latencies.

3.2 Latency Sensitivity of Execution time

The techniques we are studying are meant to hide latency and hence the performance after incorporating the technique should be less sensitive to latency than original code. Fig 2 illustrates execution time versus latency for three selected benchmarks. (All the 8 benchmarks are not presented due to lack of space and similarity in behavior between the programs. Interested readers can find them in [14].) In most of the benchmarks, software pipelining starts out better, but as latency increases, software prefetching catches up or even outperforms. To be fair in comparison, software pipelining without (with) unrolling should be compared with software prefetching without (with) unrolling. One may observe that in CONV, software prefetching with unrolling exhibits perfect latency insensitivity. Among all the techniques studied, software

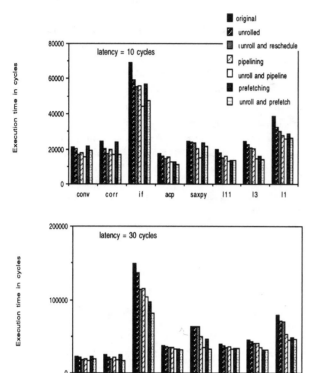

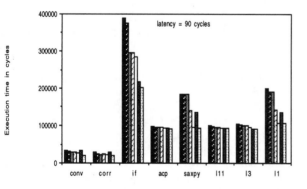

Figure 1: Comparison of Execution Time

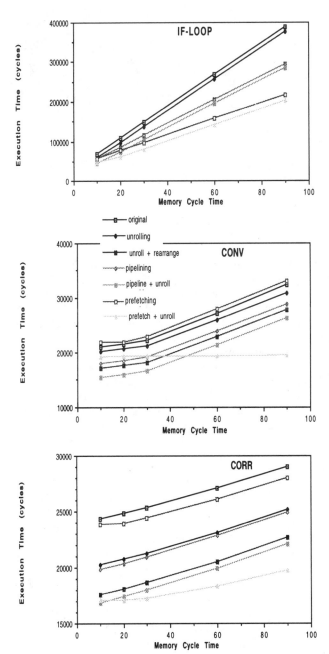

Figure 2: Execution Time vs Latency

prefetching (unrolled) exhibits lowest sensitivity to latency in most of the benchmarks.

In medium or large loops, one or two iterations are sufficient to hide lower latencies and hence software pipelining with no runtime overhead behaves better than software prefetching at lower latencies. Software controlled prefetching is a very interesting technique, but there is run-time overhead associated with it. The issuing of each prefetch instruction consumes an extra cycle. If the registers with the addresses cannot be preserved till the actual LOAD, the address calculation may have to be duplicated. (During our trace generation, we always preserved the addresses and avoided duplicate address generation, and hence the effect of this overhead is not evident in our results.) In a naive implementation, software prefetching could easily yield a performance deterioration. Porterfield [20] had obtained increase in execution time with software prefetching. Among the results presented by Mowry et al. [18], in the case of indiscriminate prefetching, 3 out of their 13 benchmark programs exhibited increase in execution time. Among our 8 programs, for CONV, software prefetching without unrolling deteriorates the performance, but when unrolling and other optimizations are applied, the performance improves.

At low latencies, the overhead of executing extra prefetch instructions can deteriorate the performance. But as latency increases, the extra prefetch instructions get executed for free and the overhead associated with prefetching gets nullified. In software prefetching, it is easy to increase the prefetch distance. Software pipelining is more restricted, since a register has to be associated with the preloaded data. Software prefetching does not increase register lifetimes as software pipelining does. Software prefetching has the capability to mask higher latencies than software pipelining.

Loop unrolling has no risks or overheads associated with it that may nullify the benefits of the technique. If sufficient unused registers to unroll the loop are available, compilers may incorporate the technique safely, since loop unrolling is a relatively risk-free approach. Loop unrolling often reduces loop overhead such as branches and indexing, and improves performance. If possible optimizations are not properly incorporated, the speed up in software pipelining and software prefetching may become less than unity, but loop unrolling will never result in less than unity speed up. Unrolling alone without code rearrangement also results in benefits due to reduction in branch instructions and loop overhead.

3.3 Latency Sensitivity of Speed Up

Fig 3 illustrates the comparison for the geometric mean of the speed up for the 8 benchmarks. Several important observations can be made from this figure. The performance improvement for loop unrolling becomes less significant as latency increases. At lower latencies, the performance of unrolling and static scheduling is comparable to naive software pipelining and software prefetching. At low latencies, software pipelining is better than software prefetch-

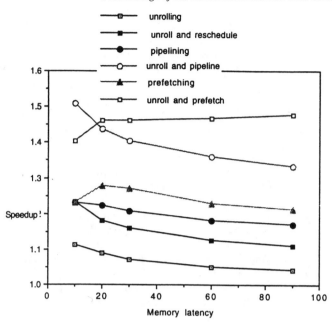

Figure 3: Mean Speed up vs Latency

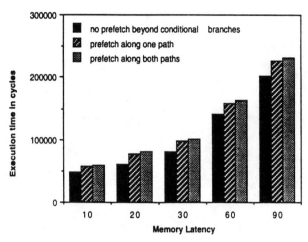

Figure 4: Danger of lifting loads above conditional branches

ing. The difference between the two techniques narrows down as latency increases and software prefetching outperforms software pipelining. Loop unrolling and other optimizations can significantly improve the performance of software pipelining and software prefetching. This figure reiterates our conclusion that software pipelining is suitable at lower latencies and software prefetching is more effective at higher latencies. One may refer to Appendix I for exact values of speedup at latencies of 10, 30 and 90 cycles. As latency increases from 10 to 90 cycles, the improvement contributed by static scheduling with unrolling reduces from 23% to 11%, that of software pipelining (with unrolling) reduces from 51% to 33% and that of software prefetching (with unrolling) increases from 40% to 48%.

3.4 Effect of lifting loads above conditional branches

Our results in the previous sections employ no aggressive anticipatory loading (or in other words, we do not lift loads above data dependent conditional branches). In Fig 4, we present results from software controlled prefetching with anticipatory or speculative loads for the IFLOOP program, which has conditional branches embedded in the loop. The execution time with speculative loading of only the load in the THEN case, and speculative loading of the loads in both the THEN and ELSE cases are compared to the case with no speculative loads. In all of the cases that we studied, speculative loading was seen to deteriorate performance from the no speculative load case. This suggests that speculative loading and extra memory traffic from superfluous loads are often detrimental. Rogers and Li [22] explained algorithms to aid in lifting loads above conditional branches, but our studies warn about the over-

head of superfluous fetches and extra memory bandwidth requirement that it may create. Our results support the approach of Gornish et al. [8] who incorporated an algorithm in their compiler, to suppress superfluous fetches. We assumed equal probability for the IF and ELSE paths. The results may have not been so pessimistic if there was a higher probability for one of the paths, and prefetches only along that path were performed. But even then, there would be some wasted traffic, and increased bandwidth requirements. Since memory bandwidth is a bottleneck in most high performance architectures, we would not recommend such an approach. Aggressive prefetching will be fruitful only in architectures with extra bandwidth. The effect of superfluous fetches on the performance of prefetching schemes was discussed by Mowry [19] also.

3.5 Compiler Issues

All the techniques studied in this paper require assistance from the compiler. In loop unrolling, the compiler has to unroll loops, manipulate indices accordingly, and rearrange the instructions within the loop to increase the load distances. Modern optimizing compilers perform loop optimizations very efficiently. The compiler assistance required in software pipelining is more complex than that for loop unrolling, since loads have to be moved across iterations. Software controlled prefetching requires still more sophisticated compiler intervention. The compiler has to insert prefetch instructions in such a way to guarantee sufficient load distance to hide latency. At the same time, the data should not be loaded very much earlier than required which may result in replacement of the data from the cache before it is actually used in computations. The compiler should minimize the number of prefetch instructions by unrolling the loops and making use of cache locality, and generating prefetches for only potential cache misses. The compiler has to minimize or suppress anticipatory (superfluous) prefetches.

4   Summary and Concluding Remarks

Loop unrolling, software pipelining and software prefetching techniques were quantitatively compared in this paper. One major conclusion from the study is that at low memory latencies, software pipelining without any hardware support outperforms software cache prefetching which requires ISA and microarchitectural changes. Software prefetching has the run-time overhead of issuing extra prefetch instructions and this overhead may cancel the benefits of prefetching at low latencies. Software prefetching can cause detrimental effects if the compiler is not efficient in applying various optimizations. At higher latencies, software prefetching can lead to better benefits than software pipelining, provided bandwidth has not yet become a bottleneck. Loop unrolling is a very powerful technique, and it is essential to combine loop unrolling with software pipelining and software prefetching in order to obtain true benefits from those techniques. Loop unrolling with static scheduling of loads in the unrolled loop produces a speed up of 1.23 at latency of 10 cycles and 1.11 at latency of 90 cycles. The improvement is smaller than best implementations of software pipelining or software prefetching, but loop unrolling never yields a performance deterioration. As latency increases from 10 cycles to 90 cycles, the speedup from software pipelining changes from 1.51 to 1.33, and that of software prefetching increases from 1.40 to 1.48.

Loop unrolling and software pipelining can be successfully performed in systems with no cache also (assuming the memory is pipelined or non-blocking), whereas software prefetching requires a cache (or a fast local memory). Implicit prefetching and overlapping as in loop unrolling with load hoisting and software pipelining, are possible only in load/store architectures. Explicit prefetching, such as software controlled prefetching can be done even in non load/store architectures. All the techniques are particularly suited for iterative programs.

Another conclusion is that aggressive speculative loading beyond conditional branches is often detrimental to performance. In the IFLOOP benchmark, software controlled prefetching with speculative loading was seen to increase the execution time. Unless carefully designed, any explicit prefetching scheme that lifts loads above conditional branches, can nullify the benefits of prefetching by the increase in superfluous fetches and extra memory traffic. The superfluous fetches increase the memory bandwidth requirement. Memory bandwidth is already a bottleneck in most high performance architectures, and any scheme that aggravates the bottleneck problem cannot be favored. Our studies support a conservative approach regarding speculative loads and prefetches. Perhaps the thrust of future research should be on techniques such as blocking [16] [18] which reduce bandwidth requirements rather than just smoothen requirements as in the techniques studied.

We expect our results to be true for larger programs, but detailed experiments with benchmarks such as the SPEC are required to investigate this.

References

[1] D. Bernstein and M. Rodeh, "Global instruction scheduling for superscalar machines", ACM SIGPLAN '91 Conference on Programming Language Design and Implementation, pp. 241-255, June 1991.

[2] D. Callahan, K. Kennedy and A. Porterfield, "Software Prefetching", Proceedings of the Fourth International Conference on Architectural Support for Programming Languages and Operating Systems", April 1991, pp. 40-52.

[3] T-F Chen and J-L Baer, "Reducing Memory Latency via Non-blocking and Prefetching Caches", Proceedings of the International Conference on Architectural Support for Programming Languages and Operating Systems", October 1992, pp. 51–61.

[4] W. Y. Chen, S. A. Mahlke, P. P. Chang, and H. W. Hwu, "Data access microarchitectures for superscalar processors with compiler assisted data prefetching", Proceedings of MICRO-24, 1991.

[5] P. P. Colwell, R. P. Nix, J. J. O'Donnell, D. B. Papworth and P. K. Rodman, "A VLIW architecture for a trace scheduling compiler", Proceedings of the Second International Conference on Architectural Support for Programming Languages and Operating Systems", pages 180-192, October 1987.

[6] DECchip 21064-AA Microprocessor Hardware Reference Manual, Digital Equipment Corporation, 1992.

[7] K. Ebcioglu, "A Compilation Technique for Software Pipelining of Loops with Conditional Jumps", IEEE Micro-20, December 1987.

[8] E. Gornish, E. Granston and A. Veidenbaum, "Compiler directed Data Prefetching in Multiprocessors with Memory Hierarchies", 1990 International Conference on Supercomputing, pp. 354-368.

[9] A. Gupta, J. Hennessy, K. Gharachorloo, T. Mowry and W-D Weber, "Comparative Evaluation of Latency Reducing and Tolerating Techniques", Proc. of the 18th Annual International Symposium on Computer Architecture, Toronto, Canada, May 1991, pp.254–263

[10] N. P. Jouppi, "Improving direct-mapped cache performance by the addition of a small fully associative cache and buffers", 17th International Symposium on Computer Architecture, 1990, pp. 364–373.

[11] G. Kane, "MIPS RISC Architecture", Prentice–Hall, Englewood Cliffs, N.J., 1988.

[12] A. C. Klaiber and H. M. Levy, "An architecture for software-controlled data prefetching", 18th Intl.

Symp. on Computer Architecture, May 1991, pp. 43–53.

[13] D. Kroft, "Lockup-free Instruction Fetch/Prefetch Cache Organization", Proc. of the 8th Annual Intl. Symp. on Computer Architecture, pp. 81-87, June 1981.

[14] L. Kurian and V. Reddy, "A Comparative Evaluation of Software Techniques to Hide Memory Latency", University of South Florida, Dept. of Computer Science and Engineering, Technical Report, 1994-02.

[15] M. S. Lam, "Software pipelining: An effective scheduling technique for VLIW machines", ACM SIGPLAN '88 conference on programming Language Design and Implementation, pp. 318 – 328, 1988.

[16] M. S. Lam, E. E. Rothberg and M. E. Wolf, "The Cache Performance and Optimizations of Blocked Algorithms", Proceedings of the Fourth International Conference on Architectural Support for Programming Languages and Operating Systems", 1991, pp. 63 – 74.

[17] S. Melvin and Y. Patt, "Exploiting Fine–Grained Parallelism Through a Combination of Hardware and Software Techniques", Proc. of the 18th Annual International Symposium on Computer Architecture, Toronto, Canada, May 1991, pp.287-296

[18] T. C. Mowry, M. S. Lam and Anoop Gupta, "Design and Evaluation of a Compiler Algorithm for Prefetching", Proceedings of the International Conference on Architectural Support for Programming Languages and Operating Systems", October 1992, pp. 62 – 73.

[19] T. Mowry, "Tolerating Latency Through Software-Controlled Data Prefetching", Stanford University Technical Report, CSL-TR-94-628, June 1994.

[20] A. K. Porterfield, "Software Methods for Improvement of Cache Performance on Supercomputer Applications", Ph. D. dissertation, RICE COMP TR 89-93, May 1989.

[21] B.R. Rau et al. "The Cydra 5 departmental supercomputer: Design philosophies, decisions, and trade-offs", IEEE Computer, vol. 22, January 1989, pp. 12-35.

[22] A. Rogers and K. Li, "Software Support for Speculative Loads", Proceedings of the International Conference on Architectural Support for Programming Languages and Operating Systems", October 1992, pp. 38–50.

[23] D. M. Tullsen and S. J. Eggers, "Limitations of Cache Prefetching on a Bus-Based Multiprocessor", Proc. of the International Symposium on Computer Architecture, May 1993, pp. 278-288.

[24] Warren Jr. H., "Instruction Scheduling for the IBM RISC System/6000 processor", IBM Journal of Research and Development 34(1), Jan 1990, pp. 85 – 91.

APPENDIX I

Speedup from various techniques

Bench-mark	unroll	un+ sch	soft pipe	un+ pipe	soft pref	un+ pref
CONV	1.045	1.235	1.168	1.364	0.964	1.097
CORR	1.203	1.381	1.228	1.441	1.021	1.425
SAXPY	1.021	1.043	1.223	1.628	1.043	1.136
IFLOOP	1.169	1.243	1.231	1.566	1.210	1.451
ACP	1.093	1.206	1.130	1.400	1.399	1.587
L11	1.112	1.297	1.220	1.496	1.438	1.441
L3	1.086	1.193	1.225	1.680	1.526	1.730
L1	1.183	1.284	1.398	1.506	1.350	1.474
Mean	1.112	1.232	1.230	1.507	1.230	1.403

(a) 10 cycles

Bench-mark	unroll	un+ sch	soft pipe	un+ pipe	soft pref	un+ pref
CONV	1.044	1.222	1.160	1.340	0.968	1.152
CORR	1.192	1.357	1.213	1.411	1.038	1.471
SAXPY	1.000	1.000	1.286	1.809	1.387	1.911
IFLOOP	1.091	1.301	1.295	1.432	1.535	1.837
ACP	1.042	1.087	1.057	1.156	1.155	1.210
L11	1.052	1.128	1.099	1.200	1.180	1.180
L3	1.046	1.099	1.113	1.289	1.431	1.434
L1	1.113	1.123	1.487	1.723	1.617	1.702
Mean	1.070	1.159	1.207	1.404	1.269	1.461

(b) 30 cycles

Bench-mark	unroll	un+ sch	soft pipe	un+ pipe	soft pref	un+ pref
CONV	1.048	1.159	1.124	1.228	0.975	1.655
CORR	1.153	1.278	1.164	1.314	1.036	1.465
SAXPY	1.000	1.000	1.314	1.925	1.351	1.961
IFLOOP	1.033	1.320	1.318	1.369	1.791	1.932
ACP	1.016	1.032	1.021	1.056	1.056	1.072
L11	1.020	1.047	1.038	1.074	1.066	1.066
L3	1.019	1.041	1.045	1.107	1.147	1.150
L1	1.043	1.047	1.39	1.882	1.463	1.865
Mean	1.041	1.110	1.169	1.334	1.211	1.476

(c) 90 cycles

APPENDIX II

Code sequences for saxpy.equal program, with various techniques incorporated step-by-step are illustrated in this Appendix.

```
$32:    lw      $15,-4008($3)        ; load x(i) to R15
        lw      $14,-8008($3)        ; load y(i) to R14
        mul     $24,$15,a            ; a * x(i)
        addu    $25,$14,$24          ; y(i) + a*x(i)
        sw      $25,-8008($3)        ; save y(i)
        addu    $3,$3,4              ; update base register
        bne     $3,$2,$32            ; loop back
```

(a) Baseline code

```
$32:    lw      $15,-4008($3)        ; load x(i) to R15
        lw      $14,-8008($3)        ; load y(i) to R14
        mul     $24,$15,a            ; a * x(i)
        addu    $25,$14,$24          ; y(i) + a*x(i)
        sw      $25,-8008($3)        ; save y(i)
        lw      $9,-4004($3)         ; load x(i+1) to R9
        lw      $8,-8004($3)         ; load y(i+1) to R8
        mul     $10,$9,a             ; a * x(i+1)
        addu    $11,$8,$10           ; y(i+1) + a*x(i+1)
        sw      $11,-8004($3)        ; save y(i+1)
        addu    $3,$3,8              ; update base register
        bne     $3,$2,$32            ; loop back
```

(b) Loop unrolling alone (no code rearrangement)

```
$32:    lw      $15,-4008($3)        ; load x(i) to R15
        lw      $9,-4004($3)         ; load x(i+1) to R9
        lw      $14,-8008($3)        ; load y(i) to R14
        lw      $8,-8004($3)         ; load y(i+1) to R8
        mul     $24,$15,a            ; a * x(i)
        addu    $25,$14,$24          ; y(i) + a*x(i)
        mul     $10,$9,a             ; a * x(i+1)
        addu    $11,$8,$10           ; y(i+1) + a*x(i+1)
        sw      $25,-8008($3)        ; save y(i)
        sw      $11,-8004($3)        ; save y(i+1)
        addu    $3,$3,8              ; update base register
        bne     $3,$2,$32            ; loop back
```

(c) Loop unrolling and code rearrangement

```
        lw      $15,-4008($3)        ; load x(0) to R15 - (This is in the prologue)
        lw      $14,-8008($3)        ; load y(0) to R14 - (This is in the prologue)
$32:    mul     $24,$15,a            ; a * x(i)
        lw      $15,-4004($3)        ; load x(i+1) to R15
        addu    $25,$14,$24          ; y(i) + a*x(i)
        lw      $14,-8004($3)        ; load y(i+1) to R14
        sw      $25,-8008($3)        ; save y(i)
        addu    $3,$3,4              ; update base register
        bne     $3,$2,$32            ; loop back
        mul     $24,$15,a            ; last a * x(i) will be in epilogue
        addu    $25,$14,$24          ; last y(i) + a*x(i) in epilogue
        sw      $25,-8008($3)        ; save y(i), last store will be in epilogue
```

(d) Software pipelining

```
            lw      $17,-4008($3)        ; load x(0) to R17 - prologue
            lw      $7,-4004($3)         ; load x(1) to R7 - prologue
            lw      $16,-8008($3)        ; load y(0) to R16 - prologue
            lw      $6,-8004($3)         ; load y(1) to R6 - prologue
$32:        mul     $24,$17,a            ; a * x(i)
            lw      $17,-4000($3)        ; load x(i+2) to R15
            addu    $25,$16,$24          ; y(i) + a*x(i)
            lw      $16,-8000($3)        ; load y(i+2) to R14
            mul     $10,$7,a             ; a * x(i+1)
            lw      $7,-3996($3)         ; load x(i+3) to R9
            addu    $11,$6,$10           ; y(i+1) + a*x(i+1)
            lw      $6,-7996($3)         ; load y(i+3) to R8
            sw      $25,-8008($3)        ; save y(i)
            sw      $11,-8004($3)        ; save y(i+1)
            addu    $3,$3,8              ; update base register
            bne     $3,$2,$32            ; loop back
            mul     $24,$17,a            ; a * x(n-1) epilogue
            mul     $10,$7,a             ; a * x(n) epilogue
            addu    $25,$16,$24          ; y(n-1) + a*x(n-1) epilogue
            addu    $11,$6,$10           ; y(n) + a*x(n) epilogue
            sw      $25,-8008($3)        ; save y(n-1)epilogue
            sw      $11,-8004($3)        ; save y(n)epilogue
```

(e) Software pipelining in (d) with unrolling

```
$32:        fetch   -4004($3)            ; prefetch x(i+1) to cache
            fetch   -8004($3)            ; prefetch y(i+1) cache
            lw      $15,-4008($3)        ; load x(i) to R15
            lw      $14,-8008($3)        ; load y(i) to R14
            mul     $24,$15,a            ; a * x(i)
            addu    $25,$14,$24          ; y(i) + a*x(i)
            sw      $25,-8008($3)        ; save y(i)
            addu    $3,$3,4              ; update base register
            bne     $3,$2,$32            ; loop back
```

(f) Software controlled prefetching (no unrolling)

```
$32:        fetch   -4000($3)            ; prefetch x(i+2) to cache
            fetch   -8000($3)            ; prefetch y(i+2) to cache
            lw      $15,-4008($3)        ; load x(i) to R15
            lw      $14,-8008($3)        ; load y(i) to R14
            mul     $24,$15,a            ; a * x(i)
            addu    $25,$14,$24          ; y(i) + a*x(i)
            sw      $25,-8008($3)        ; save y(i)
            lw      $9,-4004($3)         ; load x(i+1) to R9
            lw      $8,-8004($3)         ; load y(i+1) to R8
            mul     $10,$9,a             ; a * x(i+1)
            addu    $11,$8,$10           ; y(i+1) + a*x(i+1)
            sw      $11,-8004($3)        ; save y(i+1)
            addu    $3,$3,8              ; update base register
            bne     $3,$2,$32            ; loop back
```

(g) Software prefetching (unrolled and optimized)

SCALABLE SHARED-MEMORY ARCHITECTURES

Minitrack Coordinator:

Josep Torrellas

Scalable Shared-Memory Architectures

Introduction to the Minitrack

Josep Torrellas

Center for Supercomputing Research and Development
and Computer Science Department
University of Illinois at Urbana-Champaign, IL 61801, USA

1   Background

Shared-memory multiprocessing is emerging as a popular approach to increase computing power, over that of sequential computing, while maintaining programmability. What makes the base shared-memory paradigm attractive is the simplicity of the programming model: all memory is in a pool and is globally shared. Furthermore, architectures that do not require a broadcast channel for interprocessor communication can potentially scale to many processors and therefore provide large-scale computing power. Such systems are loosely termed "scalable".

There are many hardware and software research issues in scalable shared-memory multiprocessors. One of the most important ones is how to handle the increasing speed mismatch between fast processors and slow, far-off memory systems. Indeed, data needs to be fetched and returned to memory, and the processor may have to remain idle during this transfer. This problem is partially eliminated with the presence of caches or local memories, which try to keep the working set close to the processor. Alternative or complementary approaches to caches are prefetching [5, 9] and multithreading [2]. Prefetching consists of fetching instructions or data before they are needed while overlapping the accesses with other computation. Both hardware and software approaches are possible. Multithreading consists of switching processes when an instruction or memory access by a process would stall the processor. When the process is finally re-scheduled, the offending condition that forced the switch is likely to have disappeared. For example, if the offending condition is a remote memory read, the data is likely to be in the cache when the process is re-scheduled.

Unfortunately, not only do processors want to access memory, they want to communicate with each other as well. This gives rise to the synchronization problem [8]. Furthermore, given that, for performance reasons, data is usually allowed to replicate in the memory hierarchy, the popular problems of data coherence and memory consistency appear. Data coherence has been studied from many different angles. There are many hardware solutions [3] (variations of directory-based schemes), compiler solutions [6], and operating system-based approaches [4]. Memory consistency models focus on how the overlapping of memory accesses from different processors to the same set of variables affects the sequence of operations seen by the program [7, 1].

While communication resulting from the sharing of data (also called true sharing) is unavoidable, other non-essential sources of communication slow the machine further. Such sources are false sharing [10] and process migration [11]. The former can appear when the unit of coherence is larger than a single word; the latter is often necessary if we want to keep the machine load-balanced. These are also active areas of research.

Another active area of research focuses on the channels used by the processors to communicate, namely the interconnection networks. Many network configurations exist. The reason is that each of them satisfies different cost/performance requirements, which range from those of busses to crossbars.

In addition to the mostly hardware research issues that we mentioned, there are countless software issues that need to be explored in these architectures. Examples are task scheduling issues, operating systems issues, and many compiler/language issues. The shared-memory paradigm is attractive because it simplifies the development of complex software systems. For instance, there are several robust commercial multiprocessor operating systems and parallelizing compilers.

Last, but not least, there is the active field of application design for these machines. Many of the efforts done by developers of applications for these machines result in feedback for the architecture and system designers. Overall, the field of scalable shared-memory architectures is one of the most exciting and vast areas of research in computer systems nowadays.

2 Scope of the Minitrack

The papers that have been accepted for this mini-track are good examples of the variety of research topics involved in building scalable shared-memory architectures. The first paper, *"Using Hints to Reduce the Read Miss Penalty for Flat COMA Protocols"*, discusses a hardware optimization for the cache coherence protocol of cache-only memory architectures. Examples of such machines are the Kendall Square Research KSR-1 and the DDM-1 from the Swedish Institute of Computer Science. The second paper, *"Decoupled Pre-Fetching for Distributed Shared Memory"*, discusses hardware support for data prefetching. The third paper, *"Modeling Load Imbalance and Fuzzy Barriers for Scalable Shared-Memory Multiprocessors"*, focuses on the synchronization and load imbalance problems. It uses an analytical model to estimate the impact of these issues. Finally, *"A Survey of Software Solutions for Maintenance of Cache Consistency in Shared Memory Multiprocessors"* discusses schemes that use the compiler to keep data coherent.

Acknowledgments

I would like to thank all the authors that submitted papers to this minitrack; unfortunately, only a few papers could be published. Thanks also to the many reviewers who offered their time and expertise. Finally, thanks to my assistant, Donna Guzy, for her help and Trevor Mudge for his advice.

References

[1] S. Adve and M. Hill. Weak Ordering - A New Definition. In *Proceedings of the 17th Annual International Symposium on Computer Architecture*, pages 1–13, May 1990.

[2] A. Agarwal. Performance Tradeoffs in Multithreaded Processors. In *IEEE Transactions on Parallel and Distributed Systems*, volume 3, pages 525–539, September 1992.

[3] A. Agarwal, R. Simoni, J. Hennessy, and M. Horowitz. An Evaluation of Directory Schemes for Cache Coherence. In *Proceedings of the 15th Annual International Symposium on Computer Architecture*, pages 280–289, May 1988.

[4] W. Bolosky, R. Fitzgerald, and M. Scott. Simple but Effective Techniques for NUMA Memory Management. In *Proceedings of the 12th ACM Symposium on Operating System Principles*, pages 19–31, December 1989.

[5] T. F. Chen and J. L. Baer. A Performance Study of Software and Hardware Data Prefetching Schemes. In *Proceedings of the 21st Annual International Symposium on Computer Architecture*, pages 223–232, April 1994.

[6] H. Cheong and A. V. Veidenbaum. Compiler-Directed Cache Management in Multiprocessors. In *IEEE Computer*, pages 39–47, June 1990.

[7] K. Gharachorloo, D. Lenoski, J. Laudon, P. Gibbons, A. Gupta, and J. Hennessy. Memory Consistency and Event Ordering in Scalable Shared-Memory Multiprocessors. In *Proceedings of the 17th Annual International Symposium on Computer Architecture*, pages 15–26, May 1990.

[8] J. R. Goodman, M. K. Vernon, and P. J. Woest. Efficient synchronization primitives for large-scale cache-coherent multiprocessors. In *Proceedings of the 3rd International Conference on Architectural Support for Programming Languages and Operating Systems*, pages 64–73, April 1989.

[9] T. Mowry, M. Lam, and A. Gupta. Design and Evaluation of a Compiler Algorithm for Prefetching. In *Proceedings of the 5th International Conference on Architectural Support for Programming Languages and Operating Systems*, pages 62–73, October 1992.

[10] J. Torrellas, M. S. Lam, and J. L. Hennessy. False Sharing and Spatial Locality in Multiprocessor Caches. In *IEEE Trans. on Computers*, pages 651–663, June 1994.

[11] J. Torrellas, A. Tucker, and A. Gupta. Evaluating the Performance of Cache-Affinity Scheduling in Shared-Memory Multiprocessors. In *IEEE Transactions on Parallel and Distributed Systems*. To appear 1994. A short version appeared in ACM Sigmetrics 1993.

Proceedings of the 28th Annual Hawaii International Conference on System Sciences — 1995

Using Hints to Reduce the Read Miss Penalty for Flat COMA Protocols*

Mårten Björkman, Fredrik Dahlgren, and Per Stenström

Department of Computer Engineering, Lund University
P.O. Box 118, S-221 00 LUND, Sweden

Abstract

In flat COMA architectures, an attraction-memory miss must first interrogate a directory before a copy of the requested data can be located which often involves three network traversals. By keeping track of the identity of a potential holder of the copy—called a hint—one network traversal can be saved which reduces the read penalty.

We have evaluated the reduction of the read miss penalty provided by hints using detailed architectural simulations and four benchmark applications. The results show that a previously proposed protocol using hints actually can make the read miss penalty larger because when the hint is not correct, an extra network traversal is needed. This has motivated us to study a new protocol using hints that simultaneously sends a request to the potential holder and to the directory. This protocol reduces the read miss penalty for all applications but the protocol complexity does not seem to justify the performance improvement.

1. Introduction

Cache-coherent NUMA (CC-NUMA) and cache-only memory architectures (COMA) are two emerging styles of building scalable shared-memory architectures. Examples of the former type include the Stanford DASH [14] and the MIT Alewife [1] whereas the Swedish Institute of Computer Science's Data Diffusion Machine (DDM) [13] and Kendall Square Research's KSR1 [4] are examples of the latter type. Both styles use processing nodes that consist of processors, caches, and a portion of the distributed main memory. In contrast to CC-NUMA machines, main memory in COMA is converted into huge caches called *attraction memories*, that support replication of data not only across caches, but also across memories.

The main advantage of COMA as compared to CC-NUMA machines is that a vast majority of replacement cache-misses can be handled in the local attraction memory [17]. However, to handle cache misses that cannot be carried out locally, a mechanism is needed that locates the node in which a copy of the memory block resides. DDM and KSR1—examples of hierarchical COMAs—use a hierarchical directory structure. Therefore, the latency of

locating a copy can include several directory lookups. This is in contrast to in CC-NUMA machines where a single directory lookup locates a copy.

COMA machines can also locate copies using a single directory lookup as in CC-NUMA machines which is the basic idea behind the flat COMA (COMA-F) proposal by Stenström *et al.* [17]. When a cache miss cannot be serviced by the local attraction memory, the miss request is sent to a directory which then forwards the request to an attraction memory that keeps a copy of the block. This attraction memory then returns the copy to the requesting node. While the whole transaction often includes three network traversals, two network traversals would suffice, did the requesting node know where to retrieve a copy.

To be able to send the read-miss request directly to a holder of the block, one can associate an identifier of the potential block holder—called a *hint*—with each attraction-memory block-frame. This concept was incorporated in a COMA-F protocol by Gupta *et al.* in [12]. If the hint is correct, the copy is retrieved in two network traversals but if the hint turns out to be wrong, the directory has to be interrogated. Since this costs the latency of an extra network traversal, the hints must be correct in at least fifty percent of the cases to reduce the read miss penalty.

We evaluate in this paper the performance improvement using hints on a simulated flat COMA machine and four benchmark applications. While we evaluate the protocol using hints according to [12], we find that the savings can be offset by the extra network traversals associated with unsuccessful hints. This motivates us to study a new protocol using hints that simultaneously sends a request to the potential holder as well as to the directory; clearly, unsuccessful hints do not introduce extra miss latency in this protocol. Although we find that this protocol cuts the read-miss penalty—in some case by 14%—the improvement is limited by the small fraction of misses that can use hints and the low success rate of hints.

In the next section, we review the latency associated with read misses in protocols for CC-NUMA and COMA machines and Section 3 presents a new COMA protocol that uses hints to reduce the read-miss penalty. We present our architectural simulation results in Sections 4 and 5 before we conclude in Section 6.

*This work was supported by the Swedish National Board for Technical Development (NUTEK) under the contract P855.

2. CC-NUMA and Flat COMA Protocols

Penalties for memory operations, i.e., the number of cycles a processor is stalled waiting for a memory operation to complete, are important to combat in shared-memory multiprocessors. While the penalty in servicing write operations can be eliminated by exploiting relaxed memory consistency models [8], as we assume in this paper, penalties associated with read misses—read miss penalties—are much harder to attack.

Many techniques have been proposed to reduce read miss penalties including prefetching [15,5,6] and update-based cache-coherence protocols [10,7]. In this paper, we focus on penalty reduction and cost of COMA protocol optimizations as compared to CC-NUMA protocols. The framework for our comparison is the coherence protocol in DASH [14] and in the flat COMA protocol proposed by Gupta *et al.* [12]. The review of these protocols, that appear in Sections 2.1 and 2.2 and that we simulate in Section 5, provides an intuition as to how *hints* can make a flat COMA protocol performing better. We then review the original flat COMA protocol with hints in Section 2.3.

The general structure of the CC-NUMA and COMA machines we consider in this paper appears in Figure 1. It consists of a number of processing nodes that each contains a processor, a private cache, and a portion of the main memory. The processing nodes are connected by a general interconnection network for which the only requirement is that a request sent from one node to another always uses the same path (i.e. FIFO order is preserved).

2.1 A CC-NUMA Protocol

Data and code pages are initially mapped to the various memory modules in a CC-NUMA machine. The node in which a specific page is mapped is called the *home node* of that page and the memory blocks it contains.

Replication of memory blocks is only supported across the private caches and consistency among cached memory blocks is maintained by a system-level write-invalidate protocol. The basic mechanism consists of a directory

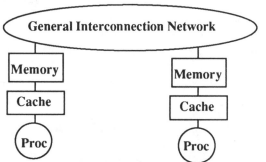

Figure 1: General structure of the CC-NUMA and COMA architectures.

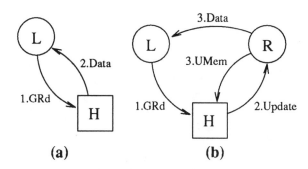

Figure 2: A global read request when the block is (a) SHARED or UNCACHED (b) MODIFED.

entry associated with each memory block that keeps track of which caches have copies using a presence-flag vector. Moreover, the directory entry also encodes the state of the memory copy which can be *UNCACHED*, *SHARED*, or *MODIFIED*. Similarly, each cache copy can be in one of three states: *INVALID*, *SHARED*, or *DIRTY*.

Let us now recapitulate the cache read-miss transactions in the DASH protocol. (For more details, the reader is referred to [14].) To simplify the discussion, we refer to the node in which the cache miss originates as the *local node*; a node other than the local node and the home node that is involved in the cache-miss transaction is referred to as a *remote node*.

If Local (L) is not the same as Home (H), a cache miss results in a global read-miss request (*GRd*) to Home. If the memory copy is *SHARED* or *UNCACHED*, a copy is returned to Local. This read-miss transaction includes two network traversals (or *hops*) and is shown in Figure 2a. If the memory block is *MODIFIED*, however, the copy must be retrieved from Remote (R) which keeps the only copy in state *DIRTY*. This is done by sending an update request to Remote (*Update* in Figure 2b). When Remote receives the request, it sends a fresh copy to Home (*UMem*) as well as to Local (*Data*). When Home receives the copy, the state of the memory block is changed to *SHARED*. We note that when Local, Home, and Remote are different nodes, a read-miss transaction includes three hops whereas if Home is either the same as Local or Remote, it requires less than three hops.

Whether a read miss is serviced in zero, two, or three hops in CC-NUMA depends on (i) the location of Home with respect to Local and (ii) the state of the memory copy. First, if Local is the same as Home and if the memory copy is clean, i.e., in state *UNCACHED* or *SHARED*, the read miss can be serviced locally; if the memory block is in state *MODIFIED*, the read miss is serviced in two hops. Second, if Local is not the same as Home but the memory copy is clean, the read miss is serviced in two hops, whereas if the memory copy is in state *MODIFIED*, three hops are needed. We note that if a page is mapped to Local, then all Local's misses to that page are serviced in at most two hops. Especially in the absence of invalidations, all misses are serviced locally.

The way CC-NUMA machines reduce the number of hops per cache read miss is by a careful mapping of pages to nodes. This mapping strives at increasing the likelihood of finding the home node in the local node. Unfortunately, the absence of support for page replication limits this approach. This is why COMA machines have a potential to reduce the number of hops per cache read miss by using hardware support for replication at the main-memory level.

2.2 A Flat COMA Protocol

To support replication of memory blocks at the main-memory level, COMA machines convert each memory module into a huge cache by associating tag and state bits with each memory block-frame. Coherence across these main-memory caches, referred to as *attraction memories* (AM), is maintained by a system-level write-invalidate protocol.

Owing to the replication of memory blocks at the main-memory level, a vast majority of the cache replacement misses[1] can be handled by the local AM [17]. On the other hand, cold misses to memory blocks belonging to pages mapped to other nodes and coherence misses must be handled remotely. Since memory blocks can migrate across memories, a mechanism is needed to locate an AM that has a copy for remotely serviced misses. The Data Diffusion Machine[13] and the Kendall Square Research's KSR1[4] employ a hierarchical directory mechanism that may introduce several directory lookups before the copy is located. This is in contrast to in CC-NUMA machines where a single directory lookup (in Home) is needed to locate the copy. In [17], it was shown that the latency caused by the hierarchical mechanism can offset the gains of the low replacement-miss latency even if pages are randomly distributed in a CC-NUMA machine.

The flat COMA (COMA-F) as proposed by Stenström *et al.* in [17] uses a similar notion of a home node for each memory page as in CC-NUMA. Unlike CC-NUMA, however, a memory copy is not necessarily allocated in Home's AM even if it is clean. Instead, another dynamically assigned node—the *master* of the memory block—is responsible for a "master copy" of the block and will service all AM read-miss requests. Each directory entry consists of a pointer to the current master and a presence-flag vector to keep track of memory copies. We next study the

---

1. Misses that result from size or associativity constraints in the private caches in the absence of invalidations.

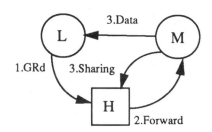

Figure 3: Flow of a global read-miss transaction in a flat COMA protocol.

protocol for inter-node AM read misses in the protocol proposed in [12]. Like in Section 2.1, we refer to the requesting node as Local and the node that keeps the directory as Home. In addition, we refer to the node that keeps the master copy as the Master and any other node involved in an inter-node read-miss transaction as Remote.

Each directory entry can be in two stable states, *EXCLUSIVE* and *SHARED*, that indicate that there is exactly one or more than one memory copy in the system, respectively. Moreover, the directory state can be also in a transient state, *WAIT_INVALIDATE*, indicating that an ownership transaction is in progress.

A cache read-miss that cannot be serviced in the local AM results in a global read-miss request (*GRd*) which is sent to Home as shown in Figure 3. Home then forwards the request to Master (*Forward*) that returns a copy to Local (*Data*). Local fills the AM as well as the private cache with the block. Home will not change the directory state (if ever) until it receives the transfer request from Master (*Sharing* in Figure 3).

Ownership transactions are handled according to Figure 4. When Home receives an ownership request (*GWr*), it forwards it to the Master (*WForward*) and the state of the directory entry becomes *WAIT_INVALIDATE*. From now on, all incoming read miss as well as ownership requests will be rejected and have to be retried. When Master receives the forward request, it returns a copy of the block to Local (*WData*) and notifies Home (*Transfer*). When Home receives this message, the state becomes *EXCLUSIVE* and Local is deemed the new master. In parallel, Home issues invalidations to all sharers (called Remote in Figure 4) and sends a message to Local (*WrAck*). Local will receive all invalidation acknowledgments (*IAck*) as in the DASH protocol [14].

While the transient state *WAIT_INVALIDATE* prevents a race condition if a global read-miss or another ownership request arrives at Home during an ownership transaction, other race conditions can occur. Assume that an ownership request arrives at Home during a global read-miss transaction when Home has sent *Forward* to

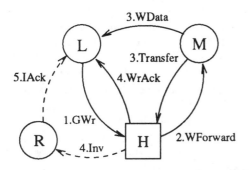

Figure 4: Flow of an ownership transaction in a flat COMA protocol.

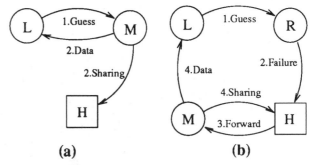

(a)　　　　　　　　　**(b)**

Figure 5: Flow of a global read-miss transaction using hints. (a) Successful hint (b) Unsuccessful hint.

Master (see Figure 3). Since the network preserves FIFO order between any two nodes, Home will receive the *Transfer* message in the ownership transaction **after** it has received the *Sharing* message from Master which guarantees that the directory information cannot be obsolete. Another race can occur when Home subsequently issues invalidations to all sharers. It can so happen that Local receives an invalidation before *Data* in Figure 3 has arrived. This could result in a block fill of inconsistent data. This problem is solved as in the DASH by retrying the read-miss transaction, once the *Data* message arrives.

Handling replacements of AM blocks is a challenge to COMA protocols not apparent in CC-NUMA protocols. While AM copies that are not master copies can be simply discarded, a new master has to be nominated if the master copy has to leave room for another copy. Strategies for doing this is beyond the scope of the paper. (The interested reader is referred to [17].)

In summary, while a flat COMA is expected to have fewer global read misses than CC-NUMA machines, global read-miss transactions often involve three hops when CC-NUMA machines involve two hops. This is because Home does not keep any memory copy in general; rather the current master has to provide it. In the next section we will study how COMA protocols can use the notion of a hint to avoid the detour of read-miss requests via Home.

2.3 Hints: Avoiding Three-Hop Misses

To be able to service a global AM read-miss transaction in two hops, Local could associate with each AM block-frame an identifier—called a *hint* in [12]—of a potential master. If the hint is correct, a copy of the memory block can be retrieved in two hops. While the success rate of a hint depends on the heuristics used to guess who the current master is, we postpone the discussion of the usefulness of various hint heuristics to Section 3.2.

Let us review how the basic global read-miss transaction in Figure 3 can be changed to support hints. In Figure 5, we show the read-miss transaction flow when (a) the

hint is successful and (b) when the hint is wrong. Unlike the flat COMA protocol with no hints, the read request is sent to the potential master (*Guess*). If the hint is correct, Master supplies *Data* and sends a sharing request (*Sharing*) to Home. Home updates the state of the directory entry as in the protocol with no hints. If the hint is wrong, however, the remote node that is no longer Master (R in Figure 5) forwards the read request to Home (*Failure*). Home then forwards the read request to the current Master as in the original protocol.

One could use the notion of hints for ownership requests as well. Although such transactions are sketched in [12], we have not incorporated them in our simulated protocols. Instead, the ownership requests are handled according to the transaction flow of Figure 4.

While successful hints can reduce the number of hops in global read-miss transactions by one, unsuccessful hints add another hop to the latency; at least half the guesses must be successful to reduce the overall read miss penalty. We study in the next section a new protocol extension that does not add an extra network hop when the hint is wrong.

3. A New Flat COMA Protocol using Hints

Instead of forwarding the read-miss request to Home, when the hint is wrong, Local could simultaneously send the read-miss request to both Home and the potential master. If the hint is correct, Home could drop the read-miss request. Conversely, if the hint is wrong, the incorrectly inferred master could discard it. This is the general idea of the new flat COMA hint protocol extension. We present in Section 3.1 how the global read-miss transaction has to be changed for the new protocol. Then in Section 3.2 we discuss previously proposed hint heuristics as well as proposing a new one.

3.1 Protocol Transactions

In Figure 6a, the flow of a global read-miss transaction in the case of a successful hint is shown. A global read-miss request (*GRd*) is sent from Local to Home. This request

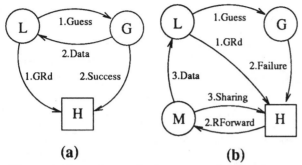

Figure 6: Flow of a read-miss transaction for the new protocol. (a) Successful hint (b) Unsuccessful hint.

carries the identity of the hint. Simultaneously, a *Guess* message is sent to a potential master (G in Figure 6a). If G has a copy of the block, it will respond with *Data* to Local and Home is notified by the *Success* message so that it updates the directory state. Since the identity of the guessed master is contained in the *GRd* message sent to Home, Home can drop the message if G has a copy. The flow of an unsuccessful global read-miss transaction is shown in Figure 6b. If Home notices that G does not have a copy according to the directory entry, it will forward the read request (*RForward*) to the current Master which responds to the read request in the same manner as in the COMA protocols in Section 2. Therefore, an unsuccessful hint can be serviced in three hops, instead of four using the protocol in Section 2.3. Moreover, this protocol only requires that G has a copy; and not a **master** copy.

A complication arises if G sends a request to Home to give up its AM copy (replacement) and Home receives a global read-miss request before the replacement request from G has arrived at Home. Home would then conclude that the read-miss request is serviced by G and would drop the request. To solve this race condition, G sends a *Failure* message to Home if it has no copy. Home then services this request in the same way as a failure request in the original hint protocol in Section 2.3.

3.2 Hint Heuristics

Two hint heuristics, called *shared hints* and *invalid hints*, where proposed in [12]. Invalid hints consider the node that most recently invalidated the block as the Master, whereas shared hints consider the node that most recently provided a copy as the Master. To support hints, we note that the identity of the node that invalidated or supplied the block must be available in the invalidation requests or in the data replies. Moreover, shared hints associate with each AM block a $\log_2 N$ pointer, given N nodes; invalid hints can use the empty block frame because the block is invalid.

Invalid hints work well for applications in which data is supplied on a read miss from the same node that invali-

dated the copy prior to the miss. This situation shows up in applications with producer-consumer data where the producer will both invalidate the data and subsequently provide it to a consumer. By contrast, in applications with migratory data [11], a block will be typically invalidated by one node and subsequently supplied by another. Gupta *et al.* [12] studied the success rate of read misses using invalid hints and found that it is less than 50% for applications where migratory data dominate; for applications with producer-consumer data, the success rate was high.

Shared hints in the terminology used by Gupta *et al.* [12] consider the latest node that provided the copy as the one that is the current Master. Gupta *et al.* [12] used shared hints to optimize ownership transactions only, but did not consider it for optimizations of read-miss transactions which is in contrast to what we do in this study. To do this, we let the latest node that provided the copy act as the next one to provide it. While this heuristic is expected to work well for producer-consumer data, as do invalid hints, it is also expected to work well for migratory data when a block always migrates among nodes in the same order.

We note that the new protocol presented in this section is expected to perform better than the one in Section 2.3 because it does not introduce extra network hops when the hint is wrong. However, a successful hint requires an extra message—in essence the *GRd* message in Figure 6a. This will result in a higher traffic than the original hint protocol in Section 2.3 which as a secondary effect can increase the read miss penalty. Note, however, that the new protocol does not involve more messages in read-miss transactions as compared to the COMA protocol with no hints.

The usefulness of hints is dictated by (i) the fraction of misses that can use hints and (ii) the success rate of the hints. Whereas coherence misses can often use hints, we note that cold misses in general can not be optimized because the hint heuristics discussed require that the block has been in the AM before.

4. Simulation Methodology

In order to study the performance improvement obtained by the COMA protocols in the previous sections, we have developed detailed architectural simulation models using the CacheMire Test Bench [3]; a program-driven simulation platform for shared-memory multiprocessors. A simulator consists of two parts: (i) a functional model of multiple SPARC processors driven by a parallel program and (ii) a memory-system simulator. The processors in the functional simulator are delayed according to the timing characteristics of the memory-system simulator. Thus, an interleaving of global memory references that conforms with the target system is maintained.

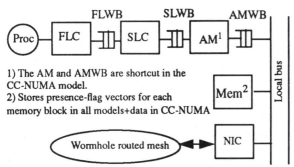

1) The AM and AMWB are shortcut in the CC-NUMA model.
2) Stores presence-flag vectors for each memory block in all models+data in CC-NUMA

Figure 7: Simulated processing node organization.

The detailed organization of the CC-NUMA and the COMA processing node models appears in Figure 7. It consists of a SPARC processor connected to a 2 Kbyte, write-through, and direct-mapped first-level cache (FLC in Figure 7). The write buffer of the FLC (denoted FLWB) is connected to a direct-mapped second-level cache (SLC). To focus on the relative performance of our CC-NUMA and COMA models, we vary the size of the SLC in the simulations. In the CC-NUMA model, the SLC is lockup-free and copy-back and connected through its request buffer directly to the local bus. The SLC is filled from either the local memory module or from a memory module in another node. By contrast, in the COMA models, the SLC is write-through and interfaces directly to an infinitely sized attraction memory (AM) which in turn is connected to the local bus through its request buffer (AMWB). The particular location of the AM is motivated by the fact that it has to be interrogated on each SLC miss. The block size in the FLC, in the SLC, as well as in the AM is 16 bytes. The FLWB contains eight entries and the SLWB and the AMWB both contain 16 entries. In all models, a memory module stores a presence-flag vector for each memory block; in CC-NUMA, the data block for each memory block is also contained in this module.

Regarding the timing parameters, the processors are clocked at 100 MHz (1 pclock = 10 ns). We handle all instruction and private data references as if they hit in the FLC. These references and all shared data references that hit in the FLC take 10 ns to service and do not stall the processor. The SLC access time is 30 ns and an access that misses in the FLC but hits in the SLC takes 6 pclocks (including 3 pclocks to fill the FLC). The AMs in the COMA models and the fully-interleaved memory modules in the CC-NUMA model have an access time of 90 ns. The time for an FLC block fill from the AM is 18 pclocks whereas an FLC block fill from the memory module takes 30 pclocks. The difference stems from that the latter also includes two local bus accesses that each takes 60 ns.

We simulate systems of 16 processing nodes interconnected by a single 4-by-4 wormhole routed synchronous mesh[2] that is clocked at 100 MHz and with a flit size of 64

bits. A request requires two flits whereas a reply (containing data) requires six flits. It takes on average 12 pclocks and 16 pclocks to transfer a request and a reply from one node to another, respectively, in a conflict free system. We simulate contention in all parts of the machine though.

The latency involved in a global read-miss transaction depends on the initial mapping of pages among nodes. The allocation we assume maps the 4 Kbyte pages to the nodes in a round-robin fashion; consecutive virtual pages end up in nodes with consecutive node numbers. On the other hand, the latency encountered by ownership transactions are completely hidden because we assume release consistency [9] and an aggressive lockup-free second-level cache design. Finally, synchronizations use queue-based locks and we allocate a single lock per memory block to avoid false sharing.

To evaluate the performance of the implemented protocols, four benchmark programs summarized in Table 1 are used. The programs are written in C, compiled with gcc (version 2.1) with optimization level -O2, using ANL macros [2] to express parallelism. Three of the applications (MP3D, Water, and Cholesky) are part of the SPLASH suite [16] and the fourth application—the multigrid version of Ocean—has been provided to us from Stanford University. MP3D uses 10K particles for 10 time steps. Cholesky was run using the bcsstk14 benchmark matrix. Water uses 288 molecules for 4 time steps, and Ocean works on a 128x128 grid with tolerance 10^{-7}. All statistics are gathered in the parallel sections.

Table 1: Benchmark programs.

Benchmark	Description
MP3D	3-D particle-based wind-tunnel simulator
Water	Water molecular dynamics simulation
Cholesky	Cholesky factorization of a sparse matrix
Ocean	Ocean basin simulator

5. Experimental Results

We first study the relative performance of the various protocols by looking at the effects on the execution time in Section 5.1. Then in Section 5.2 we focus on the efficiency with which the protocol extensions using hints reduce the average number of network hops for read-miss transactions. Finally in Section 5.3 we study to what extent the COMA protocols with hints affect the network traffic.

2. While a separate request and reply mesh is a customary solution to avoid deadlock [14], we simplify our models by using infinite network buffers in each network switch.

5.1 Effects on the Execution Time

The experimental evaluation considers five systems. We first compare the performance of the CC-NUMA protocol according to Section 2.1 (denoted NUM) with the flat COMA protocol according to Section 2.2 with no hints (denoted COM). The execution times for the four applications on top of these systems appear in Figure 8 normalized to the execution time of COM. For each application, we consider three SLC cache sizes: 4, 16, and 64 Kbytes. To see the fraction of the execution time that stems from handling cache misses and synchronizations, we have decomposed each execution-time bar into three sections: The bottommost section is the busy time, the middle section is the read-miss penalty, and the topmost section is the time spent waiting for a lock to be granted. (The time waiting for writes to perform is eliminated because we assume release consistency [9].)

Comparing CC-NUMA with COMA with no hints with 4 Kbyte caches first, we see that the execution time for CC-NUMA is between 13% (MP3D) and 100% (Ocean) longer than COMA which stems from the relative number of cold, coherence, and replacement misses in the applications. Whereas all replacement misses can be handled locally in the COMA model (we assume infinite AMs), most replacement misses result in global read-miss transactions in CC-NUMA. In Table 2, the miss rates for each application decomposed into cold, coherence and replacement misses are shown. In Ocean and Cholesky, the replacement miss component dominates the total miss rate which explains why COMA performs significantly better than CC-NUMA for these applications. By contrast, the difference in performance between CC-NUMA and COMA is smaller for MP3D where coherence misses dominate. As we consider larger SLCs, the difference between CC-NUMA and COMA vanishes as we can see in Figure 8 for the 64 Kbyte SLC systems. These results are consistent with [17].

Table 2: Cold, coherence, and replacement miss rate components for 4, 16, and 64 Kbyte SLCs.

Appl.	Cold miss rate	Coh. miss rate	Repl. m. rate (4 Kb)	Repl. m. rate (16 Kb)	Repl. m. rate (64 Kb)
MP3D	1.6%	8.9%	6.7%	6.5%	1.8%
Water	0.01%	0.2%	0.8%	0.3%	0.1%
Chol.	0.8%	0.2%	4.5%	0.8%	0.2%
Ocean	0.03%	0.6%	11%	5.8%	1.9%

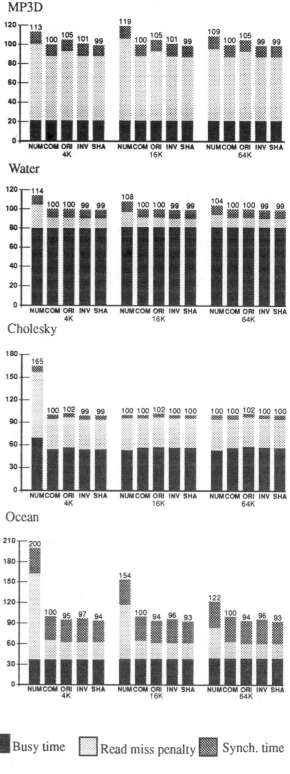

Figure 8: Execution times relative to Flat COMA with no hints for all simulated systems at various SLC cache sizes (4, 16, and 64 Kbytes).

We next consider the three COMA protocols using hints. ORI refers to the original COMA protocol that involves an extra network hop if the hint turns out to be wrong in Section 2.3 and that uses the shared hint heuristic according to Section 3.2. We do not consider the invalid hint heuristic for this protocol because of the low success rate and because of the devastating effect wrong hints have on the performance of this protocol. We also simulate the new COMA protocol in Section 3 using invalid hints (INV) and shared hints (SHA).

Starting with the original protocol using hints (ORI) and for systems with 64 Kbyte second-level caches, we see in Figure 8 that it does better than the COMA protocol with no hints (COM) only for Ocean, where the execution time is 6% shorter. Ocean contains producer-consumer data as a result of nearest neighbor communication in the multigrid solver. Therefore, shared hints have a high success rate. For the other applications, ORI exhibits mixed results; while the execution time for Water is virtually unaffected, ORI does worse than COM for MP3D and Cholesky. The fact that the execution time is between 2 and 5% longer for these applications as compared to COMA with no hints suggests that the success rate is less than 50%. Migratory data dominates in MP3D and Cholesky. The fact that ORI shows poor performance indicates that data does not migrate among nodes in the same order which would be beneficial for shared hints.

Continuing with the new protocols using shared (SHA) and invalid (INV) hints, we see that they perform somewhat better than the COMA protocol with no hints in some cases, but never worse. This is due to the fact that they do not introduce extra latency for unsuccessful hints. Both hint heuristics do best for Ocean because of its producer-consumer data dominance, although SHA does best. Although it is difficult to make out from Figure 8, SHA manages to cut the read-miss penalty in COMA with no hints by 14%. The reason why SHA is better than INV is that SHA also can shortcut misses to migratory data when the latest supplier of the data block on a miss is the same as the current one. This happens in Ocean for the barrier counter that is read and written by all processors in turn. Due to the deterministic order of how locks are granted by the queue-based lock mechanism, barrier counters tend to migrate among nodes in the same order, giving SHA an advantage over INV. This also explains why we see a shorter synchronization stall time for SHA than INV in Ocean.

Overall, although the new protocol with shared hints performs better than the original protocol with shared hints for all applications, the performance improvement over COMA without hints is significant for Ocean only. In the next two sections, we will analyze in detail the reasons for the modest improvements of hints.

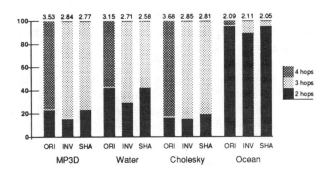

Figure 9: Distribution of 2, 3, and 4 hop read-miss transactions in the protcols using hints.

5.2 Effects on the Number of Network Hops

To analyze how successfully the new protocols using hints reduce the number of network hops, we counted the average number of hops needed to carry out each read-miss transaction using hints.

Depending on the location of Local, Home, Master, and Remote with respect to each other, read-miss transactions could be serviced in two network hops with the original COMA protocol with no hints. To separate out the effects of how successfully hints can cut the number of network hops, we charge a network hop for all requests in a read-miss transaction even if the source and the destination is the same node. For example, if Local and Home refer to the same node, we charge a network hop for the global read-miss request (*GRd*) in Figure 3. Therefore, the average number of hops for coherence misses in the original COMA protocol with no hints is three.

In Figure 9, we show the average number of network hops needed for misses using hints on top of each bar for the three COMA protocols. Considering the original protocol using hints (ORI) first, we note that it requires 3.53, 3.15, and 3.68 hops for MP3D, Water, and Cholesky, respectively; more hops are needed than in the protocol without hints. To understand why this is the case, we also show in Figure 9 the fraction of misses using hints that require two, three, and four hops. While we also record the miss transactions that have to be retried due to other pending coherence actions on a block, such transactions contribute marginally to the statistics. From the distribution, we clearly see that a majority of the misses in ORI need four hops. These four-hop miss transactions stem from unsuccessful hints. Because of the apparent low successful rate of hints, ORI does worse than the COMA protocol with no hints for MP3D and Cholesky. The read-miss penalty in Water is a small fraction of the overall execution time; hence unsuccessful hints have a marginal effect.

Looking at the new protocols using hints (SHA and INV), we see that the average number of hops is lower than three for all applications. Specifically, virtually all four-hop misses have been wiped out because a miss request exploiting hints is sent to the potential master as well as to Home in these protocols, simultaneously. Unfortunately, because of the low success rate of hints, most misses still need three hops in all applications except Ocean which is why we see modest improvements in the execution times. Another important observation is that shared hints do consistently better than invalid hints for all applications; the fraction of two-hop misses is higher in ORI and SHA than in INV.

5.3 Effects on Network Traffic

One negative effect of the new hint protocols as compared to the original hint protocol is the extra message needed for each read-miss transaction. These messages increase traffic and could increase the contention which as a secondary effect could affect the read-miss penalty. To study whether this is a significant effect, we first measured the average bandwidth needed, measured in Mbytes per second, for each application which we show in Figure 10 for the COMA protocol with no hints. We see that MP3D requires more than twice the bandwidth of the other applications. It appears that MP3D and Cholesky are the only applications where the network could saturate.

In Figure 11 we show the total network traffic for each application and for the different protocols with hints, normalized to the traffic of the COMA with no hints assuming 4 Kbyte SLCs. Whereas the original protocol using hints requires (ORI) at most 6% more traffic than the protocol with no hints, the new protocols using hints do not require significantly more traffic. The only case where the traffic gets significantly higher is for the Water application under the INV protocol. Fortunately, Water needs considerably less bandwidth than the other applications as we see in Figure 10 so the extra traffic is not an important issue.

Comparing the traffic of ORI and SHA, we see that the difference is typically less than 10%, indicating that the traffic increase due to extra messages sent in SHA protocols is negligible compared to the traffic caused by other coherence messages. Finally, if we compare the traffic

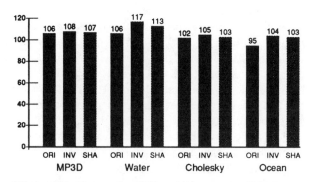

Figure 11: Network traffic relative to the COMA protocol with no hints (100%).

caused by INV and SHA, we see that SHA does better thanks to its higher success rate for hints.

6. Concluding Remarks

Flat COMA protocols manage to remove global read-miss transactions for replacement cache misses because of the attraction memories which act as huge main-memory caches. Unfortunately, other miss types such as coherence misses may involve as many as three network traversals because the directory must be interrogated before a copy can be located.

In this paper, we have studied how COMA protocols can use hints to find the node that keeps a copy without interrogating the directory. This can cut the number of network traversals by one. The first contribution is a new protocol for using hints that does not introduce extra network traversals if the hint is wrong. Secondly, we propose a new hint heuristic that considers the last node that provided the copy as the one that is going to provide a copy when the next attraction-memory read miss is encountered.

We evaluate these new protocols and compare their performances with previously proposed COMA protocols using detailed architectural simulations and four applications. Our new protocol with the enhanced hint heuristic performs better than previous COMA protocols, and the read-miss penalty is improved by 14% for one out of the four applications. For the other three applications, however, the improvement is marginal. The reasons for this are the low fraction of read misses that can use hints and the low success rate of the hint heuristic. While the hint heuristics seem successful for producer-consumer data, they perform poorly under migratory sharing which seems especially hard to deal with. In addition, since a protocol that exploits hints is more tricky and because it also needs some extra state in terms of storage for the identity of a potential holder of a copy, we feel that the improvement in performance that hints can provide does not justify the cost.

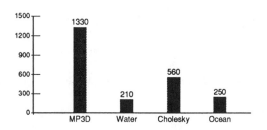

Figure 10: Bandwidth need for the COMA protocol with no hints.

Acknowledgments

We want to thank our colleague Håkan Grahn and the anonymous reviewers for numerous comments on an earlier version of this paper.

References

[1] Agarwal, A. *et al.* "The MIT Alewife: A Large-Scale Distributed-Memory Multiprocessor," in *Proceedings of the 1st Workshop on Scalable Shared-Memory Multiprocessors.* Kluwer Acedemics, 1991.

[2] Boyle, J. et al. *"Portable Programs for Parallel Processors".* Holt, Rinehart, and Winston Inc. 1987.

[3] Brorsson, M., Dahlgren, F., Nilsson, H., and Stenström, P. "The CacheMire Test Bench - A Flexible and Effective Approach for Simulation of Multiprocessors," in *Proceedings of the 26th Annual Simulation Symposium*, pp. 41-49, March 1993.

[4] Burkhardt III, H. et al. *"Overview of the KSR1 Computer System."* Technical Report KSR-TR-9202001, Kendall Square Research, Boston, February 1992.

[5] Dahlgren, F., Dubois, M., and Stenström, P. "Fixed and Adaptive Sequential Prefetching in Shared-Memory Multiprocessors," in *Proceedings of 1993 International Conference on Parallel Processing*, Vol. I, pp. 56-63, 1993.

[6] Dahlgren, F., Dubois, M., and Stenström, P. "Combined Performance Gains of Simple Cache Protocol Extensions," in *Proceedings of the 21th Annual International Symposium on Computer Architecture*, pp. 187-197, April 1994.

[7] Dahlgren, F. and Stenström, P. "Using Write Caches to Improve Performance of Cache Coherence Protocols in Shared-Memory Multiprocessors," accepted for publication in *Journal of Parallel and Distributed Computing*. June 1994.

[8] Gharachorloo, K., Gupta, A., and Hennessy, J. "Memory Consistency and Event Ordering in Scalable Shared-Memory Multiprocessors," in *Proceedings of the 17th Annual International Symposium on Computer Architecture*, pp. 15-26, May 1990.

[9] Gharachorloo, K., Gupta, A., and Hennessy, J. "Performance Evaluation of Memory Consistency Models for Shared-Memory Multiprocessors," in *Proceedings of ASPLOS IV*, pp. 245-257, April 1991.

[10] Grahn, H., Dubois, M., and Stenström, P. "Implementation and Evaluation of Updata-Based Cache Protocols Under Relaxed Memory Consistency Models," accepted for publication in *Future Generation Computer Systems,* July 1994.

[11] Gupta, A. and Weber, W-D. "Cache Invalidation Patterns in Shared-Memory Multiprocessors," in *IEEE Transaction on Computers,* 41(7), pp. 794-810, July 1992.

[12] Gupta, A., Joe, T., and Stenström, P. *"Performance Limitations of Cache-Coherent NUMA and COMA Multiprocessors and the Flat-COMA Solution,"* Technical report, Stanford University, CSL-TR-92-524, October 1992.

[13] Hagersten, E., Landin, A., and Haridi, S. "DDM - A Cache-Only Memory Architecture," In *IEEE Computer*, Vol. 25, No. 9, pp. 44-54, September 1992.

[14] Lenoski, D. *et al.* "The Stanford Dash Multiprocessor," in *IEEE Computer*, Vol. 25, No. 3, pp. 63-79, March 1992.

[15] Mowry, T. and Gupta, A. "Tolerating Latency through Software-Controlled Prefetching in Scalable Shared-Memory Multiprocessors," in *Journal of Parallel and Distributed Computing*, pp. 87-106, June 1991.

[16] Singh, J.P., Weber, W.-D., and Gupta, A. "SPLASH: Stanford Parallel Applications for Shared-Memory," in *Computer Architecture News*, 20(1):5-44, March 1992.

[17] Stenström, P., Joe, T., and Gupta, A. "Comparative Performance Evaluation of Cache-Coherent NUMA and COMA Architectures," in *Proceedings of the 19th Annual International Symposium on Computer Architecture*, pp. 80-91, May 1992.

Decoupled Pre-Fetching for Distributed Shared Memory

Ian Watson & Alasdair Rawsthorne
iwatson@cs.man.ac.uk, arawsthorne@cs.man.ac.uk

Dept. Computer Science, University of Manchester
MANCHESTER M13 9PL, England.

Abstract

Distributed Shared Memory is an architectural technique for providing a global view of memory in a distributed store parallel machine by introducing mechanisms which make copies of remote areas of memory when required. One of the major problems of such a system is the performance penalties incurred due to the need to wait for areas of memory to be copied. This can be ameliorated to a certain extent using user annotations, compile time analysis or run-time prediction to aid pre-fetching of data. This paper proposes a decoupled run-time technique for pre-fetching in a Distributed Shared Memory environment which is applicable in circumstances where static analysis is difficult and the access patterns are sufficiently irregular that run-time prediction may fail. The proposal is in the form of a dual processor structure where one processor performs a partial evaluation of the program and thereby anticipates the need for data fetches before they are required by a second processor which performs the full evaluation.

1: Introduction

Commercial parallel computers which present a machine wide view of memory have, until fairly recently, had a physically shared store structure resulting in limited extensibility. More highly parallel machines have used physically distributed store and presented the programmer with message passing models of computation for inter process communication. More recently, it has become much more widely accepted that, at the programmers model level, a global view of memory is highly desirable even if the machine has a physically distributed store structure.

Distributed shared memory can be implemented in a variety of ways. Advanced multi-processor caching schemes such as that incorporated in the Stanford DASH machine [1] use techniques similar to those found on shared memory multi-processor systems. Other machines such as the DDM [2] and the KSR1 [3] use schemes which have commonalities with virtual memory and are sometimes termed 'Virtual Shared Memory' or VSM. The

different approaches seem to reflect differing views concerning the spatial locality of 'cached' data and hence the size of memory block or page used. The techniques described in this paper tend towards larger units and try to exploit the spatial locality within those units; we therefore describe our principles in the context of VSM although most of it is also applicable to cache systems.

One major problem with VSM and associated techniques is that if global data is found, by a processor, not to be resident in its local memory, then the current thread of computation must wait for that data to be fetched remotely and hence performance is impaired. One solution to this problem is to make the processor switch threads at this point; this technique is at the heart of many approaches to parallel computing from Dataflow to 'parallel slackness' in PRAM related ideas [4]. One notable attempt at latency hiding by multiple threading is the TERA machine proposed by Smith [5]. The drawback with thread switching is that it implies a change of context. In order to minimize the impact of this it is either necessary to provide specialized facilities for multiple contexts or to minimize the context carried by a thread. The former probably implies duplicated register banks, caches etc. while the latter leads in the direction of fine grain parallelism. A further detailed analysis of these consequences is outside the scope of this paper but the experience of the authors has led to a belief that it is better to avoid the problems than to attempt to solve them!

An obvious way to avoid the problems is to attempt to predict the future usage of data and 'pre-fetch' operands into local memory before they are needed. Pre-fetching has been studied extensively to hide latencies in a number of environments ranging from uni-processors with 'on-chip' cache to distributed memory multi-processors with multiple levels of caching.

'Software' based pre-fetching schemes use information inserted either by the programmer or compiler in anticipation of future data usage. They normally require hardware support in the form of special instructions; for example those defined by the DEC-Alpha [6]. A comprehensive study of loop based compiler directed pre-fetching in scientific applications has been reported by

Mowry et al. [7]; they observe that, although the techniques work well for a range of programs, those which use irregular addressing present problems. They further note that, in non-scientific codes, where irregular addressing patterns are common, software based pre-fetching is likely to be considerably more difficult. Similar results have been reported by Tullsen & Eggers [8]; they additionally observe that a significant proportion of cache misses are due to 'false' invalidations caused by sharing of cache blocks. The need to re-fetch invalidated pages is almost impossible to predict using compile-time methods.

'Hardware' based schemes use dynamic information about blocks which are currently cached to predict future usage [9]. Their performance is heavily influenced by choosing the correct prediction algorithm and may be less successful than software schemes for programs with a wide variety of access patterns, for example large 'strides' through an array. A more elaborate scheme has been proposed by Baer & Chen [10][11] which keeps a dynamic data access prediction table based on data accesses related to program counter values and strides observed between previous data accesses. The scheme uses a pseudo program counter with jump prediction which runs ahead of the real program counter to perform the pre-fetching using the stored information. This technique overcomes, to a certain extent, the disadvantages of the simpler hardware schemes.

Fetch-Execute decoupling [12][13] is a technique which was originally proposed to overcome the latency of main memory accesses in high performance single computer systems, usually with heavily interleaved main memory. The program instruction streams are separated into those which are concerned with address calculations and those which operate on the data and are run in separate hardware units. The fetch is performed ahead of the execute in order to overcome the memory latency; the fetched data is normally buffered in a FIFO queue and consumed by the execute unit. Decoupled machines do not seem to have gained favour although recent studies [14] have produced optimistic results for decoupled architectures on a wide variety of programs.

Decoupling is clearly a pre-fetching technique, although, to our knowledge, it has not been studied in the context of cache pre-fetching in multi-processors. Lee et al. [15] proposed a scheme where pre-fetches are initiated from an instruction lookahead buffer in a uni-processor environment but this does not involve decoupling the fetch and execute and is more an application of pipelining.

Decoupling is relatively complex and, in most proposals, requires specialized hardware. It is doubtful whether, in the context that most pre-fetching has been studied, it would be a cost-effective proposition. However, in a VSM environment, one major task is to cache larger blocks of data in the local 'main' memory of a processor and overcome large communication latencies. In these circumstances, the penalty for a 'miss' is large and the need for longer term prediction accuracy is greater. This paper therefore investigates the application of decoupling to pre-fetching in this environment.

The scheme proposes the use of 'off the shelf' CPUs with the necessary extra functionality provided in an external memory management unit for each processor, thus avoiding the need for much specialized hardware. In many cases the decoupling can be achieved by running identical code in the two CPUs and there is thus no need for specialized compiler technology. It is believed that the application of decoupling in a VSM system has a number of potentially interesting advantages. Spatial locality can be exploited to achieve decoupling in circumstances where it would break down in other environments and allows pre-fetching of data structures common in non-numeric programming (lists, trees etc.) where loop based techniques do not work. Additionally, if the pre-fetching is wholly non-speculative (which, it is believed, can be achieved for a wide range of programs) the occurrence of 'write' misses and resulting page invalidations can be predicted. The exploitation of this latter property is not investigated in the paper but mentioned as an additional motivation for the proposed scheme.

The major part of the paper concentrates on the physical structure of a single computational processor. A parallel machine would comprise a collection of such units interconnected by a high speed network. Although the details of network structure are important to a physical implementation, we do not wish to detail them here. Network structures such as that developed for the Thinking Machines CM5 [16] would certainly be applicable.

The techniques described are specifically concerned with the problems associated with pre-fetching. A complete system based on these ideas would, of course, need to address issues of distributed memory coherence and consider how the pre-fetching scheme would interact with the distributed memory model. Such issues are beyond the scope of this paper and are a subject for further study. However, our simulator implements a distributed memory model which is similar to (and believed to be equivalent to) the 'release consistency' [17] model implemented in the DASH prototype [1]. We consider this to be sufficient to provide a basic validation of the ideas.

2: Virtual Shared Memory Principles

Virtual Shared Memory is essentially just an extension of well known virtual memory principles. Each processor in a parallel system has local random access memory which is accessed via a Memory Management Unit (MMU). The virtual address space is common to all processors but their local memory will, at any time, hold only a fraction of it. The MMU records those areas of virtual memory which are currently in local memory and performs the address translation necessary to access them. If access is made to an area of memory which is not currently resident, the MMU must signal this 'miss' allowing for a copy of the appropriate memory to be made, from another processor, before the computation proceeds. The ideas described in this paper are concerned with minimizing the cost associated with making such copies.

If a processor wishes to perform a 'write' access it must ensure that the effects of this write are observed correctly by other parallel processors in the system. The normal way of ensuring this is to gain 'ownership' of the area of memory and invalidate all other copies. This may sound like a high cost operation in a parallel system, but there is evidence that, as long as one assumes an overlying programming model with a sensible shared variable strategy, the memory of the system can be maintained in a consistent state with relatively small overhead [18]. Again, the pre-fetching techniques under consideration are intended to reduce the cost by obtaining prior knowledge of the requirement to obtain ownership.

There are some alternatives in the implementation of VSM systems which are important but do not effect the basic principles and we have made simplifying assumptions in subsequent discussions.

- Page, segment or item based copying. The simplest implementation would probably use a fixed size page as the unit managed and copied by the VSM system. The use of a smaller unit such as a sub-page segment or single data item may result in lower data transfer overheads and more efficient use of memory at the expense of more complex MMU requirements and possibly less exploitation of spatial locality. In the following descriptions we will assume the use of a fixed size page for simplicity.
- The ownership of an area (page) of virtual memory. If a processor needs a copy of a page it must know where to obtain it from. We will assume that the information is available using one of the many distributed directory schemes described in the literature [1].

3: Decoupled VSM Structures

3.1: A Simple Read-Fetch Problem

Consider a section of a parallel program, running on a processor of a parallel system which implements VSM, which operates on (for the moment reads) elements of an array which are mapped on to multiple pages of virtual memory. We will use the array data structure as the main focus of our preliminary discussion; it is probably the most important data structuring mechanism in parallel computation and also simplifies the initial descriptions. Assume that many of the elements of the array are accessed

but in a manner which is not readily determinable at compile time and that the pages which hold the array are scattered around separate memories of the system.

A simple example of such code (in a suitable HLL!) might be:-

```
for i = 0 to N do
    sum = sum + A[f(i)]
```

The function f is assumed to be defined elsewhere; it returns integer values which are within the bounds of the array but which, for successive values of i, are distributed across all possible values in a way which is not predictable except by computing the function at run time. This does not necessarily mean that successive accesses to the array A have no spatial locality, just that it cannot readily be predicted and hence neither static nor simple dynamic run-time pre-fetching techniques can be used to predict the usage of elements of A.

In these circumstances there is a high probability that a processor performing this computation will attempt to make memory accesses to addresses for which there are no local copies in the processor's local memory. The memory management unit will therefore signal that the page must be fetched from another memory in the system. We do not, at this point, wish to discuss the detail of how this is achieved but, in any real system, the communication overheads and network latency will ensure that hundreds of machine cycles will elapse before the copy appears in local memory and the computation can proceed. Clearly, this will have a significant impact on the performance of the system; given that the incidence of such page 'misses' will increase with an increasing number of parallel processors, it is likely that the performance of any parallel machine implementing VSM using a simple 'copy on demand' system will exhibit poor parallel speed-up.

3.2: Decoupling the Fetch

Techniques related to Decoupling can, however, enable us to do a significant amount of prediction at run-time. In any modern or structured approach to the above program, the variable i would be local to a small section of the program; probably allocated on the stack. We will assume therefore that the store location holding i is, and will remain, local to the processor on which the section of code is running and any accesses to it can be made rapidly (in a real processor, we could probably assume that it was in cache). Computations involving only such local variables will therefore never require data to be fetched from elsewhere and can always proceed unhindered. In this case, therefore, the generation of the addresses required to access A can run independently, i.e. they can be **decoupled**.

In a normal approach to decoupling, where we are trying to mask latencies which occur during main store

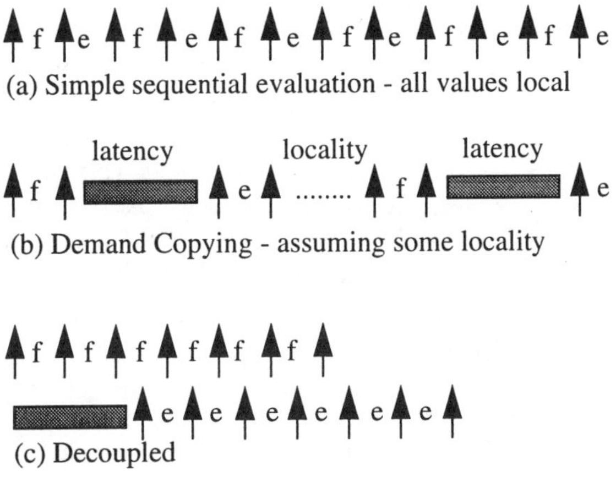

(a) Simple sequential evaluation - all values local

(b) Demand Copying - assuming some locality

(c) Decoupled

Figure 1. Possible VSM Execution Sequences

access, the code performing address generation and data accessing is generated separately from that which uses the data. This is then run on separate fetch and execute units with the phasing adjusted so that instructions using the data are delayed by the store latency. The fetched data is normally held in a FIFO queue between the fetch and execute units to accommodate small variations in phasing.

In the VSM environment the latency can vary significantly depending on whether or not the data already exists in local store. Using the structure just described, we would need to delay the execution unit by a time equal to, or greater than, the upper bound which we set for a remote transfer. We would also need to provide a mechanism for queuing local data values in correct order and inserting remote ones in the correct place when available.

We will not examine the detail of such a structure as we propose to develop a more flexible approach. However, this simple model serves to examine the effects of the decoupling.

Returning to our simple array example; the fetch unit would compute values of i and f, and issue addresses to form the queue of data values. The execution unit, delayed by the appropriate amount, would consume these to form the final value of 'sum'. Figure 1. shows a comparison of various execution patterns which might occur with our simple program under various conditions.

1(a) shows the sequential fetch and execute cycles which would occur on a single processor where all data were local. 1(b) shows a demand copying VSM system where, assuming some locality of access to copied pages, the execution time would be extended by idle periods equal to the time that it takes to copy a page from a remote processor. 1(c) shows the effect of decoupling assuming that the total fetch time is greater than the latency. In these circumstances, the performance is improved over the serial case due to the pipeline overlap of the fetch and execute phases (assuming that they are not significantly extended by being separated). This pipelining effect is a bonus; the

major achievement of the decoupling is that it has eliminated most of the idle periods due to the copying latency.

Although the example may look over simple it should be noted that there are real computations which are amenable to such techniques; for example, a simple matrix multiply. However, many computations are not sufficiently simple that the fetch and execute can be separated totally, this requires that both the data addresses and the outcome of any control transfers rely only on local values. If a computation were to use global values either to calculate the address of further values or in the evaluation of a conditional control transfer, we would encounter a long delay around the fetch/execute loop needed to cope with the maximum latency. We will return to this issue later following a discussion of an improved physical structure.

3.3: A More Flexible Approach

When attempting to apply the principle of decoupling to VSM, we must recognize the major difference between communications which take place between a processor and its local 'main' memory and those which require the use of communication across a network to another processor's memory. The first have a short fixed predictable latency and the total time required to communicate multiple values is almost directly proportional to their number. The second are longer and, furthermore, the latency may not be either predictable or uniform depending on the characteristics of the communication system and network. In general, because of a significant communication 'setup' time, it is much more efficient to fetch a number of values at a single time rather than fetch them individually. Indeed one of the major reasons for the use of VSM is to exploit locality so that the cost of communication can be amortized over multiple accesses. We therefore have an environment where access latencies to non-local values may vary from a few machine cycles to maybe a thousand or more and we will not know until the access is made. Even then, if it is a remote access and the characteristics of the communication system are non-uniform, we can probably only predict an upper bound. In these circumstances, the simple extension of existing decoupled structures described above is not ideal.

A much more flexible structure results if we consider the fetch and execute sections to be less closely coupled and, in fact, complete CPUs which are each capable of performing the full range of fetch and execute computations. We propose a dual CPU structure in which the processors run with one lagging the other; in general the leading one will be performing the fetch function while the other performs the execution, particularly that associated with global values. However, we have a wide range of possibilities depending on how we compile and divide the code between them. There are also several options for

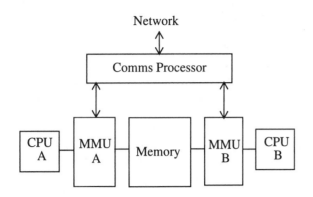

Figure 2. Decoupled VSM Processor Structure

achieving the necessary phasing between the processors and this will be discussed later. The processors have Memory Management Units with special functionality. An outline of this physical structure is shown in Figure 2.

Assume, for the moment, that the CPUs A & B are each allocated their own stack space in virtual memory where they hold local variables. It is assumed that the computation will consist of parallel 'threads' and the local variables belonging to a particular thread will never be accessed from outside one processor. However, global variables are common to both CPUs A & B and can be accessed from anywhere. MMU A has the following properties:-

- A read access to a local variable will always succeed and return a value.
- A write access to a local variable will always succeed and modify the value.
- A read access to a global variable may succeed or result in a page fault. In either case, we continue with the computation in CPU A, but in the case of a page fault, notify the Comms Processor that the page is needed. It is assumed that the comms processor will have a record of pages currently being fetched and will initiate a fetch if necessary. The value returned by this access could be a special **null**. (see later for a more complete discussion)
- A write access to a global variable will not be performed by the MMU A in any circumstances but a request will be issued for an exclusive copy of that page (invalidating other page copies) and the computation will proceed.

MMU B performs normal address translation with all reads and writes completed.

Return, for the moment, to the simple program example. We can make use of the new structure in similar way to the previous one with code running on CPU A which calculates array addresses and causes the fetching of pages

of global virtual memory into local memory by trying to read the array. However, because we have not formed a queue of operands, the code which runs on CPU B must repeat the address calculations before accessing memory. As long as we have a page replacement strategy which does not reject pages which have recently been accessed from CPU A, all global variables required by the computation will be available for it to complete normally in CPU B. The functionality we have defined for the MMU also allows us to also achieve the correct result by running the complete program, phased appropriately, on both CPUs. If the elements of the array were not local when accessed in A we would simply form spurious values of A's local copy of 'sum'.

This may not, at first sight, seem to be an improvement, particularly as we would, by running the complete code twice, lose the performance advantages of pipelining the fetch and execute. One benefit though, is that such a structure can be built using 'off the shelf' integrated CPU components rather than the more specialized custom circuits which might be required for dedicated fetch/ execute hardware. In addition, acceptable performance can probably be achieved without specialized compiler technology because of the ability to run the same code, although higher performance might result with more intelligent separation of fetch and execute functions. The major benefits of this structure become apparent when we move to more complex examples.

4: Extended use of Decoupled VSM

4.1: Simple Linked Structures

Traditional fetch/execute decoupling copes only with cases similar to those described above where the phases can be separated fully. This is because we are normally trying to hide a small fixed latency and, if the value being fetched is required to progress the next fetch computation we must wait for that time before proceeding. In decoupled VSM, the situation is somewhat different. The major latency we are trying to hide is that of a remote fetch of a copy of memory and, assuming we use a page based VSM system we would hope that each fetch would result in the copying of a significant number of global values which, due to spatial locality, we would be using in the future. We can make use of this to extend the capability of our decoupled system. Traditional uses of decoupling usually only work well for array like data structures with relatively simple access patterns like those described above. An operation on a structure like a linked list, for example, is likely to perform very poorly because the fetching of each element of the list is totally dependent on the previous. We believe that, with appropriate compilation techniques, decoupled VSM can hide remote access latencies in many of these more complex cases.

Let us consider a linked list composed of elements described by the following C like definitions:-

```
typedef
    struct cell{
            int value;
            struct cell *next;
            } cell;
cell *list;
```

And a computation of the form:-

```
{
cell *ptr;
sum = 0;
ptr = list;
while (ptr != NULL)
  {
  sum = sum + ptr->value;
  ptr=ptr->next;
  }
}
```

This is the list based equivalent of the array example, simply traversing the list and summing the values. The major problem with this program is that each data item fetch uses an address which is contained in the previous element of the list and is likely to cause long pauses in the fetching process if a remote access is required. In practice, we would hope that, in a paged demand copying VSM system, a significant number of cells would be grouped on to pages (how well this happens depends critically on the memory management strategy in a practical system, but locality within pages is not an unreasonable assumption) and only a fraction of the accesses would result in a 'miss'. However, they would still have a significant impact on performance. Figure 3. indicates the form of the execution which would result.

The access to 'value' will cause a suspension if the cell pointed to is not local. When the value is available, either following a suspension or due to locality, the sum will be followed by the assignment and test of the next pointer.

The nature of the program is such that these suspensions in the fetch phase are inevitable, however, given adequate locality, we can use decoupling techniques to minimize the effect of them on the progress of the overall

f1 = ptr->value
e = sum +
     f2 = ptr->next , while ..

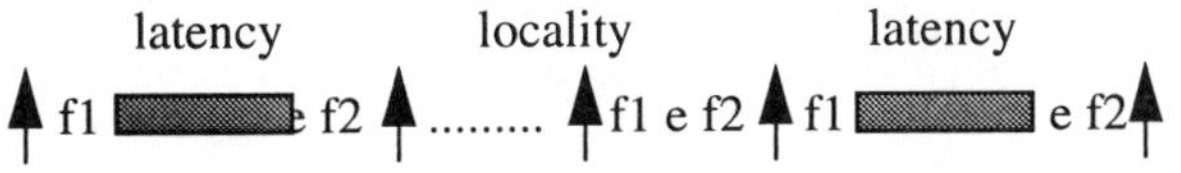

latency   locality   latency

Figure 3. Demand Copying VSM system

computation. It is possible to identify that part of the loop which is concerned with the fetch and separate it simply by omitting the statement in the body of the loop concerned with the addition:-

```
while (ptr != NULL)
  {
  ptr=ptr->next;
  }
```

If we run this on CPU A of our structure together with the complete program on B, we might expect to obtain the execution pattern shown in Figure 4.

f = while (ptr!=NULL), ptr->next
f' = ptr =
f &e = complete loop including 'sum'

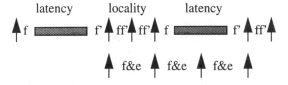

latency   locality   latency

Figure 4. Decoupled VSM list program.

The ability of CPU B to progress unhindered is determined by the latency L, the fetch time F (=ff' above), the total loop execution time E (= f&e above) and the number of consecutive elements N of the structure which are either grouped on a single page or found locally on other pages already fetched. As long as:-

$$N *E > L + N * F \text{ or } N > L/(E-F)$$

then the elements will always be available in B's store when required. In order to see whether this is realistic, consider some typical values. Compiling the loop for a SPARC, we get F=9 instructions and E=14. If we assume an instruction execution time of 25nS and a latency of 5μS this requires N ≥ 40. Given that, for more complex loops the value of E-F would almost certainly be significantly greater than this, the technique seems promising.

We need to note here that CPU A does suspend when it discovers a value which it needs for an address calculation but is not available from memory. In an earlier description of the MMU functionality we mentioned that the MMU might return a special 'null' value to CPU A if a global value were not available. If we were able then to propagate this null through subsequent computations we could suspend CPU A if it were ever used as an address (or as the operand to a test which might cause a control transfer). An alternative, but simpler, solution would be to plant 'critical' load instructions in the code when an access was made for a global value which was to be used as above. This could probably be achieved using an 'off the shelf' CPU whereas the previous solution would probably require special hardware. The disadvantage is that it requires compile time analysis.

4.2: More Complex Structures

The list is a simple example of a linked structure which represents the other major large data structuring technique (apart from arrays) that we are likely to encounter in real computation. In practice, in parallel systems, it is likely that linked tree/graph structures will be important with parallel sections of a program operating on sub-trees. It should be clear that, as long as the trees are built in a way that ensures some locality, similar principles to those used above will apply.

A further issue which needs discussion, is the way in which data structures, of all types, are used. The examples we have considered so far have the common property that the size of the computation is fixed; the array example goes around the loop N times and the list example follows the list to its end. The important feature is, in fact, that the test which terminates the loop is a function of values that are certain to be local when the test is made and therefore the 'fetch' can be separated into a smaller loop which can be allowed to 'run ahead' fetching values which are known to be required. There are computations, however, where the requirement for future parts of a structure depends on the value of those currently being processed. This happens with all sorts of data structures including arrays, typically where the computation involves searching the structure for a particular value contained in it.

To keep it simple, consider searching a list with a loop of the form:-

```
while (ptr!= NULL) && (!found)
  {
    found= (ptr->value == 42)
    ptr=ptr->next;
  }
```

Here it is not possible to identify a smaller loop which can be separated from the main computation to pre-fetch values because all parts of the computation are required in the loop test.

The solution we could consider is to omit that part of the test which depends on the loop body from the fetch computation, reducing it to be identical to the simpler loop case above.

Because of the nature of the dual CPU structure and the MMU, the effect of running this loop in CPU A will be to cause those values which *might* be used in the computation to be fetched avoiding any suspensions in CPU B, but

without affecting the result of the final computation. Clearly there is the danger of doing wasted work and we need to devise mechanisms to prevent CPU A running too far ahead.

4.3: The CPU Phasing

We have described the two CPUs in our structure running code with a delay between them. In order to produce a proposal for a practical system we need to consider in a little more detail how this is done. We need to cater for cases where CPU A suspends because it needs the value of a non-local variable and, although we have not shown it happening in our examples so far (because we hope to avoid it in most cases) the case of CPU B suspending if there has been a delay in a global value arriving. In both these cases, the need to suspend will be signalled by the MMU.

To ensure the lack of suspensions, we need to keep B delayed by the correct amount, however, particularly in the more complex cases we have mentioned where we might consider some speculative fetching, we also do not want to let A get too far ahead, filling the real store with copies too far in advance.

The solution proposed is that each CPU has its own Program Counter and fetches instructions as normal from memory. Either CPU may have its progress of instruction execution halted by a miss signalled by its MMU. In addition CPU A may be stalled if its execution gets too far ahead of CPU B. The simplest way to achieve this is to keep a count of pages fetched by A which is decremented when the page is first used by B. If this count exceeds a pre-determined limit then CPU A is stalled until a further decrement.

By removing the explicit delay between the two CPUs, the potential for efficient execution in the absence of MMU induced suspensions is increased. CPU A will start executing code to ensure that required global values are made local. CPU B will start at the same time and only suspend if its MMU signals a 'miss', it will be restarted by the arrival of the page of information requested by A. In this way the delay will only be introduced when necessary resulting in the minimum total execution time.

5: Simulation Experiments

The evaluation of a system of the type described is very difficult to perform with any degree of confidence unless very detailed simulation is performed. Many cache pre-fetching schemes have been evaluated using trace driven simulation, but we felt that the distortion of access patterns caused by VSM misses would be sufficiently severe that such techniques would be doubtful. We have therefore developed a detailed instruction level simulator for the proposed structure. The CPU used is an idealized load/store RISC with no pipelining or first level cache, this was thought sufficient to produce a realistic assessment of the wider decoupled VSM ideas without introducing the complexity of simulating a real CPU. However, this decision implied the need to produce code for the idealized processor from a suitable high level language. It was felt that C was the obvious choice to give access to a range of existing benchmarks. We therefore have produced a modified version of the Princeton lcc system [19] which compiles directly to the simulator instruction set.

Three programs were chosen for our initial investigation. Two of them are 'scientific' codes with relatively regular accessing patterns and therefore could probably be handled by other pre-fetching techniques. However, it is important to show that our scheme works as expected on such access patterns. The third uses a tree data structure which has been allocated dynamically and, unless one could make very optimistic forecasts about the behaviour of a dynamic memory manager, would almost certainly defeat most software and hardware pre-fetching methods.

5.1: MMult - Matrix Multiply

MMult is a 64x64 blocked matrix multiply distributed statically over 32 processors, each producing a 2x32 component of the result. The input matrix values are initialized across the processors in a way which ensures the need for full communication of values. The result matrix is not produced using 'in place' update of one of the input matrices thus avoiding invalidation traffic.

5.2: Nbody - Gravitational Attraction

Nbody is a simple N-body problem calculating the gravitational attraction and resulting velocity and position of 512 particles over a number of iterations. Each of 32 processors is allocated a group of 16 particles and the computation involves calculating the forces between those and all other 512. There are a variety of ways of writing this program, some of which are more sympathetic to distributed memory. We have chosen a method similar to that of the SPLASH[20] 'Water' benchmark where the number of particle computations can be halved by updating the forces on a pair of particles for each calculation. This is at the expense of global updates to particles not 'belonging' to a single processor. This is done with the aid of locks and barriers as in the SPLASH suite.

The global data structures are invalidated by a write update each time around an iteration. Due to the relatively simple nature of the gravitational calculations this is a much more severe test of pre-fetching performance than more realistic applications such as 'Water'. However, it was thought that its inclusion would provide an interesting comparison to the other programs which should be expected to decouple well.

5.3: TSpell - Spelling Checker

TSpell is a simplified version of the UNIX 'sp' utility. Given an input word it produces a list of 'close' matches. This involves searching a complete dictionary. The dictionary is held as a binary tree; the example used here is of 2047 words with equal sections of the search distributed across 32 processors. The original dictionary is generated in a single processor thus requiring remote copies to be taken.

5.4: Results

The first two benchmarks were run with identical code on the two CPUs of each processor. For TSpell, the code was separated into fetch and execute sections manually at the C source level. All benchmarks were run on a 32 processor simulator using a page size of 128 bytes (which is considered typical of a real VSM page size). The results are presented for remote fetch latencies of 150 and 600 CPU cycles. The simulation assumes the existence of a communications processor and therefore much of the communication time does not appear in the results. However, it is recognized that some disturbance of CPU performance is inevitable and therefore a communication overhead of approximately 30 cycles per message is included for a message request received; the message reply overhead for page copies is included in the latency. The locks and barriers used in Nbody are implemented in C code and therefore contribute a realistic factor.

The results are presented in bar chart form showing proportions of Execute, Fetch, Communications and Synchronization (lock and barrier) time. The left hand bar of each pair shows normalized execution time with pre-fetching disabled. The figures shown are the average over the active processors, because of the symmetrical nature of the benchmarks, the variation is minimal.

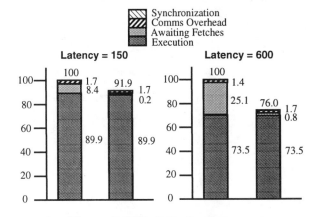

Figure 5. MMult Performance

As can be seen in Figure 5 MMult achieves almost perfect pre-fetch performance. The small pre-fetch time observed is due to the initial latency fetching the first page. The communication overhead remains constant in terms of number of cycles although, as presented, the percentage increases slightly. The data copied is identical, only the timing is affected by the pre-fetch.

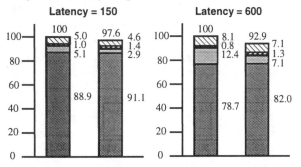

Figure 6. Nbody Performance

Figure 6 shows the simulation results for Nbody. All remote address calculations are done using local variables and therefore we might expect good pre-fetching performance. However, the presence of global updates with locking and barrier synchronization has a detrimental effect as expected and the fetch waiting time is reduced only by a factor of two. This is very similar to the results presented by Chen & Baer [11] for their hardware prefetching scheme on the SPLASH Water benchmark. Given that the program uses very regular addressing patterns we would have expected that our method would perform similarly to a good hardware scheme. No pre-fetching method could be expected to perform well in the presence of continuous global updates.

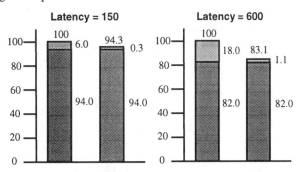

Figure 7. TSpell Performance

TSpell performance is shown in Figure 7. Again following an initial start-up delay, the time spent waiting for remote fetches is very small. A small communication overhead is present for the processor which holds the original copy of the dictionary; this is not shown in the chart.

A dictionary tree entry is 34 bytes and therefore the computation time per node needs to occupy approximately one quarter of the latency to achieve efficient pre-fetching, the string comparisons in the program used ensures this. The success of this locality based decoupling will depend on the interaction between the page size, the number of

spatially local items per page and the computation time per item. Optimistically one might expect the computation time to be proportional to the item size thus cancelling the effect of less local items per page.

Results have been presented for two values of latency which are representative of the minimum and maximum values encountered on a machine such as the KSR 1. As can be seen the ratio between the waiting times with and without pre-fetching is approximately constant. Further experiments outside this range, although not presented here, confirm this result.

6: Conclusions

A technique has been described where the effects of latency in a distributed memory parallel system can be reduced by a pre-fetching technique related to Fetch-Execute decoupling. One major feature of the proposed scheme is that it can be implemented using standard CPU components and that, in many cases, complex compilation techniques are not required.

The ideas have been subject to a preliminary investigation by simulation and it has been demonstrated that significant increases in performance can be obtained for a range of program types. For regular array based problems the performance is comparable with that which might be expected from the best software or hardware schemes. However, we have also demonstrated good performance on a non-scientific problem with addressing patterns which would almost certainly defeat othe pre-fetching methods.

Intuitively, we would also expect our scheme to operate well for irregular addressing patterns which occur in scientific problems which handle sparse structures and those which use 'randomizing' algorithms.These are areas where more detailed simulation results are required.

Further work is also required in a number of other areas. We need to develop a compilation system which will identify 'critical' loads and also separate fetch and execute code when necessary. The feasibility of a hardware implementation must be studied in more detail, covering issues such as caching, memory bandwidth and the exact structure of the memory management units.

Although we intend to continue our evaluation using more complex existing benchmarks, in particular those from the SPLASH [20] suite, the current shared memory programming models which make frequent use of locks and barriers need to be reviewed. It is doubtful if a programming model, which tries to maintain close consistency, is workable for large scale distributed shared memory systems. More advanced parallel programming models such as those described by Reinhardt et al. [21] may provide a more efficient way of using the facilities of such a structure. This is important because these models attempt to use memory models which are less consistent and thus require less synchronization. There is no doubt that our decoupled pre-fetching performance will benefit from such an approach. Therefore, programming models for distributed shared memory must be studied alongside memory consistency models and this will reflect back into the facilities required at the machine level to support them.

7: References

[1] D.Lenoski, J.Laudon, K.Gharachorloo, A.Gupta, J.Hennessey, "The Directory-Based Cache Coherence Protocol for the DASH Multiprocessor", Proceedings of the 17th. Annual Symposium on Computer Architecture, May 1990, pp. 148-159.

[2] D.H.D. Warren and S.Haridi, "The Data Diffusion Machine - a Scalable Shared Virtual Memory Multiprocessor", Proceedings of the 1988 International Conference on Fifth Generation Computer Systems, pp 943-952, Tokyo, Japan, Dec 1988.

[3] J.Rothnie, "Overview of the KSR1 Computer System", Technical Report TR-9202001, Kendal Square Research, 1992.

[4] Valiant L.G., "A Bridging model for Parallel Computation", CACM, August 1990, Vol 33 No. 8, pp103-111.

[5] Smith. B et al. The TERA Computer System" ICS90 ACM Press 1990, pp1-6.

[6] Digital Equipment Corporation, "Alpha Architecture Handbook". 1992.

[7] T.C. Mowry, M.S. Lam, A. Gupta, " Design and Evaluation of a Compiler Algorithm for Prefetching", Fifth International Conference on Architectural Support for Programming Languages and Operating Systems, September 1992, pp. 62-73.

[8] D.M. Tullsen, S.J. Eggers, "Limitations of Cache Prefetching on a Bus-Based Multiprocessor", Proceedings of the 20th. Annual Symposium on Computer Architecture, May 1993, pp. 278-288.

[9] R.Bianchini, T.J.Leblanc, "A Preliminary Evaluation of Cache-Miss-Initiated Prefetching Techniques in Scalable Multiprocessors", Technical report 515, University of Rochester, May 1994.

[10] J-L. Baer, T.F. Chen, "An Effective On-chip Preloading Scheme to Reduce Data Access Penalty", Proceedings of Supercomputing '91, pp. 176-186, 1991.

[11] T.F. Chen, J-L Baer, "A Performance Study of Software and Hardware Data Prefetching Schemes", Proceedings of the 21st. Annual Symposium on Computer Architecture, April1994, pp. 223-232.

[12] J. E. Smith, "Decoupled Access/Execute Computer Architecture," ACM Transactions on Computer Systems, Vol. 2, No. 4, November 1984, pp. 289-308.

[13] J.R. Goodman, J.T. Hsieh, K. Liou A.R. Pleszkun, P.B. Schechter, H.C. Young, "PIPE - A VLSI Decoupled Architecture" Proceedings of the 12th. Annual Symposium on Computer Architecture, June 1985, pp. 20-27.

[14] P. L. Bird, N. P. Topham and A. Rawsthorne, "The Effectiveness of Decoupling," ACM International Conference on Supercomputing, Tokyo, Japan, 1993.

[15] R.L. Lee, P.C. Yew, D.H. Lawrie, "Data Prefetching in Shared Memory Multiprocessors", Proceedings of the 1987 Conference on Parallel Processing, pp28-31.

[16] C.E. Leiserson et al. "The Network Architecture of the Connection Machine CM5", Proceedings of the Fifth ACM Symposium on Parallel Algorithms and Architectures, July 1992.

[17] K.Gharachorloo, D.Lenoski, J.Laudon, P.Gibbons, "Memory Consistency and Event Ordering in Scalable Shared Memory Multiprocessors",Proceedings of the 17th. Annual Symposium on Computer Architecture, May 1990, pp. 15-26.

[18] K.Gharachorloo, A.Gupta, J.Hennessey, "Performance Evaluation of Memory Consistency Models for Shared Memory MultiProcessors", Fourth International Conference on Architectural Support for Programming Languages and Operating Systems, April 1991, pp. 245-259.

[19] C.W. Fraser, D.R.Hanson, "A Code Generation Interface for ANSI C", Research Report CS-TR-270-90, Princeton University, July 1990.

[20] J.P.Singh, W.Weber, A.Gupta, "SPLASH : Stanford Parallel Applications for Shared Memory", Computer Architecture News, 20(1), pp 5-44, March 1992.

[21] S.K.Reinhardt, J.R.Larus, D.A.Wood, "Tempest and Typhoon: User-Level Shared Memory", Proceedings of the 21st. Annual Symposium on Computer Architecture, pp 325-337 April 1994.

Modeling Load Imbalance and Fuzzy Barriers for Scalable Shared-Memory Multiprocessors *

Alexandre E. Eichenberger
Advanced Computer Architecture Laboratory
EECS Department, University of Michigan
Ann Arbor, MI 48109-2122

Santosh G. Abraham
Hewlett Packard Laboratories
1501 Page Mill Road
Palo Alto, CA 94304

Abstract

We propose an analytical model that quantifies the overall execution time of a parallel region in the presence of non-deterministic load imbalance introduced by network contention and by random replacement policy in processor caches. We present a novel model that evaluates the expected hit ratio and variance introduced by a cache accessed with a cyclic access stream. We also model the performance improvement of fuzzy barriers, where the synchronization between processors at the end of a parallel region is relaxed. Experiments on a 64-processor KSR system which has random first-level caches confirms the general nature of the analytic results.

1 Introduction

Load imbalance and synchronization costs can have a significant influence on the execution of parallel programs. In most parallel scientific and engineering applications, processors repetitively update large data-structures in parallel and synchronize themselves with synchronization barriers. Therefore, the overall execution time of these parallel applications is significantly affected by the load imbalance present between synchronization points.

A common source of load imbalance is *systemic load imbalance*, where the workload is unevenly partitioned among the processors as a result of which certain processors consistently arrive late at a synchronization point. Systemic imbalance arises when some processors are assigned a larger share of the overall computation and/or communication requirements. Systemic imbalance can be handled effectively by static partitioning of the workload so that each processor is assigned an equitable workload.

Another important source of load imbalance is *non-deterministic* imbalance, where processors fail to reach a synchronization point simultaneously but typically the processor arriving last changes on each iteration. Non-deterministic load imbalance is generated by several factors: the workload associated with a processor may change from cycle to cycle; the interprocessor communication may incur random delays due to contention; there may be contention for hardware or software resources. Non-deterministic load imbalance can be reduced by dynamic scheduling policies which redistribute the workload to idle processors.

On uniform-memory access machines such as Cray and Convex multiprocessors, non-deterministic load imbalance can be reduced by dynamic scheduling policies which redistribute the workload to idle processors. This approach is less effective on scalable shared-memory parallel machines which have non-uniform memory access times. In such scalable systems, redistribution of the workload is associated with high data movement costs. As a result, these systems are more sensitive to non-deterministic load imbalance.

While the systemic load imbalance is mostly determined by the load imbalance of an application, the non-deterministic load imbalance is also dependent on architectural characteristics of a parallel machines, i.e. the frequency and variation in random delays due to memory or communication contention. It is therefore important to develop an understanding of the impact of non-deterministic load imbalance while designing a scalable shared-memory machine.

In this paper, we develop an analytical model of the execution time of a parallel region in the presence of non-deterministic load imbalance. The execution time is modeled as three parts: computation time, memory reference time, and communication time. The

*This research was supported in part by ONR grant N00014-93-1-0163.

processes do not execute in isolation however: they are assumed to synchronize at the boundaries of the parallel region. Therefore, the overall execution time of a parallel region also takes into account the idle time at the synchronization barriers, where each process idles until all processes reach the barrier.

The first contribution of this paper is the performance analysis of caches with random replacement policy. Whereas random replacement have been previously investigated from the uniprocessor perspective [1], we analyze these caches in a multiprocessor system. We demonstrate that the load imbalance is exacerbated by caches with random replacement policy because the overall execution time may be governed by the processor making the worst replacement decisions.

We analyze cache performance on cyclic access streams because these access stream are common in data-parallel programs that access large data structures. We characterize these access streams as a function of the set size and access stream length. We present the first algorithm that constructs the Markov chains describing the behavior of a cache with random replacement for any cyclic access streams and for any degree of set-associativity. Although the chains grow exponentially in the access stream length and degree of set-associativity, we determine analytic expressions for both the mean and the variance of the cache hit ratio for two-way set-associative caches. This work extends the results in [1] by introducing a new closed form solution for the two-way set-associative cache with random replacement and by investigating the variance of its performance.

The second contribution is the performance analysis of fuzzy barriers, a technique that efficiently tolerates non-deterministic load imbalance without requiring expensive load redistribution. Fuzzy barriers proposed by Gupta [2], achieve this goal by executing independent operations, called *slack*, while waiting for the synchronization. Since there are programming as well as other costs associated with increasing the number of independent computations, it is important to be able to quantify the reduction in idle time due to the introduction of slack in fuzzy barriers.

To our knowledge no analytic model for the performance improvement due to fuzzy barriers has been presented. In a two-processor system, we derive analytically the reduction in idle time due to the buffering provided by independent operations but the general case is not tractable. We carried out a large number of simulations and validated an empirical function that is similar in form to the analytic function. According to this function, the idle time is approximately proportional to the variance of the thread execution time and inversely proportional to the amount of slack.

This paper is organized as follows. First, we present the performance model of caches with random replacement policy in Section 3 and the communication performance model in Section 4. We develop the overall execution time of a parallel region in the presence of non-deterministic load imbalance in Section 5. We determine the execution time improvements due to fuzzy barriers in Section 6. We present measurements that confirm the general nature of the analytic results using experimental runs on the KSR multiprocessor system which has random first-level caches in Section 7. We conclude in Section 8.

2   Related Work

Smith and Goodman [1] have compared the behavior of several cache replacement policies. They provide a closed form solution for the expected hit ratio of caches with random replacement accessed by cyclic access streams exceeding the set associativity by one cache line. Recently, Schlansker *et al* [3] have investigated the design of placement-insensitive caches and studied the random replacement policy. Both studies recommend this replacement policy, but focus on the average random replacement performance and not on its variance.

The source of execution time performance variance has been studied. Adve and Vernon [4] quantified the fluctuation of parallel execution times due to random delays and non-deterministic processing requirements. Dubois and Briggs [5] investigated the performance fluctuation generated by memory contentions and obtained an analytical formula describing the expected number of cycles and its variance for memory references in tightly coupled systems. Sarkar [6] provided a framework to estimate the execution time and its variance based on the program's internal structure and control dependence graph.

The effects of load imbalance are investigated in several articles. Kruskal and Weiss [7] investigated the total execution time required to complete k tasks for various distributions. Madala and Sinclair [8] quantified the performance of parallel algorithms with regular structures and varying task execution times. Durand *et al* studied the impact of memory contention on NUMA parallel machines and provided experimental measurements [9].

Simulation results show that the idle time generated by partial synchronization barriers [10] [11] is significantly lower than that generated by normal synchronization barriers. Greenbaum [10] showed that near-optimal idle time is achievable through Boundary Synchronization, a relaxed synchronization scheme where boundary computations are executed first within each thread. Gupta [2] investigated Fuzzy Barriers, where a region of statements are executed while waiting for the synchronization. Techniques that detect and increase the number of independent operations are presented in [2] [12]. These papers bounded the performance of their *weak*-synchronization schemes by the performance of *strong*- and *no*- synchronization respectively for the upper and the lower bound, but do not propose tighter bounds.

3 Performance of Cache with Random Replacement

Random replacement policy [16] has been implemented in several caches. The advantages of this technique are its simplicity and its low cost. Another advantage of random replacement, is that it does not exhibit the same performance discontinuities as LRU for workloads differing slightly in size, as observed by Smith and Goodman [1]. Schlansker *et al* [3] investigated large secondary caches with random replacement and concluded that they perform better than LRU, especially with high fill ratio.

Cyclic access streams have been used in previous studies of caches [1][3] and are comomon in large data-parallel applications [3], where operations are repetitively executed on large data structures. Cyclic access streams can be viewed as a worst case of temporal sequences and illustrates, as such, an important aspect of cache performance breakdown. Thus cyclic access streams are not intended to be representative of average cache performance, but represent an important component of cache behavior.

3.1 Cache Model

We propose a model that quantifies the expected hit ratio and its variance for a cyclic access stream in an n-way associative cache with random replacement, described by the following three parameters:

n	the set associativity of the cache
l	the length of the cyclic access stream
r	the number of times this access stream is repeated

Assuming an initially empty cache, we can model the behavior of one cache set, determine its content and its transitions (hits or misses) for each of the lines accessed in a cyclic access stream. Figure 1 A illustrates the behavior of a two-way set-associative cache accessed twice by the lines 'ABC'. After the three first compulsory misses, the cache contains either the line tuples 'AC', 'BC', or 'CX'. When the line 'A' is accessed for the second time, the line tuples 'BC' and 'CX' result in replacement misses. However, the line tuple 'AC' results in a hit. The two remaining accesses proceed similarly.

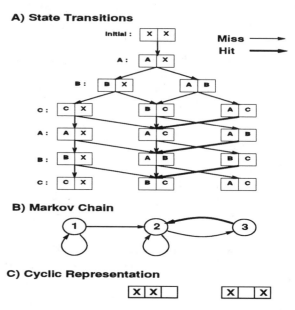

Figure 1: State transitions for a cyclic access stream of length three ($n = 2$, $l = 3$, and $r = 2$)

The state transitions present a regular pattern, illustrated by the Markov chain of Figure 1 B. State 1 represents the transient effect, where one of the initial lines ('X') remains in the set. State 2 corresponds to the state always containing the two most recently accessed lines. Finally, State 3 corresponds to the state containing the current line and the least recently accessed line. For this access stream, all deterministic replacement policies correspond to a cycle in the Markov chain of Figure 1 B. For example, the LRU and OPT replacement policies correspond to the cycle {2} and {2,3} respectively.

We introduce now an algorithm that builds the Markov chain associated with the steady state behavior ($r \to \infty$) of a cache with random replacement policy accessed by a cyclic access stream. The idea behind this algorithm is to focus on when these lines were last accessed: in a cyclic access stream of length l, the ages spans from 0 to $l - 1$. We represent the cache state by l adjacent boxes with increasing age from left to right. Furthermore, a cross in the ith box means that the cache currently holds the line of age i. Figure 1 C illustrates this representation for the steady-states State 2 and 3. With this representation, we can formulate the cache invariant as follows:

I1 there are exactly n crosses in a n-way set-associative cache,

I2 there is a cross in the leftmost box, as the most recently accessed line must be in the cache.

All states in the steady-state Markov chains must respect these two invariants. Therefore, there are exactly $\binom{l-1}{n-1}$ different states. Furthermore, the transition rules between states, corresponding to a new line access, can be formulated as follows:

R1 the rightmost box is moved to the leftmost position (rotates to the right), as the oldest line in the stream becomes the most recent one,

R2 after rotating the boxes, the invariant **I2** may be violated. If so, the invariant is restored by moving one of the crosses to the leftmost box. This corresponds to a cache miss and the choice of the cross is guided by the cache replacement policy. With the random replacement policy, we must investigate all possible replacements.

We construct the steady state Markov chain with the following algorithm: we compute all states that respect the invariants **I1** and **I2**, and we compute the transition from each state by following the transition rules **R1** and **R2**. Furthermore, all transitions originating from a single state are equally likely. Figure 2 A illustrates this algorithm for an access stream of length 4 in a two-way set-associative cache.

The transient effects of the cache correspond to states where some initial lines are not part of the cyclic access stream. We introduce a new transition rule, corresponding to the replacement of one of these unrelated lines:

R3 After rotating the boxes, if the leftmost box is empty and the number of lines that are part of the cyclic access stream is smaller than n, add a cross in the leftmost box.

We construct the transient state Markov chain with the following algorithm: we build the steady-state Markov chain for the set-associativity one through n; then we connect the Markov chains using the transition rule **R3**. Furthermore, all transitions originating from a single state are equally likely.

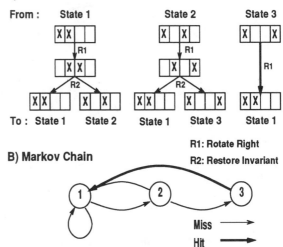

Figure 2: Steady state transitions for a cyclic access stream of length four ($n = 2$, $l = 4$, and $r \to \infty$)

3.2 Hit Ratio and Variance

The first step in determining the cache performance is to obtain the probability distribution of hits. Once its distribution has been determined, the expected hit ratio and its variance are easily computed.

3.2.1 Steady-State

The Markov chains of the steady-state are ergodic[1], thus allowing us to compute the state distribution π by solving the following equations:

$$\pi = \pi P \quad \text{and} \quad \sum_i \pi_i = 1 \qquad (1)$$

where P is a Markov chain transition probability matrix. The hit ratio and variance associated with a Markov chain is obtained as follows:

$$E[hit\ ratio] = \sum_{i \in hit\ states} \pi_i * 1$$

$$Var[hit\ ratio] = E[(hit\ ratio)^2] - E^2[hit\ ratio] \qquad (2)$$

We solve equations (1) and (2) for a two-way set-associative cache accessed by a cyclic access stream of length $l \geq 3$. The corresponding Markov chain is illustrated in Figure 3. Since a hit occurs only in State L-1, the expected hit ratio is equivalent to the

---

[1] A Markov chain is ergodic if it is irreducible, aperiodic, and positive recurrent for all states

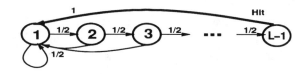

Figure 3: Markov chain of the steady-state transitions for an cyclic access stream of length L ($n = 2$, $l = L$, $r \to \infty$)

probability of State L-1: π_{L-1}. The probability state distribution is defined as follows

$$\pi_i = \frac{1}{2}\,\pi_{i-1} \text{ for } i = 2, \cdots, l - 1 \qquad (3)$$

Solving (1) with (3), we obtain the following state distribution:

$$\pi_i = \frac{2^{l-i}}{2^l - 2} \qquad (4)$$

It results in the following steady-state hit ratio and variance:

$$E[hit\ ratio] = \frac{1}{2^{l-1} - 1}$$

$$Var[hit\ ratio] = \frac{2^{l-1} - 2}{\left(2^{l-1} - 1\right)^2} \qquad (5)$$

Equation (5) is valid for any cyclic access stream of length $l \geq 3$ for a two-way set-associative cache with random replacement. For shorter streams, the expected hit ratio is one and its variance zero.

3.3 Performance Distribution

We can now estimate the performance of a cache with random replacement for a single processor within a given parallel region, assuming that cache performance is dominated by cyclic memory reference streams. First, we determine the number of cyclic memory references $\mathcal{M}_{em}$ generated by one processor within this parallel region. We model this number as a function of the number of processors p and the data size d:

$\mathcal{M}_{em}(p, d)$	number of memory references within a parallel region,
d	size of the data within a parallel region
p	number of processors within a parallel region
t_h, t_m, t_Δ	cache hit penalty, miss penalty, and their difference ($t_\Delta = t_m - t_h$)

Then, we determine the number of competing lines for each set, the access stream length l, which is the

overall stream length divided by the product of words per line and number of sets in the cache. Thus, even when the overall stream length is large, the access stream length for each set can be quite small. Given l, we compute the expected hit ratio and its variance, using Equations (5) for two-way set-associative caches with random replacement. Using the properties of the Central Limit theorem,[2] we assume that for a sufficient number of memory references, the cache performance is normal distributed. A similar assumption was used in [4] [10] [5] , and our measurements on the KSR1 corroborate this assumption. Assuming that the behavior of each set is independent and identically distributed, we obtain the following expected time and variance for the overall execution time spent in the memory system:

$$E[cache] = \mathcal{M}_{em}(p, d)\,(t_m - t_\Delta\,\mu_{hit})$$

$$Var[cache] = \mathcal{M}_{em}(p, d)\,t_\Delta^2\,\sigma_{hit}^2 \qquad (6)$$

where the variance of the cache performance is proportional to the square of the difference between hit and miss penalty and proportional to the number of memory references.

4 Communication Performance

In this section, we attempt to quantify the influence of non-determinism introduced by communication delays. Our approach is based on analyzing a parallel region to extract its communication behavior and predicting its performance distribution on a given parallel machine. This method allows us to get a clearer understanding of whether the random delays generated by a given data size, d, number of processors, p, and parallel machine affect the overall performance of that parallel region significantly.

The communication behavior of a parallel region is characterized by the number of communication events $\mathcal{E}_{vents}$ generated by each processor within its parallel region. The primary factors determining $\mathcal{E}_{vents}$, are the communication pattern and the data partitioning of the parallel region. For example, an algorithm using near-neighbor communication generates communication proportional to $\sqrt{d}$ and $\sqrt{d/p}$ when partitioned along one and two dimensions respectively, where d is the dimension size. Other architectural and hardware factors such as network topology and *automatic update* [15] also have a secondary effect on $\mathcal{E}_{vents}$.

---

[2] The Central Limit Theorem states that the sum of a sufficiently large number of random variables approaches a normal distribution, no matter what the form of their density function is.

4.1 Performance Distribution

Assuming that the delays are independent identically normally distributed random variables $X_1, \cdots, X_{\mathcal{E}_{vents}}$ with parameters μ_{event} and σ^2_{event}:

$\mathcal{E}_{vents}$	number of communication events for one processor within a parallel region
μ_{event}	expected duration of communication events
σ^2_{event}	variance of communication events

the sum of these normally random variables, Y, is a normal random variable with parameters $E[comm]$ and $Var[comm]$ defined as follows

$$E[comm] = \mathcal{E}_{vents}(p, d)\, \mu_{event}$$

$$Var[comm] = \mathcal{E}_{vents}(p, d)\, \sigma^2_{event} \qquad (7)$$

Understanding how $\mathcal{E}_{vents}$ evolves for increasing number of processors and larger data sets is also crucial in estimating the performance of a parallel region.

5 Performance of a Parallel Region

Given the cache normal random processes with parameters defined in equation (6) and the communication normal random processes with parameters defined in equation (7), the cumulative execution time of processor i is itself a normal random process X_i with parameters

$$\mu_p = E[cache] + E[comm] + E[comp]$$

$$\sigma^2_p = Var[cache] + Var[comm] \qquad (8)$$

where $E[comp]$ is the expected computation time. The results of this equation correspond to the expected execution time of a single processor and its variance. The overall performance of this parallel region for p processors correspond to the expected maximum $\max(X_1, \cdots, X_p)$. Based on the asymptotic extremal distribution [17], the extreme value can be asymptotically approximated for independent identically distributed normal distribution with parameters μ_p and σ_p as follows [17]:

$$\sigma_p = \sqrt{\mathcal{M}_{em}\, t^2_\Delta\, \sigma^2_{hit} + \mathcal{E}_{vents}\, \sigma^2_{event}}$$

$$E[idle\ time] \simeq \sigma_p \left\{ \sqrt{2\log p} - \frac{\log\log p + \log 4\pi}{2\sqrt{2\log p}} \right\}$$
$$(9)$$

The first factor of Equation (9), σ_p, is highly machine and parallel region dependent. The second factor in Equation (9) however, is machine independent, proportional to $\sqrt{2\log p}$, and quantifies the intuition that the more processors in the system, the more likely one processor is expected to be significantly slower than the average. This factor is consistent with the estimated total time derived by Kruskal and Weiss [7]. Equation (9) specifically corresponds to the time spent idling in the synchronization barrier due to random replacement and network contention.

Finally, the overall performance of a parallel region corresponds to the expected execution time of a single processor and the expected idle time, defined as follows:

$$E[par\ region] = \mu_p + E[idle\ time] \qquad (10)$$

Equation (9) and (10) approximate the influence of random delays without systemic workload imbalance. In the presence of systemic workload imbalance, these equations allow us to quantify which percentage of the measured idle time is generated by random delays and which percentage is due to the systemic workload imbalance.

6 Performance of a Parallel Region with Fuzzy Barriers

In a fuzzy barrier [2], processors execute independent operations between arriving at a barrier and leaving a barrier. We refer to the execution time of these independent operations as the *slack* of a synchronization barrier. While this technique does not address the problem of systemic workload imbalance, it can significantly reduce the effect of random delays.

We can gain an intuitive understanding of the benefit of fuzzy barriers by studying a two-processor system with discrete Bernoulli delays. A similar two-processor model was mentioned by Kung [18] in the context of Semi-Synchronized Iterative Algorithm but left unsolved. Consider the execution time of a parallel region, delayed by one discrete delay with probability $1/2$ and bounded by a slack equivalent to τ discrete delays. By iterating over this parallel region, we see that one of the processors can be up to τ delays faster than the other one without waiting at the barrier.

Because the relative difference between the two processors is bounded, and because the delays are discrete, the number of states is finite and equal to $2\tau + 1$. The Markov chain associated with this model is shown in Figure 4, where the state label is the amount by

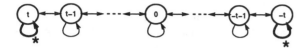

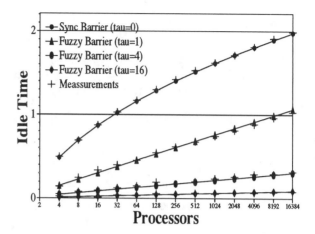

Figure 5: Idle time for a fuzzy barrier with $\tau = 0, 1, 2, 4, 8, 16$ for a parallel region with standard deviation $\sigma_p = 0.5$.

Figure 4: Markov chain for the two-processor Bernoulli-delay model of fuzzy barriers

which one processor is ahead of the other. The steady-state probability distribution of the Markov chain is uniform. Its expected idle time corresponds to the probability of traversing the starred edges in Figure 4 and is equal to:

$$E[idle\ time] = \frac{1}{4} \cdot \frac{1}{\tau + 1/2} \qquad (11)$$

We see that the expected idle time for a two-processor Bernoulli-delay model is inversely proportional to the slack τ, the execution time of the independent operations.

We now consider extending this result for fuzzy barriers with p processors and normal distributed delays with parameters μ_p and σ_p. Extending Equation (11) for the normal case is impractical, because the idle time is a function of all previous delays in all processors. Instead, we present an empirical mathematical approximation.

By running a large number of simulations for a normal distribution we find that the expected idle time is linear in the logarithm space. Curve fitting this slope with the result of the Bernoulli-delay model of Equation (11) in the logarithm space, we obtained the following approximation:

$$E[idle\ time] \simeq .6238 \cdot \frac{\sigma_p^2}{\tau + 1/2} \log p, \qquad \tau \geq 2\sigma_p \quad (12)$$

where σ_p and τ are respectively the standard deviation of a single processor execution time and the slack of the fuzzy barrier. The average error between the simulation and the approximation for $\sigma_p = .5, 1, 2, 4$ and $\tau = 1, 2, 4, 8, 16, 32, 64$ is less than 12 percent.

Figure 5 compares the simulation results and the approximation as computed with Equation (12) for $\mu = 10$ and $\sigma = 1/2$,. The average error in expected idle time between the simulation and the approximation is less than seven percent.

Equation (12) relates the amount of idle time due to random delays with standard deviation σ_p when using a fuzzy barrier, where the slack is τ. This equation is accurate when $\tau \geq 2\sigma_p$, namely when the probability of having delays shorter than τ is at least 68

percent. Otherwise, the idle time behaves more like Equation (9). To the best of our knowledge, this result is the first that quantifies the performance of a *weak*-synchronization scheme. Previous articles [10] [11] bounded the performance of week-synchronization using the performance of *strong-* and *no-* synchronization for the upper and the lower bounds respectively.

7 Measurements

We performed several experiments to validate our models. We ran two synthetic programs to measure the idle time generated by random replacement policy and network contention on a 64-processor KSR1. Furthermore, we investigated the benefit of fuzzy barriers on a real application with complex data streams: a sparse solver.

7.1 Cache Generated Idle Time

We measured the steady-state behavior of the two-way cache with random replacement of the KSR1 parallel machine. Each KSR1 cell contains a data and an instruction primary-cache, each 256 KB (random replacement, 2-way associative, 64 sets) as well as a 32 MB secondary-cache (LRU replacement, 16-way associative, 128 sets). One run consists of accessing the primary cache r times with a cyclic access stream of length l. Our results are averaged over a thousand runs.

We measured the expected hit ratio and its variance, and compared these measurements with the analytical results of Equation (5). Figure 6 illustrates the hit ratio for one up to ten competing lines per set. For three competing lines (cyclic access), the hit ratio is around 34 percent, larger than LRU (0 percent) and smaller than OPT (50 percent).

Figure 7 illustrates the measured and analytical variance of the hit ratio. The measured variance is larger than the one computed by Equation (5). We believe that this difference is partially due to the fact that we could not turn off the hardware interrupts. These inaccuracies are more significant in Figure 7 than in Figure 6 because the variance is a secondary effect.

Figure 8 illustrates the idle time generated by a cyclic access stream of length three and four. These measurements are specific to the KSR1[3]. They were obtained by measuring a large number of runs on a single node and by using these runs to simulate a system with large numbers of processors. The measurements are compared with the results of Equation (9), with the total number of memory reference $\mathcal{M}_{em}$ set to 1920 and 2560 for three and four competing lines respectively. The standard deviation used is the one shown in Figure 7.

The hit ratio of an individual processor for three competing lines mapped in a single set is 34%. However, the results presented in the graph demonstrates that the effective hit ratio is reduced to 30% for 64 processors because all processors wait for the processor that made the worst replacement decisions.

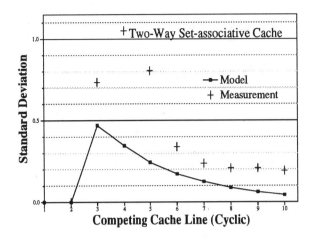

Figure 7: Variance in a two-set associative cache ($r = 1920$)

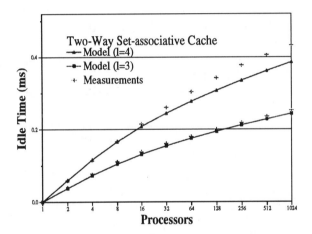

Figure 8: Idle time generated by two-way associative cache with three/four competing lines (1920/2560 accesses)

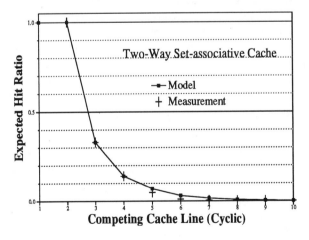

Figure 6: Hit ratio in a two-set associative cache ($r = 1920$)

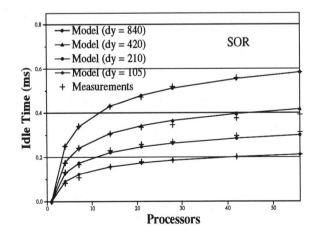

Figure 9: Idle time generated by communication delays for SOR for four different data sizes

---

[3] The measurement of the cache-generated idle time is dependent on the time difference between the hit and miss penalty of the cache. On the KSR1, this difference is 47 cycles ($t_\Delta = 2.35\ \mu s$).

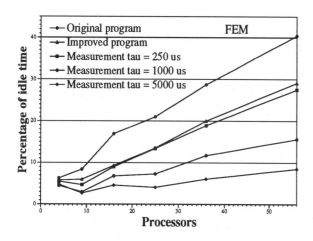

Figure 10: Overall percentage of idle time in FEM-ATS

7.2 Communication Generated Idle Time

We implemented a relaxation algorithm (SOR) where each element is averaged with its four neighbors to measure the idle time generated by communication. The relaxation is performed in parallel with two alternating arrays, thus avoiding additional communication due to race conditions among processes.

The two-dimensional data of size (d_x, d_y) is partitioned along the x-dimension, and the number of data per processor is kept constant, to avoid interferences with the memory subsystem. The resulting communication per processor is $4d_y$ elements because each processor acquires one element in write mode (the element to update) and one element in read mode (east or west neighbor element) for each of the $2d_y$ elements of the overlap region. On the KSR1, the unit of communication is a cache line of 16 words, and therefore the total number of communication events per processor ($\mathcal{E}_{vents}$) is equal to $4\lceil d_y/16 \rceil$. On the KSR1, we estimated the standard deviation of a single communication event (σ_{event}) by running our program for 56 processors and obtained $17\mu s$ [15].

Figure 9 illustrates the idle time generated by communication delays in the SOR program on the KSR1. We notice that the idle time indeed varies as described in Equation (9). For example, multiplying the data size (d_y) by four doubles the idle time spent at a synchronization barrier.

7.3 An Example: a Sparse Solver

The two previous synthetic programs presented a highly regular memory access and communication behavior respectively. These programs were useful to

demonstrate the presence of random delays and to validate our models. In this section, we investigate the behavior of a complete parallel application, to demonstrate the usefulness of our model for random delays and fuzzy barriers.

We analyze the behavior of FEM-ATS [13], an application which solves a system of complex linear equations iteratively using a diagonal-preconditioned symmetric gradient method. This application presents a highly irregular memory and communication pattern due to a sparse matrix multiplication and is therefore a good example of a complex application. In this paper, we used an input data size of 20033 complex elements for the FEM-ATS application.

An iteration consists of eight vector operations and three synchronization barriers. The data are partitioned along one dimension among processors and can result in systemic workload imbalance, as some of the elements may require more computation and/or communication depending on the non-zero pattern of the sparse matrix.

Figure 10 illustrates the percentage of time spent in synchronization overhead, which include the synchronization cost, the idle time due to random delays, and the idle time due to systemic workload imbalance. The upper curve corresponds to the behavior of the original FEM code, the second curve corresponds to the behavior of the improved FEM code, and the three remaining curves plot the additional performance improvements that could be achieved with a slack of 250, 1000, and 5000 μs per relaxed synchronization barriers. In the improved FEM code, the slack accounts for approximately 5 percent of the total execution time and results in an overall performance improvement of 4.8 percent, yielding an overall speedup of 37 for 56 processors.

8 Conclusion

Load imbalance and synchronization costs can have a significant influence on the execution of parallel programs. While systemic load imbalance can be handled effectively by static partitioning, reducing the effect of non-deterministic load imbalance is more problematic on scalable shared-memory parallel machines, because the dynamic redistribution of the workload results in high data movement costs on machines with non-uniform memory access times.

In this paper, we develop an analytical model of the execution time of a parallel region in the presence of non-deterministic load imbalance. The overall execution time of a parallel region is modeled using four components: computation time, memory reference time, communication time, and synchronization time. We identify caches with random replacement policy as a source of non-deterministic load imbalance in multiprocessor systems. We present a novel way for representing the steady-state and transient behavior of an n-way set-associative cache with random replacement under a cyclic access stream of length l. For a two-way set-associative cache, we derive expressions for the mean and variance of the hit ratio distribution. We demonstrate using measurements on the KSR that the idle time generated by caches with random replacement can be significant.

Fuzzy barriers insert a slack, τ, consisting of independent operations, while waiting for the synchronization. Though it is an important concept that has been suggested and used by several researchers, to our knowledge the effect of τ on overall idle times has not been previously evaluated. We present an empirical mathematical approximation for the idle time on a p-processor system, directly proportional to the variance of the execution time of a single processor and inversely proportional to τ. This model enables a qualitative understanding of the benefit of introducing slack.

References

[1] J. E. Smith and R. J. Goodman, "Instruction cache replacement policies and organization," *IEEE Trans. Computers*, vol. C-34, pp. 234–241, March 1985.

[2] R. Gupta, "The fuzzy barrier: A mechanism for high speed synchronization of processors," *Proc. Int. Conf. Arch. Support Prog. Lang & OS*, pp. 54–63, 1989.

[3] M. S. Schlansker, R. Shaw, and S. Sivaramakrishan, "Randomization and associativity in the design of placement-insensitive caches," Technical Report HPL-93-41, HP Laboratories, June 1993.

[4] V. S. Adve and M. K. Vernon, "The influence of random delays on parallel execution times," *ACM SIGMETRICS Conf. Meas. Model. Comp. Sys.*, pp. 61–73, 1993.

[5] M. Dubois and F. A. Briggs, "Performance of synchronized iterative processes in multiprocessor systems," *IEEE Trans. Soft. Eng.*, vol. SE-8, pp. 419–431, Jul 1982.

[6] V. Sarkar, "Determining average program execution times and their variance," *Proc. ACM SIGPLAN Conf. Prog. Lang. Des. & Impl.*, vol. 24, no. 7, pp. 298–312, 1989.

[7] C. P. Kruskal and A. Weiss, "Allocating independent subtasks on parallel processors," *IEEE Trans. Soft. Eng.*, vol. SE-11, pp. 1001–1016, October 1985.

[8] S. Madala and J. B. Sinclair, "Performance of synchronous parallel algorithms with regular structure," *IEEE Trans. Par. & Dist. Sys.*, vol. 2, pp. 105–116, January 1991.

[9] M. D. Durand, T. Montaut, L. Kervella, and W. Jalby, "Impact of memory contention on dynamic scheduling on numa multiprocessors," *Proc. Int. Conf. Par. Proc.*, vol. 1, pp. 258–267, 1993.

[10] A. Greenbaum, "Synchronization costs on multiprocessors," *Paralled Computing*, vol. 10, pp. 3–14, 1989.

[11] C. S. Chang and R. Nelson, "Bounds on the speedup and efficiency of partial synchronization in parallel processing systems," Research Report RC 16474, IBM, 1991.

[12] R. Gupta, "Loop displacement: An approach for transforming and scheduling loops for parallel execution," *Proc. Supercomp. '90*, pp. 388–397, 1990.

[13] D. Windheiser, E. Boyd, E. Hao, S. G. Abraham, and E. S. Davidson, "KSR1 multiprocessor: Analysis of latency hiding techniques in a sparse solver," *Proc. Int. Par. Proc. Symp.*, pp. 454–461, April 1993.

[14] E. Rosti, E. Smirni, T. D. Wagner, A. W. Apon, and L. W. Dowdy, "The KSR1: Experimentation and modeling of poststore," *ACM SIGMETRICS Conf. Meas. Model. Comp. Sys.*, 1993.

[15] E. L. Boyd, J.-D. Wellman, S. G. Abraham, and E. S. Davidson, "Evaluating the communication performance of mpps using synthetic sparse matrix multiplication workloads," *Proc. Int. Conf. Supercomp.*, pp. 240–250, jul 1993.

[16] R. L. Mattson, J. Gecsei, D. R. Slutz, , and I. L. Traiger, "Evaluation techniques for storage hierarchies," *IBM Systems Journal*, vol. 2, pp. 78–117, 1970.

[17] H. David, *Order Statistics*. New York: Wiley, 1981.

[18] H. T. Kung, "Synchronized and asynchronous parallel algorithms for multiprocessors," in *Algorithms and Complexity: New Directions and Recent Results* (J. Traub, ed.), pp. 153–200, New York: Academic, 1976.

A SURVEY OF SOFTWARE SOLUTIONS FOR MAINTENANCE OF CACHE CONSISTENCY IN SHARED MEMORY MULTIPROCESSORS

Igor Tartalja and Veljko Milutinović

Department of Computer Engineering
School of Electrical Engineering
University of Belgrade
POB 816
11000 Belgrade, Yugoslavia
E-mail:{etartalj, emilutiv}@ubbg.etf.bg.ac.yu

ABSTRACT: *This paper represents a comprehensive survey of software solutions for maintenance of cache consistency in shared memory multiprocessor systems. The lack of widely known, acceptably systematic, and flexible classification in this research field has been our basic motivation for this work. We have proposed here a classification based on a set of ten carefully selected criteria that we considered most relevant. Existing solutions have been described and decomposed on the basis of this classification. Different solutions correspond to various points of an abstract multidimensional criterion-space. Such generalized approach enables the points corresponding to non-existent but potentially useful solutions to be noticed and selected for exploration.*

1. INTRODUCTION

Shared memory multiprocessor systems represent an efficient architectural support for applications characterized with significant data sharing among parallel processes. The efficiency of these systems can be significantly improved if cache memories are used. Presence of cache memories is important for two reasons. First, because of the speed difference between the processor and the main memory. Second, because of the access contention for both, the interconnection network and the memory modules. A shared cache [YEH83] helps about the speed difference, but not about the access contention. Private caches enable most of the memory references to be satisfied locally, which decreases the contention on both the interconnection network and the memory modules.

One problem which is inherent to the use of private cache memories is potential inconsistency of the memory system. If several processes on several processors access the shared data, several copies of shared data will exist in private cache memories. If these data are changeable, after a change made by one processor, other copies become out of date. They should be either invalidated or modified before some other processor gets to use them. This problem is being worked on for at least two decades now. Consequently, there exists a variety of possible solutions to the problem. Two major approaches are the hardware and the software maintenance of the consistency of private caches.

Hardware approaches make the consistency maintenance

This research was partially sponsored by the FNRS. For further information refer to emilutiv@ubbg.etf.bg.ac.yu

Proceedings of the 28-th IEEE/ACM Hawaii International Conference on System Sciences, Maui, Hawaii, U.S.A., January 3-6, 1995.

fully transparent for all levels of software, which simplifies the programming model of the multiprocessor system with private cache memories, but increases the hardware complexity (and usually the price) of the system. One recent survey of hardware approaches is given in [TOMAŠ93].

Software approaches [WULF72, GOTTL82, PFIST85, BRANT85, EDLER85, SMITH85, CHERI86, VEIDE86, MCAUL86, LEE87b, CHEON88, CYTRO88, CHEON89, MIN89, BENN90b, TARTA92, DARNE93] lift the transparency of the problem above the operating system level or the compiler level. This complicates the programming model to some extent (which is not necessarily a large drawback), but decreases the complexity of the hardware support (which can be significant). Also, software approaches tend to be more efficient than hardware approaches, in a class of non-numeric applications characterized with the predominantly migratory data [ADVE91]. This survey of software approaches can be treated as the continuation of the effort which started with the above mentioned survey of hardware approaches [TOMAŠ93].

Motivation to do the classification and the survey presented in this paper comes from the lack of a wide, systematic, and flexible classification and a corresponding survey of software solutions. Existing survey papers in the field of cache consistency focus mostly on the hardware solutions. For example, papers [ARCHI86] and [EGGER88] present and compare (using simulation methodologies) hardware schemes based on snooping. Paper [AGARW88] gives a survey and an evaluation of hardware schemes based on directories. Paper [TOMAŠ93] contains the most comprehensive survey of only hardware solutions. Paper [STENS90] contains both hardware and software solutions, but the included solutions are not presented into details, and many recent software solutions are missing. Paper [CHEON90] gives a comparative analysis of three software solutions based on the assistance of compiler, developed by Cheong and Veidenbaum. Paper [MIN92] contains a view of software solutions, and proposes one relatively narrow classification of software solutions.

This paper proposes a set of criteria for the classification of software solutions. Existing software solutions are presented in the context of these criteria. After that, the proposed classification is generalized through the introduction of an abstract space of relevant criteria. Each specific software solution is associated with one specific point (specified with multiple coordinates) of the multidimensional criterion space. This type of generalization marks the points with no known solution associated. Some of these points correspond to solutions which are potentially useful under the circumstances.

The paper is organized as follows. Second section proposes a set of classification criteria, defines the basic classes of software solutions, and mentions typical examples for each class. Third part contains a wide survey of existing solutions, based on the above mentioned classification. Fourth part introduces a generalization of the above classification, and points to some potentially useful solutions, not found so far in the open literature.

2. A PROPOSAL FOR THE CLASSIFICATION OF SOFTWARE SOLUTIONS

One of the most widely cited definitions of memory system consistency (coherency) is the Censier-Feautrier definition from [CENSI78]. It states that "a memory scheme is coherent if the value returned on a load instruction is always the value given by the latest store instruction with the same address." This definition enables the copies of shared data temporarily to contain different values. It is only important that the value is updated before it is read. The possibility to delay the consistency maintenance related activities to the moment when they are necessary, decreases the frequency of the consistency maintenance related activities, and consequently the system overhead. Most of the software solutions exploit this possibility to do the consistency maintenance related activities with a delay.

The widely used basic classification criterion is the placement of the consistency maintenance mechanism, in hardware or in software. Hardware solutions make the consistency problem completely transparent to the user, and to all software levels. Software solutions make the consistency problem visible to either the operating system, or the compiler. The virtual machine accessible to the programmer which uses the compiler or the operating system primitive operations must be consistent. This classification has a drawback, since some solutions are hybrid in their nature, and not always easy to classify according to the hardware/software division line. Often, the consistency maintenance algorithm is implemented in software, with a more or less significant hardware support. Still, this paper starts from the hardware/software division, primarily because of the continuation with the widely adopted basic classification of [STENS90] and [TOMAŠ93].

Of the papers which, among other issues, treat the classification of software solutions, the most complete one is the paper by Min and Baer [MIN90]. Their classification is based on several criteria (some of those criteria we have accepted and reproduced in this paper) and encompasses a relatively small number of existing solutions. It will be referred to here as the Min-Baer's classification. This paper proposes a set of 10 criteria which is believed to be wide enough to create clear distinctions among the existing software solutions. Given criteria are not fully orthogonal, i.e. some criteria are derived from another ones. Although, the classification method is flexible enough to enable the widening of the criterion set with new criteria, if and when so required by a newly generated solution. For each criterion, we define a set of corresponding classes. Each class is illustrated with examples from the open literature (a reference to the original paper is included). Also, a "wild card" class is introduced, referred to as (*), which can be associated with any criterion. If a given criterion is irrelevant for some solution, it will be assumed that the solution is marked as (*), in relation to that criterion.

Criterion #1: **Dynamism (D).** Decisions about the consistency maintenance activities to take, can be made at compile time (statically), or at run time (dynamically).

Classes: Static schemes (s) as in [WULF72, VEIDE86, CHEON89], or dynamic schemes (d) as in [SMITH85, BENN90b, TARTA92].

Comment: In this work, only the schemes that require absolutely no compile time analysis, are referred to as dynamic schemes. Consequently, some of the schemes that make the invalidation related decisions at run time, but do perform some compile time analysis, are classified as static schemes.

Criterion #2: **Selectivity (S).** Explicit consistency maintenance related activities (e.g., invalidation) can be done on the entire cache memory (i.e., without any spatial discrimination), or on only a portion of the cache memory (i.e., selectively).

Classes: Indiscriminative schemes (i) as in [VEIDE86], or selective schemes (s) as in [CHEON88, CYTRO88, TARTA92].

Comment: The schemes referred to as selective are characterized with a wide range of granularity of data which can be the subject of the consistency maintenance activities. For example, in the case of the IBM RP3 [BRANT85], there exists a wide plethora of objects, all of them of different sizes, which can be the subject of the invalidation actions. The granularity differences are not reflected through this criterion; however, there is another criterion (to be introduced later) which covers the granularity issue.

Criterion #3: **Restrictiveness (R).** The consistency maintenance related activities can be performed for preventive purposes (conservatively), or only when absolutely necessary (restrictively).

Classes: Conservative schemes (c) as in [VEIDE86, SMITH85], or restrictive schemes (r) as in [CHEON89, TARTA92].

Comment: This criterion could result in a fine division, with much more than just two classes. One could introduce a measure called the level of restrictiveness, defined as the ratio of absolutely necessary consistency maintenance related activities and the total number of performed consistency maintenance related activities, averaged over a number of benchmark programs. An absolutely restrictive scheme would have this ratio equal to 1.

Criterion #4: **Adaptivity (A).** The consistency maintenance algorithm can be fixed or adaptive to the characteristics of the access patterns to the data objects.

Classes: Fixed schemes (f) as in [SMITH85, CYTRO88, CHEON89, TARTA92], or adaptive schemes (a) as in [BENN90b].

Comment: So far, only one adaptive scheme was noticed in the open literature [BENN90b], and there is no need to introduce a finer measure called the level of adaptivity. However, as the time goes by, and other adaptive schemes are introduced, a need may arise for a measure like the level of adaptivity.

Criterion #5: **Locality (L).** The consistency maintenance algorithm may reduce the misses only locally (inter-block reduction), or globally (intra-block reduction).

Classes: Local schemes (l) as in [SMITH85, VEIDE86], or global schemes as in [CHEON89, TARTA92].

Comment: Obviously, this criterion is an extension of the restrictiveness criterion, and is irrelevant for the absolutely conservative schemes (those without any reduction of misses).

Criterion #6: **Granularity (G).** The size and structure of the unit object varies from one consistency maintenance algorithm to the other.

Classes: Line (l) also referred to as cache line or cache block as in [CHEON89], or page (p) as in [WULF72, SMITH85], or segment (s) as in [TARTA92], or flexible object (f) as in [BRANT85, BENN90b].

Comment: To some extent, this criterion extends the selectivity criterion. In the case of fully indiscriminative schemes, this criterion is irrelevant.

Criterion #7: **Blocking (B).** The basic program block in the consistency maintenance process varies in size and structure from one algorithm to the other.

Classes: Critical region (c) as in [SMITH85, TARTA92], or epoch (e) as in [MCAUL86, VEIDE86, LEE87, CHEON89, MIN89], or subroutine (s) also referred to as procedure as in [CYTRO88], or the entire program (p) as in [WULF72].

Comment: Actually, terms like "computational unit" [MCAUL86], "loop" [VEIDE86], "epoch" [LEE87, MIN89], "task level" [CHEON89], and similar, refer to the issue which is essentially the basic consistency block. Consequently, one entire class was introduced, to encompass all these cases.

Criterion #8: **Positioning (P).** Instructions to implement the consistency maintenance algorithm can be positioned at various places in the program.

Classes: Entry/exit into/from the critical region (e) as in [SMITH85, TARTA92], or loop boundary (b) as in [VEIDE86, CHEON89], source/sink of the data dependency (d) as in [CYTRO88], or interrupt procedure (i) as in [CHERI86].

Comment: Some of the schemes do comparisons at each reference (using specialized hardware support), which can also be treated as a consistency maintenance related activity. However, this criterion considers only the special instructions for consistency maintenance (invalidate, flush, post, or similar).

Criterion #9: **Updating (U).** The main memory can be updated at the time of cache write, or with some delay.

Classes: Write-through (t) as in [CHEON89], or write-back (copy-back) (b) as in [CYTRO88, BENN90b], or hybrid which implies both write-through AND write-back (h) as in [SMITH85], or alternative (a) which implies either write-through OR write-back as in [TARTA92].

Comment: One should notice the difference between the hybrid schemes which (as in [SMITH85]) offer write-through for private data and write-back for shared data, on one hand, and alternative schemes which (as in [TARTA92]) proposes one or the other approach to be used exclusively.

Criterion #10: **Checking (C).** Conditions of inconsistency can be checked using several techniques.

Classes: Checking the data type or the reference type (r) as in [WULF72, LEE87a, MIN89], or program structure analysis (s) as in [BRANT85, VEIDE86], or data dependency analysis (d) as in [CYTRO88], or run-time information comparison (c) as in [CHEON89], or monitoring of the traffic on the interconnection network (m) as in [CHERI86].

Comment: The classification based on this criterion should be treated conditionally. Some schemes include more than one technique for detection of inconsistency. For example, this is the case with the scheme in [CHEON88]. In such cases, the schemes is classified according to the technique which dominates. However, for completeness, the presence of other techniques will be indicated accordingly (using slashes, e.g. c/+s+d+r/).

3. AN OVERVIEW OF EXISTING SOFTWARE SCHEMES

This section contains a relatively wide overview of existing software schemes for maintenance of consistency among private cache memories. Using the criteria and the classes introduced in the previous section, a (ten element) set of attributes is associated with each presented scheme. These attributes determine the place of a given scheme in the proposed classification. In accordance with the (first) dynamism criterion, this section is divided into two subsections. One deals with static schemes, and the other with dynamic schemes.

For the reason of presentation consistency, each scheme description of this section includes the elements as follows.
* In the first paragraph:
  (a) Information about the authors and the home institution of their research, project that the research was part of, and the major references to the original work.
  (b) The essence of the contribution, or the major characteristic of the research, in as few words as possible.
* In the second paragraph:
  (c) Description of the scheme, in which the level of details is related to the impact of the scheme, its relevance to the class under consideration, and the amount of data available through the open literature.
* In the third paragraph:
  (d) Final discussion of the scheme (advantages, disadvantages, and possibly a discussion of some specific issues).

At the end, the ten-element descriptor vector is given, which defines the place of the scheme within the overall classification used in this work.

3.1. Static Schemes

Static schemes predominantly rely on the program analysis at compile time. Analysis points to potential causes of inconsistency, and additional information is added to the program, to avoid the fatal inconsistency related errors during the program execution. This additional information includes, but is not limited to, issues like marking of data, marking of references, and insertion of special instructions. This analysis (and related actions) eliminate the need for processors to communicate during the execution of the critical parts of the code, which makes the static schemes well scalable. On the other hand, static solutions degrade the system performance, because the precise prediction of memory conflicts due to the cache inconsistency is not possible (actions are done on the basis of some kind of "worst case" analysis, not on the basis of "deterministic optimum" analysis).

3.1.1. The C.mmp page marking from Carnegie-Mellon University

Wulf and Bell from Carnegie-Mellon University, working on the C.mmp project, among the first, in [WULF72] have noticed the problem of multiple values of shared variables existing concurrently in private cache memories of different processors in a multiprocessor system. The essence of the proposed method for the maintenance of cache consistency is in keeping the read-write shared data out of the cache at all times.

Only the read-only shared pages can be cached in the private cache memories. Particularly this is the case with pages that contain shared instructions. Pages are marked as "cacheable" using a bit which is reserved for this purpose in the relocation registers.

This scheme is extremely conservative, which enables a relatively easy realization, but decreases the processing power considerably [OWICK89].

Classification: (D:s,S:*,R:c,A:f,L:*,G:p,B:p,P:*,U:*,C:r).

3.1.2. The Ultracomputer program structure analysis from NYU

Gottlieb and his coauthors [GOTTL82, GOTTL83], and later Edler with his coauthors [EDLER85], as well as McAuliffe in his Ph.D. thesis [MCAUL86], propose the approach for software maintenance of cache consistency in the Ultracomputer multiprocessor developed at the New York University. The essence of the approach is that the cacheing of read-write shared data is permitted, in the intervals of the program execution when the read-write shared data are used exclusively by one processor.

The Ultracomputer supports two instructions for software managing of cache memories. These instructions are inserted into the user code at compile time. The release instruction frees one cache memory entry, without copying the data (from that entry) into the main memory. This means that the release instruction prevents memory traffic. According to [GOTTL83], the main memory is updated according to the write-back approach. In a later paper [EDLER85], a combined approach is used: write-back for private data, and write-through for shared data. Independently of the cache consistency maintenance, the release instruction can be used, at the exit from a begin-end block, to free the space in cache that was used by the local variables. In the context of cache consistency maintenance, the read-write shared variables are kept in cache only during the time intervals when it is guaranteed that they will be accessed only for read. At the end of these intervals, the variable has to be removed from the cache using the release instruction, and marked as non-cacheable. The second of the two cache consistency maintenance instructions is the flush instruction which copies data from the cache memory entry into the main memory, without erasing the entry. For private data, the flush instruction must be executed when blocking a task, because it may happen that the execution of the task continues on another processor. For data shared by a parent-task and its child-tasks, instructions flush and release are executed before the spawn operation. The variable which was private before a new task was created, now becomes shared, and has to be marked as non-cacheable; however, its value in the main memory is up-to-date.

After the child-tasks are completed, the parent task can continue to work with the same variable, treating it as a private variable, and therefore cacheable. The first next reference to that variable will place its current value into the cache. All activities described here can be done on the segment level, or on the cache level.

This scheme is less conservative compared to the Wulf and Bell scheme. Still, this cacheing scheme has no restrictiveness in the invalidation of shared data. The scheme supports only the locality of references within "safe" intervals. The consistency maintenance related instructions can be made selective with the segment-level granularity; however, something like that would slow them down, due to the required scan through cache directory.

Classification: (D:s,S:s,R:c,A:f,L:l,G:l,B:e,P:b,U:h,C:s).

3.1.3. The RP3 flexible data invalidation from IBM T.J.Watson Research Center

Brantley, McAuliffe, and Weiss in [BRANT85], as well as Pfister with coauthors in [PFIST85], propose a cache consistency maintenance scheme which is similar (but more flexible as far as granularity of data) compared to the one from the NYU Ultracomputer. The research was done at the IBM T. J. Watson Research Center, and was intended for the IBM's RP3 multiprocessor.

At compile time, shared data are marked as cacheable, if they are used exclusively in the given program block. Data marked as non-cacheable in one program block may become cacheable in the next program block, and vice versa. Also at compile time, data are marked as volatile or not, which helps in the efficient managing of the temporary cacheable data. In short, all data include two attributes: cacheability and volatility. These attributes are also specified on the level of segment and page descriptors, for specific segments and specific pages. They are also applied to segment tables and page tables. On the other hand, the RP3 includes a number of different data invalidation instructions: line invalidation, page invalidation, segment invalidation, user space invalidation, supervisor space invalidation, as well as invalidation of all volatile data (which can exist in many different segments or pages). The main memory is updated using the write-through approach.

In general, the cache consistency maintenance strategy of the IBM RP3 scheme is still very conservative; however, its selective invalidation is more flexible in the sense that the granularity of the invalidation can be varied. Consequently, in the case of the IBM RP3 scheme, software designer can use more powerful "tools" in his effort to minimize the probability that a data item is "expelled" from the cache although it may be needed later.

Classification: (D:s,S:s,R:c,A:f,L:l,G:f,B:e,P:b,U:t,C:s).

3.1.4. Cache on/off control from University of Illinois

Veidenbaum proposes in [VEIDE86] a relatively simple static software scheme for cache consistency maintenance in the Cedar multiprocessor, at the University of Illinois. The scheme assumes the program structure based on parallel/serial loops, which are widely used to express parallelism in numeric applications. The essence of the scheme is that compiler inserts special purpose instructions for cache consistency maintenance only at loop boundaries, and at subroutine call points.

Assuming that the main memory value of the shared variable is current, which is achieved here using the write-through approach, the incoherence happens when a value fetched from the cache is different from the value in the main memory. According to this definition, Veidenbaum gives a formal proof of the lemma about the necessary conditions for inconsistency. When processor P_j ($j=1,2,...$) fetches the variable X, the inconsistency will happen if: (1) the value of the variable X is present in the cache memory of the processor P_j, and (2) the new value of X is placed into the main memory, by the processor P_k ($k \diamond j$, $k=1,2,...$), since the processor P_j had accessed the variable X last time. Detection of the necessary conditions of inconsistency can be based on the data dependency graph. As indicated in Figure 1, the inconsistency will happen if the following is satisfied: (1) P_j executes instruction S1 which writes into or reads from X; (2) another processor P_k ($k \diamond j$) executes instruction S2 which writes a new value into X; and (3)

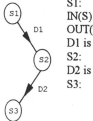

S1: $X \in IN(S1) \lor X \in OUT(S1)$
IN(S) - set of variables read by instruction S
OUT(S) - set of variables written by instruction S
D1 is output dependency or antidependency
S2: $X \in OUT(S2)$
D2 is flow dependency
S3: $X \in IN(S3)$

Figure 1. Data dependency graph containing the conditions of inconsistency

P_j executes instruction S3 which reads from X again.

Instructions for the cache consistency maintenance are as follows: (1) Flush (or Invalidate according to [CHEON90]) which deletes the contents of the entire cache (indiscriminative invalidation); (2) Cache-on which enables the cache, i.e. enables all references to go through the cache; (3) Cache-off which disables the cache, i.e. forces all references to bypass the cache. The proposed cache coherence maintenance algorithm is applied at compile time - each instruction in the program is examined, and where necessary, the above mentioned cache consistency maintenance related instructions are inserted, before, inside or after the loops as well as before/after procedure calls, as follows:

(1) DoAll: Cache memory can be enabled, because there is no inconsistency hazard, since there is no data dependency between different iteration of the loop. The loop is expanded with Cache-on and Flush instructions, so each processor, at the beginning of the iteration assigned to that particular processor, enables its own cache, and deletes the old contents.

(2) DoAccross: Parallelisation is possible with additional synchronization, because of the data dependency between different iterations. Consequently, conditions of inconsistency can arise, and the Cache-off instruction should be inserted in the loop. However, the cache could be enabled, but, in that case, the Flush instruction should be is inserted after the synchronization-related wait-on-semaphore operation, in the appropriate iteration on another processor (which contains the sink of data dependency). With respect to other details, the treatment of the DoAccross loop is the same as the treatment of the DoAll loop.

(3) Serial loop: Cache memory can be enabled because the loop is entirely executed on one processor, which is the consequence of the fact that the structure of data dependencies between

iterations disables any parallelisation. Instructions Cache-on and Flush have to be inserted before the loop.

(4) DoEnd: If the cache was enabled before the loop, and disabled in the loop, the Cache-on instruction is inserted after the loop. If the cache was enabled before the loop, and enabled (fully or partially) in the loop (because the loop was of the type DoAll or DoAccross), the Flush instruction is inserted after the exit from the loop.

(5) Call: Instruction Cache-off is inserted before the call; if the cache is enabled before the call, instructions Cache-on and Flush are inserted after the call.

As it can be seen, the algorithm includes no analysis of individual data dependencies for each particular instruction. It only does the preventive disabling and flushing of the cache, at the boundaries of those loop types in which the non-consistency condition can be created. Consequently, this algorithm is very conservative, its restrictiveness of invalidation is very low, and the invalidation is non-selective.

Classification: (D:s,S:i,R:c,A:f,L:l,G:*,B:e,P:b,U:t,C:s).

3.1.5. Program analysis and reference marking from University of Illinois

Lee, Yew, and Lawrie in [LEE87a, LEE87b] propose a scheme which is based on the static analysis of program structure and the marking of individual references. The research was done at the University of Illinois.

The approach starts from the notion of epoch, which refers to either a parallel loop, or a piece of sequential code between two parallel loops. First, the program is analyzed and segmented into a sequence of epochs. Second, for each data item, its cacheability status is marked for each epoch separately (the cacheability status of a data item may change from one epoch to the other). The marking is done at compile time, using the Paraphrase, a parallelizing FORTRAN compiler. Within an epoch, all references to a variable accessed by a number of processors, but at least by one processor for write, are marked as non-cacheable (references to other variables are marked as cacheable). References marked as non-cacheable bypass the cache at execution time, and access the main memory directly. At the end of each epoch, the invalidation of the cache contents is done, so that the processor obtains up-to-date values from the main memory, at the next reference to the variable. The main memory is updated using the write-back approach.

This algorithm efficiently supports the intra-epoch localities. However, the cache is flushed at the end of each epoch, which means that the inter-epoch localities are not supported, which degrades the performance of the scheme.

Classification: (D:s,S:i,R:c,A:f,L:l,G:*,B:e,P:b,U:b,C:r/+s/).

3.1.6. Fast selective invalidation from University of Illinois

Cheong and Veidenbaum in [CHEON88] propose another software scheme for consistency maintenance which originated from research done at the University of Illinois. The speed of invalidation is close to the case of the indiscriminative invalidation, but its selectivity is such that it enables a better hit ratio.

It is assumed that the value of a variable in shared memory is always valid, because the write-through approach is used. Also, it is assumed that the synchronization variables are not cached. Each word in cache has a change bit associated to it.

When set, this bit tells that the word is potentially invalid (in another paper which originated from the same research [CHEON90], this bit is defined in the inverse way). When a new line is entered into the cache, the corresponding change bits are set to 0 (zero). Also, a write to cache sets this bit to 0. The Invalidate instruction only sets the change bits to 1 - it does not perform the actual invalidation. The setting of change bits is done in one cycle, for all change bits in the cache. That is why the invalidation is as fast as in the case of the indiscriminative invalidation. At compile time, the Invalidate instructions are inserted at the critical places in the program (loop boundaries), in the same way as in a previously described scheme [VEIDE86]. Also, each word in cache has a clear bit associated with it. This bit, when set, tells that nothing was read/written from/into the corresponding word. The Clear-cache instruction sets the clear bits of the entire cache memory to 1 (one), which brings the cache into the initial clear state. Marking of references is done at compile time, as follows. All references, for which it can be guaranteed that they will not fetch an invalid data copy, are marked as cache-read. Other references are marked as memory-read. The marking algorithm is applied to each procedure separately. It is assumed that the cache is always cleared at the beginning of a procedure (using the Clear-cache instruction). References to data which are only read within a procedure are marked as cache-read; also, all references to read-write data coming chronologically before the first write to the same data, are marked as cache-read. Other references are marked according to specific rules. For cache hit, it is required not only that address and validity tags match, but also that the reference is either a cache-read, or a memory-read with the change bit set to 0.

In this scheme, the invalidation instructions are inserted into the program statically. The same applies for marking of references. However, the Invalidate instruction here only points at the occurrence of a situation in which a non-up-to-date contents may appear in cache memory. Decisions of the actual invalidations are made at execution time. The hit is prevented for only those memory read references with the change bit in the accessed word set. This approach has two good sides. First, invalidation has no impact on cache-read references, i.e. the invalidation is selective. Second, when a variable is read more than once within a single iteration of a DoAll loop, although all reads are marked as memory-read, the invalidation will refer only to the first read; the other reads will be satisfied in the cache memory (intra-cycle restrictive invalidation). Although, the algorithm for inserting the Invalidate instruction is conservative - preventive invalidation is done at the boundaries of parallel loops (inter-cycle conservative invalidation).

Classification: (D:s,S:s,R:c,A:f,L:l,G:l,B:e,P:b,U:t,C:c/+s+d+r/).

3.1.7. Programmable cache from IBM T.J.Watson Research Center

Cytron, Karlovsky, and McAuliffe in [CYTRO88] propose a solution for cache consistency maintenance in shared memory multiprocessors, which is based on a detailed static analysis of data dependencies for all instructions in the program. The authors were with the IBM T.J. Watson Research Center and with the University of Illinois, at the time when the work was published.

As in other static schemes special instructions for cache memory management are inserted into the program at compile time, as follows: (a) Post is the instruction which passes the value of the local data copy into the location of the original data in main memory; (b) Invalidate is the instruction which destroys the local data copy; and (c) Flush is the instruction which performs an activity that is a combination of the previous two instructions. A write-back cache memory is assumed, which is large enough that replacement of lines in cache could be neglected. The line size is equal to one memory word. Each address in the global address space is marked in one of the following three ways: (a) Cacheable - data copies on these addresses can exist in private cache memories at all times (read-only shared data and private data); (b) Temporarily cacheable - data at these addresses can be placed into the cache memory, and the compiler 'is responsible for making decisions about the instances in time when these data are to be flushed or invalidated (read-write shared data); (c) Non-cacheable - data from these locations are not allowed to be placed into the cache memory (shared data with the activity dynamics such that the consistency maintenance does not pay off, due to a relatively large overhead). The cacheability status of an address is determined in three steps: (a) First, all variables are marked as Temporarily cacheable; (b) Second, the locations in the program are determined where the cache management instructions are to be inserted; (c) Third, the variables which require no consistency maintenance are marked as Cacheable, and those accessed only after invalidation are marked as Non-cacheable; other variables remain to be Temporarily cacheable (these would require a special analysis to determine how profitable it would be to perform the consistency maintenance activity in the case of each particular variable). The proposed algorithm relies on some information obtained from the parallelizing compiler, like the information about the possibility to parallelize a loop (if the loop is parallel or serial), the data dependency graph, and similar. Instruction Post(X) is inserted after the instruction which writes into a shared variable X, if it (the instruction which writes) is a source of the crossing flow dependency. The term "crossing" refers to the case when the sink of the dependency can be executed on another processor. Also, if the variable X is inter-procedure live after the procedure P (which is the subject of the analysis), the instruction Post(X) is inserted after the last write to X (within the procedure P). Hence, the instruction Write is followed by the instruction Post(X) in the case of the following sequence:

$$\text{Write } (P_i, X) \rightarrow \text{Read}(P_j, X) \quad (j \Leftrightarrow i)$$

Authors propose two different algorithms for insertion of the instruction Invalidate. The first one is less complex. It is linearly dependent on the number of flow dependencies in the analyzed program. However, it can generate unnecessary invalidations, because it is based on a conservative invalidation strategy: invalidate instruction is inserted before each reading of the variable X, if the variable X is a sink of a crossing flow dependence. Also, if a shared variable X could have been defined before the entry into the procedure P, the Invalidate(X) instruction is inserted before the first reading of the variable X in the procedure P. Hence, instruction Invalidate(X) is inserted before the read operation, when the above mentioned write-read sequence exists. However, it would be quite enough to invalidate the variable X before the second reading, only when the following sequence exists:

$$\text{Ref}(P_j, X) \rightarrow \text{Write } (P_i, X) \rightarrow \text{Read}(P_j, X) \quad (j \Leftrightarrow i)$$

Consequently, the authors propose a better, but a more complex algorithm for insertion of the invalidation instructions (an algorithm which is quadratically dependent on the number of flow dependencies). The Invalidate(X) instruction is inserted before the sink of the crossing flow dependency, if the source of the analyzed flow dependency acts as a sink in at least one output dependency, or in at least one anti dependency, in relation to the variable X. Instruction Flush(X) generates both operations - the passing of X into the shared memory, and the invalidation of X in cache memory (of the processor which executed the instruction). Instruction Flush is inserted after the source of the direct dependency, substituting for the instructions Post and Invalidate, in instances where such substitution can be done without causing unnecessary misses.

This scheme is very restrictive to the invalidations within a procedure. This is due to the fact that both the program structure analysis and the data dependency analysis are performed at compile time. However, the problem of unnecessary invalidations on the inter-procedure level is still there.

Classification: (D:s,S:s,R:r,A:f,L:g,G:l,B:s,P:d,U:b,C:d/+s+r/).

3.1.8. Version control from University of Illinois

Cheong and Veidenbaum in [CHEON89] propose a scheme which represents an improvement of their "fast selective invalidation" scheme. It is referred to as the "version control scheme," and was also developed at the University of Illinois. It is based on the static analysis of the parallel program tasking structure, and a dynamic control of the variable version, using appropriate hardware support.

Essence of the approach is in the notion that, whenever a write is made to a shared variable, a new "version" of its contents is formed. In the case of DoAll loops, there is no data dependency between iterations (iterations of the DoAll loop form tasks on the same level of the task execution graph), and there is no hazard of another processor needing the new version of the shared variable. Therefore, no consistency maintenance related activities are needed within a DoAll loop - a temporary inconsistency of the memory system is allowed. However, before the processor passes the task level boundary, the most recent version of the variable in cache must be stored into the main memory. Each processor keeps a private evidence about the current version of each shared variable (scalar or vector) in main memory. For that purpose, a Current Version Number is maintained (CVN). When passing to the next task level (e.g., after the exit from a DoAll loop), processors execute the instructions (inserted by the compiler, based on the static program analysis) for incrementing of the current version number, for all variables being written at the previous task level. At the same time, each cache line contains a field with the information about the Birth Version Number (BVN). The BVN is updated at the loading of each cache line from main memory. After a read miss and the loading of the cache line, BVN is equal to CVN. At each cache write, BVN is made equal to CVN + 1 (the number of the next version). At each access to a shared data item in cache, CVN and BVN are compared. If BVN is smaller than CVN, the data item in cache is stale, and the access is declared a miss. If BVN is equal or greater than CVN, the data item in cache is valid, and the access is declared a hit (after a write to a variable, BVN = CVN + 1, and BVN is greater than CVN on the same task level).

The version control scheme [CHEON89], compared with the previous two schemes of the same authors [VEIDE86 and CHEON88], demonstrates a better performance, due to the respecting of temporal locality of references, over the task execution level boundary [CHEON90]. Direct consequence of this is an increased cache hit ratio. This advantage is paid by a more complex hardware support for consistency maintenance, compared to other schemes.

Classification: (D:s,S:s,R:r,A:f,L:g,G:l,B:e,P:b,U:a,C:c/+s/).

3.1.9. Timestamps from University of Washington

Min and Baer in [MIN89, MIN92] propose, independently of Cheong and Veidenbaum, the "timestamps" scheme, which is in its essence very similar to the version control scheme.

Each shared data structure is assigned a counter to it, which is incremented at the end of each epoch in which the data structure could be modified. Each word in cache is assigned a "timestamp". This timestamp is set to "counter + 1" when that word is modified. At the access to cache memory, a word is valid if the value of the timestamp is equal to or greater than the value of the corresponding counter. The Min-Baer counter correspond to the Cheong-Veidenbaum CVN. The Min-Baer timestamp corresponds to the Cheong-Veidenbaum BVN. The Min-Baer epoch corresponds to the Cheong-Veidenbaum task level.

Basic difference between the timestamps approach and the version control approach is in the fact that Min and Baer also propose a very sophisticated marking of references, which supports better the localities between dependent tasks in a DoAccross loop.

Classification: (D:s,S:s,R:r,A:f,L:g,G:l,B:e,P:b,U:t,C:c/+s+r/).

3.1.10. One-bit time stamps from Rice University

Darnell and Kennedy from Rice University in [DARNE93] propose a new scheme based on timestamping. Their scheme requires considerably less complex hardware support then appropriate schemes [CHEON89] and [MIN89], although it achieves at least the same hit ratio.

One bit, called "epoch bit," is associated with each cache line, in order to notify any arbitrary access to the cache line during current epoch of the program execution. All epoch bits are reset at each epoch boundary. Invalidate instructions, are inserted statically by compiler at the end of each epoch (before reset of the epoch bits). Invalidation can be related to the whole array (conservative analysis of the program) or only to some parts of the array that have been written during the current epoch. In run time, these instructions actually invalidate only the cache lines that have not been accessed during the epoch. Practically, invalidate instruction copies the epoch bit to the valid bit.

As it have been shown through simulation study, this scheme has almost always better hit ratio than scheme proposed by Min and Baer [MIN89]. Hardware support, on the other hand, is very simple - each cache line is enlarged with one bit (epoch) and no additional bits are required in instructions or private memory.

Classification: (D:s,S:s,R:r,A:f,L:g,G:l,B:e,P:b,U:*,C:c/+s/).

3.2. Dynamic solutions

Dynamic software solutions maintain the consistency of private caches entirely at run time (the same as hardware solutions). They are implemented in the kernel of the operating system. Consequently, they do not contribute to compiler complexity (in static schemes, one multiprocessor system requires a number of different compilers - one for each language). Since the consistency maintenance decisions are done at execution time, dynamic approaches do not have to do any preventive actions; it is possible that only the actions which are absolutely necessary to be done. Dynamic approaches are difficult to apply in the cases where the parallelism is modeled via parallel loops. Consequently, dynamic solutions are not so suitable for numeric applications, which are primarily based on a programming model characterized by parallel loops. On the other hand, dynamic solutions are a natural solution for non-numeric concurrent applications, frequently based on a programming model with an explicit management of sharing, like through the usage of critical regions or monitors.

3.2.1. One time identifiers from University of California at Berkeley

Smith in [SMITH85] proposes a solution for dynamic maintenance of cache consistency which is entirely based on the application of operating system level primitive operations for control of the exclusive access to critical regions. This research was done at the University of California at Berkeley.

In the case of the conventional page-organized memory, at each access to a page, the real page address is calculated from the virtual page address, using the hashing function. To avoid unnecessary repetitions of this operation, a translation lookaside buffer (TLB) can be introduced. It is a cache in which the address tag contains the virtual page address, and the data field contains the real page address. Smith proposes that both each TLB entry and each line in the processor cache are expanded with another field, which represents a unique marking of a shared data page. This field is referred to as OTI (one time identifier). When a new TLB entry is loaded, a new and unique value is placed into its OTI field. This value is read from a special incrementing register. When an entry for a shared page is accessed for the first time, the entry is loaded into the cache from the main memory. At the same time, the OTI field value from the TLB is passed to the OTI field in the cache. All subsequent accesses to this variable check if the value of the OTI field in cache matches the value of the OTI field in the TLB. If a match occurs, the access is treated as a hit, otherwise it is a miss. After the exit from a critical region, processor executes the instructions that invalidate all TLB entries of the pages which belong to shared data being protected by the just exited critical region. At the first next access to shared data, the corresponding TLB entry is loaded again, and a new value for the OTI field is obtained. This enables that all later accesses to stale data are treated as misses, because the value of the OTI field in the TLB is different than the value of the OTI field in the cache. Next, Smith proposes a selective write-through, as follows. Updating of shared data is done with the write-through approach (which guarantees that the main memory is always updated for shared data), while the updating of the private data is done using the write-back approach.

Good side of the OTI scheme is the complete decentralization of the cache consistency maintenance, as it is the case with practically all static schemes, and it is not the case with practically all hardware schemes. Consistency is maintained at each processor autonomously, without any communications with other processors in the system. However, the scheme requires a relatively complex hardware support (the OTI extension in the TLB and the cache, comparators for the OTI fields, etc.). Also, at the exit from a critical region no possibility remains for restriction in executing the invalidation instructions (here, the invalidation is done as a preventive action).

Classification: (D:d,S:s,R:c,A:f,L:l,G:l,B:r,P:e,U:h,C:c).

3.2.2. Consistency on interrupt request from Stanford University

Cheriton, Slavenburg, and Boyle in [CHERI86] propose a combined hardware-software solution for the maintenance of cache consistency in virtually addressed private cache memories. This research was done at the Stanford University, and was a part of the VMP multiprocessor project. The essence of the solution is in the hardware-based determination of the inconsistency conditions and generation of the interrupt request, and the software-based activities aimed at the consistency maintenance.

The idea of this scheme is based on the concept of virtual memory. Page faults are determined in hardware. Fetching of new pages form the secondary memory is done in software. The proposed cache memory page size is relatively large (up to 512 bytes), and the proposed hardware for the transfer of data blocks is relatively fast (40 Mbytes/sec). Consequently, cache memory misses are relatively rare, and can be processed in software. on the operating system level. The same concept is extended into the domain of cache consistency maintenance. The hardware based bus monitor detects the inconsistency conditions, and informs the local processor about that, by issuing an interrupt request. In response, processor executes the interrupt routine, and performs the consistency maintenance related activities (within the interrupt routine). The same consistency maintenance mechanism is used both for the shared pages and the pages that contains entries of the page table. The same mechanism also resolves the problem of aliases in the virtually addressed cache memory. The main memory is viewed as a sequence of cache page frames. A page in a frame can be in one of the following two states: shared or private. In the shared state, the page frame contains the least recently written page value, while the local cache memories can contain multiple copies of that particular page. In the private state, only one cache memory contains a copy of the page, which is the only copy of that page in the system. Each bus monitor has a private table of actions. For each page frame, this table defines the activity to be done by the monitor when the address from that page appears on the bus. If the corresponding page frame is not in a private cache memory, no action is needed. If the page in cache memory is shared, the monitor has to ignore all read-shared requests; all read-private and assert-ownership requests have to be aborted, followed by an interrupt to the local processor (during the processing of that interrupt request, the processor invalidates the page in cache memory). If the page in cache memory is private, the monitor has to issue an interrupt request for each transaction related to that page (during the processing of that interrupt, if the page was dirty, processor performs a write-back into the main memory; if the transaction was read-private or assert-ownership, processor invalidates the page in cache; if the transaction was read-shared, processor changes the page state into shared). The processor which was performing the aborted transaction, detects the abortion, and starts the transaction again. Using this protocol, the request for a shared copy of a shared page is satisfied immediately. The request for a shared copy of a private page results in the abortion of the transaction and the passing of the ownership. Consequently, the processor which requested the page succeeds in the next try. The request for a private copy of a shared page is satisfied immediately, but triggers the invalidation of all copies of that page in all cache memories. The request for a private copy of a private page is aborted and causes the passing of the ownership, which enables the success on the next try.

The completely hardwized detection of inconsistency conditions results in a very restrictively applied invalidation;

however, the size of the cache page (which must be relatively large, so that the interrupts related to misses are relatively rare) makes the invalidation poorly selective in the case of shared data of fine granularity.

Classification: (D:d,S:s,R:r,A:f,L:g,G:p,B:p,P:i,U:b,C:m).

3.2.3. Conditional invalidation from University of Belgrade

Authors of this survey, in their paper [TARTA92] propose a class of dynamic software schemes for maintenance of cache consistency, based on the testing at the entry into a critical region, with a goal to avoid unnecessary invalidations. The work was performed at the University of Belgrade, in cooperation with the NCR Corporation.

Consistency maintenance activities are performed at the entry/exit into/from the critical region (the program code region with an exclusive access to the shared data segment). Of the three schemes that they propose, the "version verification" scheme is the most restrictive, and the one which utilizes the existing inter-regional locality of references the best. At the entry into the critical region, the real version of the shared segment (information from the shared segment table) is explicitly compared with the local and private information about the least recently used segment version. If the versions do not match, selective invalidation of the shared segment is done. If the shared memory is updated using the write-back approach, the updating of the shared segment original (in main memory) is done at the exit from the critical region.

A simulation analysis has shown the advantages of the restrictively applied invalidation, even if the number of processors is relatively small (up to 16). This was especially the case if the mostly-read shared segments prevail.

Classification: (D:d,S:s,R:r,A:f,L:g,G:s,B:r,P:e,U:a,C:c).

3.2.4. Adaptive software cache management from Rice University

Bennett, Carter, and Zwaenepoel in [BENN90a, BENN90b] propose a dynamic adaptive software maintenance of consistency, within the Munin project at Rice university. Munin supports several consistency maintenance mechanisms, and in each particular case uses the one which fits the best the prevailing class of shared objects for that particular case (the access type is relevant when making the decision about the specific mechanism to use).

Generally in DSM (Distributed Shared Memory) systems, the memory inconsistency problem exists because the virtual address space is physically distributed on several local memories. Consequently, one memory address can be mapped into a number of memory modules. Munin is a program system which makes the above problem completely transparent for the application. For the purpose of memory consistency maintenance, programmer informs the system about the expected way of access to shared objects. The classes of objects are: (a) write-once, (b) private, (c) write-many, (d) result, (e) synchronization, (f) migratory, (g) producer-consumer, (h) read-mostly, and (i) general read-write. A study has shown [BENN90b] that the number of general read-write objects is relatively small. Also, it was shown that parallel programs behave differently in different phases of their execution. Except in the initialization, most of the accesses are of the read type. Finally, it was noticed that the average period between two accesses to synchronization objects is considerably

longer than the average access period for other shared objects. In addition to traditional mechanisms for consistency maintenance in DSM systems (replication, invalidation, migration, and remote load/store), Munin supports one new mechanism - delayed update. When a process modifies a shared data item, the new value is not immediately sent to remote servers, to update their copies. Instead, the sending is postponed till the first next synchronization, and all changes are sent in one package. Between the synchronization, each process forms its own queue of delayed updates. This queue is flushed at the time of the next synchronization. Some objects are written only once (at the initialization), and later only read. These objects are maintained by replication, and accessed only locally. Private objects are those accessible to all processes, but really being accessed by one processor only. Accesses to private objects are local, and they are not managed by Munin. The write-many objects are those being written into many times between two synchronization points. The delayed update mechanism proves to be very efficient for the consistency maintenance of these objects (weak consistency). The result objects collect the writes from several processes, and make them available for reading to only one process. The delayed update mechanism is very useful here, as well. For the synchronization objects, the consistency is maintained using the distributed locks mechanism. Migratory objects are accessed in one time interval by one process only (within the critical region). The consistency is achieved efficiently if, at the exit from the critical region of one process, the object and the associated distributed lock for that critical region, are migrated onto the processor to execute the first next process from the waiting queue for the corresponding critical region. The producer-consumer objects are those being written into by one process, and being read by a number of other processes. The consistency is maintained by the so called "eager object movement" to the processors to need them, before the actual need arises (and the related request is issued). The mostly-read objects are maintained by replication, and by updating via broadcast, after the writes which are relatively rare. The general read-write objects are those that can not be put into any of the above described classes. Consistency of these objects is maintained through a mechanism which is based on the Berkeley Ownership scheme for consistency maintenance of cache memories.

The adaptivity of this consistency scheme (based on the dynamic nature of objects) has a very positive impact on the overall performance of the system and the application. The simulation studies have shown [BENN90b] that, for a given application (e.g., Quicksort), this software adaptive method can decrease the bus traffic for over 50% compared to the conventional hardware write-update, and for over 85% (compared to the write-invalidate mechanism).

Classification: (D:d,S:d,R:r,A:a,L:g,G:f,B:p,P:*,U:*,C:*).

4. GENERALIZATION OF THE PROPOSED CLASSIFICATION OF SOFTWARE SOLUTIONS

The set of criteria introduced earlier in the paper enables each software solution to be described with a set of attributes. These attributes are related to the ten criteria, and correspond to different possible classes of the applied criteria. A ten-tuple of attributes was associated with each one of the presented solutions. The proposed classification method can be easily generalized, through the introduction of an abstract space of criteria. Each one of the presented solutions can be treated as a point in such a space, to be explained next.

Coordinates of the multidimensional discrete space of criteria correspond to the chosen criteria, and the discrete values on these coordinates correspond to the classes of the applied criteria, i.e., to the attributes. The number of criteria determines the dimension of the space. The number of classes for each criterion determines the number of discrete values that exist on the corresponding coordinate.

If the abstract space is described with a large enough number of criteria (complete space), each point corresponds to one of the existing solutions. If the abstract space is described with a smaller number of criteria (reduced space), one point may correspond to a larger number of existing solutions. This situation tells that either some important criterion was not taken into consideration, or that the solutions are practically the same (e.g. [CHEON89] and [MIN89]) or semantically similar (e.g. [MIN89] and [DARNE93]), but different in implementation, resulting in different performance and/or complexity. On the other hand, if some criterion is not relevant for some solution, than the axes related to this criterion has to be extended with the value (attribute) "irrelevant." This action prevents the propagation of the solution over all points along the coordinate of the irrelevant criterion. All above enables that all points in the complete space come into one-to-one correspondence with the existing solutions. In that case, the classification boils down to the positioning of a given solution to a given point in the space.

For illustration purposes, Figure 2. shows a reduced three-dimensional space (3D) formed out of the first three criteria (dynamism, selectivity, and restrictiveness). Some points in this reduced space correspond to several solutions; however, only one representative solution was shown. For example, the point (s,s,r) contains not only the scheme from [CHEON89], but also the schemes from [CYTRO88] and [MIN89]. Also, the point (d,s,r) contains not only the scheme from [TARTA92], but the scheme from [BENN90b], as well.

If the coordinates of the space are treated as discrete and bounded, which is the case with the abstract criterion space discussed here, the total possible number of points in this space is given by:

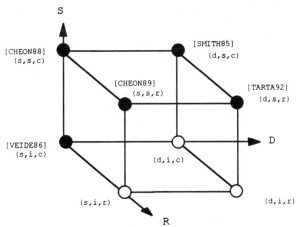

1. Dynamics (D): static (s) or dynamic (d)
2. Selectivity (S): indiscriminative (i) or selective (s)
3. Restrictiveness (R): conservative (c) or restrictive (r)

Figure 2. An example of a reduced 3D abstract criterion space

$$Q = \prod_{i=1}^{N} Ci \qquad (1)$$

where Ci refers to the number of classes for the i-th criterion (i=1,...,N). The number of theoretically different software schemes, according to equation (1), for the concrete case of the ten-criterion abstract space presented here, is equal to Q=40960. Of course, this number should be considered just as an illustration, for one possible classification, not as a general conclusion.

The combinations of attributes (N-tuples of attributes) that correspond to non-existing solutions are referred to as "free points." Some of these "free points" can serve as guides to new solutions which are potentially useful (some of the "free points" correspond to solutions that make no sense, and of those that do make sense some may not be very useful in given circumstances). It should be noticed that, based on the knowledge about the characteristics of classes that characterize a new solution, one could roughly estimate the performance of the solution, without analyzing its details.

A relatively large number of new and potentially useful solutions can be found in the "plane" of adaptive static schemes. Using the semantic information about the access methods to a shared object, at compile time, appropriate instructions could be inserted into the code, to support the mechanism which is "optimal" for the given access method.

6. CONCLUSIONS

This paper represents an effort to encompass and classify the existing work in the field of software based algorithms for the maintenance of cache consistency in shared memory multiprocessor systems. A set of ten classification criteria is proposed. Each criterion results in several classes. These classes serve as attribute values for description and classification of existing approaches.

The basic criterion, the dynamism of the approach, is used to divide the surveyed schemes into two essential groups: (a) static, which do the program analysis for detection of inconsistency conditions at compile time, and (b) dynamic, which detect the inconsistency conditions at run time.

After the field is widely surveyed, and the correspondence between schemes and attributes is established, a generalization of the proposed classification is introduced. It is based on an N-dimensional criterion space. Each scheme which is essentially different from other existing schemes corresponds to a point in that space. This generalization enables the following to be accomplished:

* With the state-of-the-art in the field, it can be detected that some solutions are essentially the same (because they belong to the same point in the criterion space), although they are declared as formally different (because they have been introduced independently of each other, in time and space).

* With the development of the field, it can be determined if a set of criteria (and related classes) is defined widely enough, so that essentially different solutions can be associated to different points in the space.

* As far as the future contributions in the field, the "empty" points in the criterion space can serve as guides towards new solutions (as it was the case with the Mendelieyev classification system in chemistry).

Through a careful inspection of the criterion space, one can notice that a part of the criterion space which corresponds to static and adaptive schemes is "empty" at the time. This means that some potentially good new solutions can be found in this part of the criterion space, and the research in that direction is encouraged.

7. REFERENCES

[ADVE91]   Adve,S.V., Adve,V.S., Hill,M.D., Vernon,M.K., "Comparison of hardware and software cache coherence schemes," Proceedings of the 18th Annual International Symposium on Computer Architecture, May 1991, pp.298-308.

[AGARW88] Agarwal,A.,Simoni,R., Hennessy,J., Horowitz,M., "An evaluation of directory schemes for cache coherence," Proceedings of the 15th Annual International Symposium on Computer Architecture, May 1988, pp.280-289.

[ARCHI86] Archibald,J., Baer,J.-L., "Cache coherence protocols: evaluation using a multiprocessor simulation model," ACM Transactions on Computer Systems, Vol.4, No.4, November 1986, pp.273-298.

[BENN90a] Bennett,J.K., Carter,J.B., Zwaenepoel,W., "Munin: Distributed shared memory based on type-specific memory coherence," Proceedings of the 1990 Conference on Principles and Practice of Parallel Programming, March 1990, pp.168-176.

[BENN90b] Bennett,J.K., Carter,J.B., Zwaenepoel,W., "Adaptive software cache management for distributed shared memory architectures," Proceedings of the 17th Annual International Symposium on Computer Architecture, June 1990, pp.125-134.

[BRANT85] Brantley,W.C., McAuliffe,K.P., Weiss,J., "RP3 processor-memory element," Proceedings of the 1985 International Conference on Parallel Processing, August 1985, pp.782-789.

[CENSI78] Censier,L.M., Feautrier,P., "A new solution to coherence problem in multicache systems," IEEE Transactions on Computers, Vol.C-27, No.12, December 1978, pp.1112-1118.

[CHERI86] Cheriton,D.R., Slavenburg,G.A., Boyle,P.D., "Software-controlled caches in the VMP multiprocessor," Proceedings of the 13th Annual International Symposium on Computer Architecture, June 1986, pp.366-374.

[CHEON88] Cheong,H., Veidenbaum,A.V., "A cache coherence scheme with fast selective invalidation," Proceedings of the 15th Annual International Symposium on Computer Architecture, May 1988, pp.299-307.

[CHEON89] Cheong,H., Veidenbaum,A.V., "A version control approach to cache coherence," Proceedings of the International Conference on Supercomputing 89, June 1989, pp.322-330.

[CHEON90] Cheong,H., Veidenbaum,A.V., "Compiler-directed cache management in multiprocessors," IEEE Computer, Vol.23, No.6, June 1990, pp.39-47.

[CYTRO88] Cytron,R., Karlovsky,S., McAuliffe,K.P., "Automatic management of programmable caches," Proceedings of the 1988 International Conference on Parallel Processing, 1988, pp.229-238.

[DARNE93] Darnell,E., Kennedy,K., "Cache coherence using local knowledge," Proceedings of the Supercomputing '93, November 1993, pp.720-729.

[EDLER85] Edler,J., Gottlieb,A., Kruskal,C.P., McAuliffe,K.P., Rudolph,L., Snir,M., Teller,P., Wilson,J., "Issues related to MIMD shared-memory computers: the NYU Ultracomputer approach," Proceedings of the 12th Annual International Symposium on Computer Architecture, June 1985, pp.126-135.

[EGGER89] Eggers,S.J., Katz,R.H., "Evaluating the performance of four snooping cache coherency protocols," Proceedings of the 16th Annual International Symposium on Computer Architecture, June 1989, pp.2-15.

[GOTTL82] Gottlieb,A., Grishman,R., Kruskal,C.P., McAuliffe,K.P., Rudolph,L., Snir,M., "The NYU Ultracomputer - designing a MIMD, shared-memory parallel machine (Extended abstract)," Proceedings of the 9th Annual International Symposium on Computer Architecture, 1982, pp.27-42.

[GOTTL83] Gottlieb,A., Grishman,R., Kruskal,C.P., McAuliffe,K.P., Rudolph,L., Snir,M., "The NYU Ultracomputer - designing an MIMD, shared memory parallel computer," IEEE Transactions on Computers, Vol.C-32, No.2, September 1983, pp.175-189.

[LEE87a]   Lee,R.L., Yew,P.-C., Lawrie,D.H., "Multiprocessor cache design considerations," Proceedings of the 14th Annual International Symposium on Computer Architecture, June 1987, pp.253-262.

[LEE87b]   Lee,R.L., "The effectiveness of caches and data prefetch buffers in large-scale shared memory multiprocessors," Ph.D. Thesis, TR 670, Center of Supercomputing Research and Development, Univ. of Illinois at Urbana-Champaign, Aug. 1987.

[MCAUL86] McAuliffe,K., "Analysis of cache memories in highly parallel systems," Ph.D. Thesis, TR 269, Courant Institute of Mathematical Sciences, NY University, May 1986.

[MIN89]   Min,S.L., Baer,J.-L., "A timestamp-based cache coherence scheme," International Conference on Parallel Processing, 1989, pp.I23-I32.

[MIN90]   Min,S.L., Baer,J.-L., "A performance comparison of directory-based and timestamp-based cache coherence schemes," Proceedings of the 1990 International Conference on Parallel Processing, August 1990, Vol.I, pp.305-311.

[MIN92]   Min,S.L., Baer,J.-L., "Design and analysis of a scalable cache coherence scheme based on clocks and timestamps," IEEE Transactions on Parallel and Distributed Systems, Vol.3, No.1, January 1992, pp.25-44.

[OWICK89] Owicki,S., Agarwal,A., "Evaluating the performance of software cache coherence," Proceedings of the 3rd International Conference on Architectural Support for Programming Languages and Operating Systems, April 1989, pp.230-242.

[PFIST85] Pfister,G.F.,et.al., "The IBM research parallel processor prototype (RP3): Introduction and architecture," Proceedings of the 1985 Parallel Processing Conference, pp.764-771.

[SMITH85] Smith,A.J., "CPU cache consistency with software support and using one time identifiers," Proceedings of the Pacific Computer Communication Symposium, Seoul, Korea, October 1985, pp.142-150.

[STENS90] Stenstrom,P., "A survey of cache coherence schemes for multiprocessors," IEEE Computer, Vol.23, No.6, June 1990, pp.12-24.

[TARTA92] Tartalja,I., Milutinović,V., "An approach to dynamic software cache consistency maintenance based on conditional invalidation," Proceedings of the 25th Annual Hawaii International Conference on System Sciences, January 1992, pp.457-466.

[TOMAŠ93] Tomašević,M., Milutinović,V., "A survey of hardware solutions for maintenance of cache coherence in shared memory multiprocessors," Proceedings of the 26th Annual Hawaii International Conference on System Sciences, January 1993, Vol.1, pp.863-872

[VEIDE86] Veidenbaum,A.V., "A compiler-assisted cache coherence solution for multiprocessors," Proceedings of the 1986 International Conference on Parallel Processing, 1986, pp.1029-1036.

[WULF72]   Wulf,W.A., Bell,C.G., "C.mmp - a multi-mini processor," Proceedings of the Fall Joint Computer Conference, Montvale, N.Jersey, December 1972, pp.765-777.

[YEH83]   Yeh,P.C.C., Patel,J.H., Davidson,E.S., "Shared cache for multiple-stream computer systems," IEEE Transactions on computers, Vol.C-32, No.1, January 1983, pp.38-47.

LOW ENERGY ILP PROCESSORS

Minitrack Coordinator:

Michael A. Schuette

Low Energy ILP Processors

Minitrack Coordinator - Michael A. Schuette

Motorola, Inc.

A major trend in the computing industry is the move towards computers in portable products. This can be seen as the sales of laptops now surpass desktops, the emergence of a new class of devices known as Personal Digital Assistants (PDA's), and the growth in the sale of consumer electronics devices such as pagers, cellular phones, viewmen. For a large number of these products, battery life is an important consideration.

Often a major determinant of the battery life of these products is the energy consumption of the embedded computing system. Therefore it is important to devise low energy computing systems for these products. However. the computing system is often utilized to perform such functions as image processing, voice recognition, handwriting recognition, signal processing, data compression/decompression as well as more general purpose computing and execution of a non-trivial operating system. The sum total of the performance requirements can approach that of some modern desktops. This minitrack is intended to invite discussion of how techniques, appropriate to high performance ILP processors, can be used to reduce the energy consumption of such computing systems.

Basically, energy in CMOS-based computing systems is consumed primarily in logic transitions. During execution of a function on such a system a set of logic transitions occurs. The energy consumed in executing the function depends on the number and magnitude of the transitions. The energy consumed by a single transition varies as $C*V^2$, where C is the capacitance being switched by the transition and V is the supply voltage. Reducing the energy consumed in executing the function, then involves reducing the number of transitions, the capacitance, or the supply voltage.

The supply voltage has the most significant effect on the energy consumed. Its minimum value is often dictated by the maximum clock speed at which the system is to be run. The greater the clock speed, the greater the minimum supply voltage must be.

Time to execute a given function in a computing system, and therefore its performance, is often approximated by I*CPI*T, where I is the instruction count needed to execute the function, CPI is the average number of clock cycles per instruction, and T is the clock cycle time. In ILP computing systems these quantities are reduced by several means: use of superscalar techniques to reduce CPI, use of pipelining to reduce T, enhancing the locality of communications through the use of memory hierarchies to reduce T, use of optimizing compilers to reduce I and CPI, etc.

Viewed from an energy consumption perspective, these same techniques can also reduce energy consumption. Techniques employing hardware parallelism allow the system to maintain constant performance while reducing the clock rate. A reduction in the clock rate allows the system to be run at a reduced supply voltage. Memory hierarchies reduce the capacitance that must be switched when accessing information, and optimizing compilers reduce the number of transitions or more fully utilize the hardware parallelism. These techniques, even though they reduce N, C, or V, may also cause one or more of the other factors to increase. Thus their effectiveness in reducing energy consumption depends on the degree to which these two effects balance out.

Chandrakasan, et al. [1] investigated the issue of using parallelism to reduce energy consumption. In their paper they examine the energy consumption of a simple data path while varying its degree of parallelism and their estimate of the complexity of the associated control circuitry. Their results showed that for a $2\mu m$ technology, keeping performance of the data path constant by lowering the clock rate, energy consumption could be reduced by a factor of 9 with a degree of parallelism of 10 and a reduction of the supply voltage to 1.4V.

There is evidence in commercial products to support their general conclusions. Examination of several of the leading CPU's for moderate performance, low power applications [2],[3],[4], reveals that each employs a fair degree of pipelining and/or parallelism. These same processors, implemented using little or no parallelism, could easily run at a higher clock rate to achieve the same level of performance. The fact that this simpler implementation was not chosen suggests that parallelism does affect power consumption.

Chandrakasan, et al., appropriately note that to achieve the full energy savings there must be a commensurate degree of parallelism in the software being executed on the data path. Most applications will not have the degree of parallelism needed to fully utilize a data path with degree of parallelism of 10 and so the optimum degree of hardware parallelism will be less. The optimum degree of parallelism for any given application depends upon the degree of parallelism in the application and the degree to which that parallelism can be made manifest by the compiler.

Evaluation of ILP compiler techniques for their ability to reduce energy consumption by enhancing the exploitable parallelism in the application has not occurred. However, initial investigation has been done into the effects of rescheduling of instructions on the number of logic transitions that occur [5]. This investigation has revealed that by rescheduling of instructions to minimize the number of logic transitions within the control logic, switching activity can be reduced by 20-30%. The study did not consider the effects of rescheduling on the amount of switching activity on the CPU data bus caused by the alteration in the sequence of instructions that is fetched across it.

To achieve the high performance that ILP processors are capable of requires a memory subsystem of commensurate performance. Often memory hierarchies are employed to achieve this performance. Memory hierarchies also are capable of reducing energy consumption because they spatially localize communications, thereby reducing the capacitance that is switched.

Past research has investigated optimum cache design to support maximum performance. Bunda, et al. [6] have examined cache design for minimum energy consumption. Many of the standard cache design techniques still apply, however the optimum design points differ. For example, their results indicate that smaller line sizes are better. In addition, it was found that the addition of a small buffer between the cache and CPU to hold the most recently accessed line can significantly reduce energy consumption by reducing the frequency with which the full cache must be accessed.

Another approach to reducing energy consumption lies in the choice of the instruction set architecture (ISA) and encoding. RISC instruction sets have been shown to be more amenable to superscalar and pipelining techniques. This in itself suggests that they may be more energy efficient. However, most instruction sets tend to have 32 bit instructions. Work by Bunda, et al. [6], has shown that a RISC instruction set with16 bit instructions can significantly reduce the memory traffic associated with fetching the instruction stream with little performance degradation and thus save energy. Specifically, the results show that on average instruction traffic is reduced by 35% while performance ranges from 13% slower with 0 wait state memory to 19% greater for 3 wait state memory on a system with no cache.

There is some question as to what style of architecture best exploits instruction level parallelism while minimizing power consumption. Processors such as the ARM [2], and Hitachi SH7xxx [3] utilize conventional architectures, whereas the Hobbit [4] employs a stack architecture. It is claimed in [4] that the stack architecture enables a more energy efficient memory system to be used, namely through a smaller data cache, that provides the throughput and latency required to support a machine pipelined to the degree of Hobbit.

In conclusion, recent research has shown that there are a variety of performance enhancing techniques used in ILP processors that have the potential to reduce energy consumption. They either reduce the amount of capacitance being switched or permit the system to maintain performance but operate at a reduced supply voltage. The key to their effectiveness lies in the balance between this energy savings and the energy increase that results from any added circuitry or increased activity in existing circuits.

Except for [1], none of the previous work considers the effect on energy consumption that improved performance has by permitting a lowering of the supply voltage. It can be reasonably asserted that not all increases in performance of a computing system will permit the system to maintain performance but run at a lower supply voltage. There are natural breakpoints in the supply voltage that are being standardized upon, such as 5V, 3.3V, 2.2V, etc. Thus if the technique does not improve performance sufficiently to allow the system to be run at the next lowest breakpoint, then there will be no energy savings. However, one must view the problem in the context of combining several techniques together that give a sufficient performance boost to allow the next lower level of supply voltage to be used.

The challenge in this area is to not only devise techniques that save energy, but specifying the conditions under which energy is saved. The difficulty in determining the effectiveness of any technique lies in the implementation dependence of energy consumption and upon whether or not the system is capable of utilizing the improved performance to permit a reduction in the supply voltage

[1] Chandrakasan, A., et al. "Low Power CMOS Digital Design", IEEE Journal of Solid-State Circuits, April 1992, pp 473-483

[2] Furber, S., et al. "Amulet1: A Micropipelined ARM", CompCon '94, Feb 1994, pp 476-485

[3] Freet, P., "The SH Microprocessor: 16-bit fixed Length Instruction Set Provides Better Power and Die Size", CompCon '94, Feb 1994, pp 486-488

[4] Argade, P., "Hobbit: A High-Performance, Low-Power Microprocessor", CompCon '93, Feb 1993, pp 88-95

[5] Su, C.C., et al. "Low Power Architecture Design and Compilation Techniques for High-Performance Processors", CompCon '94, Feb. 1994, pp 489-498

[6] Bunda, J., et al, "Increasing Instruction Fetch Energy-Efficiency of a VLSI Microprocessor", Technical Report, Dept. of Computer Sciences, University Texas at Austin, 1992

Energy Efficient CMOS Microprocessor Design

Thomas D. Burd and Robert W. Brodersen

University of California, Berkeley

Abstract

Reduction of power dissipation in microprocessor design is becoming a key design constraint. This is motivated not only by portable electronics, in which battery weight and size is critical, but by heat dissipation issues in larger desktop and parallel machines as well. By identifying the major modes of computation of these processors and by proposing figures of merit for each of these modes, a power analysis methodology is developed. It allows the energy efficiency of various architectures to be quantified, and provides techniques for either individually optimizing or trading off throughput and energy consumption. The methodology is then used to qualify three important design principles for energy efficient microprocessor design.

1: Introduction

Throughput and area have been the main forces driving microprocessor design, but recently the explosive growth in portable electronics has forced a shift in these design optimizations toward more power conscious solutions. Even for desktop units and large computing machines, the cost of removing the generated heat and the drive towards "green" computers are making power reduction a priority.

An energy-efficient design methodology has been developed for signal processing applications, resulting in a strategy to provide orders of magnitude of power reduction [1]. These applications have a fixed throughput requirement due to a real-time constraint given by the application (e.g. video compression, speech recognition). Microprocessors targeted for general purpose computing, however, generally operate in one of two other computing modes. Either they are continuously providing useful computation, in which case maximum throughput is desired, or they are in a user interactive mode, in which case bursts of computation are desired.

A framework for an energy-efficient design methodology more suitable for a microprocessor's two operating modes will be presented. Using simple analytic models for delay and power in CMOS circuits, metrics of energy efficiency for the above modes of operation will be developed and their implications on processor design will be presented. This paper will conclude with the application of these metrics to quantify three important principles of energy-efficient microprocessor design.

2: CMOS Circuit Models

Power dissipation and circuit delays for CMOS circuits can be accurately modelled with simple equations, even for complex microprocessor circuits. These models are dependent upon six variables which an IC designer may control to either individually minimize or trade off power and speed. These models hold only for digital CMOS circuits, and are thus not applicable to bipolar or BiCMOS circuits.

2.1: Power Dissipation

CMOS circuits have both static and dynamic power dissipation. Static power arises from bias and leakage currents. While statically-biased gates are usually found in a few specialized circuits such as PLAs, their use has been dramatically reduced in CMOS design. Furthermore, careful design of these gates generally makes their power contribution negligible in circuits that do use them [2]. Leakage currents from reverse-biased diodes of MOS transistors, and from MOS subthreshold conduction [3] also dissipate static power, but are insignificant in most designs.

The dominant component of power dissipation in CMOS is therefore dynamic, and arises from the charging and discharging of the circuit node capacitances found on the output of every logic gate. This capacitance, C_L, can be expressed as:

$$C_L = C_W + C_{FIX} \qquad \text{(EQ 1)}$$

C_W is the product of a technology constant and the device width, W, over which the designer has control. C_W is composed of the subsequent gates' input capacitance and part of the diffusion capacitance on the gate output. C_{FIX} is composed of the remaining part of the diffusion capacitance which is purely technology dependent, and the capacitance of the wires interconnecting these gates which may be minimized by efficient layout.

For every low-to-high logic transition in a digital circuit, C_L incurs a voltage change ΔV, drawing an energy $C_L \Delta V V_{DD}$ from the supply voltage at potential V_{DD}. For each node $n \in N$, these transitions occur at a fraction α_n of the clock frequency, f_{CLK}, so that the total dynamic switching power may be found by summing over all N nodes in the circuit:

$$Power = V_{DD} \cdot f_{CLK} \cdot \sum_{i=1}^{N} \alpha_i \cdot C_{L_i} \cdot \Delta V_i \qquad \text{(EQ 2)}$$

Aside from the memory bitlines in CMOS circuits, most nodes swing a ΔV from ground to V_{DD}, so that the power equation can be simplified to:

$$Power \cong V_{DD}^2 \cdot f_{CLK} \cdot C_{EFF} \qquad \text{(EQ 3)}$$

where the effective switched capacitance, C_{EFF}, is commonly expressed as the product of the physical capacitance C_L, and the activity weighting factor α, each averaged over the N nodes.

During a transition on the input of a CMOS gate both p and n channel devices may conduct simultaneously, briefly establishing a short from V_{DD} to ground. In properly designed circuits, however, this short-circuit current typically dissipates a small fraction (5-10%) of the dynamic power [4] and will be omitted in further analyses.

2.2: Circuit Delay

To fully utilize its hardware, a digital circuit's clock frequency, f_{CLK}, should be operated at the maximum allowable frequency. This maximum frequency is just the inverse of the delay of the processor's critical path. Thus, the circuit's throughput is proportional to 1/delay.

Until recently, the long-channel delay model (in which device current is proportional to the square of the supply voltage) suitably modelled delays in CMOS circuits [5]. However, scaling the minimum device channel length, L_{MIN}, to below 1 micron (which is common in today's process technology), degrades the performance of the device due to velocity saturation of the channel electrons. This phenomenon occurs when the electric field (V_{DD}/L_{MIN}) in the channel exceeds 1V/um [6].

$$Delay \cong \frac{C_L}{I_{AVE}} \cdot \frac{V_{DD}}{2} \cong \frac{C_L \cdot V_{DD}}{k_V \cdot W \cdot (V_{DD} - V_T - V_{DSAT})} \quad \text{(EQ 4)}$$

The change in performance can be analytically characterized by what is known as the short-channel or velocity-saturated delay model shown in Equation 4. I_{AVE} is the average current being driven onto C_L, and is proportional to W, the technology constant k_V, and to first-order, V_{DD}. V_T is the threshold voltage (typically 0.5 - 1.0 volts) and is the minimum V_{DD} for which the device can still operate. For large V_{DD}, V_{DSAT} is constant, with typical magnitude on order of V_T. For V_{DD} values less than $2V_T$, V_{DSAT} asymptotically approaches $V_{DD} - V_T$.

2.3: Circuit Design Optimizations

The designer can minimize some of the variables in Equations 3 and 4 to either individually or simultaneously minimize the delay and power dissipation. This can be accomplished by minimizing C_{EFF}, while keeping W constant. The following three methods for minimizing C_{EFF} can be correlated so they may not always be individually optimized.

First, the switching frequency, α, can be minimized to reduce power dissipation without affecting the delay. This optimization shows the best promise for significant power reduction. The α factor can be minimized by a number of techniques such as dynamically gating the clock to unused processor sections and selecting cell/module topologies that minimize switching activity.

Another approach is to minimize the number of nodes, which will minimize the total physical capacitance, and likewise reduce the power. However, this method may come at the expense of computation per cycle, as in the example of reducing a 32-bit datapath to a 16-bit datapath.

The third approach is to reduce C_{FIX} by minimizing the interconnect capacitance, which optimizes both power and delay. Since speed has always been a primary design goal, this is already done as general practice.

Although it beyond the control of the designer, it is worth noting the impact of technology scaling on power and delay. Capacitances scale down linearly with technology parameter L_{MIN} while transistor current stays approximately constant if V_{DD} remains fixed (constant-voltage technology scaling). Thus, delay scales linearly with L_{MIN} for constant power; likewise, power scales linearly with L_{MIN} for constant delay. Essentially, technology scaling is always beneficial.

2.4: Trading off Delay and Power

The remaining three variables under the designer's control can only be used to trade-off delay and power. As the voltage is reduced, the delay increases hyperbolically as the supply voltage approaches V_T. Meanwhile, the power drops due to the product of the squared voltage term and the frequency (inverse of the delay) term. Thus, by operating at various values of supply voltage, a given processor architecture can be made to cover a large range of operating points as demonstrated in Figure 1.

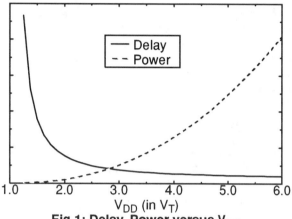

Fig 1: Delay, Power versus V_{DD}

Another method for trading off delay and power is to vary the device width W. However, the trade-off is dependent on how large C_{FIX} is with respect to C_W. Empirical data shows these capacitances are typically on the order of the same size for transistors with minimum width. As the width is increased above the minimum value, the power increases but the delay is decreased. However, C_W soon dominates C_{FIX}, and then power scales linearly with width, while the delay remains approximately constant. Thus, there is a delay-power trade-off, but only over a small range of delay values.

Scaling the clock frequency is a third approach which is most beneficial if it is coupled with voltage scaling. If the clock frequency is reduced, the delay may be increased (keeping it equal to $1/f_{CLK}$) by reducing the supply voltage and thus saving power. If the voltage is kept constant, then power and throughput reduce linearly with clock frequency.

3: Energy Efficiency

No single metric quantifies energy efficiency for all digital systems. The metric is dependent on the type of computation the system performs. We will investigate the three main modes of computation: fixed throughput, maximum throughput, and burst throughput. Each of these modes has a clearly defined metric for measuring energy efficiency, as detailed in the following three sections.

Throughput, T, is defined as the number of operations that can be performed in a given time. When clock rate is inversely equal to the critical path delay, throughput is proportional to the amount of concurrency per clock cycle (i.e. number of parallel operations) divided by the delay, or equivalently:

$$Throughput \equiv T = \frac{Operations}{Second} \propto \frac{Concurrency}{Delay} \quad \text{(EQ 5)}$$

Operations are the units of computation at the highest level of the design space. Valid measures of throughput are MIPS (instructions/sec) and SPECint92 (programs/sec) which compare the throughput on implementations of the same instruction set architecture (ISA), and different ISAs, respectively.

3.1: Fixed Throughput Mode

Most real-time systems require a fixed number of operations per second. Any excess throughput cannot be utilized, and therefore needlessly dissipates power. This property defines the fixed throughput mode of computation. Systems operating in this mode are predominantly found in digital signal processing applications in which the throughput is fixed by the rate of an incoming or outgoing real-time signal (e.g.: speech, video).

$$Metric|_{FIX} = \frac{Power}{Throughput} = \frac{Energy}{Operation} \quad \text{(EQ 6)}$$

Previous work has shown that the metric of energy efficiency in Equation 6 is valid for the fixed throughput mode of computation [5]. A lower value implies a more energy efficient solution. If a design can be made twice as energy efficient (i.e. reduce the energy/operation by a factor of two), then its sustainable battery life has been doubled; equivalently, its power dissipation has been halved. Since throughput is fixed, minimizing the power dissipation is equivalent to minimizing the energy/operation.

3.2: Maximum Throughput Mode

In most multi-user systems, primarily networked desktop computers and supercomputers, the processor is continuously running. The faster the processor can perform computation, the better. This is the defining characteristic of the maximum throughput mode of computation. Thus, this mode's metric of energy efficiency must balance the need for low power and high speed.

$$Metric|_{MAX} = ETR = \frac{E_{MAX}}{T_{MAX}} = \frac{Power}{Throughput^2} \quad \text{(EQ 7)}$$

A good metric for measuring energy efficiency for this mode is given in Equation 7, henceforth called the Energy to Throughput Ratio, or ETR (E_{MAX} is the energy/operation, or equivalently power/throughput, and T_{MAX} is the throughput in this mode). A lower ETR indicates lower energy/operation for equal throughput or equivalently indicates greater throughput for a fixed amount of energy/

operation, satisfying the need to equally optimize through-put and power dissipation. Thus, a lower ETR represents a more energy efficient solution. The Energy-Delay Product [7] is a similar metric, but does not include the effects of architectural parallelism when the delay is taken to be the critical path delay.

In most circuits, however, ETR is not constant for different values of throughput. The throughput can be adjusted with the delay-power trade offs shown in Section 2.4; but, unfortunately, none of the methods perform linear trade-offs between energy/operation and throughput, and only V_{DD} allows the throughput to be adjusted across a reasonable dynamic range.

Because energy/operation is independent of clock frequency, the clock should never be scaled down in maximum throughput mode; only the throughput scales with clock frequency, so the ETR actually increases. Increasing all device widths will only marginally decrease delay while linearly increasing energy. Generally, it is optimal to set all devices to minimum size and only size up those lying in the critical paths.

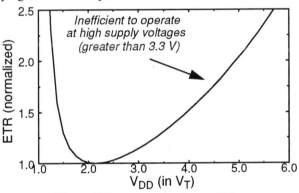

Fig 2: ETR as a function of V_{DD}.

As shown in Figure 2, V_{DD} can be adjusted by a factor of almost three ($1.4V_T$ to $4V_T$) and the ETR only varies within 50% of the minimum at $2V_T$. However, outside this range, the ETR rapidly increases. Clearly, for supply voltages greater than 3.3V, there is a rapid degradation in energy efficiency.

To compare designs over a larger range of operation for the maximum throughput mode, a better metric is a plot of the energy/operation versus throughput. To make this plot, the supply voltage is varied from the minimum operating voltage (near V_T in most digital CMOS designs) to the maximum voltage (3.3V- 5V), while energy/operation and delay are measured. The energy/operation can then be plotted as a function of delay, and the architecture is completely characterized over all possible throughput values.

Using the ETR metric is equivalent to making a linear approximation to the actual energy/operation versus throughput curve. Figure 3 demonstrates the error incurred in using a constant ETR metric. For architectures with

similar throughput, a single ETR value is a reasonable metric for energy efficiency; however, for designs optimized for vastly different values of throughput, a plot may be more useful, as Section 5.1 demonstrates.

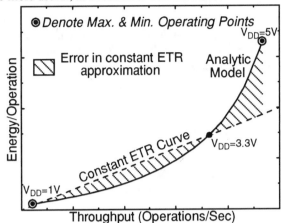

Fig 3: Energy vs. Throughput metric.

3.3: Burst Throughput Mode

Most single-user systems (e.g. stand-alone desktop computers, portable computers, PDAs, etc.) spend a fraction of the time performing useful computation. The rest of the time is spent idling between user requests. However, when bursts of useful computation are demanded, e.g. spread-sheet updates, the faster the throughput (or equivalently, response time), the better. This characterizes the burst throughput mode of computation. The metric of energy efficiency used for this mode must balance the desire to minimize power dissipation, while both idling and computing, and to maximize throughput when computing.

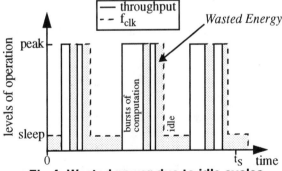

Fig 4: Wasted power due to idle cycles.

Ideally, the processor's clock should track the periods of computation in this mode so that when an idle period is entered, the clock is immediately shut off. Then a good metric of energy efficiency is just ETR, as the power dissipated while idling has been eliminated. However, this is not realistic in practice. Many processors do not having a power saving mode and those that do so generally support only simple clock reduction/deactivation modes. The hypothetical example depicted in Figure 4 contains a clock reduction (sleep) mode in which major sections of the processor are powered down. The shaded area indicates the processor's idle cycles in which power is needlessly dissipated, and whose magnitude is dependent upon whether the processor is operating in the "low-power" mode.

$$E_{MAX} = \frac{Total\ Energy\ Consumed\ Computing}{Total\ Operations} \quad (EQ\ 8)$$

$$E_{IDLE} = \frac{Total\ Energy\ Consumed\ Idling}{Total\ Operations} \quad (EQ\ 9)$$

Total energy and total operations can be calculated over a large sample time period, t_S. T_{MAX} is the peak throughput during the bursts of computation (similar to that defined in Section 3.2), and T_{AVE} is the time-average throughput (total operations / t_S). If the time period t_S characterizes the computing demands of the user and/or target system environment (T_{AVE}), then a good metric of energy efficiency for the burst throughput mode is:

$$Metric|_{BURST} = METR = \frac{E_{MAX} + E_{IDLE}}{T_{MAX}} \quad (EQ\ 10)$$

This metric will be called the Microprocessor ETR (METR); it is similar to ETR, but also accounts for energy consumed while idling. A lower METR represents a more energy efficient solution.

Multiplying through Equation 8 by t_S•(fraction of time computing) shows that E_{MAX} is the ratio of compute power dissipation to peak throughput T_{MAX}, as previously defined in Section 3.2. Thus, E_{MAX} is only a function of the hardware and can be measured by operating the processor at full utilization.

E_{IDLE}, however, is a function of t_S and T_{AVE}. The power consumed idling must be measured while the processor is operating under typical conditions, and T_{AVE} must be known to then calculate E_{IDLE}. However, expressing E_{IDLE} as a function of E_{MAX} better illustrates the conditions when idle power dissipation is significant.

Equation 9 can be rewritten as:

$$E_{IDLE} = \frac{[Idle\ Power\ Dissipation] \cdot [Time\ Idling]}{[Average\ Throughput] \cdot [Sample\ Time]} \quad (EQ\ 11)$$

With the Power-Down Efficiency, β, is defined as:

$$\beta = \frac{Power\ dissipation\ while\ idling}{Power\ dissipation\ while\ computing} = \frac{P_{IDLE}}{P_{MAX}} \quad (EQ\ 12)$$

E_{IDLE} can now be expressed as a function of E_{MAX}:

$$E_{IDLE} = \frac{[\beta \cdot E_{MAX} \cdot T_{MAX}] \cdot [(1 - T_{AVE}/T_{MAX}) \cdot t_S]}{[T_{AVE}] \cdot [t_S]} \quad (EQ\ 13)$$

Equation 14 shows that idle power dissipation dominates total power dissipation when the fractional time spent computing (T_{AVE}/T_{MAX}) is less than the fractional power dissipation while idling (β).

$$METR = ETR\left[1 + \beta\left(\frac{T}{T_{AVE}} - 1\right)\right], \quad T \geq T_{AVE} \quad (EQ\ 14)$$

The METR is a good metric of energy efficiency for all values of T_{AVE}, T_{MAX}, and β as illustrated below by analyzing the two limits of the METR metric.

Idle Energy Consumption is Negligible ($\beta \ll T_{AVE}/T_{MAX}$): The metric should simplify to that found in the maximum throughput mode, since it is only during the bursts of computation that power is dissipated and operations performed. For negligible power dissipation during idle, the METR metric in Equation 14 degenerates to the ETR, as expected. Likewise, for perfect power-down ($\beta=0$) and minimal throughput ($T_{MAX}=T_{AVE}$), the METR is exactly the ETR.

Idle Energy Consumption Dominates ($\beta \gg T_{AVE}/T_{MAX}$): The energy efficiency should increase by either reducing the idle energy/operation while maintaining constant throughput, or by increasing the throughput while keeping idle energy/operation constant. While it might be expected that these are independent optimizations, E_{IDLE} may be related back to E_{MAX} and the throughput by β (T_{AVE} is fixed):

$$\frac{E_{IDLE}}{E_{MAX}} \cong \frac{P_{IDLE}/T_{AVE}}{P_{MAX}/T_{MAX}} = \beta \cdot \frac{T_{MAX}}{T_{AVE}} \quad (EQ\ 15)$$

Expressing E_{IDLE} as a function of E_{MAX} yields:

$$METR \cong \frac{\beta \cdot E_{MAX}}{T_{AVE}}, \quad \text{(Idle Energy Dominates)} \quad (EQ\ 16)$$

If β remains constant for varying throughput (and E_{MAX} stays constant), then E_{IDLE} scales with throughput as shown in Equation 15. Thus, the METR becomes an energy/operation minimization similar to the fixed throughput mode. However, β may vary with throughput, as will be analyzed further in Section 4.4.

4: Design Optimizations

Many energy efficiency optimization techniques developed for the fixed throughput mode of computation are applicable to the a microprocessor operating in either the maximum or burst throughput modes though not always yielding equal gains. Those techniques that successfully apply to microprocessors are outlined below

If processors are compared without a target system's requirements in mind, then ETR is a reasonable metric of comparison. However, if the targeted system resides in the single-user domain and the required average operations/second T_{AVE} can be characterized, then METR is a better metric of comparison.

4.1: Fixed Throughput Optimization

Orders of magnitude of power reduction have been achieved in fixed throughput designs by optimizing at all levels of the design hierarchy, including circuit implementation, architecture design, and algorithmic decisions [1].

One such example is a video decompression system in which a decompressed NTSC-standard video stream is displayed at 30 frames/sec on a 4" active matrix color LCD. The entire implementation consists of four custom chips that consume less than 2mW [1].

There were three major design optimizations responsible for the power reduction. First, the algorithm was chosen to be vector quantization which requires fewer computations for decompression than other compression schemes, such as MPEG. Second, a parallel architecture was utilized, enabling the voltage to be dropped from 5V to 1.1V while still maintaining the throughput required for the real-time constraint imposed by the 30 ms display rate of the LCD. This reduced the power dissipation by a factor of 20. The reduction in clock rate compensated for the increased capacitance; thus, there was no power penalty due to the increased capacitance to make the architecture more parallel (though it did consume more silicon area). Third, transistor-level optimizations yielded a significant power reduction.

4.2: Fixed vs. Max Throughput Optimization

Since the fixed throughput mode is a degenerate case of the max throughput mode, the low-power design techniques used in the fixed throughput mode are also applicable to the maximum throughput mode. This is best visualized by mapping the procedure for exploiting parallelism onto the Energy/operation vs. Throughput plot. There is a two-step process to exploit parallelism for the fixed throughput mode as shown in Figure 5.

Step 1: Ideally, doubling the hardware (arch1->arch2), doubles the throughput. Although the capacitance is doubled, the energy per operation remains constant, because two operations are completed per cycle

Step 2: Reduce the voltage to trade-off the excess speed and achieve the original required throughout. With this parallel architecture, the clock frequency is halved, but the throughput remains constant with respect to the original design.

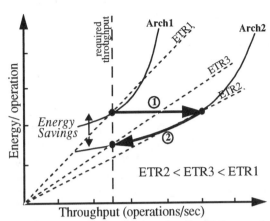

Fig 5: Energy minimization for fixed throughput.

For a processor operating in the maximum throughput mode of computation, it is favorable to reduce the ETR as much as possible, thus, only step 1 is required. In the above example, the final efficiency may even be reduced by decreasing the voltage as was done in step 2.

The energy-throughput trade-off of the maximum throughput operation allows one processor to address separate market segments that have different throughput and power dissipation requirements by simply varying the value of the supply voltage. In essence, a high-speed processor may be the most energy efficient solution for a low throughput application, if the appropriate supply value is chosen. Unfortunately, there are practical bounds that limit the range of operation (e.g. the minimum and maximum supply voltages), preventing one processor from spanning all possible values of throughput.

4.3: Maximum Throughput Optimization

Simply scaling voltage and device sizes are methods of trading off throughput and energy; but they are not energy efficient if used alone since they do not reduce the ETR. However, the architectural modifications that allowed the voltage to be reduced in the fixed throughput mode, do reduce ETR. Conversely, clock frequency reduction, as is common in many portable computers today, does not decrease ETR (it actually increases it) as shown in Section 3.2).

There are three levels in the digital IC design hierarchy. Energy efficient design techniques can drastically increase energy efficiency at all levels as outlined below. Many techniques have corollaries between the fixed and maximum throughput modes, although some differences arise, as noted.

Algorithmic Level: While the algorithm is generally implemented in the software/code domain, which is removed from processor design, it is important to understand the efficiency gains achievable. Similar gains are possible in hardware-implemented algorithms found in signal processing applications.

By using an algorithm implementation that requires fewer operations, both the throughput is increased, and less energy is consumed because the total amount of switched capacitance to execute the program has been reduced. A quadratic improvement in ETR can be achieved [7]. This does not always imply that the program with the smallest dynamic instruction count (path length) is the most energy efficient, since the switching activity per instruction must be evaluated. What needs to be minimized is the number of primitive operations: memory operations, ALU operations, etc. In the case of RISC architectures, the machine code closely resembles the primitive operations, making this optimization possible by minimizing path length. However, in CISC architectures, the primitive operations per each machine instruction need to be evaluated, rather than just comparing path length.

The design of the ISA, however, which does impact the hardware, may be optimized for energy efficient operation. Each instruction must be evaluated to determine if it is more efficient to implement it in hardware, or to emulate it in software.

Architectural Level: The predominant technique to increase energy efficiency is architectural concurrency; with regards to processors, this is generally known as instruction-level parallelism (ILP). Previous work on fixed throughput applications demonstrated an energy efficiency improvement of approximately N on an N-way parallel/pipelined architecture [5]. This assumes that the algorithm is fully vectorizable, and that N is not excessively large.

Moderate pipelining (4 or 5 stages), while originally implemented purely for speed, also increases energy efficiency, particularly in RISC processors that operate near one cycle-per-instruction. More recent processor designs have implemented superscalar architectures, either with parallel execution units or extended pipelines, in the hope of further increasing the processor concurrency.

However, an N-way superscalar machine will not yield a speedup of N, due to the limited ILP found in typical code [8][9]. Therefore, the achievable speedup, S, will be less than the number of simultaneous issuable instructions, and yields diminishing returns as the peak issue rate is increased. S has been shown to be between two and three for practical hardware implementations in current technology [10].

If the code is dynamically scheduled in employing superscalar operation, as is currently common to enable backwards binary compatibility, the C_{EFF} of the processor will increase due to the implementation of the hardware scheduler. Even in statically scheduled architectures such as VLIW processors, there will be extra capacitive over-

head due to branch prediction, bypassing, etc. There will be additional capacitance increase because the N instructions are fetched simultaneously from the cache, and may not all be issuable if a branch is present. The capacitance switched for unissued instructions is amortized over those instructions that are issued, further increasing C_{EFF}.

The energy efficiency increase can be analytically modelled. Equation 17 gives the ETR ratio of a superscalar architecture versus a simple scalar processor; a value larger than one indicates that the superscalar design is more energy efficient. The S term is the ratio of the throughputs, and the C_{EFF} terms are from the ratio of the energies (architectures are compared at constant supply voltage). The individual terms represent the contribution of the datapaths, C_{EFF}^{Dx}, the memory sub-system, C_{EFF}^{Mx}, and the dynamic scheduler and other control overhead, C_{EFF}^{Cx}. The 0 suffix denotes the scalar implementation, while the 1 suffix denotes the superscalar implementation. The quantity C_{EFF}^{C0} has been omitted, because it has been observed that the control overhead of the scalar processor is minimal: $C_{EFF}^{C0} << C_{EFF}^{D0,M0}$ [11].

$$ETR|_{RATIO} = \frac{S\left(C_{EFF}^{D0} + C_{EFF}^{M0}\right)}{\left(C_{EFF}^{C1} + C_{EFF}^{D1} + C_{EFF}^{M1}\right)} \quad \text{(EQ 17)}$$

Whether ILP architecture techniques can yield significant energy efficiency improvement is not inherently clear. The presence of C_{EFF}^{C1} due to control overhead, and increase of C_{EFF}^{M1} (with respect to C_{EFF}^{M0}) due to unissued instructions, may even negate the increase due to S. Current investigation is attempting to quantify these terms and the resulting efficiency increase for a a variety of superscalar implementations.

Other aspects of architecture design can be optimized for improved efficiency. One example is the reduction of extraneous switching activity by gating the clock to various parts of the processor when possible [12]. Another example is the minimization of the lengths of the most active busses.

Circuit level: The design techniques implemented at this level are similar for the fixed and maximum throughput modes. For example, the topologies for the various subcells (e.g. ALU, register file, etc.) should be selected by their ETR, and not solely for speed. Low-swing bus drivers are currently being investigate for high-speed operation; but, these drivers are also applicable to low power design because the energy per transition drops linearly with the voltage swing (ΔV is reduced, not V_{DD}).

The basic transistor sizing methodology is to reduce every transistor not in the critical path to minimum size to minimize C_{EFF}. There are a number of other techniques to minimize effective capacitance which are also viable for optimizing energy efficiency [1].

4.4: Burst Throughput Optimization

If the energy consumed while idling is negligible compared to that consumed during bursts of computation, then the METR metric simplifies to the ETR metric, and all the design optimizations to increase energy efficiency in the maximum throughput mode are equivalently valid in the burst throughput mode.

However, if the energy consumption during idle dominates the total energy consumption, then different optimizations are required. As was shown in Equation 14, this occurs when the fractional time spent computing (T_{AVE}/T_{MAX}) is less than the fractional power dissipation while idling (β). Then the METR optimization is to minimize β and E_{MAX}, as seen from Equation 16. Furthermore, the exact optimization depends on whether β changes as the throughput T is varied as shown below.

β *is independent of throughput*: This case generally applies to processors with no power-down mode for idle periods; if the clock frequency remains the same (or proportional) during both computation and idle periods, then the idle power dissipation tracks the compute power dissipation. If the throughput is now increased while E_{MAX} is held constant (e.g. using parallelism, as was shown in Figure 5 to decrease the ETR), the METR remains constant because the increase in compute power dissipation causes the idle power dissipation to increase as well.

The METR can be optimized by minimizing E_{MAX}, similar to the fixed throughput mode optimization. By reducing V_{DD} to scale down both throughput and E_{MAX}, the processor's efficiency can be maximized. The efficiency will keep improving as V_{DD} is reduced until $E_{IDLE} < E_{MAX}$, and the energy consumption during idle is not dominant anymore; decreasing V_{DD} any further will have little effect on the energy efficiency.

β *varies with throughput*: This is common for processors that implement idle power down modes; the power dissipation during idle is not proportional to the power dissipation during computation. So, for constant idle power dissipation, or equivalently, constant E_{IDLE}, it is most efficient to deliver as much throughput as possible, since any increase in computational power dissipation is negligible compared to the total power dissipation. In practice, β will be less than inversely proportional to throughput (e.g. due to latency switching between operating modes) so that E_{IDLE} is not independent of throughput. However, energy efficiency will continue to increase with throughput until idle power dissipation is no longer dominant.

By itself, the processor hardware can only provide a moderate value of β, which is the ratio of the power dissipated executing a nop instruction to the power dissipated executing a typical instruction. While executing nop instructions, the internal state of the controller and datap-

ath is not changing ($\alpha = 0$), but the clock line is still transitioning every cycle. The processor's clock dissipates a sizable fraction of the total power, anywhere from 10% to 50%. Even if the clock is gated to those pipeline sections executing nop instructions, the instruction-memory access per cycle will continue to dissipate power. If the processor is used in a laptop computer, and T_{AVE} is on the order of 1 SPECint92 (high estimate for user's average operations/second) and β is reasonably estimated as 0.2, it is not energy efficient to increase the peak throughput of the processor beyond 5 SPECint92. Thus, to deliver a more tolerable response time to the user, energy efficiency will have to be degraded.

It is imperative that the operating system intervene to provide further reductions in β. In doing so, β will typically become a function of throughput because the operating system can decouple the compute and idle regimes' power dissipation. The hardware can enable software power down modes by providing instructions to halt either parts of the processor or the entire thing, as is becoming common in embedded microprocessors.

Independent of β's relation to throughput, the METR metric indicates poor energy efficiency whenever the energy/operation consumed idling dominates total energy consumption. If β is constant, the energy efficiency is maximized by reducing E_{MAX} through V_{DD} reduction, until the throughput is roughly T_{AVE}/β. If β is inversely dependent on throughput, then the energy efficiency is maximized by increasing the throughput, and possibly V_{DD}, until E_{MAX} is roughly equal to E_{IDLE}.

5: Design Principles

A few examples are presented below to demonstrate how energy efficiency can be properly quantified. In doing so, three design principles follow from the optimization of the previously defined metrics: a high-performance processor is usually an energy-efficient processor; reducing the clock frequency does not increase the energy efficiency; and lastly, idle power dissipation limits the efficiency of increasing deliverable throughput.

5.1: High Performance is Energy Efficient

Table 1 lists two hypothetical processors that are similar to ones available today -- B targets the low-power market, and A targets the high-end market; both are fabricated in the same technology, which allows an equal comparison. SPEC is either SPECint92, or if a floating point unit is present, the average of SPECint92 and SPECfp92 [7]. A misused metric for measuring energy efficiency is SPEC/Watt (or Dhrystones/Watt, MIPS/Watt, etc.). Processor B may boast a SPEC/Watt eight times greater than A's, and declare that it is eight times as energy efficient. This metric only compares operations/energy, and does not weight that B has 1/15th the performance.

Table 1: Comparison of two processors

Proc.	SPEC (T_{MAX})	Watts	V_{DD}	SPEC/Watt ($1/E_{MAX}$)	ETR (10^{-3})
A	150	30.0	3.3	5.0	1.33
B	10	0.25	3.3	40.0	2.50

The ETR (Watts/SPEC^2) metric indicates that processor A is actually *more* energy efficient than processor B. To quantify the efficiency increase, the plot of energy/operation versus throughput in Figure 6 is used because it better tracks processor A's energy at the low throughput values. The plot was generated from the delay and power models in Section 2.

According to the plot, processor A would dissipate 0.154 W at 10 SPEC, or 60% of processor B's power, despite the low V_{DD} ($1.31V_T$) for A. Conversely, A can deliver 31 SPEC at 0.25W ($V_{DD}=1.66V_T$), or 310% of B's throughput. This does assume that processor A can be operated at this supply voltage.

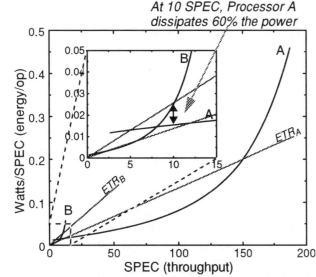

Fig 6: Energy vs Throughput of Processors A & B

While the ETR correctly predicted the more energy-efficient processor at 10 SPEC, it is important to note that processor A is not more energy efficient for all values of SPEC, as the ETR metric would indicate. Because the nominal throughput of the processors is vastly different, the Energy/Operation versus Throughput metric better tracks the efficiency, and indicates a cross-over throughput of 8 SPEC. Below this value, processor B is more energy efficient.

5.2: Clock Reduction is not Energy Efficient

A common fallacy is that reducing the clock frequency f_{CLK} is energy efficient. In maximum throughput mode, it is quite the opposite. At best, it allows an energy-throughput trade-off when idle energy consumption is dominant in burst throughput mode.

In the maximum throughput mode, energy is independent of f_{CLK}, so as the latter is scaled down, the throughput decreases, and the ETR increases, indicating a less efficient design. If f_{CLK} is halved, the power is also halved. However, it takes twice as long to complete any computation, so the energy/operation consumed is constant. Thus, if the energy source is a battery, halving f_{CLK} is equivalent to doubling the computation time, while maintaining constant computation per battery life.

In the burst throughput mode, clock reduction may trade-off throughput and operations per battery life (i.e. energy/operation), but only when E_{IDLE} dominates total energy consumption ($\beta >> T_{AVE}/T_{MAX}$) and β is independent of throughput such that E_{IDLE} scales with throughput. When this is so, halving f_{CLK} will double the computation time, but will also double the amount of computation per battery life. If the user is engaged in an application where throughput degradation is acceptable, then this is a reasonable trade-off. If either E_{MAX} dominates total energy consumption, or β is inversely proportional to throughput, then reducing f_{CLK} does not affect the total energy consumption, and the energy efficiency drops.

If V_{DD} were to track f_{CLK}, however, so that the critical path delay remains inversely equal to the clock frequency, then constant energy efficiency could be maintained as f_{CLK} is varied. This is equivalent to V_{DD} scaling (Section 3.2) except that it is done dynamically during processor operation. If E_{IDLE} is present and dominates the total energy consumption, then simultaneous f_{CLK}, V_{DD} reduction may yield a more energy efficient solution.

5.3: Faster Operation Can Limit Efficiency

If the user demands a fast response time, rather than reducing the voltage, as was done in Section 5.1, the processor can be left at the nominal supply voltage, and shut down when it is not needed.

For example, assume the target application has a T_{AVE} of 10 SPEC, and both processor A and B have a β factor of 0.1. If the processors' V_{DD} is left at 3.3V, B's METR is exactly equal to its ETR value, which is 2.5×10^{-3}. It remains the same because it never idles. Processor A, on the other hand, spends 14/15ths ($1 - T_{AVE}/T_{MAX}$) of the time idling, and its METR is 3.2×10^{-3}. Thus, for this scenario, processor B is more energy efficient.

However, if processor A's β can be reduced down to

0.05, then the METR of processor A becomes 2.26×10^{-3}, and it is once again the more energy efficient solution. For this example, the cross-over value of β is 0.063.

This example demonstrates how important it is to use the METR metric instead of the ETR metric if the target application's idle time is significant (i.e. T_{AVE} can be characterized). For the above example, a β for processor A greater than 0.063 leads the metrics to disagree on which is the more energy efficient solution. One might argue that the supply voltage can always be reduced on processor A so that it is more energy efficient for any required throughput. This is true if the dynamic range of processor A is as indicated in Figure 6. However, if some internal logic limited the value that V_{DD} could be dropped, then the lower bound on A's throughput would be located at a much higher value. Thus, finite β can degrade the energy efficiency of high throughput circuits due to excessive idle power dissipation.

6: Conclusions

Metrics for energy efficiency have been defined for three modes of computation in digital circuits. The appropriate metric for the fixed throughput mode, typical of most digital signal processing circuits, is energy/operation. Two other modes which apply to the operation of a microprocessor are maximum throughput and burst throughput modes.

A good energy efficiency metric for the maximum throughput mode is energy/operation versus throughput, which can be approximated with a constant ETR value. Many of the techniques developed for low power design in the fixed throughput mode can be successfully applied to the energy efficient design of a processor in the maximum throughput mode.

However, a better metric to describe more typical processor usage is the Microprocessor ETR, or METR; it includes the energy consumption of the idle mode, which can dominate total energy consumption in user-interactive applications. Decreasing the energy consumption of the idle mode is critical to the design of a energy efficient processor and complete shut down of the clock while idling is optimal. If this cannot be accomplished, then it is imperative that the operating system implement a power down mode so that the idle power dissipation becomes independent of the computing power dissipation. Then the METR optimization will maximize the throughput delivered to the user in an energy efficient manner. Otherwise, if idle power dissipation is proportional to the compute power dissipation, achieving energy efficient operation requires the throughput to be minimized.

An organized analytical approach to the optimization of power in microprocessor design, based on metrics that include the requirement of both throughput and energy, as well as actual application operation, allow the designer to quantify energy efficiency and provide insights into the design issues of energy efficient processor design.

This research is sponsored by ARPA.

References

[1] A. Chandrakasan, A. Burstein, R.W. Brodersen, "A Low Power Chipset for Portable Multimedia Applications", *Proceedings of the IEEE International Solid-State Circuits Conference*, Feb. 1994, pp. 82-83.

[2] T. Burd, *Low-Power CMOS Cell Library Design Methodology*, M.S. Thesis, University of California, Berkeley, 1994.

[3] S. Sze, *Physics of Semiconductor Devices*, Wiley, New York, 1981.

[4] H. Veendrick, "Short-Circuit Dissipation of Static CMOS Circuitry and Its Impact on the Design of Buffer Circuits", *IEEE Jour. of Solid State Circuits*, Aug 1984, pp. 468-473

[5] A. Chandrakasan, S. Sheng, R.W. Brodersen, "Low-Power CMOS Digital Design", *IEEE Journal of Solid State Circuits*, Apr. 1992, pp. 473-484.

[6] R. Muller, T. Kamins, *Device Electronics for Integrated Circuits*, Wiley, New York, 1986

[7] M. Horowitz, T. Indermaur, R. Gonzalez, "Low-Power Digital Design", *Proceedings of the Symposium on Low Power Electronics*, Oct. 1994.

[8] D. Wall, *Limits of Instruction-Level Parallelism*, DEC WRL Research Report 93/6, Nov. 1993.

[9] M. Johnson, *Superscalar Microprocessor Design*, Prentice Hall, Englewood, NJ, 1990.

[10] M. Smith, M. Johnson, M. Horowitz, "Limits on Multiple Issue Instruction", *Proceedings of the Third International Conference on Architectural Support for Programming Languages and Operating Systems*, Apr. 1989. pp 290-302

[11] T. Burd, B. Peters, *A Power Analysis of a Microprocessor: A Study of the MIPS R3000 Architecture*. ERL Technical Report, University of California, Berkeley, 1994.

[12] S. Gary, et. al.; "The PowerPC 603 Microprocessor: A Low-Power Design for Portable Applications", *Proceedings of the Thirty-Ninth IEEE Computer Society International Conference,* Mar. 1994, pp. 307-315

Energy-Efficient Instruction Set Architecture for CMOS Microprocessors

John Bunda,* Donald Fussell
Department of Computer Sciences
The University of Texas at Austin
Austin, Texas 78712
{bunda,fussell}@cs.utexas.edu

W. C. Athas
Information Sciences Institute
University of Southern California
Marina del Rey, California
athas@isi.edu

Abstract

Concern over power dissipation in CMOS microprocessors is increasing, not just for portable battery-based applications, but also for performance-driven designs, where power may soon displace silicon area as the principal design constraint. Traditional methods of power management, such as reduced operating voltage, exotic packaging, and low-power "sleep modes" can help mitigate the problem, but limits and drawbacks of these methods motivate examination of processor architecture tradeoffs from a power perspective.

This research was undertaken to validate the hypothesis that instruction set architecture can have a significant effect on power – a smaller program encoding is more energy-efficient than a larger one. In this paper we explore the relationship of code density and instruction set richness to the energy cost of fetching and delivering instructions to the execution resources. These effects are of particular interest to instruction-level parallel machines where speculative and multiple-path instruction fetching is necessary to exploit high execution bandwidth.

1 Introduction

On-chip memory and off-chip communication are two large components of the power budget for a typical microprocessor. Therefore, inefficiency in the instruction fetch mechanism can be expected to have significant energy cost. Instruction fetch rate and density of compiled code have first-order effects on performance; it should not be surprising that these also strongly influence electrical power demands. This can be critical in instruction-level parallel processors which require

high instruction fetch bandwidth to support parallel instruction issue and multiple-path branch following.

In this paper, we examine the effects of code density within a model of instruction fetch power. Through analytic models and simulation, we explore the relative energy-efficiency of two instruction encodings for the same microarchitecture. Using measurements of switching behavior on key instruction transport circuit nodes, we relate code density and and instruction set richness to instruction fetch power. We examine these trade-offs for a single-level off-chip store, and extend the model to include on-chip caches. The results presented in this paper demonstrate a significant advantage for a 16-bit instruction encoding for a RISC-style microarchitecture when compared to the more typical fixed 32-bit format.

2 CMOS switching energy.

CMOS circuits operate by switching the states of capacitive nodes between voltage levels that arbitrarily correspond to "zero" and "one" logic values. The switching energy for a state change at a given circuit node is proportional to:

$$E_{sw} = \frac{1}{2}CV^2$$

where C and V are capacitance and voltage respectively.

For complementary CMOS circuits, maintaining a node at a fixed voltage level is practically free. In these circuits, virtually all energy is dissipated when changing states from one logic value (voltage) to the other. This permits us to separate low-level circuit technology issues like capacitance, clock frequency, and voltage from higher-level issues like duty factor, fanout, and capacitance ratios.

---

*John Bunda is now with IBM Corporation, 9737 Great Hills Trail, Austin, Texas 78759

If charge sharing and other transient effects are ignored, the switching energy of a CMOS circuit over some period of time can be approximated as the product of the number of state changes at each node that occur during that time and E_{sw} for that node. The number of state changes at a circuit node depends on both the data traffic at that node (the information stored there) and the circuit implementation (static or dynamic).

For a static CMOS circuit that transports a stream of data, switching energy over time is proportional to the cumulative number of times a bit in the stream differs from its immediate predecessor. For dynamic (precharged, or domino) circuits, however, stream history is erased because between data holding states, the node is reset to a default state. For precharged circuits, switching energy is proportional to the number of times the data state differs from the precharged state.

The actual cost of a node state change depends on many variables, including the global system circuit. It is impossible to convert directly from state changes to absolute energy units without more information. However, state change information is often sufficient to compare relative energy-efficiency of different implementations of the same basic function.

The question is how to apply this model in a way to evaluate architectural decisions – capacitance values for every circuit node in a processor are not ordinarily available, much less complete node histories. However, compared to an arbitrary CMOS circuit, microprocessors have very regular structure, making it possible to discuss *classes* of circuit nodes. For certain high-level node classes, we can fairly easily obtain state histories. Moreover, while precise capacitance values might be unknown, the number of connections to key circuit nodes is usually defined by the microarchitecture, so we can reliably estimate capacitance *ratios*. Furthermore, in evaluating specific trade-offs, relative energy-efficiency of possible implementations can be nearly as useful as absolute energy values.

We developed methods to assess the power characteristics of two different instruction encodings for the same basic RISC microarchitecture. The two instruction set architectures are DLXe, a variant of DLX [4], which features thirty-two bit, three-address instructions, and D16, a sixteen-bit, two-address encoding for the same microarchitecture. The idea is to create a level playing field by holding the execution engine constant, and varying only the encoding scheme of the operations it supports.

The two instruction sets display measurable differences in code density and instruction traffic. The code density advantage for D16 yields comparable or better instruction processing performance than DLXe despite increased path length, primarily due to reduced instruction traffic [1, 3]. The reduction in instruction traffic yields better cache miss ratios and fewer memory latency cycles, which can more than offset the increase in instruction count. The hypothesis investigated in this paper is that all else being equal, this reduction in traffic yields lower instruction fetch power. Since different instruction sets could display quite different switching activity on instruction fetch circuit nodes, supporting this conjecture requires some analysis.

In evaluating the energy-efficiency of the instruction fetch mechanism for each instruction set, we are concerned primarily with two classes of circuit nodes, the pins through which instructions are fetched from off-chip memory, and, if an integrated instruction cache is present, nodes comprising the cache bit lines. This simplification allows us to subordinate much implementation detail, and only requires assumptions about capacitance ratios among critical nodes.

3 Instruction-fetch energy-efficiency.

Our first step in estimating the energy cost of fetching instructions is to characterize instruction traffic and node switching factors of each instruction set for both static and dynamic CMOS implementations of instruction transport circuits. With a simple software architecture simulator, we monitor state changes as instruction words are fetched. In this model, each instruction word passes through a single 32-bit Instruction Register. A series of benchmark programs was run, counting the total number of fetches through the register and the number of state changes at the Instruction Register outputs. This yields figures for total instruction traffic and switching factors for static and dynamic implementations of the Instruction Register.

For a given program, the D16 machine executes more instructions, but fetches fewer total instruction words, and traffic is reduced by an average of 36 percent (see Table 1). However, the static CMOS switching factor f is slightly higher for the D16 machine, most likely due to the higher information density of D16 instructions The bits of D16 instructions "work harder" since each bit must convey more information. Static switching factors for both instruction sets are only moderately sensitive to the particular application program.

Program	$\frac{T_{D16}}{T_{DLX_e}}$	f_{D16}	f_{DLX_e}
ackermann	0.83	0.45	0.36
as16	0.68	0.43	0.35
cbubble	0.55	0.50	0.27
cqueens	0.74	0.41	0.30
cquick	0.63	0.44	0.35
ctowers	0.57	0.46	0.36
grep	0.66	0.45	0.32
linpack	0.56	0.46	0.34
mat	0.59	0.46	0.30
dhrystone	0.72	0.43	0.33
pi	0.59	0.44	0.31
solver	0.62	0.44	0.35
tex	0.67	0.43	0.34
ipl	0.65	0.46	0.37
whetstone	0.60	0.44	0.33
Average	0.64	0.45	0.34

Table 1: D16/DLXe instruction traffic and static CMOS switching factors.

These traffic and switching factor measurements can be used to estimate relative instruction fetch energy cost for each instruction set. For example, if the processor must fetch all instructions externally (has no integrated instruction cache), instruction fetch energy will be proportional to the product of the switching factor and total traffic. Averaged over the benchmark suite, the ratio of the estimated instruction fetch energies is:

$$\frac{f_{D16} * T_{D16}}{f_{DLX_e} * T_{DLX_e}} = \frac{0.45 * 0.64}{0.34 * 1.0} = \frac{0.29}{0.34} = 0.85$$

That is, if all instruction traffic is through a 32-bit wide static CMOS register, D16 instructions can be fetched with 15 percent less switching energy than DLXe instructions.

For almost any modern microprocessor, this Instruction Register model is a gross oversimplification of the fetch mechanism. In the next section, we extend the model to account for the effects of instruction caches and dynamic circuit implementations.

3.1 Effects of an instruction cache.

Performance considerations aside, the high energy cost of off-chip communication makes an integrated cache an attractive strategy for reducing power. A cache allows satisfaction of many instruction fetch requests without incurring pin traffic. Assessing the power trade-offs with on-chip caches is more complex, since we must account not only for capacitance ratios between pin and cache nodes, but for the varying capacitance of cache nodes for different cache geometries. Moreover, varying the cache geometry and size influence both the power to operate the cache and the cache miss rate.

Exhaustive simulation to count actual node state changes for a large number of cache sizes and organizations is somewhat impractical. However, to the extent that switching activity is distributed uniformly over total instruction traffic, it is possible to estimate energy directly from cache miss rates.

The cache memory array is organized as a collection of fixed-size *blocks* (lines). A block is defined as the unit of cache memory associated with a single cache tag. Each block holds an aligned, contiguous sequence of bytes from main memory. The cache read port is one block wide. A *cache miss* occurs when a requested block of memory is not held in the cache. On a cache miss, the entire cache block is loaded with the corresponding memory contents. A *cache access* is the activation of the cache circuits to drive the value of a selected cache block to the bit lines of the cache read port.

The performance cost of a cache miss is latency; from a power standpoint, a cache miss is expensive because the energy cost of switching I/O pins normally considerably exceeds the cost of driving even a very long wire on the chip. By the same token, a small cache can be constructed with shorter wires and with fewer cells connected by each wire (reducing parasitic capacitance) compared to a large cache, and therefore costs less energy to operate. The model must address these fundamental trade-offs.

Total instruction fetch energy cost for a given program is defined as the sum of that used to access the instruction cache and that used to fetch instructions from external memory when a cache miss occurs. Let E_{access} be the average switching energy for a cache access, where f_{access} is the switching factor on the cache bit lines, and *BlockSize* and *SetSize* denote the dimensions of the cache in the block size in bits and the number of blocks, respectively.

$$E_{access} = f_{access} * BlockSize * SetSize$$

In this formula, both dimensions of the cache are weighted equally. It bears mention that a for a differential sense-amp cache design, DC power is of greater concern, a larger block size can have higher energy cost than a longer bit line, in which case increased weight should be assigned to the *BlockSize* term. Most differential designs also behave like dual-rail dynamic circuits, meaning the switching factor is always 1, and power is strictly a function of the number of cache accesses.

On a cache miss, additional switching energy is dissipated loading the requested instructions from external memory. Let E_{load} be the average switching energy to load a missed block from external memory. Each miss generates traffic proportional to the cache *BlockSize*, f_{load} is the switching factor of a pin node, and E_{pin} is the switching energy for a state change of a pin node.

$$E_{\text{load}} = f_{\text{load}} * BlockSize * E_{pin}$$

Instruction fetch switching energy over the execution of a given program can be estimated in terms of the total number of instruction fetches and the number of cache misses as follows:

$$E_{\text{ifetch}} = IFetches * E_{\text{access}} + CacheMisses * E_{\text{load}}$$

This model has some important simplifications; for example, power for driving cache word line selects is not included. Since select lines are orthogonal, switching factor at these nodes is relatively low (though loading is proportional to the block size). In most cache implementations, however, and power is dominated by driving of the bit-line outputs. Also ignored is power at the address outputs to the external memory subsystem. Like power at the cache word lines, this should be linear in the number of off-chip accesses. And since each fetch address generates multiple data transfer transactions (the cache block size is probably larger than the width of the memory port) it is probably also reasonable to assume that the data transfer portion dominates. It is worth noting, however, that the effect of these assumptions is to *understate* the power benefits of reducing instruction traffic.

We use this model to predict the relative instruction fetch energy cost for identical programs running on D16 and DLXe processors. We examine three progressively more complicated designs. The first is a simple power-naive approach in which each instruction is fetched with a cache access. Multiplexors below the cache are used to select the requested instruction word from the block. No state is saved between successive fetches. In the second, each cache line is buffered below the cache, and as long as the instruction stream can be fetched from the buffer, the cache is not accessed. This scheme is similar to what one might expect to encounter in a parallel-dispatch or superscalar processor implementation. A steep diminishing return curve for longer cache blocks led to the third refinement, which incorporates sub-blocking of long cache lines to reduce extraneous miss reload traffic.

Empirically measured average switching factors for static and single-rail dynamic CMOS circuits of the Instruction Register as described above are shown in Table 2. In the models, we assume static CMOS inputs at the off-chip memory interface. We measure a single-rail domino-style bit-line driver instead of a differential sense-amp to reduce switching factor.

We arbitrarily estimate the pin switching energy E_{pin} as a weight κ times E_{access} per bit for a 16K-byte cache, and conservatively select $\kappa = 10$ (weighting the cost per bit of an external memory access at ten times the cost per bit of operating a 16K cache).

ISA	f_{load} Static CMOS	f_{access} Dynamic CMOS
D16	0.45	0.58
DLXe	0.34	0.68

Table 2: Average instruction circuit switching factors.

To determine cache miss rates, **dinero** [5] was applied to D16 and DLXe address traces for three programs from our benchmark suite large enough to have interesting cache behavior (**assem, latex,** and **ipl**). Cache miss ratios were obtained for cache sizes ranging from 1K to 16K bytes, and for block sizes varying from 8-256 bytes. For sake of simplicity, we consider only direct-mapped placement. Figure 1 plots E_{ifetch} for both D16 and DLXe for **assem**. The two other programs behave similarly, and are not presented here (see [2, 3]).

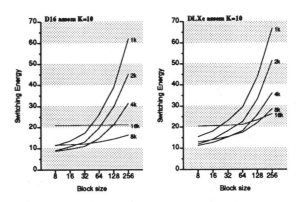

Figure 1: Instruction fetch energy for **assem**.

The graphs show that while larger cache blocks reduce the cache miss rate, the savings is not sufficient to recover the energy cost of fetching instructions that are never issued due to branches into and out of the middle of a cache block. With smaller caches, high miss rates lead to high pin traffic, and the cost of external traffic dominates. As the cache grows large enough to capture the program working set, sensitivity to block size decreases, but beyond a certain point, marginal hit rate improvement decreases while the cost of a cache block access grows linearly.

Because they reflect capture of the working set, the curves for 16K caches are dominated by cache bit line (rather than external pin) energy, and appear nearly identical for both instruction sets. This is misleading because in this model, the cache is operated for each instruction word fetch. The D16 machine executes 25 percent more instructions, but total traffic is 40 percent less than for the DLXe machine. If the bit cost weight of external to internal traffic were to exceed our conservative estimate of 10, the higher external traffic would result in a larger increase for DLXe than for D16.

3.2 Cache block buffering.

The locality of instruction fetch references means that a very good hit rate can be achieved with a simple, relatively small cache, even if the cache is organized as a simple buffer [6]. This can be exploited to reduce power by diminishing the total number of cache accesses. The idea is to buffer the most recently fetched cache block, and operate the cache only when a requested instruction is not held in the current buffer, i.e. a *block miss*. Fetching multiple instructions per cache access is not a new idea, most parallel-issue and superscalar machines exploit this same locality to increase instruction processing performance. The scheme can be trivially adopted to reduce power in a single-issue processor by performing a cache-tag comparison of the requested instruction with the tag for the current block before operating the cache. This is usually just a compare-equal of high-order address bits. This block buffering scheme is pictured in Figure 2.

The block buffer could be thought of as another cache, with a miss in the block buffer "cache" resulting in retrying the request in the instruction cache. Figure 3 shows the relationship between block size and block hit rate for the three benchmark programs at different block sizes. The figure shows that the block hit rate curve flattens between 32 and 64 bytes for for both D16 and DLXe. Block sizes larger than 64 bytes do not significantly affect block hit rate for either machine, presumably due to branching. For D16, note that the block hit rate for a 32-byte block exceeds 80 percent, and the block hit rate for both machines peaks at over

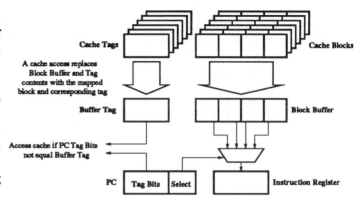

Figure 2: Block buffered cache.

90 percent.

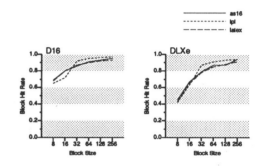

Figure 3: Block size and block hit rate.

The drawback to larger block sizes shown above is the cost of fetching unneeded instructions. However, a buffered cache tends to favor larger blocks. Especially if a block is large enough to capture a loop body, it is possible for the processor to operate for extended periods with no traffic overhead at all.

With a block buffer, cache access does not occur on every instruction fetch but only when the needed instruction is not in the block buffer. Therefore, the number of block misses replaces the number of instruction fetches in the computation of switching energy:

$$E_{\text{ifetch}} = BlockMisses * E_{\text{access}} + CacheMisses * E_{\text{load}}$$

Figure 4 shows that block sizes of up to 256 bytes are reasonable as long as the cache is large enough to capture the working set. With moderate cache and block sizes, the strategy yields energy savings of 40% to 50% over the non-buffered design. The energy-inefficiency of large caches displayed by the non-buffered approach is eliminated. Only at very

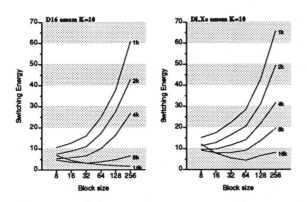

Figure 4: Instruction fetch energy with block buffered cache.

small block sizes does the 16K block-buffered cache have higher energy cost than the smaller arrays.

With a block buffered cache, the D16 code density advantage (more instructions per block) yields even better reductions in traffic and switching energy. D16 instruction fetch is 40% to 50% more energy-efficient than DLXe instruction fetch.

3.3 Cache sub-blocks.

Block buffering exploits instruction locality and block hit rate to reduce cache accesses and therefore energy. The strategy exploits locality to reduce the need to operate the cache. However, a remaining drawback to larger blocks is the high energy cost of filling those blocks from off-chip memory. As block size increases, so does the traffic in instructions that are fetched unnecessarily because they are never issued. Beyond a certain block size, this component can eliminate any savings due to cache access reduction.

There is no need, though, to fill an entire cache block on a cache miss. Cache sub-blocking, or sectoring, has been used in many cache designs, usually to conserve tag array space and control overhead (rather than energy). In a sub-blocked design, each cache block is divided into several sub-blocks, with all sub-blocks in the block being associated with a single tag.

The principal drawback of sub-blocking is a higher cache miss rate, since a cache miss can occur on each sub-block within a block. On the other hand, each cache miss generates a smaller amount of external traffic, and the probability of a fetched instruction actually being dispatched is considerably increased.

To estimate instruction fetch energy for a sub-blocked cache, we substitute *SubBlockSize* for

BlockSize in the computation of the formula for E_{load} from Section 3.1:

$$E_{\text{load}} = f_{\text{load}} * SubBlockSize * E_{pin}$$

Because external traffic has a much higher energy cost, reducing it even slightly can be expected to dramatically reduce total instruction fetch energy. The magnitude of E_{pin} determines how critical this optimization can be, but its effect is significant even with our conservative estimate. Figure 5 shows the reduction in external traffic using 8-byte sub-blocks in the cache (interpolation can be used to estimate the difference for intermediate sub-block sizes).

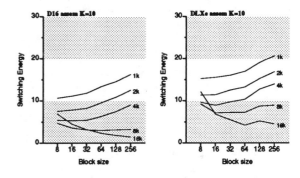

Figure 5: Instruction fetch energy with block buffering and sub-blocks.

As one might expect, the reduction in energy is most significant when the cache is too small to hold the working set, and off-chip traffic is high. The Y axis of the graph has been rescaled to accentuate the differences along the curves. When the cache is "too small", sub-blocking can be a significant win. In this scenario, energy was reduced by about a factor of three for all programs considered. This sub-blocking strategy also increases the energy-cost advantage of the denser D16 instruction encoding. In some cases, the worst-case block size/energy for D16 is better than the best-case for DLXe. All else equal, the D16 advantage is averages roughly 40 percent, and proportional to code density. Block buffering and sub-blocking significantly increase the energy efficiency over the base design. For larger cache arrays, the efficiency is increased by as much as a factor of eight.

4 Conclusions

This paper presents the results of some experiments that demonstrate a model for quantitative evaluation of power on instruction fetch circuits. This approach is based on a simplified model of switching energy, cache miss rates, and instruction traffic, and is used to compare and contrast instruction fetch energy-efficiency of two different instruction encodings for the same microarchitecture. Measured switching factors over instruction streams were used with miss ratios to characterize power sensitivity to the instruction set and cache structure and configuration.

The principal result is that all else being equal, increasing code density can have a very large payoff in energy efficiency, even if this increases path length and switching factor. This benefit is directly proportional to traffic reduction, and in a high-performance system, this effect is compound, since it will be observed at each level of a multilevel memory hierarchy.

In any of the scenarios considered, the 16-bit instructions of the D16 ISA are fetched with greater energy-efficiency than the 32-bit DLXe instructions. The richness of a fixed 32-bit instruction set has costs which must be carefully weighed in power-critical applications. Block buffering and cache sub-blocking are very effective in reducing cache accesses and off-chip traffic, respectively, and judiciously applied, could significantly reduce power without unnecessarily compromising performance.

Curiously, the energy and performance benefits of instruction caches do not necessarily always coincide. For example, sub-blocking reduces traffic at the expense of higher miss rate. If performance is critical, the power benefits of a sub-blocking scheme must be balanced by the net performance provided by the speculative prefetching provided by larger-granularity sub-blocks.

Future work should include empirically testing the validity of the state-change and traffic models of switching energy. The model could be enhanced to include the power burden for word-line and address drivers, and more accurate estimates of the relative cost of off-chip communication to on-chip wiring loads would be useful. The energy cost of instruction decoding for the two instruction sets should be investigated.

The particular strategies to reduce power demonstrated in this paper might be at odds with other performance, packaging, or technology constraints of a given design point. Nonetheless there are clearly numerous other opportunities for increasing the energy-efficiency of microprocessor designs at the architectural and microarchitectural levels that could be evaluated using similar techniques.

Acknowledgments

Thanks to Bob Masleid, Nestoras Tzartzanis, and the referees for their thoughtful criticism of early drafts.

References

[1] J. D. Bunda, D. K. Fussell, W. C. Athas, and R. M. Jenevein. 16-bit vs. 32-bit instructions for pipelined architectures. In *Proceedings of the 20th International Symposium on Computer Architecture*, pages 237–246, May 1993.

[2] John Bunda, W. C. Athas, and Donald Fussell. Increasing instruction fetch energy-efficiency of a VLSI microprocessor. Technical Report TR 92-40, Department of Computer Sciences, The University of Texas at Austin, 1992.

[3] John D. Bunda. *Instruction-Processing Optimization Techniques for VLSI Microprocessors*. PhD thesis, The University of Texas at Austin, Austin, Texas, 1993.

[4] John L. Hennessy and David A. Patterson. *Computer Architecture: A Quantitative Approach*. Morgan Kaufmann Publishers, Inc., Palo Alto, CA, 1990.

[5] Mark D. Hill. Dinero cache simulator, 1992.

[6] Mark D. Hill et al. Design decisions in SPUR. *Computer*, pages 8–22, November 1986.

Appendix

Table 3 gives cache miss totals for the three cache benchmark programs for both full-block and sub-block caches. Table 4 shows misses in the block buffer for each.

	ISA	Full Block Reload on Miss Cache Block Size (bytes)						Eight-Byte Sub-Blocks Cache Block Size (bytes)					
		8	16	32	64	128	256	8	16	32	64	128	256
assem													
1K	D16	32288	19904	12782	9969	7566	6127	32288	34582	36871	41808	45863	51113
	DLXe	62370	37098	23977	15433	11663	8991	62370	64772	67627	71879	80772	87938
2K	D16	20801	13314	8499	6849	5483	4288	20801	22955	24707	29027	33278	38876
	DLXe	41655	25755	17320	11008	8421	6720	41655	45123	49982	54059	62307	69564
4K	D16	11645	7403	4709	3864	3229	2659	11645	13029	14446	17689	21351	26618
	DLXe	27617	17105	11336	7311	5763	4275	27617	30681	34743	38774	48269	54330
8K	D16	4201	2420	1443	1132	827	610	4201	4415	4788	5785	6995	7898
	DLXe	14279	9367	6232	4183	3372	2587	14279	16379	18899	21807	27157	30631
16K	D16	1147	638	355	208	123	69	1147	1147	1147	1147	1147	1147
	DLXe	4264	2430	1453	952	1072	938	4264	4402	4585	5070	8268	10395
ipl													
1K	D16	276467	167422	107910	84227	62706	68798	276467	295706	328416	383859	415087	501189
	DLXe	402487	246608	167808	118918	95170	93601	402487	432775	478458	530438	616721	729450
2K	D16	161067	102807	66463	107910	48092	42996	161067	177204	198797	239470	308421	363878
	DLXe	210052	126785	86393	62975	60606	58390	210052	226862	260205	308282	412416	514778
4K	D16	99164	60432	41573	66463	29846	28383	99164	108866	125728	152513	212474	288493
	DLXe	124843	74577	54315	39598	33524	26972	124843	134752	161790	194758	250361	302509
8K	D16	17641	10720	6780	41573	3855	3370	17641	19180	21127	24413	30045	39377
	DLXe	78795	46433	34206	23734	18867	16257	78795	84782	103838	124508	159763	210710
16K	D16	8436	4954	3041	6780	1366	1267	8436	8999	9684	10813	12399	15797
	DLXe	29001	16530	10467	6857	4743	4075	29001	30798	34542	39294	44948	59937
latex													
1K	D16	966342	625054	478122	368917	320573	301081	966342	1054085	1223552	1394334	1595759	1827352
	DLXe	1693044	1028048	671987	471435	379999	339729	1693044	1797795	1944511	2126821	2453371	2830746
2K	D16	671269	432969	358282	286279	256001	229798	671269	740139	917518	1087886	1295456	1525392
	DLXe	1170367	716266	470530	336354	273710	238794	1170367	1261109	1386414	1564101	1870220	2208279
4K	D16	344728	235391	171538	131354	122772	116941	344728	393747	465745	543993	684203	838187
	DLXe	728038	437657	288352	208566	173443	148269	728038	780069	862822	995463	1223768	1434184
8K	D16	187832	124402	95090	69580	61993	71952	187832	213751	261116	299111	373725	498297
	DLXe	436099	265520	182285	134502	114976	95087	436099	473085	539308	640226	839266	998052
16K	D16	116812	74735	54168	38532	33885	31000	116812	131467	155897	175168	217335	267896
	DLXe	224468	134454	87486	63234	49506	41375	224468	242881	270396	313715	375036	469483

Table 3: Instruction cache misses.

ISA	Benchmark Program	Total Instructions	Block Size					
			8	16	32	64	128	256
assem	D16	302600	86482	54677	37284	25493	18505	12760
	DLXe	245873	122589	72820	46805	29239	29173	13738
ipl	D16	5454311	1689280	1357357	374722	235548	181037	159581
	DLXe	4844964	2418230	1551295	560329	363990	305304	236202
latex	D16	116782293	3303327	2089498	1346811	1042733	868332	757629
	DLXe	9091141	4706934	2860397	1863159	1259471	989519	765549

Table 4: Instruction misses in block buffer.

Cache Designs for Energy Efficiency

Ching-Long Su and Alvin M. Despain

Advanced Computer Architecture Laboratory
University of Southern California

Abstract

Caches usually consume a significant amount of energy in modern microprocessors (e.g. superpipelined or superscalar processors). In this paper, we examine contemporary cache design techniques and provide an analytical model for estimating cache energy consumption. We also present several novel techniques for designing an energy efficiency cache, which include block buffering, cache sub-banking, and Gray code addressing. The experimental results suggest that both block buffering and Gray code addressing techniques are ideal for instruction cache designs which tend to be accessed in consecutive sequence. Cache sub-banking is ideal for both instruction and data caches. Overall, these techniques can achieve an order of magnitude energy reduction on caches.

1 Introduction

Energy efficiency is important to mobile computing applications (e.g. notebook computers, consumer electronics, and cellular phones). They not only require high performance, but also low energy consumption for longer battery life. Another driving force behind designing for energy efficiency is that power consumption is becoming the limiting factor in integrating more transistors on a single chip or on a multi-chip module due to cooling, packaging and reliability problems.

Power consumption in CMOS has three components: dynamic power consumption, short circuit current power consumption, and static power consumption. With proper circuit design techniques, the latter two components can be reduced and are negligible compared to the dynamic power consumption. The dynamic power consumption of a CMOS circuit can be described by

$$P_g = 0.5 f f_d C_L V_{dd}^2$$

where f is the clock frequency, f_d is the switching activity, C_L is average capacitance loading of the circuit, and V_{dd} is the supply voltage. To minimize power consumption, we can reduce f_d, C_L or V_{dd}.

Many researchers have been studying low voltage design techniques [2,8]. However, lowering the supply voltage may create other design problems such as reduced noise margin, increased cross talk, etc. Other researchers are exploring instruction set architectures and novel memory management schemes for low power, processor design using self-clocking, static and dynamic power management strategies, etc. Some other research has been done in minimizing the switching activity of the circuit in order to minimize power. This method is orthogonal to supply voltage reduction and process optimization and thus can be used to further reduce power consumption once the supply voltage and process of the processor are chosen. Currently most of the work has been carried out in the layout [17] and logic levels [9,12,16].

In this work, we focus mainly on minimizing the energy consumption of instruction and data caches on advanced processors for ILP (Instruction-level Parallelism), in which caches usually consume a significant amount of energy. In order to understand how energy is consumed on caches, we develop an analytical model in which energy consumption on different cache components can be easily estimated. We also propose some novel ideas for designing an energy efficient cache. The proposed cache design is validated by software simulation of benchmark program running on a superpipelined processor.

This paper consists of seven sections. Section 2 briefly describes some related work on cache designs targeted for high performance and low power. Section 3 shows the methodology used in this study. Section 4 investigates several experimental cache structures used in this work. Section 5 presents the evaluation results. Section 6 discusses cache design decisions for energy optimization. Finally, concluding remarks are offered in Section 7.

2 Related Work

The performance of cache designs have been widely studied for several decades [5,10,11]. In general, caches are designed as direct-mapped or set associative. A direct-mapped cache has the advantages of a low cost and a faster hit time. However, the cache miss rate is usually high when the cache size is not big. On the other hand, a set associative cache has a lower miss rate with a higher design cost and a longer hit time.

There have been few studies of cache designs for energy efficiency compared to the number of studies on cache designs for high performance. Jouppi suggested a two-level cache structure consumes less power than a single-level organization (assuming the area devoted to the cache is the same) [7]. Bunda investigated the impact of a 16-bit instruction set design to the instruction-fetch energy [1]. Memory addressing by using Gray code has shown a significant bit switching reduction on the instruction address path compared to the traditional 2's complement memory addressing [14].

3 Methodology

This paper presents a study of cache designs for energy efficiency. The methodology used in this study is the following. First, we provide an analytical model for estimating energy consumption for different cache components. Second, we evaluate energy consumption of traditional cache designs based on this analytical model. Third, a novel cache design targeted for energy efficiency is proposed. Finally, the energy consumption of the proposed caches are evaluated and compared to the traditional cache designs. The work load used in this study is a set of Prolog benchmark programs running on a RISC-like micro-processor, the VLSI-BAM [14]

3.1 Cache Energy Model

Figure 1(a) shows the organization of a traditional direct-mapped cache design. When the processor performs a memory access operation, the reference address is first sent to the Memory Address Register (MAR). The contents of the MAR then drives the address bus and is stored into the address buffers of the direct-mapped cache which is composed from two memory arrays: tag memory and data memory. The reference address to a direct-mapped cache using bit selection mapping function is divided into several fields. They are block, index, and tag fields.

The block field of the reference address is used to locate the position of the referenced data in a cache block. The index field of the reference address is used to locate the referenced data block in the data memory arrays. The tag field of the reference address is used to compare with the tag stored in the tag memory array located by the index field of the reference address. If there is a match (i.e. a hit), then the referenced data will be stored into the Memory Data Register (MDR). The contents of the MDR are then transferred to the CPU core through the data bus. In the case when the tag comparison does not match (i.e. a miss), the reference address is then sent out of the chip through the address pads. The requested cache block will eventually be ready to be transferred into the chip. This cache block is then written to the cache through the data pads.

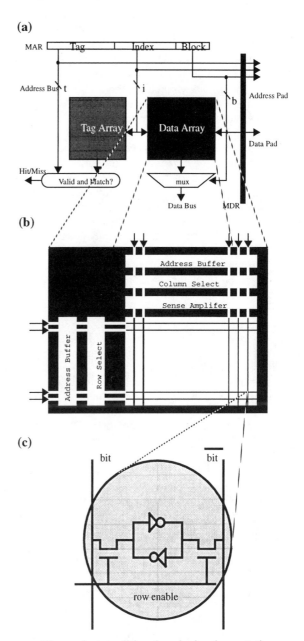

Figure 1: A traditional cache implementation

Figure 1(b) shows the micro-architecture of the cache design, in which there are four components: the memory cell array, the row select, the column select, and the bit line control circuit including a sense amplifier as well as a read/write circuit. The design of a memory cell is shown in the Figure 1(c).

The total energy consumption of a cache can be divided into three different components: the *memory addressing path*, the *cache memory*, and the *I/O path*.

The *memory addressing path* of a cache includes the address bus and the address decoding logic. Usually the capacitance of a decoding logic is a lot less than that of the address bus. Therefore, energy consumption of the memory addressing path is dominated by the address bus. In other words, the bit switching activities on the address bus will directly affect the energy consumption of the memory addressing path.

The *cache memory* includes the read/write circuitry, the tag memory array, and the data memory array. Both tag and data memory arrays usually dominate the energy consumption of this cache component. The energy consumption of both memory arrays depends on their designs (e.g. dynamic or static logic). In a dynamic circuit design, bit lines are pre-charged on every access. The pre-charge value is usually around 2.5V in a circuit design for 5V. If the value on a bit-line will be set to 1, this bit-line is charged from 2.5V to 5V. On the other hand, if the value on the bit line will be set to 0, this bit line is then discharged from 2.5V to 0V. In this case, the amount of energy consumed on the bit lines is the same whether the values on the bit lines are 1 or 0. Therefore, the amount of energy consumption of the cache memory in dynamic logic will depend on the number of accesses, instead of the values on the bit lines. On the other hand, in a static circuit design, there are no pre-charges on the bit lines. The amount of energy consumption on the tag and data memory array directly depends on the bit switch activities of the bit lines. Since most of the cache memory cell designs used in advanced microprocessor's use dynamic logic, the energy model of cache memory in this study is based on dynamic logic. The energy impact of cache designs in static logic will only be briefly discussed.

The *I/O path* of a cache includes the I/O pads and the connected address and data buses. Usually the capacitance of the I/O pads is larger than that on the address and data buses in current microprocessor designs. Energy consumption of this cache component therefore is dominated by the energy consumed during the bit switching of the I/O pads. Since the I/O pads are only accessed whenever there is a cache miss event, the bit switching rates of the I/O pads are also affected by the cache hit rate.

To design a cache for energy efficiency, the energy consumption of all three cache components must be minimized. The design goal of a cache is to minimize the overall cache energy E_{cache}, which is calculated by the summation of the energy consumption of the memory address path $E_{address\_path}$, the cache memory E_{cell_array}, and the I/O path E_{I/O_path}. Since the energy consumption of the memory address path is dominated by the switching rates of the address bus, it is reasonable to estimate $E_{address\_path}$ by multiplying the bit switching rate on the address bus $Addr\_bus\_bsr$ with some scaling factor.

The E_{cell_array} for a cache in dynamic logic is estimated by the summation of weighted access frequencies of the cache tag memory arrays Tag_access and data memory arrays $Block\_access$. This is because the bit lines of a cache cell array in dynamic logic are always precharged. The energy consumption of the bit lines of a cache in dynamic logic depends on the number of precharges (e.g. accesses) instead of the bit switching activi-

ties.

The E_{I/O_path} for a cache is estimated by the weighted bit switching rate of the address pads $Addr\_pad\_bsr$ and weighted bit switching rate of the data pads $Data\_pad\_bsr$, since the energy consumption of the I/O path is dominated by the bit switching rates of the I/O pads.

$$E_{cache} = E_{address\_path} + E_{cell\_array} + E_{I/O\_path}$$

$$E_{address\_path} = \alpha * Addr\_bus\_bsr$$

$$E_{cell\_array} = \beta * Tag\_access + \chi * Block\_access$$
(Dynamic Logic)

$$E_{address\_path} = \delta * Addr\_pad\_bsr + \varepsilon * Data\_pad\_bsr$$

Addr_bus_bsr	Bit switching rates of address bus
Tag_access	Access rates of bit-lines in cache tag arrays
Block_access	Access rates of bit-lines in cache block array
Addr_pad_bsr	Bit switching rates of address pads
Data_pad_bsr	Bit switching rates of data pads
$\alpha,\beta,\chi,\delta,\varepsilon$	Constants depending on VLSI implementation.

3.2 Benchmark Programs

The benchmark programs used in this study are described in Table 1. These benchmark programs are selected from the Aquarius benchmark suite [4]. These benchmark programs contain millions of execution cycles. Applications of these benchmark programs include list manipulation, data base queries, theorem provers, and a circuit generator.

Benchmark	Instructions	Description
boyer	27,494,723	An a Boyer-Moore theorem prover.
browse	18,883,712	Build and query a database
nand	1,064,197	A circuit generator
reducer	1,695,417	List manipulation

Table 1: Benchmark programs

The benchmark programs are compiled through the Aquarius Prolog compiler front-end [18] and an optimizing compiler backend [13] for VLSI-SLAM. An instruction-level simulator of VLSI-SLAM is used to monitor bit switching activities of cache behaviors when benchmark programs are running.

4 Experimental Cache Structures

In this section, we briefly describe the experimental caches used in this study. They includes conventional cache designs, block buffering[1], cache sub-banking[16], and Gray code addressing[14].

4.1 Conventional Caches

The basic structure of a direct-mapped cache has been shown in the Figure 1. An *N*-way set associative cache can be constructed by several *N*-times-smaller direct-mapped caches. Since there are *N* blocks that need to be checked on each reference, each of the *N* tags in a set must be read and compared in parallel in order to keep a set associative cache hit time similar to that of a direct-mapped cache.

From the performance point of view, a set associative cache has a potentially better hit rate than a direct-mapped cache of the same size. However, the hit time for a set associative cache is slightly higher than a direct-mapped cache due to the additional *N-1* multiplexes to select the hit block.

From the energy point of view, a set associative cache has potentially more bit switches of the tag and data bit lines than a direct-mapped cache of the same size since several cache banks are accessed in parallel. However, the energy consumption of each bit line in a set associative cache is less than a direct-mapped cache of the same size since the capacitance of the bit line is smaller. How the decreased energy due to smaller bit line capacitance compares to the increased energy due to more bit switches in a set associative cache depends on the VLSI implementation. One certain win in energy efficiency for a set associative cache is its less energy consumed on the I/O pads since its miss rate is less than that in a direct-mapped cache of the same cache size.

4.2 Block Buffering

In the conventional cache design discussed in the previous section, one or more blocks are accessed (read or write) on each reference. These blocks usually have a size ranging from 4 to 16 words in current microprocessor designs. For applications with a high spatial locality in which the next access data is likely to be located at the same block of the latest access, the total number of cache accesses can then be reduced by "buffering" the most recently fetched cache block. The energy consumption for accessing the buffer will be a lot less than that for accessing the cache.

A basic structure of a *block-buffered cache* [1] is presented in Figure 2. The block buffer itself is, in effect, another cache which is closer to the processor than conventional on-chip caches. The processor checks if there is a block hit (i.e. the current access data is located at the same block of the latest access data). If it is a hit, the data is directly read from the block buffer and the cache is not operated. The cache is operated only when there is a block miss. An application with high spatial locality can significantly benefit from block buffering. For example, if the energy consumed by accessing a bit of a block buffer and a cache bit line are α and 10α, assume the block size is 128 bits and the bit switching factor is 30%. To access the

cache and the block buffer requires energy 384α (calculated by $128 * 0.3 * 10\alpha$) and 38.4α (calculated by $128 * 0.3 * \alpha$) respectively. In the case of accessing four consecutive memory addresses located in the same cache block, a block-buffered cache only needs one cache access and four block buffer access. The total energy consumption will be 499.2α. Compared to 1536α, energy consumed in a conventional cache design in which four cache accesses are needed, the block buffered cache only consumes 32.5% of total energy consumed by a traditional cache design.

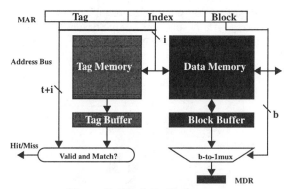

Figure 2: Block Buffering

From an energy point of view, a block-buffered cache saves energy consumed by unnecessary cache accesses. The amount of energy saved by block buffering strongly depends on the spatial locality and the block size. The higher the spatial locality of the access patterns (e.g. an instruction sequence), the larger the amount of energy can be saved by block buffering. The block size is also important to block buffering. Excluding the impact to the cache hit rate of the cache block size, a small block may result in limiting the amount of energy saved by the block buffered cache and a large block may result in increasing unnecessary energy consumption of the unused data in the block.

From a performance point of view, one advantage of block buffering is its short block buffer access time. If accessing a cache is in a critical path of a processor, the clock speed of the processor can be improved by block buffering. In this case, a block buffer hit takes only one processor cycle and a block buffer miss may take more than one processor cycle. The performance improvement of block buffering therefore depends on the hit rate of the block buffer and how much faster processor clock speed can be improved by block buffering.

4.3 Cache Sub-banking

A cache block is usually an access unit for cache references in conventional cache designs. The whole cache block is read or written at the same time. The requested data is selected from the accessed block by the block offset field of the reference address. Since the location of the requested data in a cache block is "known" (specified directly from the block offset field of the reference address) before accessing the cache, there is no need to consume energy on accessing un-requested data located in the same cache block. In order to separate energy management of each data in the cache block, the data memory array is partitioned into several banks, named *cache sub-banking*. Each cache bank can be accessed individually.

A basic structure for cache sub-banking is presented in Figure 3. The data memory array is, in effect, divided into several sub-banks. In each cache access, only the cache sub-bank where the desired data located is activated (i.e consuming energy). Therefore, a sub-banked data memory array with N sub-banks only consume $1/N$ energy of the total energy consumed by a traditional data memory array.

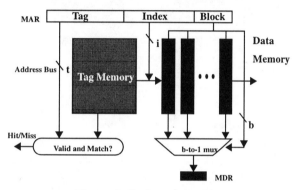

Figure 3: Cache sub-banking

Like block buffering, cache sub-banking saves energy consumed by unnecessary data accesses. Unlike block buffering, the amount of energy saved by cache sub-banking does not depend on the spatial locality of the access patterns. Excluding the impact on the cache hit rate of the cache block size, a larger block size will save more energy.

One advantage of cache sub-banking over block buffering is that the effective cache hit time of a sub-bank cache can be as fast as a conventional performance-driven cache design since the sub-bank selection logic is usually very simple and can be easily hidden in the cache index decoding logic. With the advantage of maintaining the cache performance, cache sub-banking is very attractive.

One disadvantage of cache sub-banking over a block buffering is that the energy consumption on tag memory array cannot be saved by cache sub-banking. This will cause a large impact on total energy consumption when the block size is small (e.g. less than 2 words). However, the impact will be a lot smaller if the block size is large (e.g. more than 4 words).

4.4 Gray Code Addressing Caches

Memory addressing used in a traditional processor design is usually two's complement representation. Two

consecutive memory addresses are represented by two consecutive two's complement representations in a binary sequence. One advantage of using two's complement representation as memory addressing is its fast memory address calculation by well-developed binary adders. However, from a bit switching point of view, a two's complement representation sequence may not be the best. Since there is a significant amount of energy consumed on the memory address path (including the address buses and the decoding logic) and sequential memory address access often be seen in an application with high spatial locality, it is important to reduce bit switching activities of the memory address path in a cache design.

A Gray code is a function G(i) of the integers i, that for each integer N >= 0 is one-to-one for 0 =< i =< 2^N-1, and that has the following property: The binary representation of G(i) and G(i+1) differ in exactly one bit, shown in Table 2. Using Gray code sequence for memory addressing can significantly reduce bit switching on the memory address path. A formal definition of Gray code sequence is described as follows [3],

Gray Code Representation

1. $G_1 = 0, 1$.

2. Let $G_k = g_0, g_1,..., g_{2k-2}, g_{2k-1}$. G_{k+1} is formed by first preceding all members of the sequence G_k by 0, then repeating G_k with the order reversed and all members preceded by 1. In other words,

$$G_{k+1} = 0g_0, 0g_1,..., 0g_{2k-2}, 0g_{2k-1}, 1g_{2k-1}, 1g_{2k-2},..., 1g_1, 1g_0$$

For example, $G_2 = 00, 01, 11, 10$ and $G_3 = 000, 001, 011, 010, 110, 111, 101, 100$. Clearly the foregoing construction ensures that consecutive members of a Gray code sequence differ in exactly 1 bit.

Gray code	Decimal Equivalent	Gray code	Decimal Equivalent
0000	0	1100	8
0001	1	1101	9
0011	2	1111	10
0010	3	1110	11
0110	4	1010	12
0111	5	1011	13
0101	6	1001	14
0100	7	1000	15

Table 2: Gray code representation and decimal equivalent

Bit Switch Comparison

The bit switches of a sequence of numbers can be significantly different depending on the code representations. Table 3 shows an example. For the sequence of numbers from 0 to 16, shown in Table 3(a), there are 31 bit switches when the number are coded in binary representation. There are only 16 bit switches when these numbers are coded in Gray code representation. However, for the sequence numbers shown in Table 3(b), there are only 17 bit switches when they are coded in binary representation. There are 29 bit switches when these numbers are coded in Gray code representation.

0	00000	00000		1	00001	00001
1	00001	00001		3	00011	00010
2	00010	00011		7	00111	00100
3	00011	00010		15	01111	01000
4	00100	00110		14	01110	01001
5	00101	00111		12	01100	01010
6	00110	00101		13	01101	01011
7	00111	00100		9	01001	01101
8	01000	01100		8	01000	01100
9	01001	01101		10	01010	01111
10	01010	01111		11	01011	01110
11	01011	01110		2	00010	00011
12	01100	01010		6	00110	00101
13	01101	01011		4	00100	00110
14	01110	01001		5	00101	00111
15	01111	01000		0	00000	00000
16	10000	11000		16	10000	11000
bit changed	**31**	**16**		bit changed	**17**	**29**
(a)	*2's complement*	*Gray*		**(b)**	*2's complement*	*Gray*

Table 3: The bit switches of 2's Complement codes vs. Gray codes

From the above example, we see how the number of bit switches for a sequence of numbers coded in different representation. For random access patterns, Gray code and binary code have similar performance. Note that the sequence of numbers in Table 3(b) is careful selected favor to binary representation. In general, this special sequence is rather unlikely to happen. For a sequential access pattern, which is usually seen in a general processor which executes consecutive instructions in basic blocks, Gray code addressing has the least bit switching.

5 Evaluation Results

In this section, we evaluate energy consumption of the experimental cache structures. Each cache structure is evaluated for various cache configurations with different cache sizes, block sizes, and associativities. The cache sizes range from 512 to 32K bytes, the block sizes range from 8 to 32 bytes, and the set associativities range from 1 to 4. These cache configurations are represented as follows,

\<dm,2\>	a direct-mapped cache with block size 2 words
\<dm,4\>	a direct-mapped cache with block size 4 words
\<dm,8\>	a direct-mapped cache with block size 8 words
\<2lru,2\>	a 2-way set associative cache with block size 2 words
\<2lru,4\>	a 2-way set associative cache with block size 4 words
\<2lru,8\>	a 2-way set associative cache with block size 8 words
\<4lru,2\>	a 4-way set associative cache with block size 2 words
\<4lru,4\>	a 4-way set associative cache with block size 4 word
\<4lru,8\>	a 4-way set associative cache with block size 8 words

In this study, we assume the on-chip instruction and data caches are separated. The address and data pins are shared for the instruction and data caches.

5.1 Miss Rates

Figure 4 shows the miss rates of direct-mapped and set-associative instruction and data caches. The miss rates of both instruction and data caches are decreased when the cache size is increased. A large instruction cache can certainly help the hit rate. However, a large data cache may not help the hit rate as much. For example, the miss rates of \<dm,2\>, \<dm,4\>, and \<dm,8\> are 6.55%, 4.28%, and 3.42%, even when the cache size is 32K bytes.

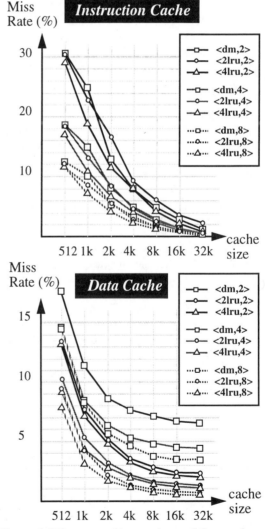

Figure 4: Miss rates of instruction and data caches

Increasing the block size significantly improves the instruction cache hit rates. A direct-mapped cache with a large block size performs better than a set associative cache of the same size. For example, the average hit rate for a 16K instruction cache <dm,8> is 98.92% which is better than the hit rates of 96.70%, 97.64%, 98.20% and 98.55% of <2lru,2>,<4lru,2>, <2lru,4>, and <4lru,4> data caches of the same size, respectively. The impact on the hit rate of a data cache while increasing the block size is not as obvious as for the instruction cache.

Increasing the degree of set associativity significantly improves the data cache hit rates. A set associative cache with a large degree of set associativity performs better than a direct-mapped cache of the same size (even with a large block size). For example, the average hit rate for the 16K data cache <2lru,2> is 97.53% which is better than the hit rates of 93.25%, 95.58%, and 96.46% of <dm,2>, <dm,4>, and <dm,8> for data caches of the same size respectively. The impact on the hit rates of an instruction cache while increasing the degree of associativity is not as obvious as to the instruction cache.

5.2 Energy Optimization of the Memory Addressing Path

Table 4 shows the normalized average bit switching rates of the address bus using traditional 2's complement addressing and Gray code addressing. The bit switching rates of the address bus using traditional 2's complement addressing are normalized to be 1.00. The bit switching rate of the instruction cache address bus using Gray code addressing is only 67% of that using 2's complement addressing. There is a 33% energy savings using Gray code addressing on the instruction cache. It is not surprising that the Gray code addressing has a significant energy reduction on the instruction cache since the sequential locality of instructions is generally quite high. The more of sequential locality, the bigger gains of energy savings by using Gray code addressing.

	Instruction Address	Data Address
2's Complement	1.00	1.00
Gray Code Addressing	0.67	0.88

Table 4: Normalized bit switching rates of the Memory Address Path

The bit switching rate of the data cache address bus in using Gray code addressing is only 88% of that in 2's complement addressing. There is about 12% energy savings by using Gray code addressing on the data cache. The energy savings on the data cache by using Gray code addressing is a lot less than that on the instruction cache because the sequential locality of data access pattern is a lot less than that of instruction access patterns.

Overall, using gray code addressing on caches can significantly reduce energy consumption of the memory address path. Traditional 2's complement code addressing

may be good for address calculation. However, from energy savings point of view, the Gray code addressing is a better choice for the memory addressing.

5.3 Energy Optimization of Cache Memory

In this section, we investigate energy optimization of data memory arrays on a block-buffered cache and a sub-bank cache. The energy savings, shown in Figure 5, are compared to conventional cache structures. <BB,N> represents a block buffered cache with a block size N bytes and <CS,BN> represents a cache sub-banking with a block size N bytes.

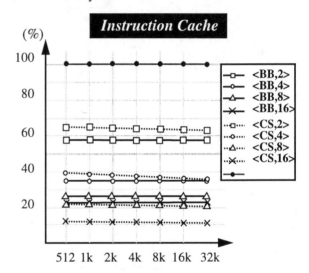

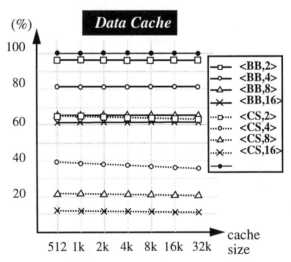

Figure 5: Energy consumption of block buffering and cache sub-banking compared to traditional caches

Block buffering reduces the number of cache accesses by buffering recently referenced cache block. The cache is accessed only when the requested data is not in the block buffer. In other words, energy is consumed only when there is a block miss. The amount of energy savings by block buffering depends on the block hit rates. The higher block hit rates, the more energy can be saved. Since the block hit rate is the rate of two consecrative hits mapping to the same block, the block hit rates only depend on the size of block. The degree of set associative and the cache size will not have any impact on the block hit rates.

Block hit rates of instruction caches are high when the block size is large. For example, the block hit rates are 41.80%, 64.35%, 74.19%, and 77.89% when the block size is 2,4,8, and 16 words (4 bytes per words). Except when a loop in the single block, the limit of block hit rates is the average length of consecutive instruction accesses in the benchmark suite. Compared to instruction caches, the block hit rates of data caches are relatively low. The block hit rates of the data caches are only 3.15%, 19.86%, 33.57%, and 39.20% when the block size is 2,4,8, and 16 words. This is because that the data access patterns tend to bounce between several regions in the working set. In general, data cache miss rates are much higher than instruction caches when the cache size is very small.

Like block buffering, cache sub-banking consumes less energy when the block size is large. For example, a sub-banking cache only consumes 63.90%, 31.11%, 20.18%, and 10.55% of energy consumed by a traditional cache with cache size 32K bytes and block size 2,4,8, and 16 words respectively. Unlike block buffering in which its energy savings is limited access pattern behavior, the energy savings of cache sub-banking is not limited by that. The larger the block size is, the more energy savings will be. The larger cache size is, the less the impact of energy consumption on tag memory array to the total energy savings of cache sub-banking.

Overall, the block buffering technique is good for instruction caches with a reasonably large block size. Especially when the block size is large enough to contain the whole loop, the instruction cache is only accessed once while executing the loop. Cache sub-banking is good for both instruction and data caches.

5.4 Energy Consumption of I/O Path

Figure 6 shows the bit switching activities of the I/O pads. As addressed in Section 3.1, the address and data pads are shared by both the instruction and data caches of the same structure. The bit switching rates of the data pads range from 0.03 to 11.89%; the bit switching rates of the address pads range from 0.07 to 3.72%. It is not surprising that the cache size has a strong impact on the bit switching rates of the I/O pads. Since the cache miss rates of instruction and data caches are decreased when the cache sizes are increased (see Figure 8), the bit switching rates of the I/O pads decreases while the cache size increases.

Increasing the degree of set associativity significantly improves the bit switching rates of the data pads. For example, the bit switching rates of data pads in 2K <dm,4>,<2lru,4>, and <4lru,4> caches are 3.52%, 1.81%,

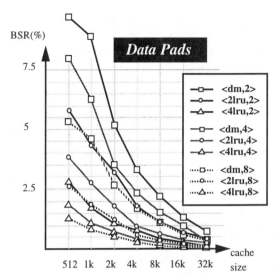

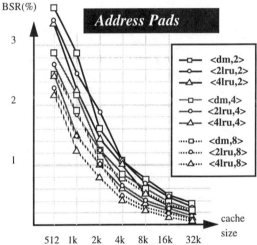

Figure 6: Energy consumption of I/O Pads

and 0.71% respectively. The reduction of bit switches of the data pads is almost half when the degree of set associativity is doubled. Increasing the block size also improves the switching rate reduction of the data pads. For example, the bit switching rates of 2K<dm,2>, <dm,4>, and <4dm,8> caches are 5.15%, 3.52%, and 2.66% respectively. The gain of bit switching rate reduction by increasing block size is still significant, although it is not as much as that by increasing the degree of set associativity.

Unlike the bit switching rates of the data pads, both increasing the degree of set associativity and increasing the block size has a similar impact on the bit switching rate reduction of the address pads. For example, the bit switching rates of address pads in 16K <dm,2>,<dm,4>, and <dm,8> caches are 0.50%, 0.36%, and 0.31% respectively. The reduction of the bit switching rates are 28% and 13.89% when the block size increases from 2 to 4 words and from 4 to 8 words. However, the bit switching rates of address pads in 16K <dm,4>,<2lru,4>, and

<4lru,4> caches are 0.36%, 0.26%, and 0.21% respectively. The reduction of the bit switching rates is 28% and 19.23% when the degree of set associativity increases from 1 to 2 words and from 2 to 4 words.

6 Discussion

In this section, we investigate the overall energy savings of the proposed cache designs. We use a cache energy model discussed in Section 3.1 to estimate the overall energy consumption of caches. The cache estimation model with the parameters used in this case study are re-printed below.

	cache size						
	512	1k	2k	4k	8k	16k	32k
β	32	64	128	256	512	1024	2048
χ	32	64	128	256	512	1024	2048

$\alpha = 4$ $\qquad$ $\delta = \epsilon = 20$

Table 7 shows the total energy consumption of traditional cache designs. The numbers represented are calculated by using the experimental parameters listed in Table 6. The cache size and the hit rate is very important to the amount of energy consumption. The cache cannot be too small because more traffic through the I/O path would consume a significant amount of energy. The cache cannot be too large, since the gain of energy savings by extra cache hits will be less than the extra energy consumed in every cache access by the larger cache size. In this case study, cache size ranging from 512 to 2K bytes seems the most energy efficient.

	512	1K	2K	4K	8K	16K	32K
<dm,2>	33.01	35.61	42.23	65.13	114.6	215.8	419.8
<2lru,2>	32.52	34.46	43.87	65.56	113.8	215.1	419.8
<4lru,2>	31.89	32.34	41.14	64.88	113.8	215.1	419.2
<dm,4>	37.77	39.43	44.42	66.62	115.6	216.4	420.2
<2lru,4>	36.81	37.13	44.69	65.64	114.9	215.9	419.8
<4lru,4>	35.35	34.37	42.51	65.21	114.3	215.5	419.6
<dm,8>	46.83	46.26	48.94	69.42	117.5	217.4	420.9
<2lru,8>	44.12	42.08	47.89	67.01	115.8	216.2	419.9
<4lru,8>	43.91	38.31	44.93	65.62	114.8	215.6	419.4

Table 7: Total energy consumption of traditional instructions and data caches.

Table 8 shows the total energy consumption of cache designs using cache sub-banking and Gray code addressing. Compared to the data in Figure 11(a), there is a significant energy savings by these novel approaches. A cache with a size ranging from 2K to 4K bytes seems the most energy efficient.

Figure 7 shows the percentage of energy consumption of cache sub-banking with Gray code addressing compared to the traditional cache design. It is not surprising the amount of energy savings favors a large block size. By using cache sub-banking and Gray code addressing in

	512	1K	2K	4K	8K	16K	32K
<dm,2>	29.13	29.53	31.71	45.57	76.86	141.2	270.2
<2lru,2>	28.65	28.38	33.36	45.99	77.02	141.3	270.2
<4lru,2>	28.02	26.27	30.62	45.32	76.01	140.5	269.7
<dm,4>	32.19	29.93	27.06	33.36	50.44	86.93	160.8
<2lru,4>	31.22	27.64	27.32	32.38	49.79	86.48	160.5
<4lru,4>	29.72	24.88	25.15	31.98	49.15	86.06	160.3
<dm,8>	40.12	34.52	27.10	27.29	34.74	52.98	92.23
<2lru,8>	37.40	30.34	26.05	24.88	32.96	51.78	91.28
<4lru,8>	37.21	26.57	23.10	23.49	32.04	51.22	90.70

Table 8: Total energy consumption of instruction and data caches with cache sub-banking and Gray code addressing.

a cache with size 32K bytes and block size 32 bytes, the total energy saving is around 80%.

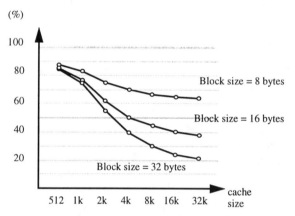

Figure 7: Energy consumption of cache sub-banking with Gray code addressing compared to the traditional cache designs

7 Conclusion

The goal of this research is to investigate the design of a cache for energy efficiency. Conventional cache design techniques are originally targeted for high performance (e.g. high miss rate and fast access time). Are these high performance cache designs also energy-efficient?

We first examine each cache components to see what part of these cache component consumes the most energy. We divided a cache structure into three different components: memory addressing path, cache memory, and I/O path. Bit switching rates on the address bus and I/O pads usually dominate the energy consumption of the memory addressing path and the I/O path. The estimation model of energy consumption on cache memory is different for caches in static and dynamic logic. Energy consumption on a cache using static logic strongly depends on the bit switching rates of the bit lines; energy consumption on a cache using dynamic logic strongly depends on the number of cache access due to the pre-charge on the bit lines for each cache access.

This paper evaluated three novel techniques for designing a cache for energy efficiency: block buffering, cache sub-banking, and Gray code addressing.

Block buffering can significantly reduce the energy consumption of an instruction cache in which there exists highly consecutive access patterns. However, the energy savings of a data cache by using block buffering is just marginal.

Cache sub-banking significantly reduces the energy consumption of both instruction and data caches. The amount of energy savings depends on the number of cache bank partitions. For example, a 64-byte cache block can be partitioned into 16 cache banks in which there are 4 bytes per bank. The energy savings of cache sub-banking can be as high as 95.55%. In other words, the energy consumption of a sub-blocking cache is an order of magnitude less than that in a traditional cache design.

Gray code addressing significantly reduces the bit switching rates of the address bus. The reduction of the bit switching rate in an instruction cache is 33% and that in a data cache is 12%.

The overall energy savings of these techniques depends on the VLSI implementation. In the case of a design with experimental parameters shown in Section 6, the total energy saving of a sub-banking cache using Gray code addressing with cache size 32K bytes is around 80%.

Acknowledgments

The authors would to thank the referees for their helpful comments. In addition, we would like to thank Steve Crago for his reviewing early drafts. The work was supported by ARPA under grant No. J-FBI-91-194.

References

[1] J. Bunda, W.C. Athas, and D. Fussell, "Evaluating Power Implication of CMOS Microprocessor Design Decisions," *Proceedings of the 1994 International Workshop on Low Power Design*, April 1994.

[2] A.P. Chandrakasan, S. Sheng and R.W. Brodersen, "Low-power CMOS digital design," *IEEE J. Solid-State Circuits*, Vol. 27, No4, 1992.

[3] J.P. Hayes, *"Computer Architecture And Organization,"* McGraw-Hill Int. Editions, 1988.

[4] R. Haygood, "A Prolog Benchmark Suite for Aquarius," Technical Report, Computer Science Department, University of California, UCB/CSD 89/509, 1989..

[5] M.D.Hill, "A case for Direct-mapped Caches," *IEEE Computer*,21,12, 1988.

[6] B. Holmer, B. Sano, M. Carlton, P. Van Roy, R. Haygood, W. Bush, and A. Despain. "Fast Prolog with an Extended General Purpose Architecture," in *Proceedings of the 17th*

Annual International Symposium on Computer Architecture*, May 1990.

[7] N.P. Jouppi, S.J.E Wilton,. "Tradeoffs in Two-Level On-Chip Caching," *The 21st Annual International Symposium on Computer Architecture*, April 1994.

[8] D. Liu, and C. Svensson, "Trading Speed for Low Power by Choice of Supply and Threshold Voltages," *IEEE Journal of Solid State Circuits*, Vol. 28, No. 1, 1993.

[9] S. Prasad and K. Roy, "Circuit activity driven multilevel logic optimization for low power reliable operation," *EDAC*, February, 1993.

[10] S. Przybylski, M. Horowitz, and J. Hennessy, "Characteristics of Performance-Optimal Multi-Level Cache Hierarchies," The 16th Annual International Symposium on Computer Architecture, May, 1989.low power reliable operation," *EDAC*, February, 1993.

[11] A.J. Smith, "A Comparative Study of Set Associative Memory Mapping Algorithms and Their Use for Cache and Memory," *IEEE Transactions on Software Engineering*, Vol. 4, No. 2, March 1978.

[12] A. Shen, A. Ghosh and S. Devadas, "On Average Power Dissipation and Random Pattern Testability of CMOS Combinational Logic Networks", *IEEE ICCAD*, Nov, 1993.

[13] C-L Su and Alvin M. Despain, "An instruction Scheduler and Register Allocator for Prolog Parallel Microprocessors," *International Computer Symposium*, 1992.

[14] C.L. Su, C.Y. Tsui, and A.M. Despain, "Low Power Architecture Design and Compilation Techniques for High-Performance Processors," *Proceedings of the IEEE COMPCON*, February 1994.

[15] C-L Su and Alvin M. Despain, "Cache Sub-banking: A Cache Design for Energy Optimization," Technical Report, ACAL-TR-94-17, USC, 1994

[16] C.Y. Tsui, M. Pedram, and A.M. Despain, "Technology Decomposition and Mapping Targeting Low Power Dissipation, *"Proceeding of the 30th Design Automation Conference*, 1993.

[17] H. Vaishnav and M. Pedram, "Pcube: A Performance driven placement algorithm for low power designs," *EURO-DAC*, September,1993.

[18] P. Van Roy and A. M. Despain, "High-Performance Logic Programming with the Aquarius Prolog Compiler," *IEEE Computer*, January 1992.

Power-efficient Delay-insensitive Codes for Data Transmission

P. Patra and D. S. Fussell

Department of Computer Sciences
The University of Texas at Austin
Austin, TX 78712-1188, USA

Abstract

We have introduced and formalized the notion of dynamic delay-insensitive codes for data communication. We describe several codes and protocols designed to optimize switching energy expended at the data pins during data transmission in asynchronous systems. These include adaptations of some existing communication methods as well as some new techniques for reducing energy used in dynamic data communication between delay-insensitive circuits.

1 Introduction and background

Current generations of CMOS VLSI systems have reached the point that power consumption more often than not is the limiting factor in the size and speed that can be obtained. This is especially true in chips designed for use in battery-powered portable systems, but it is increasingly true for high performance conventional systems as well, where exotic and expensive means to dissipate the heat generated on chip may be required to enable the system to operate at all. As a result, low voltage systems with built-in power management features are becoming common for both portable and desktop use.

Power management generally involves power down techniques to reduce dissipation by disabling portions of a circuit not currently in use. Dynamic power is the dominant source of dissipation in digital CMOS circuits (which do not use energy recovery techniques [1]). Dynamic power for clocked circuits is often approximated ([2]) as:

$$\sum_{all\ gates} p_t \cdot C_l \cdot V_{dd}^2 \cdot f_{clk}$$

where p_t is probability of a transition at a gate output during a clock cycle, C_l is the total loading capacitance of the gate, V_{dd} is the supply voltage, and f_{clk} is the clock frequency. Power management techniques aim to reduce p_t, particularly at nodes with large C_l such as I/O pins or internal bus interfaces. The effectiveness of this approach has led to increased interest in the use of asynchronous circuit design techniques, since asynchronous circuits lack a global clock and thus naturally have the property that switching only occurs in a portion of a circuit when some computation is being performed.

The class of "delay-insensitive (DI) circuits"—circuits whose external behaviors make no explicit reference to time and are independent of any (non-negative) delays in their internal components and wires—is a subclass of the class of asynchronous circuits. This class holds a great, although largely undemonstrated, potential for low-power applications since there are no global clock trees to be powered and switching activity occurs only in conjunction with useful computation or communication. For an application where particularly impressive power savings have been demonstrated using delay-insensitive circuitry, see [9].

DI systems can be expected to employ DI communication protocols not only within the computational logic of the system but also on busses used for communication between major subsystems. It has been observed that (DI) communication seems to provide better reliability and throughput ([4]) than alternative protocols for parallel transmission over large distances and between systems clocked by different clocks. Moreover, the non-synchronized transitions, inherent to DI protocols, tend to even out power drains, thereby improving overall noise characteristics.

Previous work on DI protocols for parallel bus communication has not explicitly dealt with the issue of minimizing the signal transitions required and thus the power consumed, although the importance of minimizing I/O signal transitions by means of coding was observed by both [6] and [7]. However, the former offered only an initial attempt at the problem, and the latter focused on synchronous data transmission only.

In this paper we consider ways to reduce transitions in DI data communication over a parallel bus through efficient protocols and codes. Codes and protocols are devised to reduce the number of voltage transitions at pins between chips, boards and systems and at bus interface points–possibly at the expense of higher complexity in encoding and decoding circuitry.

2 Theory of delay-insensitive codes

In our model, a transmitter (sender) circuit and a receiver circuit mutually communicate only through a set of wires of two types between them: *data wires* and *control wires*. We assume that arbitrary, undetermined non-negative delays are possible in the wires. Because only causal, but not any arbitrary temporal, relationships among events are preserved in a system in our model, one needs to encode the data-validity within the data itself in order to communicate delay-insensitively. The receiver must computationally determine if a new piece of valid data is available before consuming/accepting it. Other approaches to correct asynchronous data communication use a *delay-sensitive* control wire or signal ([8]), (1) which tracks the delay in the signal path of the data and goes active whenever data becomes valid, or (2) which goes active sufficiently late to 'practically' ensure that data has become valid. The former approach is often physically impracticable and the latter is often unacceptable for performance. Therefore, in this paper we consider purely delay-insensitive (but only bit-parallel) data communication.

Having decided to encode validity within the data, we also have to ensure 'data separation'—i.e. the receiver needs to know when a new piece of valid data is available. We assume that the receiver is capable of observing any changes in its input wires. But, whether a particular logic value pattern on its input wires is a new data value or not is defined by a *protocol* between the sender and the receiver, and the associated *code*.

Definition 1: A *code* C is a set of subsets of a finite set W. Each member of C is a *codeword*. By identifying each member of W with a unique wire, we can mechanistically interpret each subset of W to be a logic state of the data wires, $|W|$ in all, between a receiver and a transmitter. Thus, if the empty set $\emptyset$ denotes a fixed initial state, e.g., the state where all data wires are logically low, then a subset $w \in 2^W$ denotes a bit-vector (equivalently, a state of the data wires) where exactly those bits corresponding to the wires represented in w are logically opposite to their values in the initial state vector.

Example 1: Let $W = \{a, b, c\}$. If $\emptyset$ denotes state 000 of the three wires, a and c identified with the first and last wires, respectively, then $\{a, c\}$ denotes the state 101. If one is interested in only two data values, a possible code C is $\{\{a, c\}, \{a, b\}\}$.

We will henceforth use 'subset' (of W), 'state' (of data wires), or *'word'* (transmitted) interchangeably depending on the context.

Definition 2: Suppose there exists an *onto* mapping M from C to the set, V, of all the data values we are interested in transmitting. Code C is then said to be *statically* delay-insensitive (SDI) if each codeword can be unambiguously received in the presence of arbitrary wire delays when the transmitter switches the wires to the codeword from a fixed initial state/word assumed not part of C. Equivalently ([10]), $(\forall \ x, y \in C : x \subseteq y : x = y)$ holds.

However, one is usually concerned with transmission of sequences of data. Thus, we introduce and formalize the concept of a *dynamically* delay-insensitive (DDI) code as follows:

Let $D, S \subset 2^W$ such that $D \cap S = \emptyset$, $C = D \cup S$ and $I = (2^W - C)$. D and S stand for the sets of codewords called *datawords* and *spacers*, respectively. I is the set of all words that are 'invalid' or non codewords. Suppose also that an onto function M exists from D to V, the set of data values to be communicated. Furthermore, let graph G be the natural $|W|$-dimensional hypercube induced by the powerset of W, i.e. an edge exists between vertices $u, v \in 2^W$ iff $u \setminus v$ is a singleton.

Definition 3: A *hyperedge* in G exists between $x, y \in C$ if the following holds:
$(\forall \ z \in C : x \cap y \subseteq z \wedge z \subseteq x \cup y : z = x \vee z = y)$

Definition 4: A *hyperpath* exists between $x, y \in C$ if there is a sequence of one or more hyperedges in G between x and y such that all the intermediate vertices (between hyperedges) are from S.

Definition 5: A data value v is said to be *transmissible* at a dataword x if there exists a dataword y such that there is a hyperpath from x to y, and $M(y)$ is v.

Definition 6: C is a DDI code if each data value $v \in V$ is transmissible at each dataword $x \in D$.

Definition 7: A hyperpath consisting of a single hyperedge is *monotone*. A hyperpath between $x, y \in D$ is *monotone* if for some $z \in S, x \cap y \subseteq z, z \subseteq x \cup y$, there exist monotone hyperpaths between x and z, and between z and y.

Definition 8: C forms a *monotone* DDI code if each data value $v \in V$ is transmissible at each dataword $x \in D$ via monotone hyperpaths only.

It is noteworthy that DI codes have some unidirectional error-detection properties as well.

2.1 Communication protocol

With each code is associated a *protocol* of transmission : To send c after d $(c, d \in D)$, the sender follows a hyperpath from c to d, handshaking (synchronizing) with the receiver at each intermediate vertex. The signal transitions from one vertex to the next on the hyperpath is also monotonic in the sense that a wire changes its logic value at most once while wires switch from one vertex/state to the next —a general requirement on delay-insensitive logic. The receiver acknowledges each received spacer or dataword on the hyperpath that the sender follows, when ready for the next—perhaps using a separate feedback line to the sender. This way the two communicating parties synchronize with each other. Note that self-timed circuits (such as micropipelines [8]) are quite compatible with this notion of spacers, as a receiver can receive a codeword and throw it out, if it is a spacer, without affecting the underlying computation.

We observe that if the physical signals representing a codeword are sent on the wires and then consumed (i.e. received and removed) by the receiver, then a code which is SDI is also DDI. This is so because the very act of reception leaves the wires logically at their initial state represented by $\emptyset$—there is no need for additional synchronization to reset. Another way to turn a statically DI code into a dynamic one is to treat $\emptyset$ as a spacer between every two consecutive datawords transmitted.

We will use names of the sets such as W to denote their sizes, to avoid clutter, when no confusion may arise. From here on, we speak synonymously of a word sent over the wires W and its mechanistic interpretation as a state bit-vector of size $|W|$.

The map M from D to V is assumed to be one-to-one and onto in rest of the paper except in section 4.1.

3 Energy usage properties of DI transmission schemes

For large loads and long communication lines, we adopt the reasonable notion that the energy consumed in a transmission is primarily due to transitions on signal wires (or transmission lines). The computations necessary to encode or decode raw data are assumed to consume negligible power. Consequently, given a set of data values, we define the energy efficiency of a DI transmission scheme (code plus protocol) as inversely proportional to the average number of transitions on the signal wires (hence, energy consumed) per data value when a random sequence of data values is to be transmitted.

The time taken for a data value is measured in units of 'handshakes' between the sender and the receiver. The average time is the inverse ratio of the length of a random sequence of data values to the length of the corresponding sequence of codewords transmitted.

The space resource for a scheme is the number of wires used.

The possibility of multiple spacers between two data codewords allows us to use a scheme similar to 'Huffman encoding' such that the average area or space requirement can be minimized.

3.1 Some well-known DI codes

One-hot code: The sender sets to high the wire mapped to the data value being sent. After the receiver acknowledges by toggling the 'feedback' wire, the sender resets the data wire last turned high. This is a spacer condition, and the receiver acknowledges it by again toggling the lone feedback wire. At this point new data can be sent by repeating the protocol just described. The feedback wire is necessity for synchronization between the communicating parties. In the following figures for various metrics, we include the feedback transitions as well as the feedback wire. The number of data wires is W.

For this scheme, Size (number of distinct data values) = W; Space (total number of wires used) = $W+1$. Time (to transmit one data value) = 2 which is the number of synchronizations needed. Energy (used per transmission) = $2+2$ units where one unit is the energy used to make a logic transition on a communication wire. Space used is $D + 1, D = W$ because D wires are needed to permit transmission of D different data values, and one wire is used for acknowledgement.

Although this scheme is quite efficient in energy, it is often unacceptable because of very high space inefficiency.

Dual-rail code: To transmit an n-bit data value, $W = 2n$ wires are used—each bit of a data value is encoded by a pair of wires. One of the protocols used is called 4-phase handshaking, where each dataword is followed by an 'all-zero' spacer. Each dataword has ones in exactly $W/2$ bit positions. For this scheme:

$$Size = 2^{W/2}; \; Space = W + 1;$$

$$Time = 2; \ Energy = W + 2$$

Sperner code: A Sperner code of dimension W is the largest static DI code for code length W. Each word with ones at exactly $\lfloor W/2 \rfloor$ bit positions is a dataword and represents a unique data value ([10]). The following protocol makes the DI code dynamic: Initially, the wires are in the 'all-zero' (reset) state. The following steps are repeated to communicate one or more data values: The sender switches exactly $\lfloor W/2 \rfloor$ wires, as appropriate, to send a data value (dataword). The receiver acknowledges upon receiving the current dataword. The sender, then, returns the wires to the 'all-zero' or reset state. The receiver acknowledges seeing this state which in our terminology is a 'spacer'. Then, the sender is ready again to transmit the next data value, if any—by changing the present (reset) state of the wires to the next dataword/state.

This scheme yields:

$$Size \approx \frac{2^W}{\sqrt{\pi W/2}}; \ Space = W + 1;$$

$$Time = 2; \ Energy = W + 2$$

Figure 1 shows the six datawords as vertices with filled circles and the "all-zero" spacer as a vertex with empty circle on the pictured 4-cube. Recall that each vertex of a cube corresponds to a unique state of the data wires W. There exists a bijection from the set of vertices marked as datawords to the set of (six) data values.

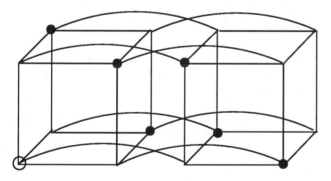

Figure 1: Sperner code: length 4 and size 4

4 Spacerless codes

The fastest way to transmit data delay-insensitively is to have no intermediate handshakes—that is, no 'spacers'. We have observed that the size of the a DDI code which is spacerless is proportional to the number of wires used, and hence, greatly limited.

DI Code	Size	Space	Time	Energy
One-hot	W	$W + 1$	2	4
Dual-rail	$2^{W/2}$	$W + 1$	2	$W + 2$
Sperner	$\approx \frac{2^W}{\sqrt{\pi W/2}}$	$W + 1$	2	$W + 2$

Table 1: Summary of some well-known DI Codes

4.1 Spacerless code: type I

One approach to designing a spacerless DDI code is the following:

Given W wires, consider the W-dimensional cube all of whose vertices are datawords, i.e., each word is a dataword. These vertices are partitioned such that a one-to-one mapping is established between the partitions and the set of data values to be transmitted. (That is, map M from D to V is not necessarily one-to-one.)

We can show that one can form a spacerless DDI code to transmit W distinct data values using W wires, where $|W|$ is a power-of-two. Abstractly, we color the vertices of a W-dimensional cube with W colors such that each vertex is adjacent to all the different W colors. Each color stands for a distinct data value and the coloring scheme is the convention for both reception (decoding) and transmission (encoding). It can further be shown that such a coloring is not possible when W is not a power-of-two.

Example 2: Figure 2 is an example for $W = 4$ with R, G, B and Y being the four "colors."

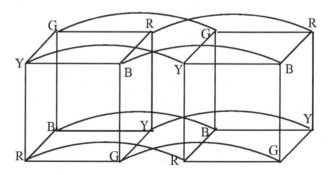

Figure 2: Spacerless code: type I, length 4 and size 4

4.2 Spacerless code: type II

Yet another approach to a spacerless DDI code is to associate exactly one dataword to each data value—in contrast to Spacerless Code I. The goal is to build the largest code of length W such that the smallest subcube containing any two datawords does not cover a third dataword—meaning that a direct transmission of an dataword following any other is possible. This eliminates the intermediate handshakes (synchronizations) associated with spacers. Now, each dataword, except one, is associated with a distinct data value. The lone special dataword represents a "repetition," i.e. when the sender needs to repeat the last data value sent via an ordinary dataword, it simply sends this special "repetition" dataword.

More precisely, this spacerless DDI code has $S = \emptyset$, and satisfies the following:

$$(\forall x, y, z \in D \; : \; x \cap y \subseteq z \; \wedge \; z \subseteq x \cup y \; : \\ z = x \; \vee \; z = y)$$

The above may be viewed as a coloring problem where *some* of the vertices of the W-cube are colored. The idea is that the remaining vertices of the smallest subcube containing a pair of colored vertices must all be uncolored, and we wish to maximize the number of colored vertices in the cube.

The upper and lower bound on the size $|D|$ of the largest spacerless DDI code of length W in this approach is conjectured to be $W + 1$, for all $W \neq 2$. For $W = 2$, the size is 2. An example of such a code for $W > 2$ is where each word with exactly $W - 1$ ones is a dataword. (The all-zero codeword is special—it may be interpreted as to stand for whatever the previous data value was. This requires storage of the last data value. Alternatively, two codewords may be assigned for each data value in order to allow back-to-back repetition of a data value. See next subsection.)

Unfortunately the size of such a code is very small—linear in code length—just as the one-hot code and the code in the previous subsection are.

For an illustration of this approach, see Figure 3. Four vertices of the 4-cube are marked R, G, B, or Y to indicate four datawords representing the four different data values. The all-zero spacer is indicated by an empty-circled vertex. Note that there is a natural equivalence relation among codes of a particular type, size and length that we are not dealing with here.

4.3 Further discussion

One need not assign two codewords for each data value (anticipating back-to-back transmission of a data value). In stead, just one codeword may be allocated to each (distinct) data value, and either of the following approaches may be taken to allow back-to-back repetition.

- An extra control wire is employed to indicate whether the last data value is being repeated. This control information can be 'event' or 'level'

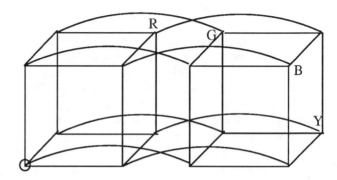

Figure 3: Spacerless code: type II, length 4 and size 4

based, i.e. a 2-phase or a 4-phase handshake protocol, respectively, may be adopted for the control wire.

- A codeword is designated as special (not bound to a fixed data value), and it is sent only when any dataword is to be repeated.

In case of the one-hot code, both the approaches above essentially call for an extra data wire—keeping the set of data values V fixed.

5 Adaptive Sperner code

We have seen how the Sperner Code introduces the "reset" handshake to allow code sizes exponential in the number of data wires used. In the following, we exploit this idea for high code size efficiency while trying to reduce the individual voltage switchings on the wires to minimize energy loss. The key to the following is the clever use of spacers (i.e., intermediate handshakes).

First note that the (minimum) energy (hence, the number of signal transitions) to switch the wires from one dataword to another is directly proportional to the *Hamming distance* ([5]) between them. When at any step all data values are equally likely to occur, the following lemma gives the mean Hamming distance between two consecutive datawords. The mean Hamming distance is also the *expected* Hamming distance when datawords are uniformly distributed (i.e., each dataword is equally likely to be the next one for transmission.)

Lemma 1: The mean Hamming distance between two datawords is

$$\left\lceil \frac{\sum_{i=0}^{n} \left(2i \times \binom{n}{i}^2 \right)}{\binom{2n}{n}} \right\rceil$$

Lemma 2: The expected Hamming distance between two consecutive datawords is $\lceil |W|/2 \rceil$.
Proof: We consider the case where $|W| = 2n$ and leave out the very similar proof for $|W| = 2n + 1$.

By the binomial theorem we get the following two equations:

$$(1 + x)^n = \sum_{i=0}^{n} \binom{n}{i} x^{n-i} \quad (1)$$

$$(1 + x)^n = \sum_{i=0}^{n} \binom{n}{i} x^{i} \quad (2)$$

Differentiating and then multiplying both sides of Eqn 2 by x,

$$nx(1 + x)^{n-1} = \sum_{i=0}^{n} i \binom{n}{i} x^{i} \quad (3)$$

Multiplying the corresponding sides of Eqns. 1 and 3,

$$nx(1 + x)^{2n-1} = \sum_{k=0}^{2n} \sum_{i=0}^{k} i \binom{n}{i}^2 x^{k} \quad (4)$$

Equating the coefficients of x^n on the two sides of Eqn 4,

$$n \binom{2n-1}{n-1} = \sum_{i=0}^{n} i \binom{n}{i}^2 \quad (5)$$

Therefore,

$$\frac{\sum_{i=0}^{n} \left(2i \times \binom{n}{i}^2 \right)}{\binom{2n}{n}} = \frac{2n \binom{2n-1}{n-1}}{\binom{2n}{n}} = n = |W|/2 \quad (6)$$

The claim follows from the above and Lemma 1 when we note that the expected Hamming distance is the mean distance between any two datawords.

(End of Proof)

5.1 Reworking the code

Using the original Sperner scheme, the number of signal transitions made to complete transmission of one data value is $W + 2$, for even W. (We will henceforth, without loss of generality, consider only even W.) The much lower value of the expected Hamming distance provides the motivation to devise a new

scheme to conserve signal transitions. In the following, we will often abbreviate the Hamming Distance function of two words as HD.

First, we observe that a dataword can be transmitted after another with Hamming distance of two between them—without intervening spacers. Second, we propose to include a few more spacers in C so that while going from a dataword to the next, one does not always have to use the 'all-zero' spacer. One method to achieve this is to augment the original Sperner code with spacers that are all the words with exactly $W/2 + K$ ones in their bit-vector representations, assuming $W > 3$. We can now state:

Lemma 3: The augmented code above is a monotone DDI code for $K = 2$.

Suppose that this specific ($K = 2$) *adaptive* Sperner code is used and that the sender uses hyperpaths without the all-zero spacer. Then, it can be shown that $x + x/2$ signal transitions and $x/2$ handshakes are necessary and sufficient to transmit any dataword b after a with $HD(a, b) = x$, $x > 2$. A possible protocol for the sender, in pseudo-code:

IF $HD(a, b) = 0$ (* the next data value is same as the current *)
THEN Send a spacer l, $HD(l, a) = 2$, followed by a.
ELSE Follow a monotone hyperpath from a to b *never* using the 'all-zero' spacer.

For Hamming distance x, $x > 2$, this scheme implies $x/2$ handshakes hence, $\lceil x/2 \rceil$ acknowledgement transitions from the receiver. So, the total number of signal transitions involved is $Max(2 + 1, x + x/2)$, for $x > 0$. For $x = 0$, the energy used is that for $2 + 1 + 2 + 1 = 6$ signal transitions.

The adaptive Sperner scheme for $K = 2$ makes a simpler case in a hierarchy of codes with diverse time and energy tradeoffs. Relative to the original Sperner scheme, the expected time is increased by $W/4 - 1$, while expected switching energy is decreased by $W/4$ even when feedback transition from the receiver is counted in.

Lemma 4: For $x < (2W+4)/3$, the protocol above always uses fewer signal transitions than the Sperner scheme.

For $x >= (2W + 4)/3$, the Sperner scheme of using the all-zero spacer is preferred for better time and energy performance. With this in mind, the sender's protocol now is:

IF $HD(a, b) = 0$ (* the next data value is same as the current *)

THEN Send any spacer $l, HD(l, a) = 2$ followed by a.

ELSE Follow a shortest, monotone hyperpath from a to b.

In Fig 4, we show the above scheme for $W = 6$. The datawords are indicated by filled circles and the spacers by empty circles on the vertices of the hypercube. To transmit the dataword 001110 after the word 111000, the adaptive scheme requires 6 signal transitions as opposed to $6 + 2$ transitions in the non-adaptive case.

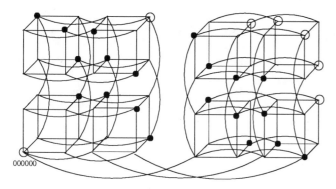

Figure 4: An adaptive Sperner code of dimension 6 (some cube edges not shown)

One can design a family of such schemes where $2 \leq K \leq W/2$.

6 Separable codes

Most algorithms for arithmetic circuits assume the input values to be in binary format. Hence, using a code such as Sperner's involves complex encoding and decoding circuitry. One approach to address this problem is to encode a condition for data validity outside the data bits. This way complexity for data validity may actually increase somewhat, but data decoding is almost trivial. For example, we can take the binary representation (x) of a data and concatenate another set of bits (y) encoding the data-validity condition to give a codeword $(x : y)$. Decoding such a codeword involves stripping off the y bits that encode the validity condition. The Berger code [3] is an example of such a 'separable' code (it is a statically DI code, too.)

6.1 Code interpretation in terms of bit-transitions

We have two choices as to how we transmit a codeword. So far we have implicitly assumed "level-encoding," i.e., a wire is set to High (Low) if the corresponding bit in the codeword to be transmitted is 1 (0). The other method, which is emphasized in this section, is to toggle the state of a wire if and only if the corresponding bit of the codeword is 1. This approach to transmission is called "transition-encoding." For example, assuming the initial state is 10101, the final state upon (complete) reception of the codeword 11000 is the state 01101. As before, because of arbitrary transmission delays in wires, no particular order of reception among causally unrelated transitions is guaranteed. The receiver acknowledges upon reception of a codeword and enters into the 'clear' state, ready for a new data value. Conceptually, the receiver removes a codeword from the channel (wires) upon reception. The sender does not have to 'erase' the previous data, by resetting the state of the data wires, in order to transmit the next data value.

Under the interpretation above, two datawords of a Sperner code can be transmitted back to back without a spacer, and each value transmitted accounts for exactly $\lfloor W/2 \rfloor$ transitions. Two disadvantages of such a scheme are: (1) the scheme cannot exploit any locality property within the data stream to reduce the total number of transitions, and (2) the sender and receiver circuits tend to be more complex because of the 'event or transition logic' implied in the scheme.

6.2 A separable DDI code

We propose one specific scheme, based on Berger code, for a DDI code that has the nice property of 'separability' mentioned above:

Suppose the sender wants to send data value b after a, both binary values being of length L (i.e. $|a|=|b|=L$). A subcode y, in binary, is formed such that y, $y = L - HD(a, b)$, is the number of bit positions where the two data values match. The binary subcode y is transition-encoded, while the data part b is level-encoded for concurrent transmission on their respective wires. Note that the length of a subcode is $\log(L + 1)$ if the number of data wires is L.

Correctness of the scheme above follows from these observations: When a codeword is being received, each transition on the data part indicates a single, unique mismatch between a pair of corresponding bits of a and b. On the other hand, the positional transitions on the subcode part indicate the number of bit matches to expect (in binary). The number of transitions increase monotonically over time in both cases. Hence, the transitions on the data part indicate monotonically increasing number of mismatches, while the transitions on the subcode part indicate monotonically increasing number of matches. Eventually, the receiver receives the counts for mismatches as well as matches, which all add up to L. At this point the codeword's reception is complete, and (only then) the data on the wires is assured to be valid.

Example 3: Suppose $b = 1100101$ is the next value while $a = 0100011$ is the present. Moreover, suppose that the present state of the subcode wires is 101. The new value of subcode y to go with b is 011, because a and b differ in 3 bit positions. Therefore, the sender sets the data wires to the state 1100101 and changes the subcode wires to state 110.

The space used for this scheme is $W = L + \log(L + 1) + 1$ wires. The expected Hamming distance between two datawords of length L is $L/2$, when each dataword is equally likely to be transmitted next. Consequently, the expected transitions on the subcode bits is no more than $\log L$ (not a tight bound). The expected energy per transmission of a data value in this scheme is bounded from above by $\lceil (L/2 + \log L) \rceil$. The size metric is 2^L and the time metric equals 1.

6.2.1 An easy extension

If the circuit complexity of transition-encoding of a large subcode y is undesirable, then one may recursively apply the separable coding scheme, described above, to encode y. When a subcode is small enough in length (e.g. $|y| = 2$), no further recursive application of the coding scheme is made. Note that each application of the coding scheme increases the total number of wires used to transmit a fixed set of data values.

7 Concluding remarks

We have characterized power efficiencies of various codes and protocols for delay-insensitive (DI) transmission of parallel data. Moreover, we have formalized and extended schemes for *static,* delay-insensitive transmission of data. We have introduced and formalized the notion of dynamic schemes for DI transmission of data, and devised some codes to achieve significantly better average-case energy efficiency of transmission. One of the ideas has been to trade in additional complexity in 'local computation' for reduction of energy used in 'non-local communication'.

The tradeoffs possible between the time required for transmission and the code density (space efficiency) are highlighted by considering *spacers* as synchronization points during transmission. If a *dataword* is interpreted in light of the spacer(s) immediately preceding

it, further optimization in transmission energy is possible, while keeping the space and time metrics about the same. In this case, encoding/decoding of a dataword is dependent on the context—the type or identity of spacers used. These observations are preliminary and need further research.

Relevant empirical and theoretical data is much needed to measure the complexity of transition-based circuits vis-a-vis level-based ones to enable a designer to choose a right coding scheme.

Acknowledgements

We thank the anonymous referees for their helpful comments.

References

[1] W.C. Athas, J.G. Koller, and L."J." Svensson. An energy-efficient cmos line driver using adiabatic switching. report ACMOS-TR-2, Information Sciences Institute, July 1993.

[2] A.P. Chandrakasan, S. Sheng, and R.W. Brodersen. Low-power cmos digital design. *IEEE Journal of Solid-State Circuits*, 27(4):473–483, April 1992.

[3] C. V. Freiman. Optimal error detection codes for completely asymmetric binary channels. *Inf Control 5*, pages 64–71, 1962.

[4] M.R. Greenstreet. *STARI: A Technique for High-Bandwidth Communication*. PhD thesis, Princeton University, January 1993.

[5] Raymond Hill. *A First Course in Coding Theory*. Clarendon Press, Oxford, 1986.

[6] P. Patra. Design of efficient and robust asynchronous circuits – a dissertation proposal (section on power-efficient DI codes), January 1994. Dept. of Comp. Sci., Univ of Texas at Austin.

[7] M.R. Stan and W.P. Burleson. Limited-weight codes for low-power I/O. In *Proceedings of the 1994 International Workshop on Low Power Design*. ACM/IEEE, April 1994.

[8] Ivan E. Sutherland. Micropipelines. *Communications of the ACM*, 32(6):720–738, June 1989.

[9] Kees van Berkel, Ronan Burgess, Joep Kessels, Ad Peeters, Marly Roncken, and Frits Schalij. A fully-asynchronous low-power error corrector for the DCC player. In *International Solid State Circuits Conference*, pages 88–89, February 1994.

[10] Tom Verhoeff. Delay-insensitive codes—an overview. *Distributed Computing*, 3(1):1–8, 1988.

Proceedings of the 28th Annual Hawaii International Conference on System Sciences — 1995

A Technique to Determine Power-Efficient, High-Performance Superscalar Processors

Thomas M. Conte   Kishore N. P. Menezes   Sumedh W. Sathaye

Computer Architecture Research Laboratory

Department of Electrical and Computer Engineering

University of South Carolina

Columbia, South Carolina 29208

Abstract

Processor performance advances are increasingly inhibited by limitations in thermal power dissipation. Part of the problem is the lack of architectural power estimates before implementation. Although high-performance designs exist that dissipate low power, the method for finding these designs has been through trial-and-error. This paper presents systematic techniques to find low-power, high-performance superscalar processors tailored to specific user benchmarks. The model of power is novel because it separates power into architectural and technology components. The architectural component is found via trace-driven simulation, which also produces performance estimates. An example technology model is presented that estimates the technology component, along with critical delay time and real estate usage. This model is based on case studies of actual designs. It is used to solve an important problem: increasing the duplication in superscalar execution units without excessive power consumption. Results are presented from runs using simulated annealing to maximize processor performance subject to power and area constraints.

The major contributions of this paper are the separation of architectural and technology components of dynamic power, the use of trace-driven simulation for architectural power measurement, and the use of a near-optimal search to tailor a processor design to a benchmark.

1   Introduction

Power limitations are increasingly nullifying some obvious superscalar advances. For example, duplicating commonly used functional units can enhance achievable parallelism [1]. Increasing duplication beyond current designs will increase power dissipation, yet current designs are already dissipating record amounts of power. Witness the 66MHz Intel Pentium that dissipates 16 watts or the 200MHz DEC Alpha AXP 21064 that dissipates 30 watts of power. Power is also directly affected by cycle time and improvements in cycle time are likely to complicate the current situation. Future increases in power dissipation may require expensive cooling and packaging techniques that significantly increase the system cost, pricing levels of performance out of the reach of all but supercomputer markets.

One source of the problem may be that architectural decisions are made largely without power usage information. Until now, obtaining such information before implementation has been extremely difficult. In the absence of this, the main emphasis has been on performance. Although high-performance designs may exist that dissipate low power, the only method for finding these designs has been through trial-and-error.

This paper presents a systematic technique to find low-power, high-performance superscalar processors tailored to specific user applications. Power in CMOS is composed of static and dynamic components. A novel approach is developed that separates the architectural contribution of dynamic power from the technology contribution. The architectural contribution is obtained via trace-driven simulation of SPEC92 benchmarks. The technology contribution is from a model based on estimates of actual designs. In reality, the constraints of circuit timing and limited real estate also impact power. Estimates of these are also included in the cost function. The function is optimized using a near-optimal search algorithm, to synthesize processor designs.

Duplication of integer functional units has been used in the Motorola 88110, the Intel Pentium and the Motorola/IBM PowerPC 604, among others [2],[3],[4]. The tradeoff between duplication and power has not been studied in detail. This paper uses the power model to address this question. Example superscalar designs are presented that achieve high parallelism by duplicating functional units while dissipating in some cases less than 25% additional power over superscalars that have little duplicated hardware. The techniques used to select these designs and the estimates of power and area are presented in the next section. Comments, conclusions and future work close out the paper.

2   Methods and Models

The processor model for this study is a superscalar engine with full-Tomasulo scheduling and pipelined functional units. To achieve high parallelism, integer and floating-point functional units are duplicated and the functional unit latencies are optimized. This paper focuses on power-centric design of the processor's execution unit and its pool of functional units. For the Alpha 21064, this unit comprises slightly over half of the chip area (from micrographs presented in [5]).

The types of functional units are shown in Table 1. A 64-bit architecture is assumed. The integer class is composed of 64-bit integer ALU units ($IALU$), 64-bit shifter hardware ($Shift$) and branch hardware ($Branch$). The floating-point units are grouped into addition ($FPAdd$), multiplication ($FPMul$) and division ($FPDiv$). $FPDiv$ is a pseudo-unit: division actually takes place in the multiplier using the quadratic convergence division method in an iterative, unpipelined fashion[1].

The data cache is accessed through three functional units: the $Load$, $Store$ and $PMiss$ units. PMiss is an abbreviation for *Pending Miss*. Any $Load$ operation that causes a cache miss is automatically coupled with a dynamically created $PMiss$ operation. These operations fetch the missing cache block independently from other cache accesses. Once a $PMiss$ operation completes, its associated $Load$ operation is allowed to execute. This scheme incorporates the lockup-free cache concepts presented by Kroft into a superscalar framework [8].

Example execution units are shown in Figure 1. In part (a) of the figure, an execution unit with no duplication is shown. This is the base design. Optimization for integer performance may result in design (b). Here the integer and the Load units have been duplicated. This allows parallel execution of independent integer instructions. A similar optimization for floating-point hardware may result in design (c).

---

[1] This algorithm can achieve the precision required by the IEEE standard at reasonable cost and speed [6] and was implemented in the RS/6000 [7]

Table 1: Functional unit types.

Class	Unit	Description
Integer	IALU	Integer arithmetic, logicals
	Shift	Bit manipulation, shifting
	Branch	Branch prediction; fault recovery
Floating-Point	FPAdd	Floating-point addition
	FPMul	Integer,floating-point multiply
	FPDiv	Integer, floating-point divide
Data-Cache	Load	Data cache read
	Store	Store-buffer/data-cache write
	PMiss	Miss repair unit (lockup-free)

2.1   An Architectural Power Model

Power dissipation in CMOS can be divided into a static and dynamic component. The static component is proportional to the product of gate leakage current (a function of the number of devices) times the supply voltage. This component is highly technology dependent. The dynamic component can be separated into architectural and technology components. To show this, assume a unit is pipelined into N stages, labeled $S_1, S_2, \ldots, S_N$. Let E_{S_i} be the *energy* consumed when stage S_i performs work[2]. The power dissipated for one instruction is:

$$P = \frac{1}{T}\left(E_{S_1} + E_{S_2} + \cdots + E_{S_N}\right) \qquad (1)$$

where T is the time it takes to execute the instruction (here $T = N$). Now consider a program fragment. Let U_{S_i} be the total *usage* of stage S_i during execution. The power dissipation now takes the form:

$$P = \frac{1}{T_{TOT}}\left(U_{S_1}E_{S_1} + U_{S_2}E_{S_2} + \cdots + U_{S_N}E_{S_N}\right), \qquad (2)$$

where T_{TOT} is the total execution time for the program fragment. The stage energies, E_{S_i}, are *technology parameters*, whereas T_{TOT} and the stage utilizations, U_{S_i}, are *architectural parameters*. This way, a simulation of the pipeline can measure the architectural parameters without any knowledge of the underlying technology.

An example helps illustrate the model. One popular myth about power usage is that pipelining can be ignored. The theory is that if any operation uses a unit, it must travel through all stages of the unit in turn, which means it consumes the same power (minus latching costs) as it would on an unpipelined unit. Figure 2 shows why this myth is false. (It has

---

[2] For now, we will assume this value is constant. Shortly, we will justify this approximation.

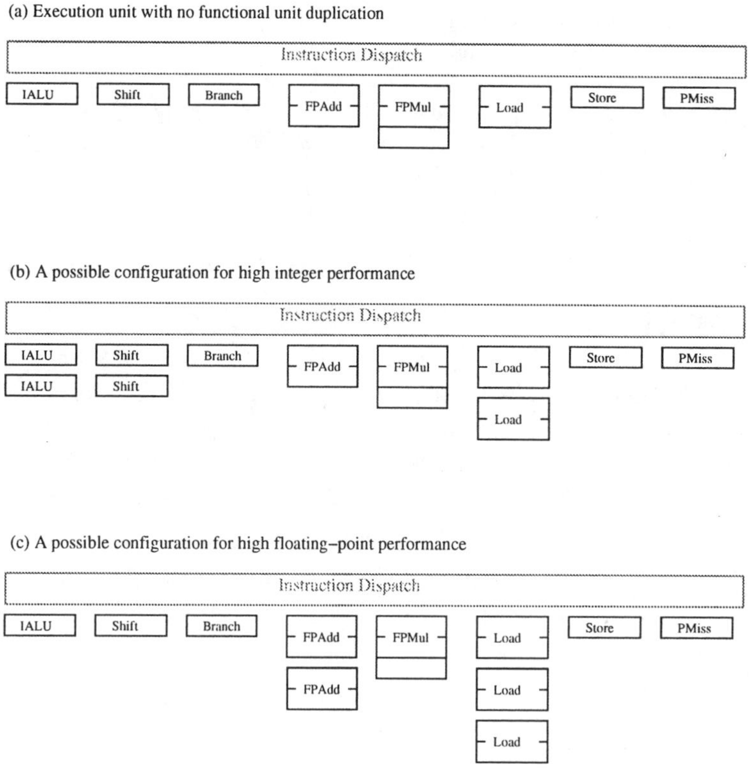

(a) Execution unit with no functional unit duplication

(b) A possible configuration for high integer performance

(c) A possible configuration for high floating–point performance

Figure 1: Example execution units.

also been disproved in [9].) Here three instructions are executed on a pipelined unit (left side of figure) and on an unpipelined unit (right side of figure). The corresponding power cost for each is shown below the figure. The unpipelined version uses 55% less power. The reason for this difference is the pipeline speedup effect, which is an architectural phenomenon.

The stage energy parameters E_{S_i} are dependent on the logical inputs to the stages. They could also be derived via trace-driven simulation. However, for this study, a further approximation of stage energy is used. We assume that every device transitions when the unit is active, which is a worst-case assumption. We also assume that the worst case stage energy is related to the average energy by a constant.[3] An example model for the stage energies is presented below.

2.2 Simulation techniques

The set of benchmarks used in this paper is shown in Table 2. The benchmarks are compiled using GCC, which schedules instructions within basic blocks using a priority-based list scheduling algorithm. This

shortens the critical dependence path of each block as much as possible, enhancing parallelism.

Architectural behavior is determined via trace-driven simulation. Traces are generated from benchmarks using the *Spike* tracing tool [10]. The simulator implements a dynamic instruction scheduling model, with the window for instruction scheduling moving between correctly predicted branches. Yeh's adaptive training branch algorithm is used to predict branch behavior, since it is currently one of the most accurate prediction schemes [11]. Since the benchmarks can generate extremely long traces, trace-sampling techniques are employed to reduce trace size and simulation time (see [12], [13] for details). Branch hardware and data cache simulation are done for the full traces, removing the possibility of sampling error for these units. The full trace is used to mark each incorrectly predicted branch in the sampled trace file. A similar approach is used to mark loads and stores that miss in the data cache.

The architectural component of dynamic power is measured during the simulation. In each cycle of the simulation, the usage of each pipeline stage is logged (i.e., U_{S_i} is incremented if S_i is busy). In addition, the simulator finds the total run time of the benchmark (i.e., T_{TOT}). This is later combined with the

---

[3]Even though the worst case is used for this study, it is not a *required* assumption of the model. A model based on average energy can be used for more accuracy. Our limited access to manufacturer implementations did not permit this.

Table 2: The benchmark set.

Class	Benchmark	Description
Integer	compress	reduces the size of files
	eqntott	conversion from equation to truth table
	espresso	minimization of boolean functions
	gcc	GNU C compiler
	li	lisp interpreter
	sc	spreadsheet program
Floating-point	doduc	Monte Carlo simulation
	hydro2d	Solves Navier Stokes equations
	mdljdp2	solves equations of motion
	ora	ray tracer through optical system
	tomcatv	vectorized mesh generation
	wave5	solves Maxwell's equations

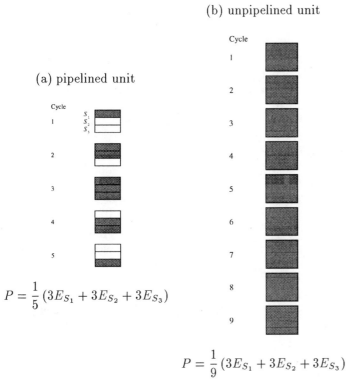

(b) unpipelined unit

(a) pipelined unit

$$P = \frac{1}{5}(3E_{S_1} + 3E_{S_2} + 3E_{S_3})$$

$$P = \frac{1}{9}(3E_{S_1} + 3E_{S_2} + 3E_{S_3})$$

Figure 2: Why pipelining matters to power dissipation.

Part (a) shows a pipelined unit executing three instructions, (b) shows an unpipelined unit executing the same three instructions. Because of the effects of pipeline speedup on parallel stage usage, the power dissipated in (b) is $5/9 = 55\%$ smaller than (a).

technology parameters (E_{S_i}'s) to find the dynamic power component using Equation 2.

2.3 Finding power-efficient processors

One goal of this study is to determine designs that achieve high performance without excessive power or area usage. Each functional unit can be duplicated as many times as power and real estate limitations allow. This freedom of design results in an extremely large design space. Exhaustive search via simulation of this space is impractical. This problem lends itself to a near-optimal search, such as simulated annealing [14].

The following is the method used to guide the simulated annealing algorithm: Consider a processor design space composed of one or more of the functional units of Table 1, each having a latency ranging from 1 to $L_{\max}$. Let P be some set of processors under consideration. A processor $p \in P$, has n_j functional units of type j and each of these functional units has a latency of ℓ_j. A concise representation of processor p is $p = \langle (\ell_0, n_0), (\ell_1, n_1), \ldots, (\ell_{k-1}, n_{k-1}) \rangle$, for k different types of functional units. At each step of the simulated annealing algorithm, the next design, p_{i+1}, is selected from the current design, p_i, using a restricted random selection procedure. The following procedure for determining a p_{i+1} from a p_i is used: (*i*) m functional units are selected at random from p_i, where m is a random integer in the range $[1, 3]$, (*ii*) the number of each of these functional units in p_i is changed by a random integer in the range $[-3, 3]$. Any number greater than the issue rate or less than 1 is rejected. For units with several possible pipeline latencies, a slightly more restrictive procedure is used to randomly alter the latencies.

A superscalar without functional unit duplication

is used as the starting point for the search: $p_0 = \langle(\ell_{MIN}, 1)\rangle_k$, where ℓ_{MIN} are the minimal allowed latencies. The goal of the search algorithm is to adjust the parameters of $p_i = \langle(\ell_j, 1)\rangle_{1 \le j \le k}$ to maximize performance and yet remain within power and real estate budgets. A detailed description of this cost function is presented below.

2.4 Performance metrics

A performance metric is needed that takes into account both architectural performance and technological considerations. *Parallelism* or *instructions per cycle* (IPC) is often used for architectural performance. IPC is ultimately limited by the issue rate (a design feature) and inter-instruction dependencies (a benchmark characteristic).

IPC alone lacks technology considerations. For example, short latency functional units produce high IPC, since dependencies are resolved quicker using shorter latencies (shallow pipeline depths). However, lower degrees of pipelining may lengthen the execution unit's critical path. This has an impact on the total time to execute a program, but is not reflected by the IPC metric. The critical path that determines cycle time is typically through the first level of the memory hierarchy (e.g., the data cache). Shallow pipelines can shift this critical path into the execution unit. Since this paper concentrates on the execution unit, the aim is to optimize on the critical path within the execution unit. This reduces the impact of the execution unit's critical path on the external cycle time of the processor.

A metric that combines IPC and critical path delay is the *critical time per instruction* (CTPI). CTPI is the ratio of the critical path delay to the number of instructions per cycle. Optimizing the execution unit for low CTPI reduces the chance of affecting the processor's cycle time. For this reason, CTPI is used in the search algorithm's cost model.

2.5 Example technology cost model

It is exceedingly difficult to obtain accurate technology estimates of the state-of-the-art, since microprocessor manufacturers rarely release this information. In the absence of this, we have constructed what we believe to be a reasonably approximate model using published results. The model considers a processor implementation technology with a budget of 1.68 million transistors and a supply voltage of 3.3 volts. This is based on the reported figures in [5] for a $0.75\mu m$ three metal-layer CMOS process technology.

Although the first-level data cache is not included in the execution unit, its miss rate impacts the overall performance of the superscalar core. A 16KB, 2-way associative data cache is assumed. This design assumes a page size of 8K bytes so that cache data store indexing can occur in parallel with TLB access. Cache misses are handled by the hardware using a lockup-free mechanism [8]. The latency to repair a missing block from the L2 cache is assumed to be 10 cycles.

The specific cost model depends on **performance**, **real estate** and **power** estimates:

Performance: Performance is measured by CTPI, where low CTPI is desirable. CTPI is calculated from the number of instructions, the number of cycles for the execution of the program, and an estimate of the critical path. The deepest pipeline stage in the execution unit is used to find the critical path using a technique presented by the authors in [13]. The function units could not be partitioned such that the cycle time is *exactly* inversely proportional to the degree of pipelining. Instead the deepest pipeline stage for each degree of pipelining is determined from our own designs. The sum of the gate delays within this stage constitutes the cycle time.

Real estate: Transistor level analysis of published work provided the approximations for each functional unit type. This model is presented in Table 3. (Since the *FPMul* unit is used iteratively for division, the *FPDiv* unit does not consume any die space and is not mentioned in the table.)

Real estate goals are expressed as a budget:

$$(\text{area of } p_i) \le (\text{area budget})$$

The area budget is based on the 1.68 million transistor budget, which includes interconnection overhead. Approximating interconnection overhead as half of this figure, and assuming that the execution unit comprises half of the total die (as is the case with the Alpha 21064), the real estate budget is taken as 25% of 1.68 million, or 420,000.

Power: Only relative power increases are required for the cost model. Therefore, power is normalized. Exact gate leakage currents for the two technologies are unpublished, but dynamic power is taken to be approximately 10,000 times larger than static power (a typical ratio). Static power is estimated using the product of the total number of transistors (which is proportional to the leakage current) times the supply voltage. The trace-driven simulation model is used for dynamic power. As stated above, the worst-case estimates are used to calculate the stage energies. This component is weighted by the square of the supply voltage [17].

Table 3: Real estate usage by functional unit type.

Functional unit	Allowed latencies	Number of transistors (by latency)					
		1	2	3	4	5	6
IALU	1–1	5068	–	–	–	–	–
Shift	1–1	6272	–	–	–	–	–
Branch	1–1	8660	–	–	–	–	–
FPAdd*	1–5	18880	19192	19504	19504**	19816	–
FPMul*	1–6	40292	41540	46196	42788	43796	46436
Load	1–4[†]	4928	4928	4928	4928	–	–
Store	1–1	4928	–	–	–	–	–
Pmiss	10	46848[‡]	46848	46848	46848	46848	46848

*Sources: [15],[16],[6] along with our own implementations.

**No change is seen in the number of transistors from latency 3 to 4 since the placement of the latches results in fewer bits that need to be latched.

[†]Load is through the data cache, which is excluded from the execution unit. However, slight overhead is required for each load operation to latch the values. Multiple load units are implemented by interleaving the cache.

[‡]Value shown is extrapolated from [8].

The power consumed by a processor p_i is constrained to a fractional increase in the power consumed by a processor without duplicated functional units (processor p_0):

$$(\text{power of } p_i) \leq K \times (\text{power of } p_0).$$

The overall goal is to minimize CTPI subject to constrained power and area budgets. An expression for the combined cost function is:

$$f(p_i) = \begin{cases} \text{CTPI}, & \text{if (area of } p_i) \leq (\text{area budget}) \ \& \\ & (\text{power of } p_i) \leq K \times (\text{power of } p_0) \\ \infty, & \text{otherwise.} \end{cases}$$

3 Experimental Results

This section presents examples of the method in action. The example cost model is used to optimize processors for increased performance via duplicated functional units. Power is limited to a fractional increase over the base case (no duplicated hardware). The power budget factor, K, is selected such that the limit of power usage is quite restrictive. Assuming that the execution unit occupies 50% of the chip area and that the power usage is uniformly distributed across the chip, a power budget of $K = 1.5$ translates into a 25% increase in power overall. This sometimes restricts performance improvement. A second budget of a 50% increase in power ($K = 2.0$) is also investigated.

Figure 3 illustrates the evolution of the cost function for li. As may be seen, an immediate attempt is

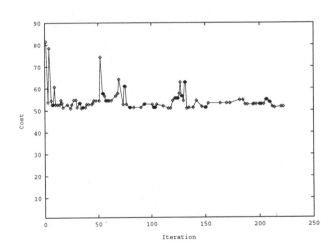

Figure 3: The cost function for li (infinities excluded from plot).

Table 4: Performance of initial designs.

Class	Benchmark	IPC	Power Index
Integer	compress	1.40	19.83
	eqntott	1.38	20.80
	espresso	1.41	21.03
	gcc	1.27	20.28
	li	1.40	21.10
	sc	1.36	25.41
Floating point	doduc	1.80	34.82
	hydro2d	1.85	28.51
	mdljdp2	2.05	34.58
	ora	1.82	26.42
	tomcatv	2.13	47.23
	wave5	1.79	28.09

made to reduce the cost from that of the initial design, p_0. Although the new cost is better than the original, the search continues for a more global minimum. The search is initially liberal in its design selections but settles into a region of the design space after the 150th iteration.

3.1 Performance of initial designs

Table 4 shows the performance of the initial designs (no duplicated functional units). Also presented is the normalized power index from the power estimators. The power index for the floating-point benchmarks is consistently higher than the integer benchmarks. Floating-point units burn higher amounts of power than integer units, due to a higher number of transistors per unit. Note the strong correlation between high IPC and high power usage: more instructions executing in parallel implies more functional units active. This correlation between power and instruction-level parallelism implies high-performance superscalars are high power designs. Our goal is to shift performance gains to less power-intensive functional units by duplicating those units.

3.2 Optimized designs

The optimized designs for each benchmark are presented below. The IPC and power index values[4] of the designs are presented graphically in Figures 4 and 5. Comparison of Figure 4 and Figure 5 shows the a general correlation between IPC and the power

---

[4] IPC is used here to measure external performance, assuming minimization of the critical path did not affect the external cycle time (see Section 2.4).

---

index. As the power budget is increased, IPC (parallelism) also increases. This is only true on a per-benchmark basis, and not true across benchmarks. Although for 125% of initial power, the IPC for *li* is greater than that for *doduc*, the power index for *doduc* exceeds that for *li*. This is because the floating-point intensive operations found in *doduc* use more power than integer intensive operations in *li*.

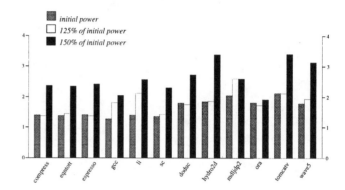

Figure 4: IPC for the benchmarks.

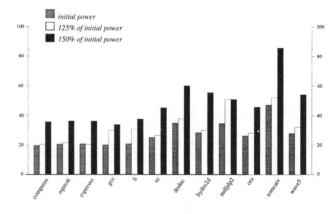

Figure 5: Power usage for the benchmarks.

Table 5 present the optimized designs for power budgets of 125% (part (a)) and 150% (part (b)).

125% power budget designs

The integer-intensive benchmarks in Table 5(a) achieve significant performance increases over the initial designs in Table 4. For example, the IPC for *gcc* improves from 1.27 initially to 1.81, and *li* increases from 1.40 to 2.12. These increases are achieved primarily by replicating the *IALU* units. The floating-point benchmarks do not have use for more than one *IALU*. The exception is *mdljdp2*, which uses four, due to a high number of address (array indexing) calculations.

Table 5: The power/area-efficient processor designs

(a) power budget 125%

Benchmark	IPC	Power Index	IALU n	IALU ℓ	Shift n	Shift ℓ	Branch n	Branch ℓ	FPAdd n	FPAdd ℓ	FPMul n	FPMul ℓ	Load n	Load ℓ	Store n	Store ℓ	PMiss n	PMiss ℓ
compress	1.37	20.6	1	1	2	1	2	1	1	5	1	6	2	1	1	1	1	10
eqntott	1.45	21.7	1	1	1	1	3	1	1	5	1	6	2	1	1	1	1	10
espresso	1.37	20.6	1	1	2	1	2	1	1	5	1	6	2	1	1	1	1	10
gcc	1.81	30.1	2	1	2	1	2	1	1	5	1	6	3	3	1	1	2	10
li	2.12	31.3	2	1	1	1	1	1	1	5	1	6	4	3	2	1	2	10
sc	1.43	26.7	1	1	2	1	3	1	1	5	1	6	2	2	1	1	1	10
doduc	1.75	37.8	1	1	2	1	1	1	1	5	2	6	1	1	2	1	1	10
hydro2d	1.86	30.1	1	1	1	1	3	1	2	5	1	6	2	1	2	1	1	10
mdljdp2	2.60	50.9	4	1	1	1	3	1	1	5	3	6	3	1	3	1	1	10
ora	1.73	28.3	1	1	1	1	3	1	2	5	1	6	2	1	2	1	1	10
tomcatv	2.12	52.3	1	1	1	1	2	1	2	5	2	6	2	1	1	1	1	10
wave5	1.94	32.0	1	1	1	1	1	1	2	5	2	6	3	1	2	1	1	10

(b) power budget 150%

Benchmark	IPC	Power Index	IALU n	IALU ℓ	Shift n	Shift ℓ	Branch n	Branch ℓ	FPAdd n	FPAdd ℓ	FPMul n	FPMul ℓ	Load n	Load ℓ	Store n	Store ℓ	PMiss n	PMiss ell
compress	2.37	35.8	3	1	2	1	1	1	1	5	1	6	1	1	3	1	1	10
eqntott	2.35	36.3	3	1	1	1	2	1	1	5	1	6	3	2	1	1	3	10
espresso	2.42	36.2	4	1	2	1	2	1	1	5	1	6	3	1	2	1	2	10
gcc	2.05	33.9	3	1	2	1	2	1	1	5	1	6	2	1	2	1	2	10
li	2.57	37.6	4	1	1	1	3	1	1	5	1	6	3	1	2	1	2	10
sc	2.30	45.3	3	1	2	1	3	1	1	5	1	6	3	1	1	1	1	10
doduc	2.73	60.0	4	1	1	1	2	1	1	5	3	6	3	1	1	1	3	10
hydro2d	3.39	55.5	4	1	4	1	2	1	2	5	3	6	3	1	1	1	2	10
mdljdp2	2.60	50.9	4	1	1	1	3	1	1	5	3	6	3	1	3	1	1	10
ora	1.92	45.7	3	1	2	1	2	1	2	5	1	6	3	1	1	1	1	10
tomcatv	3.41	85.8	2	1	2	1	2	1	1	5	2	6	3	1	1	1	1	10
wave5	3.14	54.2	4	1	3	1	2	1	2	5	2	6	4	2	2	1	2	10

There is little performance increase for the floating-point benchmarks, and in some cases the designs actually achieve a slight performance decrease. The 125% budget appears to be too restrictive for these benchmarks, preventing simulated annealing from improving the designs considerably. This is also the reason that floating-point unit duplication does not necessarily result in higher performance. This is not the case when a budget of 150% is assumed (see below).

The memory access units are optimized for multiple copies across all benchmarks. Load ports are especially important for most benchmarks, with four load ports required for *li*. Note that multiple load ports translate into high degrees of cache interleaving. With the exception of *gcc* and *li*, no more than one pending miss is needed.

In general, the parallelism available from a four

instructions per cycle lookahead is wasted for the floating-point benchmarks under the 125% budget.

150% power budget designs

The designs constrained by a 150% power budget are presented in Table 5(b). Increasing the power budget to twice the initial design has a dramatic effect on the achieved parallelism of the benchmarks. The integer benchmarks achieve parallelism values as high as 2.57 instructions per cycle (*li*). The floating-point benchmarks now achieve values significantly better than those of the Table 4 initial designs. *Tomcatv*, for example, achieves an IPC of 3.41 versus 2.13. Functional unit duplication favors the integer units, as before. *Espresso* now uses four *IALU* units, instead of the one used for the 125% power budget. In general, the 150%-budget designs are elite, high-performance superscalars. The *hydro2d* design achieves an IPC = 3.39, for example. In general, all IPC values are greater than 2.0, with the exception of *ora* (1.92). The most-popular unit to duplicate remains the *IALU* unit, with a median value of three *IALU* units. The *IALU* is one of the lowest-power units and at the same time one of the most-needed units. Other integer units are duplicated as well: *hydro2d* selects four *Shift* units and *wave5*, three[5].

The memory access units follow the general trend observed for the 125% power budget. Load ports are very important. Also, two of the floating-point benchmarks and one of the integer benchmarks require parallel data cache writes (three for *compress* and *mdljdp2*). In some cases, three pending miss units are required.

When combined, these results suggest that high performance can be achieved by technology-based allocation of units that deliver high performance without high power usage.

4   Conclusion

The number and importance of technology considerations has increased dramatically in recent years with advances in high-performance processor designs. The techniques presented in this paper make the connection between these technology considerations and the architecture level. The major contributions of this paper are the separation of architectural and technology components of dynamic power, the use of trace-driven simulation for architectural power measurement, and the use of a near-optimal search to tailor a processor to a benchmark. Although based on published design information, the example technology model has some flaws. It was presented in order to demonstrate the technique. Industry practitioners can readily develop a more accurate technology model for their internal use.

The model's predictions do match conventional wisdom: integer ALU's are best to duplicate, floating-point hardware is expensive and power-hungry, etc. With caveats in mind, several insights can be drawn from the results:

- Integer units (IAlu and Shift) achieve the highest performance per power increase,
- For higher performance designs, up to three pending misses may be required (note that this result is only valid for a miss repair penalty of 10),

- Deeply pipelined floating-point units are favored for their cycle time advantage,
- Provisions for multiple, parallel data cache reads are required,
- Up to three speculative branches active at once are needed in some cases (the PowerPC 604 currently supports two [4]),

In general, significant increases in floating-point performance will require much higher power budgets than equivalent increases in integer performance. Significant performance via duplication cannot be contemplated without taking this effect into account. The techniques in this paper find and duplicate units that produce the most performance for the least amount of power dissipation.

---

[5] Shifts are used for array index multiplication after the compiler applies strength reduction.

References

[1] T. M. Conte, "Architectural resource requirements of contemporary benchmarks: a wish list," in *Proc. 26th Hawaii Int'l. Conf. on System Sciences*, vol. 1, (Maui, HI), pp. 517–529, Jan. 1993.

[2] D. R. Ditzel and H. R. McLellan, "Branch folding in the CRISP microprocessor: reducing branch delay to zero," in *Proc. 14th Ann. International Symposium Computer Architecture*, (Pittsburgh, PA), pp. 2–9, June 1987.

[3] D. Alpert and D. Avnon, "Architecture of the Pentium microprocessor," *IEEE Micro*, vol. 13, pp. 11–21, June 1993.

[4] S. P. Song and M. Denman, "The PowerPC 604 RISC microprocessor," tech. rep., Somerset Design Center, Austin, TX, Apr. 1994.

[5] E. McLellan, "The Alpha AXP architecture and the 21064 processor," *IEEE Micro*, vol. 13, pp. 36–47, June 1993.

[6] I. Koren, *Computer arithmetic algorithms*. Englewood Cliffs, NJ: Prentice Hall, 1993.

[7] P. W. Markstein, "Computation of elementary functions on the IBM RISC system/6000 processor," *IBM J. Research and Development*, vol. 34, pp. 111–119, Jan. 1990.

[8] D. Kroft, " Lockup-free instruction fetch/prefetch cache organization," in *Proc. 8th Ann. Int'l. Symp. Computer Architecture*, pp. 81–87, May 1981.

[9] A. P. Chandrakasan, S. Sheng, and R. W. Brodersen, "Low-power CMOS digital design," *IEEE Journal of Solid-State Circuits*, vol. 27, pp. 473–484, Apr. 1992.

[10] M. L. Golden, "Issues in trace collection through program instrumentation," Master's thesis, Department of Electrical and Computer Engineering, University of Illinois, Urbana-Champaign, Illinois, 1991.

[11] T. Yeh and Y. N. Patt, "Two-level adaptive training branch prediction," in *Proc. 24th Ann. International Symposium on Microarchitecture*, (Albuquerque, NM), pp. 51–61, Nov. 1991.

[12] T. M. Conte, *Systematic computer architecture prototyping*. PhD thesis, Department of Electrical and Computer Engineering, University of Illinois, Urbana, Illinois, 1992.

[13] T. M. Conte and W. Mangione-Smith, "Determining cost-effective multiple issue processor designs," in *Proc. 1993 Int'l. Conf. on Computer Design*, (Cambridge, MA), Oct. 1993.

[14] S. Kirkpatric, C. D. Gelatt, and M. P. Vecchi, "Optimization by simulated annealing," *Science*, vol. 220, pp. 671–680, May 1983.

[15] D. W. Anderson, J. G. Earle, R. E. Goldschmidt, and D. M. Powers, "The IBM system/360 model 91: Floating point execution unit," *IBM J. Research and Development*, vol. 11, pp. 25–33, Jan. 1967.

[16] T. Asprey, G. S. Averill, E. DeLano, R. Mason, B. Weiner, and J. Yetter, "Performance features of the PA7100 microprocessor," *IEEE Micro*, vol. 13, pp. 22–35, June 1993.

[17] M. Annaratone, *Digital CMOS circuit design*. Boston, MA: Kluwer Academic Publishers, 1986.

Volume II
Table of Contents

SOFTWARE TECHNOLOGY

Program Development Tools and Environments for Parallel and Distributed Systems

Fault Tolerance in Distributed/Parallel Systems

Communication in Parallel and Distributed Systems

Volume III
Table of Contents

DECISION SUPPORT AND KNOWLEDGE-BASED SYSTEMS

Volume IV
Table of Contents

COLLABORATION SYSTEMS AND TECHNOLOGY

Groupware: User Experiences

ORGANIZATIONAL SYSTEMS AND TECHNOLOGY

Creativity/Innovation in I.S. Organizations

INTERNET and the Information Superhighway

Issues in Technology Transfer

Measuring the Effectiveness of Emerging Technologies

Volume V
Table of Contents

BIOTECHNOLOGY COMPUTING

Author Index

NOTES

NOTES

NOTES

NOTES